Go Math!™

Teacher Edition

GRADE

K

VOLUME 2

Welcome to *Go Math!*

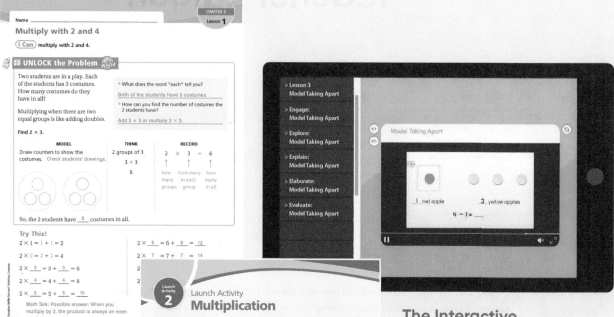

All children . . .

will see themselves and the possibilities for their future success in the materials used as part of instruction. You will see Social and Emotional Learning questions that foster a growth mindset and help children reflect on the math taught in the lesson.

The Interactive Student Edition . . .

is structured to assist children in navigating through their lesson assignments. Children start their assigned lesson and are prompted at completion to review assignment boards or to check in with you. Interactive lessons include animations, learning pathways, and appropriate intervention options to encourage high engagement with children.

Launch Activity lessons . . .

are designed for exploration and collaboration among children. Look for these activities to occur multiple times per year, with contexts to engage your students.

Bring the wonder of math . . .

to the children in your classroom through this program designed to help you, as a teacher, empower children to become mathematicians through engaging activities and thought-provoking exploration of math in authentic contexts, with social and emotional learning supports throughout.

How can I ensure children are engaged with the Mathematical Practices and Processes?

How am I supported as an educator?

How do I ensure children have the flexibility to show what they know?

Go Math! supports you as an educator to implement standards for Mathematics with teacher-to-teacher notes, Teacher's Corner, and other professional supports. Using these supports with *Go Math!*, you can meet the needs of each individual child.

- **Standards Helper,** a resource document organized by benchmark to easily see lessons, resources, and commons errors for children's learning.

- **Launch Activity,** a lesson with engaging content that introduces new concepts.

- **Teacher's Corner,** an online and interactive resource center for professional support specific to *Go Math!*, as well as other research-based supports.

The *Go Math!* lesson design integrates the Mathematical Practices and Processes throughout the Student and Teacher Editions.

- **(MP)** An MP icon indicates where in a lesson an MP standard is addressed.

The *Go Math!* program is designed to allow flexibility to solve problems using appropriate methods and strategies through discovery. The program supports exploration, rigor, fluency, and the application of real-world context.

- Teachers have the flexibility of multi-grade access on Ed to provide **prerequisite or challenge resources for children.**

- Children have access to a range of **tools and resources to model their thinking.**

- Support for **multilingual learners** is included throughout the program.

Program Authors

Edward B. Burger, PhD

Juli K. Dixon, PhD

Thomasenia Lott Adams, PhD

Edward B. Burger, PhD, is President & CEO of St. David's Foundation and President Emeritus & Professor Emeritus of Mathematics at Southwestern University in Georgetown, Texas. He has authored or coauthored numerous articles, books, and video series; delivered many addresses and workshops throughout the world; and made many radio and television appearances.

Juli K. Dixon, PhD, is a professor of mathematics education at the University of Central Florida (UCF). She has taught mathematics in urban schools at the elementary, middle, secondary, and post-secondary levels. Dr. Dixon has delivered keynotes and other presentations throughout the United States. Key areas of focus are deepening teachers' content knowledge and communicating and justifying mathematical ideas. You can find her on social media at @TheStrokeOfLuck.

Thomasenia Lott Adams, PhD, is a mathematics teacher educator/researcher in the School of Teaching & Learning and the Associate Dean of Research (ADR) in the College of Education at the University of Florida (UF), Gainesville, FL. She also serves as the college's Associate Dean of Research and Faculty Development. Dr. Adams is coauthor of the *Making Sense of Mathematics for Teaching* series (Solution Tree) and Associate Editor of *Mathematics Teacher: Learning and Teaching PreK-12* (NCTM).

Program Contributors and Consultants

Matthew R. Larson, PhD

Matthew R. Larson, PhD, is the associate superintendent for instruction at Lincoln Public Schools (Nebraska). A prolific speaker and writer, he is the coauthor of more than a dozen professional books. He was a member of the writing teams for the major publications *Principles to Actions: Ensuring Mathematical Success for All* (2014) and *Catalyzing Change in High School Mathematics: Initiating Critical Conversations* (2018). Key areas of focus include access and equity and effective stakeholder communication. He has taught mathematics at the secondary and college levels. You can find him on social media at @mlarson_math.

Contributor

Rena Petrello
Professor, Mathematics
Moorpark College
Moorpark, CA

English Language Learners Consultant

Elizabeth Jiménez
CEO, GEMAS Consulting
Professional Expert on English
  Learner Education
Bilingual Education and
  Dual Language
Pomona, California

Consultant

Valerie Johse
Math Consultant
Houston, Texas

Learning Progression

Lesson Design to Build Standards Mastery

Go Math! builds mastery of all content areas and provides a focused approach to developing children's mathematical understanding, procedural skills, and fluency. An emphasis is placed on making connections between concepts and skills as children move through a carefully-sequenced learning experience.

Building Procedural Mastery with the 5E Model

Every *Go Math!* lesson follows the same lesson design based on the 5E model of instruction.

Whole Group
Engage

Spark children's curiosity with Engage to connect prior knowledge to new mathematical content.

Small and Whole Group
Explore

In Explore, children build an understanding of new concepts through discovery and make sense of procedure using Listen and Draw or Unlock the Problem.

Math Talk questions provide entry points for mathematical discourse that explores the new concepts learned.

Small Group
Explain

In Explain, children apply their new knowledge of the lesson's mathematical concepts using Share and Show and On Your Own problems, increasing their conceptual understanding as they build towards procedural reliability.

Teachers can assess differentiation needs, providing support with supplemental activities and materials for Intervention, Language Support, and Enrichment.

Whole Group
Elaborate

The real-world problem solving in Elaborate gives children the opportunity to develop a deeper understanding of lesson concepts by practicing different solution methods.

Evaluate

Children summarize their thinking in Evaluate by connecting the I Can statement to the lesson objective. Practice and Homework problems support children's newly-learned lesson skills in their progression towards procedural fluency and automaticity.

Learning Tasks to Guide Instruction

Go Math! lesson design supports standards-driven instruction.

Promoting Exploration

The Listen and Draw and Unlock the Problem tasks are carefully crafted to promote reasoning and problem solving. Children can solve these puzzles using different strategies. These low-floor/high-ceiling tasks give every child an entry point to be successful and build understanding. Each chapter is full of real-world situations.

During these low floor/high ceiling tasks, children use their prior learning and choose manipulatives and models. Teachers provide just-in-time support, helping children engage in meaningful discourse to persevere when solving problems. Teachers lead the class to shared understanding in a student-centered environment, using the Math Talk feature to generate discussion.

Becoming More Efficient

The Share and Show tasks provide more opportunities for children to understand lesson concepts. Teachers can use the Quick Check to see if children are ready to go on, or determine how best to differentiate instruction. Teachers can assign the On Your Own problems to independently build fluency once children understand the lesson's concepts.

Building Procedural Fluency

The Problem Solving lesson tasks include real-world problems to promote procedural understanding and fluency. Teachers help children understand why the procedures are efficient and how they can be applied to solve similar problem types. Then, using the Practice and Homework helps children continue to build procedural fluency.

Launch Activity Lessons

What are Launch Activity Lessons?

Each grade's lessons are interspersed with Launch Activity lessons that introduce students to new, key areas of learning. Launch lessons highlight these important areas, and include professional development supports to help your class learn through productive perseverance and collaborative learning.

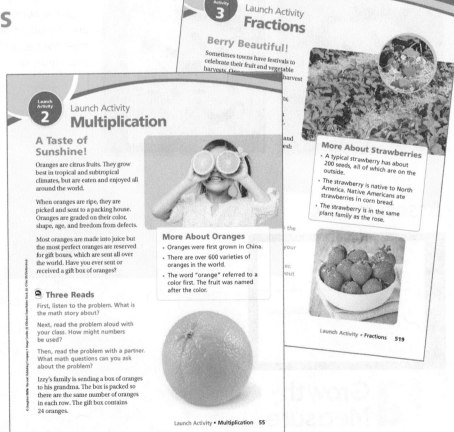

Key Components for Learning

For the Student

Student Edition*

Full-color, write-in Student Editions

Online Student Experience

Interactive practice with engaging Launch Activity lessons, hints and corrective feedback

For the Teacher

Teacher Edition*

The Teacher Edition, with all the support you need to plan lessons, build understanding, and meet the needs of all your students

Online Teacher Experience

Complete teacher support for lesson planning, assigning resources, viewing reports, and grouping, as well as flexible multi-grade access to provide both prerequisite and challenge content for standards progressions

Assessments

Online Assessments

Use a range of online assessments to benchmark student progress and inform instruction.

* Some print and digital student-facing materials are available in Spanish for Grades K–5, with companion bilingual teacher materials.

Differentiation and Small-Group Instruction

Waggle*

Interactive, adaptive practice with engaging tools and activities for students to develop fluency and mastery of the standards

Tabletop Flipchart*

Mini-lessons for math centers and small-group exploration

Readers*

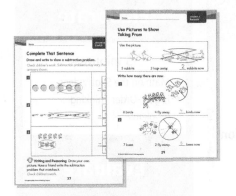

Differentiated Instruction*

Resources for Reteach, Enrich, and Fluency to meet the needs of all students

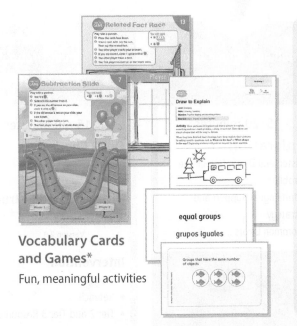

Vocabulary Cards and Games*

Fun, meaningful activities

Classroom Manipulatives Kit

Hands-on materials for modeling and understanding

Professional Learning and Implementation Support

Teacher's Corner

On-demand, bite-size articles, videos, and live events to tailor your professional learning to your specific needs

Professional Learning Cards

With Talk Moves and Language Routines

Instructional Journey

The instruction in *Go Math!* is designed from the ground up to help you nurture young mathematicians in your classroom. The small-group and whole-group activities in each lesson provide the flexibility to meet the needs of the children in your classroom.

While every classroom may look a little different, this instructional model provides a framework to organize small-group and whole-group work for meaningful learning.

How do I pace my lessons?

Your Teacher Edition includes pacing recommendations for each lesson, which you can modify for your class and your teaching style.

Whole Group
Engage

5 minutes

Readiness
- Problem of the Day
- Fluency Builder or Vocabulary Builder
- Access Prior Knowledge

Engagement
- I Can
- Making Connections
- Learning Activity

Small and Whole Group
Explore

15–20 minutes

Exploration
- Listen and Draw, Unlock the Problem
- Multilingual Support and Strategy
- Common Errors

Small Group
Explain

15–20 minutes

Quick Check
- Share and Show

Differentiated Instruction
Grab-and-Go!™
Version 2.0

Intervention
- Waggle
- Reteach
- Tier 2 and Tier 3 Resources

Language Support
- Vocabulary Activities
- Language Routines
- Multilingual Glossary

Enrichment
- Waggle Games
- Ready for More
- Enrich

Whole Group
Elaborate

5 minutes

- Math on the Spot Videos
- Higher-Order Thinking Problems

Evaluate

- I Can Reflection
- Exit Ticket
- Practice and Homework
- Fluency Practice
- Waggle

Differentiated Instruction, Practice, and Fluency

Effective instruction begins with knowing the strengths and challenges for the children in your classroom, including knowing what the children understand about a topic before they begin a new chapter.

Show What You Know

These chapter opener assessments help you to zero in on children's prerequisite knowledge, identify critical gaps, and make decisions about grouping.

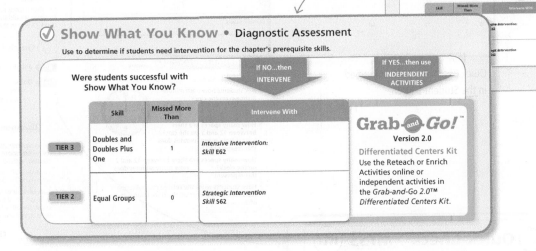

✓ Show What You Know • Diagnostic Assessment

Use to determine if students need intervention for the chapter's prerequisite skills.

Were students successful with Show What You Know?

If NO...then INTERVENE

If YES...then use INDEPENDENT ACTIVITIES

	Skill	Missed More Than	Intervene With
TIER 3	Doubles and Doubles Plus One	1	Intensive Intervention: Skill E62
TIER 2	Equal Groups	0	Strategic Intervention Skill S62

Grab and Go!
Version 2.0
Differentiated Centers Kit
Use the Reteach or Enrich Activities online or independent activities in the Grab-and-Go 2.0™ Differentiated Centers Kit.

Differentiated Instruction Options

Differentiation resources can be assigned to children who finish early (Enrich), or to children who are generally on grade level but who may need additional support (Reteach). Printable resources for differentiation are available in your teacher resources.

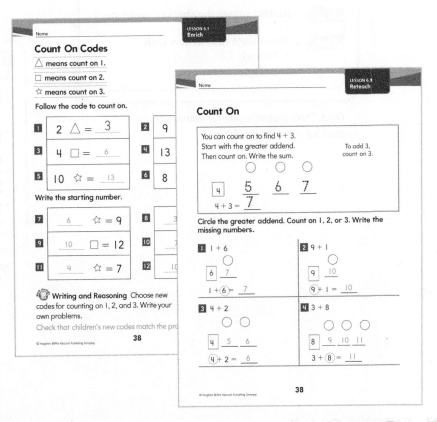

Intervention Options

Lesson level formative assessments, like the **Quick Check** items, inform intervention options for children who may be at RtI Tier 2 or 3. Children who are on grade level and above can work on the **Ready for More** activity while the other children complete the intervention activities.

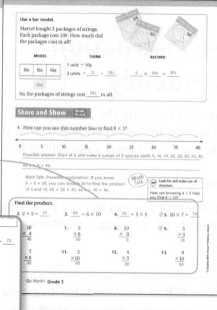

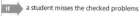

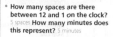

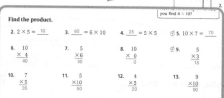

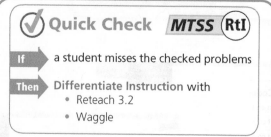

Quick Check problems identified in the Student Edition.

Use a Bar Model
Ask students to point to the bar model and say what each section represents. Ensure students understand that each section represents the cost of one package of strings. Discuss what the total length of the bar represents.

3 Explain

Share and Show

The first problem connects the learner to the learning model. Have students use the MathBoard to explain their thinking.

MP Look for and make use of structure.

Math Talk Use Math Talk to reinforce the doubles strategy students learned in the previous lesson. Students should recognize that the same reasoning that allows them to use doubles when multiplying with 4 can be used when multiplying with 10.

• **Explain how knowing 7 × 3 can help you find 7 × 6.** Possible answer: If you know 7 × 3 = 21, you can double 21 to find the product of 7 and 6: 21 + 21 = 42, so 7 × 6 = 42.

Use the checked problems for Quick Check. Students should show their answers for the Quick Check on the MathBoard.

✓ Quick Check **MTSS** **RtI**

If a student misses the checked problems

Then Differentiate Instruction with
• Reteach 3.2
• Waggle

⚠ Common Errors

Error Students may write incorrect products for multiplications with 5 because they skip counted incorrectly.

Example In Problem 7, students may write 6 × 5 = 35, instead of 6 × 5 = 30.

Springboard to Learning Remind students to keep track of the number of times they skip count. The other factor tells them how many times to skip count.

Chapter 3 • Lesson 2   116

✓ Quick Check **MTSS** **RtI**

If a student misses the checked problems

Then Differentiate Instruction with
• Reteach 3.2
• Waggle

Quick Check problems path for Intervention provided in the Teacher Edition.

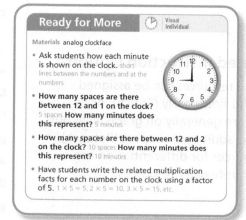

Options for on- or above-level students.

Data-Driven Decision Making

Use the chapter **Show What You Know** with the **Lesson Quick Check** and other formative assessments to diagnose children's intervention levels throughout the chapter. Intervention options are provided at point of use when beginning each chapter, during lesson instruction, and in the chapter review.

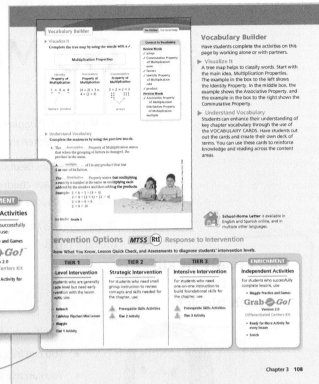

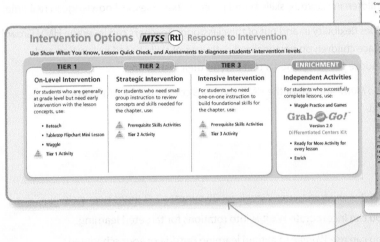

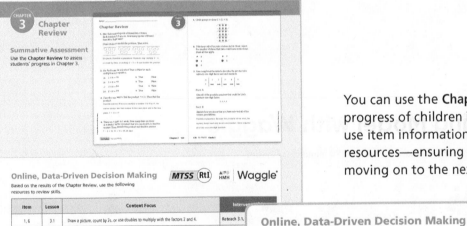

You can use the **Chapter Review** to assess the progress of children in your classroom, and then use item information to plan intervention resources—ensuring children are ready before moving on to the next chapter.

Online, Data-Driven Decision Making MTSS RtI HMH Waggle®

Based on the results of the Chapter Review, use the following resources to review skills.

Item	Lesson	Content Focus	Intervene With
1, 6	3.1	Draw a picture, count by 2s, or use doubles to multiply with the factors 2 and 4.	Reteach 3.1, Waggle
2, 8, 23	3.8	Use doubles, a number line, or the Associative Property of Multiplication to multiply with the factor 8.	Reteach 3.8, Waggle
3, 12	3.10	Use the Distributive Property with addition or subtraction or patterns to multiply with the factor 11 or 12.	Reteach 3.10, Waggle
4, 17	3.5	Use the Commutative or Distributive Property or known facts to multiply with the factor 7.	Reteach 3.5, Waggle
5, 11, 15, 21	3.6	Use the Associative Property of Multiplication to multiply with three factors.	Reteach 3.6, Waggle
7, 22	3.7	Identify and explain patterns on the multiplication table.	Reteach 3.7, Waggle
9, 18, 24	3.2	Use skip counting, a number line, or a bar model to multiply with the factors 5 and 10.	Reteach 3.2, Waggle
10, 16, 19	3.4	Use the Distributive Property to find products by breaking apart arrays.	Reteach 3.4, Waggle
13, 20	3.3	Draw a picture, use 5s facts and addition, doubles, or a multiplication table to multiply with the factors 3 and 6.	Reteach 3.3, Waggle
14	3.9	Use the Distributive Property with addition or subtraction or patterns to multiply with the factor 9.	Reteach 3.9, Waggle

FOCUSING ON THE WHOLE CHILD

HMH Go Math!™ + Waggle®

Go Math! with *Waggle* combines child-centered instruction with powerful personalization, immersing children in rigorous, skills-based practice that assesses knowledge in real time.

Waggle provides flexibility in and out of the classroom. Teachers can leverage HMH Growth Measure to place children on personalized pathways of skills-based instruction and practice, or choose the assignments that extend their instruction.

Waggle and *Go Math!* are two of the HMH solutions connected by HMH Growth Measure on *Ed*.

Can I really fit all of this into my math block?

- Plan for children to use *Waggle* for 20 minutes 2–3 times per week.
- You can incorporate *Waggle* into rotations for targeted learning.
- You can use *Waggle* to extend learning outside of your scheduled math block.

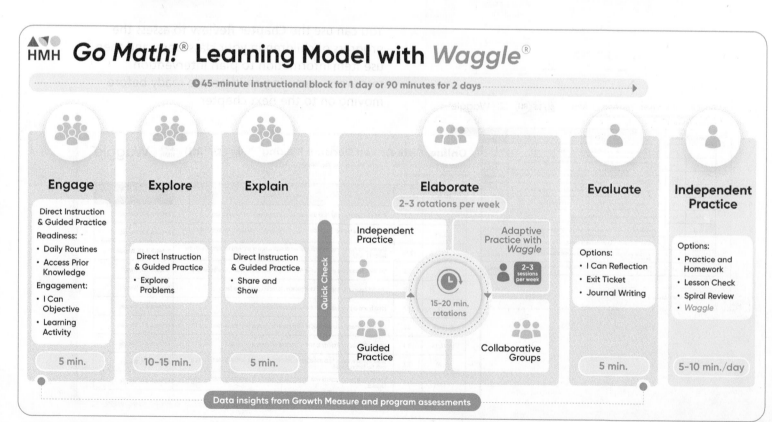

HMH Go Math!® Learning Model with Waggle®

45-minute instructional block for 1 day or 90 minutes for 2 days

Engage

Direct Instruction & Guided Practice

Readiness:
- Daily Routines
- Access Prior Knowledge

Engagement:
- I Can Objective
- Learning Activity

5 min.

Explore

Direct Instruction & Guided Practice
- Explore Problems

10–15 min.

Explain

Direct Instruction & Guided Practice
- Share and Show

5 min.

Quick Check

Elaborate

2–3 rotations per week

Independent Practice

Adaptive Practice with *Waggle*

2–3 sessions per week

15–20 min. rotations

Guided Practice

Collaborative Groups

Evaluate

Options:
- I Can Reflection
- Exit Ticket
- Journal Writing

5 min.

Independent Practice

Options:
- Practice and Homework
- Lesson Check
- Spiral Review
- *Waggle*

5–10 min./day

Data insights from Growth Measure and program assessments

How does *Waggle* work?

- Practice activities are designed to follow core instruction and assess proficiency.
- Learning activities combine instruction, practice, and formative assessments to accelerate learning.
- Waggle identifies skill gaps as children work through practice and learning activities.
- Waggle continually assesses students during practice to create personalized pathways for children and provide powerful insights for teachers.

How do I decide what to assign my students in *Waggle*?

- Teachers can use Waggle's Growth Measure-powered auto-assign. With auto-assign, children progress down their own learning path based on skill gaps and priority standards.
- Or, teachers can manually assign content based upon a particular Go Math! lesson, standard, or skill.

Waggle Activities	What They Are	When to Use Them
Skill Quizzes	• short, five-question exercises • same questions for all students • target a single skill • formative assessment	Assign **Skill Quizzes** before instruction for a quick assessment of each student's understanding of a particular skill. Assign after instruction for a brief check of understanding.
Practice	• dynamic and adaptive practice • personalized path for each student • target several related skills • provide scaffolded hints and personalized feedback	Assign **Practice** when you want students to follow a personalized path to reach proficiency. These can be used for enrichment or reteaching support.
Learn	• teach and model individual skills • conclude with a five-item skill check for students to apply what they have learned	**Learn activities** will automatically be assigned to students struggling during Practice. They can also be assigned manually when students need reintroductions or refreshers with certain skills.
Play	• focus on fluency • fun, trackable practice • utilize an item generator for unlimited, skill-based gameplay	Assign **Play** for fluency practice.

Note: Practice and Play are also available for grades 3–6.

FOCUSING ON THE WHOLE STUDENT

Social & Emotional Learning

Social and Emotional Learning (SEL) is a critical aspect of students' school experience. Inclusive and equitable mathematics environments cultivate the social, emotional, and academic competencies needed for students to contribute to a caring, thriving, and just society.

Mathematics Learning Environment

A safe, supportive, and equitable learning environment calls on mathematics teachers to:

- Cultivate a sense of belonging and community where students see themselves as mathematicians, collectively striving to develop a deep understanding of mathematics.

- Provide structures for physical and emotional safety so that mathematical sense-making is cognitively possible.

- Create space for student voice and agency as a means to productively shape students' mathematical identities.

- Provide tiered supports that meet the needs of all students to access and experience the joy, wonder, and beauty of mathematics.

- Use engaging, relevant, and culturally responsive mathematics instruction built on an understanding of how students grow and develop socially, emotionally, and academically.

- Offer frequent opportunities for students to discuss and practice anti-racism and develop collaborative solutions to address inequities using mathematics as a tool.

- Engage in mathematics teaching practices that affirm diverse social, cultural, and linguistic identities.

Adapted from *Reunite, Renew, and Thrive: SEL Roadmap for Reopening School*, CASEL, July 2020, https://casel.org/reopening-with-sel/.

CASEL's Student Competencies

SELF-AWARENESS: The abilities to understand one's own emotions, thoughts, and values and how they influence behavior across contexts.

SOCIAL AWARENESS: The abilities to understand the perspectives of and empathize with others, including those from diverse backgrounds, cultures, and contexts.

RELATIONSHIP SKILLS: The abilities to establish and maintain healthy and supportive relationships and to effectively navigate settings with diverse individuals and groups.

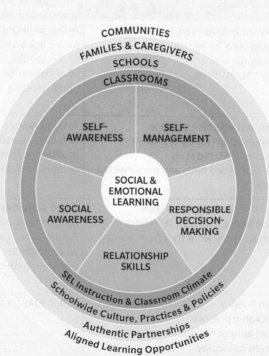

SELF-MANAGEMENT: The abilities to manage one's emotions, thoughts, and behaviors effectively in different situations and to achieve goals and aspirations.

RESPONSIBLE DECISION-MAKING: The abilities to make caring and constructive choices about personal behavior and social interactions across diverse situations.

©2020 CASEL. All Rights Reserved.

FOCUSING ON THE WHOLE STUDENT

The *HMH Go Math!* Commitment

HMH is using this framework to guide our content and services. Created in 2019, it has been used by educators across the country as a tool to reflect on and strengthen their culturally responsive teaching practices.

from *Culturally Responsive Teaching: A Reflection Guide*, New America, https://www.newamerica.org/education-policy/policy-papers/culturally-responsive-teaching-competencies/.

Reflect on one's cultural lens

Recognize and redress bias in the system

Communicate in lingusitically and culturally responsive ways

Draw on students' culture to shape curriculum and instruction

8 Competencies for culturally responsive teaching

Collaborate with families and the local community

Bring real-world issues into the classroom

Promote respect for student differences

Model high expectations for all students

Image credit: © HMH

Supporting Multilingual Learners

The *Go Math!* program includes print and online resources based on WIDA Language Support levels to provide examples of differentiated questions and strategies for multilingual learners.

Chapter-Level Language Support

The instruction highlights key academic vocabulary as well as language routines. The language routines provide opportunities for children to develop their understanding of mathematical language and concepts by listening, speaking, reading, and writing.

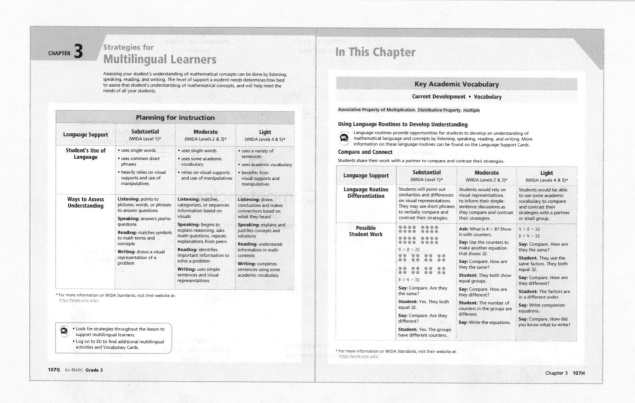

Planning for Instruction

Understanding the level of language support needed by children in your class is an important step in planning differentiation. The Planning for Instruction chart at the start of each chapter helps you explore your children's current WIDA levels.

Key Academic Vocabulary

Multilingual learners are most successful when they learn key mathematical vocabulary throughout the lessons.

Use the Language Routine Differentiations and Possible Student Work as a guide to better assess student's understanding of mathematical concepts based on their current level of language proficiency.

Lesson-Level Language Support

Every lesson of *Go Math!* includes multilingual support. These are indicated by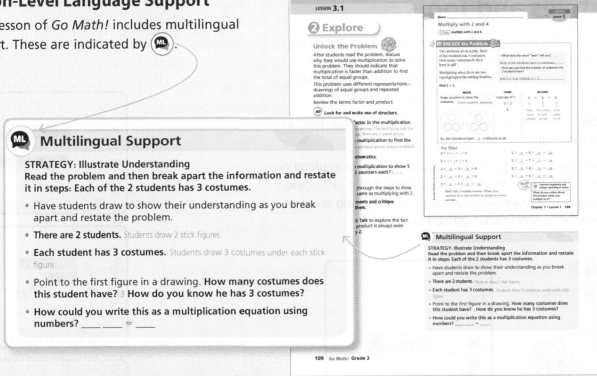

ML Multilingual Support

STRATEGY: Illustrate Understanding
Read the problem and then break apart the information and restate it in steps: Each of the 2 students has 3 costumes.

* Have students draw to show their understanding as you break apart and restate the problem.

* **There are 2 students.** Students draw 2 stick figures.

* **Each student has 3 costumes.** Students draw 3 costumes under each stick figure.

* Point to the first figure in a drawing. **How many costumes does this student have?** 3 **How do you know he has 3 costumes?**

* **How could you write this as a multiplication equation using numbers?** ____ ____ = ____

Children can access a **Glossary** in their Student Editions, an **Interactive Glossary** online, as well as a **Multilingual Glossary** available in ten languages.

Language Routines

Language Routines Cards help teachers develop children reasoning and discourse during instruction.

THREE READS

Children read a problem three times with a specific focus each time:

1. **Read** What is the problem about?
2. **Read** What do each of the numbers describe?
3. **Read** What math questions could you ask about the problem?

CRITIQUE, CORRECT, AND CLARIFY

* Children analyze an incorrect explanation or solution.
* Children work with a partner or small group to identify the error.
* Children work together to correct the sample work.

STRONGER AND CLEARER EACH TIME

* Children show their thinking with math tools and visuals.
* Children share their thinking and receive feedback with a partner or a group.
* Children revoice feedback and revise their work.

COMPARE AND CONTRAST

Children share their work with a partner to compare and contrast their strategies.

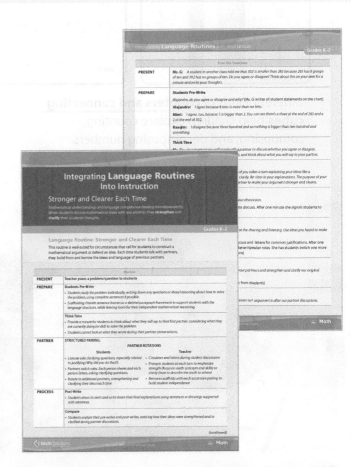

Manipulatives and Tools

Go Math! provides opportunities for children to choose manipulatives and tools to make sense of mathematics and express relationships. Flexible concrete and digital tools help children connect concepts to procedures and adapt their representations to different mathematical contexts.

By seeing how children choose tools and which tools they choose, teachers also gain insight into the connections they're making.

In *Go Math!*, children have access to manipulatives for hands-on exploration, as well as digital manipulatives to supplement and extend that exploration. Both concrete and digital manipulatives support them in making sense of situations, solving problems, and checking their reasoning.

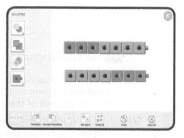

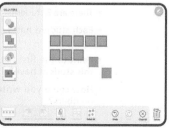

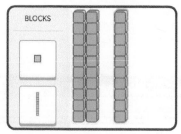

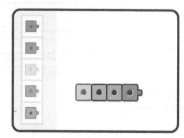
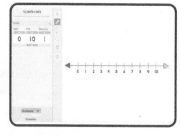

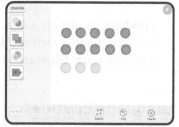

Different kinds of **counters and connecting cubes** help children explore counting, composing, and decomposing numbers.

Children can experiment with the relationships between **operations** and among **number facts**.

Image Credit: © HMH

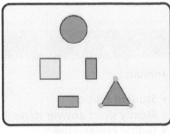

They learn properties of different **shapes** and begin to compare and sort them.

Image Credit: © HMH

Grab-and-Go!™
Version 2.0
Differentiated Centers Kit

Manipulatives are included in your Grab & Go kits. Kit contents are tailored to address the needs for each grade and may not be identical to what is shown here.

Assessments to Drive Classroom Instruction

Use a range of formative and summative assessments to measure students' understanding as they develop mastery of the standards.

Grade-Level Assessments

Resource	Assessment	Features/Purpose	Formats
HMH Student Growth Measure 40 minutes	Summative	• Administered 3 times per year using items aligned to national assessments • Monitors student growth over time • Provides data reports to guide instructional decisions • Produces a Quantile Score grade level expectation against national assessments	• Computer-adaptive digital assessment* • All items are multiple choice
Beginning/ Middle/End of Year Test 40 minutes	Diagnostic/ Summative	• Administered at the beginning, middle, or end of the school year • All items aligned to national assessments • Measures mastery of content taught in Go! Math • Individual Record Forms show standards alignment, DOK, and intervention options for each item	• PDF (Assessment Guide)
Prerequisite Skills Inventory 40 minutes	Diagnostic	• Administered at the beginning of the school year • Assess core precursor skills associated with on-grade success • Review/intervention students may need to be successful in learning grade-level standards • Individual Record Forms show standards alignment, DOK, and intervention options for each item	• PDF (Assessment Guide)
Performance Tasks 30–40 minutes	Performance Assessment (Formative/ Summative)	• Assess students' ability to use what they have learned to solve everyday problems • Include a rubric for scoring purposes • Individual Record Forms show standards alignment, DOK, and intervention options for each item	• PDF (Assessment Guide) • Constructed response format only

Chapter-Level Assessments

Resource	Assessment	Features/Purpose	Formats
Show What You Know 20 minutes	Diagnostic	• Administered at the beginning of the chapter • Assess prior knowledge from previous grades and content taught earlier in the grade • Intervention and individualized instructional recommendations are provided	• Student Edition • Mostly short answer items • Digital / Interactive*
Chapter Review 20 minutes	Summative/ Formative	• Administered at the end of the chapter • Evaluates students' mastery of concept and skills taught in the module • Hints and corrective feedback are available for all items • All items aligned to content based on national assessments	• Student Edition • Digital / Interactive*
Chapter Test 30–40 minutes	Summative/ Formative	• Administered at the end of the chapter • Evaluates students' mastery of concept and skills taught in the chapter	• Digital / Interactive* • PDF (Assessment Guide) • English and Spanish

*These assessments provide data that can be accessed through Ed.

Growth Measure

Lesson-Level Assessments

Resource	Assessment	Features/Purpose	Formats
Explain/Share and Show 15–20 minutes	Formative	• Formative assessment in every lesson • Teachers use data to determine which students need additional small-group support and which students can continue to independent practice or math center challenges	• Interactive Student Edition • Print Student Edition • Mostly short answer items
Elaborate/On Your Own 10 minutes	Formative	• As the lesson concludes, evaluates students' mastery of concepts and skills taught in the lesson • Includes step-by-step methods for students to solve problems	• Interactive Student Edition • Print Student Edition • Mix of item types from the lesson
Evaluate/Practice and Homework 20–30 minutes	Formative	• Administered at the end of the lesson • Evaluates students' mastery of concepts and skills taught in the lesson • Contains Spiral Review problems	• Print Student Edition • Mix of item types from the lesson • Digital / Interactive

Test Prep/Standards Mastery

Resource	Assessment	Features/Purpose	Formats
Standards-Based Practice 20–30 minutes	Test Prep	• Administered when additional practice is needed to achieve standards mastery with a wide variety of ways in which the standard may be assessed, the standards-based practice helps students practice key standards and skills associated with grade-level success. • Hints and corrective feedback are available for all items • Individual Record Forms show standards alignment, DOK, and intervention options for each item	• Digital / Interactive*
Getting Ready for HSA Practice Tests 40 minutes	Test Prep	• Administered to help students prepare for high stakes assessments • 3 practice tests available per grade	• Includes Constructed Response items • Digital / Interactive*

Test Prep opportunities are also available in every More Practice problem set.

*These assessments provide data that can be accessed through Ed.

DEPTH OF KNOWLEDGE (DOK)

Growth Measure

All percentages are approximations.

DOK	Growth Measure	Module Tests, Beginning, Middle, and End-of-Year, and Test Prep	Lesson/Module Practice (Formative Assessments)	Performance Assessments
DOK 1	varies**	40–45%	50–55%	0–5%
DOK 2	varies**	40–45%	40–45%	60–65%
DOK 3	varies**	5–10%	0–5%	30–35%
DOK 4	DOK 4 problems can be found in the Performance Tasks			

**The HMH Growth Measure is a computer-adaptive assessment.
The DOKs of items will vary based on students' individual experiences.

Teacher Support

Supporting Best Practices

Go Math! helps students grow by providing teachers with instruction designed around proven-effective teaching practices, such as those described in *Principles to Actions* (NCTM, 2014)[1].

- Establish mathematics goals to focus learning
- Implement tasks that promote reasoning and problem solving
- Use and connect mathematical representations
- Facilitate meaningful mathematical discourse
- Pose purposeful questions
- Build procedural fluency from conceptual understanding
- Support productive struggle in learning mathematics
- Elicit and use evidence of student thinking

Carefully crafted tasks, student-centered learning, small groups, and hands-on manipulatives play important roles in a *Go Math!* classroom. Point-of-use support helps you facilitate learning and implement research-based best practices.

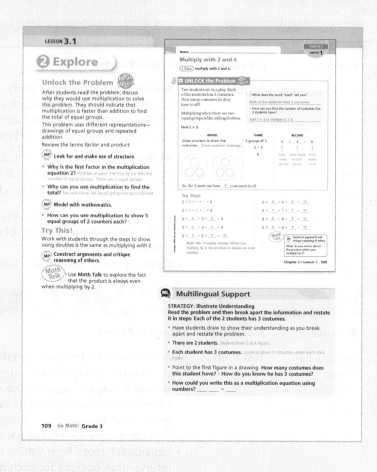

1) National Council of Teachers of Mathematics, *Principles to Actions: Ensuring Mathematical Success for All* (Reston, VA: NCTM, 2014).

Online Resources

Professional Learning Videos

Every chapter includes a professional learning video featuring a teacher or HMH author working with real students who are engaging in similar activities. The videos include modeling and discussion of effective teaching practices, as well as Language Routines and Talk Moves strategies. These strategies are key supports for multilingual students, and for *all* students in expressing their thinking.

Teacher's Corner

Go online to Teacher's Corner for on-demand, bite-size articles, videos, and other resources to tailor your professional learning to your specific needs.

Teacher's Corner™

Professional Learning Cards

The *Go Math!* Professional Learning Cards include teacher supports for Talk Moves and Language Routines. Talk Moves encourage children to verbalize their thoughts. Language Routines provide opportunities for students to internalize their mathematical thinking and describe their knowledge through writing, discourse, and engagement.

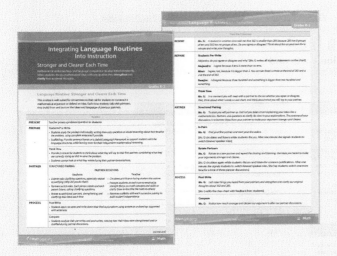

When children verbalize their thoughts and hear what classmates are thinking, they become stronger mathematicians. Math Talk tools for teachers and students help children achieve different communication aims and deepen their understanding.

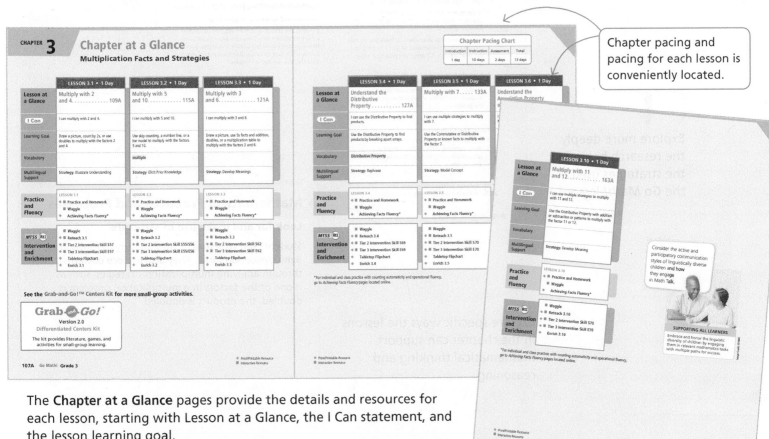

Chapter pacing and pacing for each lesson is conveniently located.

The **Chapter at a Glance** pages provide the details and resources for each lesson, starting with Lesson at a Glance, the I Can statement, and the lesson learning goal.

Multilingual Support strategies help you to plan ahead, as do lists of resources for Practice and Fluency, and Intervention and Enrichment.

Image Credit: © HMH

Teaching for Depth

Teaching for Depth gives you background about the best practices and research related to the lesson's concepts.

Identify ways the chapter lessons and activities can be extended into opportunities for students to achieve mathematical thinking and reasoning.

Gain understandings of common errors and misunderstandings students may have as they begin the work in the chapter. Then identify tools and strategies that they can use to become proficient.

CHAPTER **3** **Teaching for Depth**

Multiplication Facts and Strategies

Contexts for Multiplication

The contexts in which multiplication is explored support students' development of varied strategies for determining products for multiplication facts.

- When students are given a number of equal groups and the number of objects in each group, they may multiply or use repeated addition to find the total number of objects in all the groups.

- Arrays are similar to equal groups. Students determine the total number of objects given the number of rows and the number of objects in each row.

Strategies for Multiplication

Students develop strategies for multiplying one-digit factors when they explore ways to derive unknown facts from known facts. Such strategies assist in the process of memorizing facts. Consider 6×7.

- Students who know the product of 3×7 might choose to double 21 to get 42 to determine the product of 6×7.

- Students who can skip count by fives quickly may choose to find the product of 6×7 by finding the product of 5×7 and then adding another group of 7.

- A worthwhile activity is to ask students to generate different strategies for finding the product of similar problems and then have students choose the strategy they prefer to solve the problem.

From the Research

"If students over-practice procedures before they understand them, they have more difficulty making sense of them later." (Hiebert, 1999, p. 15)

For more professional learning, go online to Teacher's Corner.

107E Go Math! Grade 3

Properties for Multiplication

The Associative and Distributive Properties help students build fluency with multiplication by using facts they know to find unknown products.

- The Associative Property allows students to change the grouping of factors presented.

$$(4 \times 4) \times 2 = 4 \times (4 \times 2)$$
$$16 \quad \times 2 = 4 \times \quad 8$$

- The Distributive Property allows students to break apart facts they don't know into known facts.

$$8 \times \quad 7$$
$$8 \times (3 + 4)$$
$$(8 \times 3) + (8 \times 4)$$
$$24 \quad + \quad 32$$

Mathematical Practices and Processes

Look for and make use of structure.

Students **see structure** as they identify patterns in a multiplication table. They also explore patterns through applying multiplication strategies, such as if one of the factors in a multiplication problem is doubled, the product is doubled.

Explore more deeply the research behind the strategies used in the *Go Math!* lessons.

Mathematical Practices and Processes

Look for and make use of structure.

Students **see structure** as they identify patterns in a multiplication table. They also explore patterns through applying multiplication strategies, such as if one of the factors in a multiplication problem is doubled, the product is doubled.

Explore specific ways the lessons in the chapter can support mathematical thinking and reasoning.

Connect with Families and Community

Go Math! provides resources teachers can use to engage families throughout the school year.

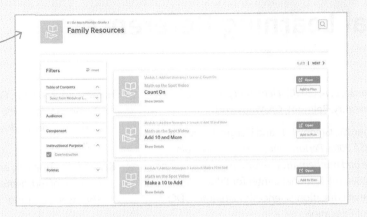

Math on the Spot video tutorials provide instruction of the math concepts covered and allow for family involvement in learning. In addition, the write-in format of the print Student Edition gives families a front-row seat to their child's thinking and progress over time, encouraging a strong home-school connection.

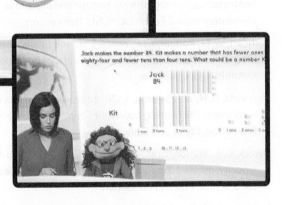

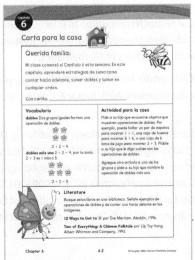

School-Home Letters

inform families about the skills, strategies, and topics students are encountering at school, extending rich dialogue beyond the classroom.

The School Home Letters are available in English, Spanish, Portuguese, and Haitian Creole.

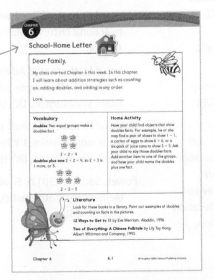

Professional Learning References

Bahr, D. L., and de Garcia, L. A. (2010). *Elementary mathematics is anything but elementary.* Belmont, CA: Wadsworth.

Baldi, S., Jin, Y., Skemer, M., Green, P. J., and Herget, D. (2007). *Highlights from PISA 2006: Performance of U.S. 15-year-old students in science and mathematics literacy in an international context* (NCES 2008–016). National Center for Education Statistics, Institute of Education Sciences. Washington, DC: U.S. Department of Education.

Battista, M. (2007). The development of geometric and spatial thinking. In F. K. Lester (Ed.), *Second handbook of research on mathematics teaching and learning: Volume 2* (pp. 843–908). Charlotte, NC: Information Age Publishing.

Burny, E., Valcke, M., and Desoete, A. (2009). *Towards an agenda for studying learning and instruction focusing on time-related competences in children.* Educational Studies. 35.10.1080/03055690902879093.

Carpenter, T. P., Franke, M. L., and Levi, L. (2003). *Thinking mathematically: Integrating arithmetic and algebra in elementary school.* Portsmouth, NH: Heinemann.

Cathcart, W. G., Pothier, Y. M., Vance, J. H., and Bezuk, N. S. (2006). *Learning mathematics in elementary and middle schools.* Columbus, OH: Pearson.

Clements, D. H., and Sarama, J. (2014). *Learning and teaching early math: The learning trajectories approach.* New York: Routledge, Taylor and Francis.

Dweck, C. S., Walton, G. M., and Cohen, G. L. (2014). *Academic tenacity: mindsets and skills that promote long-term learning.* Bill & Melinda Gates Foundation.

Furhman, S. H., Resnick, L., and Shepard, L. (2009). Standards aren't enough. *Education Week 29*(7), 28.

Fuson, K. C. (2003). Developing mathematical power in whole number operations. In J. Kilpatrick, W. G. Martin, and D. Schifter (Eds.), *A research companion to principles and standards for school mathematics* (pp. 68–94). Reston, VA: National Council of Teachers of Mathematics.

Geist, E. (2009). *Children are born mathematicians: Supporting mathematical development, birth to age 8.* Columbus, OH: Pearson.

Gonzales, P., Williams, T., Jocelyn, L., Roey, S., Katsberg, D., and Brenwald, S. (2008). *Highlights from TIMSS 2007: Mathematics and science achievement of U.S. fourth- and eighth-grade students in an international context* (NCES 2009–001 Revised). National Center for Education Statistics, Institute of Education Sciences. Washington, DC: U.S. Department of Education.

Hammond, Z. (2015). *Culturally responsive teaching and the brain: Promoting authentic engagement and rigor among culturally and linguistically diverse students.* Thousand Oaks, CA: Corwin Press.

Kennedy, L., Tipps, S., and Johnson, A. (2004). *Guiding children's learning of mathematics* (10th ed.). Belmont, CA: Wadsworth/ Thomson Learning.

Kilpatrick, J., Martin, W.G., and Schifter, D., (Eds). National Council of Teachers of Mathematics. (2003). *A research companion to principles and standards for school mathematics* (pp. 237–249. Reston, VA: National Council of Teachers of Mathematics.

Lehrer, R. (2003). Developing understanding of measurement. In J. Kilpatrick, W. G. Martin, and D. Schifter (Eds.), *A research companion to principles and standards for school mathematics.* Reston, VA: National Council of Teachers of Mathematics.

Martinez, J. G. R., and Martinez, N. C. (2007). *Teaching mathematics in elementary and middle school.* Upper Saddle River, NJ: Pearson Merrill Prentice Hall.

Martin, W. G. (2000). *Principles and standards for school mathematics.* Reston, VA: National Council of Teachers of Mathematics.

Marzano, R. J. (2003). *What works in schools: Translating research into action.* Alexandria, VA: ASCD.

National Council of Teachers of Mathematics. (1993). *Addenda Series: Number sense and operations, K–6.* In M. Leiva (Ed.). Reston, VA: Author.

National Council of Teachers of Mathematics. (2005). *Standards and Curriculum: A view from the nation, a joint report by the National Council of Teachers of Mathematics (NCTM) and the Association of State Supervisors of Mathematics (ASSM).* J. W. Lott & K. Nishimura (Eds.). Reston, VA: Author.

National Council of Teachers of Mathematics (2014). *Principles to Actions: Ensuring Mathematical Success for All.* Reston, VA: Author.

National Mathematics Advisory Panel. (2008). *Foundations for success: The final report of the National Mathematics Advisory Panel.* Washington, DC: U. S. Department of Education.

National Research Council. (2001). *Adding it up: Helping children learn mathematics.* J. Kilpatrick, J. Swafford, and B. Findell (Eds.). Washington, DC: National Academy Press.

Powell, Sarah R. (2012). Equations and the equal sign in elementary mathematics textbooks. *Elem Sch J.;* 112(4): pp. 627–648.

Reed, D. S. (2009). Is there an expectations gap? Educational federalism and the demographic distribution of proficiency cut scores. *American Educational Research Journal* 46(3), pp. 718–742.

Resnick, Lauren B. (1983). A developmental theory of number understanding. In H. P. Ginsberg (Ed.), *The development of mathematical thinking* (pp. 109–151). New York: Academic Press.

Reys, B. J., Chval, K., Dingman, S., McNaught, M., Regis, T. P., and Togashi, J. (2007). Grade-level learning expectations: A new challenge for elementary mathematics teachers. *Teaching Children Mathematics* 14 (1), pp. 6–11.

Schmoker, M. (2011). *Focus: Elevating the essentials to radically improve student learning.* Alexandria, VA: Association for Supervision and Curriculum Development.

Schneider, M. (2007). *National Assessment of Education Progress: Mapping 2005 state proficiency standards onto the NAEP scales.* Washington, DC: IES National Center for Education Statistics.

Schwartz, J. E. (2008). *Elementary mathematics pedagogical content knowledge: Powerful ideas for teachers.* Boston, MA: Pearson.

Sheffield, L. J. and Cruikshank, D. E. (2005). *Teaching and learning mathematics: Prekindergarten through middle school.* Hoboken, NJ: John Wiley and Sons.

Tracy, Dyane M.; Faneli, Beverly H. (2000). *Teaching money concepts: are we shortchanging our kids?* Retrieved from https://files.eric.ed.gov/fulltext/ED451065.pdf.

Triadafillidis, T. A. (1995). Circumventing visual limitations in teaching the geometry of shapes. *Educational Studies in Mathematics* 29(3), pp. 225–235.

Troutman, A. P., and Lichtenberg, B. K. (2003). *Mathematics: A good beginning* (6th ed.). Belmont, CA: Thomson.

Van de Walle, J. A. (1994). *Elementary school mathematics* (2nd ed.). White Plains, NY: Longman.

Van de Walle, J. A. (2007). *Elementary and middle school mathematics: Teaching developmentally* (6th ed.). Boston, MA: Pearson.

Van de Walle, J. A., and Lovin, L. H. (2007). *Teaching student-centered mathematics: Grades K–3.* Boston: Allyn and Bacon.

Wall, E., and Posamentier, A. (2007). *What successful math teachers do, Grades PreK–5 : 47 research-based strategies for the standards-based classroom.* Thousand Oaks, CA: Corwin Press.

Whitin, D. J. (2006). Learning to talk back to a statistic. In G. F. Burrill and P. C. Elliot (Eds.) *Thinking and reasoning with data and chance: Sixty-eighth yearbook* (pp. 31–39). Reston, VA: National Council of Teachers of Mathematics .

WIDA (2020). *WIDA English language development standards framework, 2020 edition: Kindergarten–grade 12.* Board of Regents of the University of Wisconsin System.

Woods, D., Ketterlin Geller, L., and Basarabi, D. (2007). Number sense on the number line. *Intervention in School and Clinic.*

TABLE OF CONTENTS
VOLUME 2

CHAPTER 13
Count, Represent, and Compare Numbers Through 15

CHAPTER 14
Count, Represent, and Compare Numbers Through 20

CHAPTER 15
Explore Addition and Subtraction to 20

CHAPTER 16
Count to 100

Image credit: ©HMH

Launch Activity 3

CHAPTER 17
Two-Dimensional Shapes

CHAPTER 20
Data

Chapter at a Glance
Addition Up to 10

	LESSON 11.1 • 1 Day	LESSON 11.2 • 1 Day	LESSON 11.3 • 1 Day
Lesson at a Glance	One More and One Less 411A	Sums Up to 7 . . . . . . 417A	Sums Up to 9 . . . . . . 423A
I Can	I can use addition and subtraction to find one more and one less.	I can write and solve addition equations with sums up to 7.	I can write and solve addition equations for sums up to 9.
Learning Goal	Add 1 and subtract 1.	Solve problems with sums to 7.	Solve problems with sums to 9.
Vocabulary			
Multilingual Support	**Strategy:** Cooperative Grouping	**Strategy:** Model Concepts	**Strategy:** Restate

Practice and Fluency	LESSON 11.1 ◆ ■ Practice and Homework ■ Waggle ◆ Achieving Facts Fluency*	LESSON 11.2 ◆ ■ Practice and Homework ■ Waggle ◆ Achieving Facts Fluency*	LESSON 11.3 ◆ ■ Practice and Homework ■ Waggle ◆ Achieving Facts Fluency*
MTSS (RtI) **Intervention and Enrichment**	■ Waggle ◆ ■ Reteach 11.1 ◆ ■ Tier 2 Intervention Skill S29/S31 ◆ ■ Tier 3 Intervention Skill E23/E24 ◆ Enrich 11.1	■ Waggle ◆ ■ Reteach 11.2 ◆ ■ Tier 2 Intervention Skill S10/S28 ◆ ■ Tier 3 Intervention Skill E10/S28 ◆ Tabletop Flipchart ◆ Enrich 11.2	■ Waggle 11.3 ◆ ■ Reteach ◆ ■ Tier 2 Intervention Skill S26 ◆ ■ Tier 3 Intervention Skill E26 ◆ Tabletop Flipchart ◆ Enrich 11.3

See the Grab-and-Go!™ Centers Kit for more small-group activities.

Grab-and-Go!™

Version 2.0

Differentiated Centers Kit

The kit provides literature, games, and activities for small-group learning.

◆ Print/Printable Resource
■ Interactive Resource

	LESSON 11.4 • 1 Day	LESSON 11.5 • 1 Day	LESSON 11.6 • 1 Day
Lesson at a Glance	Sums Up to 10 ..... 429A	Doubles 435A	Addition Word Problems 441A
I Can	I can write and solve addition equations with sums up to 10.	I can add doubles.	I can use an addition equation to solve an addition word problem.
Learning Goal	Solve problems with sums to 10.	Find the sum of doubles.	Complete addition equations to solve word problems.
Vocabulary			
Multilingual Support	**Strategy:** Define	**Strategy:** Model Concepts	**Strategy:** Identify Relationships

Practice and Fluency	LESSON 11.4	LESSON 11.5	LESSON 11.6
	◆ ■ Practice and Homework	◆ ■ Practice and Homework	◆ ■ Practice and Homework
	■ Waggle	■ Waggle	■ Waggle
	◆ Achieving Facts Fluency*	◆ Achieving Facts Fluency*	◆ Achieving Facts Fluency*

MTSS RtI Intervention and Enrichment	■ Waggle	■ Waggle	■ Waggle
	◆ ■ Reteach 11.4	◆ ■ Reteach 11.5	◆ ■ Reteach 11.6
	◆ ■ Tier 2 Intervention Skill S27/S29	◆ ■ Tier 2 Intervention Skill S22	◆ ■ Tier 2 Intervention Skill S28
	◆ ■ Tier 3 Intervention Skill E14/E27/E29	◆ ■ Tier 3 Intervention Skill E22	◆ ■ Tier 3 Intervention Skill E28
	◆ Tabletop Flipchart	◆ Enrich 11.5	◆ Tabletop Flipchart
	◆ Enrich 11.4		◆ Enrich 11.6

*For individual and class practice with counting automaticity and operational fluency, go to *Achieving Facts Fluency* pages located online.

◆ Print/Printable Resource
■ Interactive Resource

Teaching for Depth
Addition Up to 10

Encouraging Independence

As children work with addition, guide them to get into the routine of checking their work. Reread the problems. Then ask questions. Here are some examples.

- **Did you use the numbers that were used in the addition word problem?**
- **What kind of answer did you think you would get?**
- **Does your answer make sense?**

Help children explain how they solved the problems with prompts such as these:

- **Explain how you found your answer.**
- **Why did you choose that way to solve?**
- **Is there another way you could have used to solve?**

As you go through these questions, help children correct any errors they find.

From the Research

❝Children that struggled with addition up to 5 will likely feel discouraged before beginning this chapter. Culturally responsive teaching requires facilitating a shift from viewing mistakes as failure to viewing mistakes as an opportunity to learn and grow. Identify children who struggled with addition previously, and include them in a discussion about why addition was difficult for them specifically. Set them up for success by explaining how we grow by understanding and learning from our mistakes. This mindset shift helps children to become independent learners and to take ownership of their own learning.❞

(Hammond, 2015, p.115)

Make Connections

Remind children that they learned how to add numbers up to 5 in Chapter 5. Explain that in this chapter, they will use what they learned about addition to 5 and extend that learning to addition within 10.

Review the connecting cubes and addition equation with children. Explain to children how the addition equation represents the problem.

$$2 + 2 = 4$$

Mathematical Practices and Processes

Attend to precision.

In this chapter, children are given an opportunity to build addition fluency. Lesson 1 teaches the familiar concepts of *one more* and *one less* within the new context of addition. Lesson 5 introduces children to doubles facts, a strategy that will benefit them in building the automaticity of addition facts expected in first grade.

For more professional learning, go online to Teacher's Corner.

Instructional Journey

While every classroom may look a little different, this instructional model provides a framework to organize small-group and whole-group learning for meaningful student learning.

Whole Group
Engage

5 minutes

Readiness
- Problem of the Day
- Fluency Builder or Vocabulary Builder
- Access Prior Knowledge

Engagement
- I Can
- Making Connections
- Learning Activity

Small and Whole Group
Explore

15–20 minutes

Exploration
- Listen and Draw, Unlock the Problem
- Multilingual Support and Strategy
- Common Errors

Small Group
Explain

15–20 minutes

Quick Check
- ✓ Share and Show

Differentiated Instruction

Version 2.0

Intervention
- Waggle
- Reteach
- Tier 2 and Tier 3 MTSS
- Tabletop Flipchart Mini Lessons

Language Support
- Vocabulary Activities
- Language Routines
- Multilingual Glossary

Enrichment
- Waggle Games
- Ready for More
- Enrich

Whole Group
Elaborate

5 minutes

- Math on the Spot Videos
- Higher-Order Thinking Problems

Evaluate

- I Can Reflection
- Exit Ticket
- Practice and Homework
- Fluency Practice
- Waggle

Assessment

Diagnostic	Formative	Summative
• Show What You Know	• Lesson Quick Check	• Chapter Review • Chapter Test • Performance Assessment Task

Version 2.0
Differentiated Centers Kit
The kit provides literature, games, and activities for small-group learning.

Strategies for
Multilingual Learners

Understanding a child's language development is helpful in differentiating teaching and assessment. Assessing a child's understanding of mathematical concepts can be done by listening, speaking, reading, and writing. The level of support a child needs determines how best to assess that child's understanding of mathematical concepts.

Planning for Instruction			
Language Support	**Substantial** (WIDA Level 1)*	**Moderate** (WIDA Levels 2 & 3)*	**Light** (WIDA Levels 4 & 5)*
Child's Use of Language	• uses single words • uses common short phrases • heavily relies on visual supports and use of manipulatives	• uses simple sentences • uses some academic vocabulary • relies on visual supports and use of manipulatives	• uses a variety of sentences • uses academic vocabulary • benefits from visual supports and manipulatives
Ways to Assess Understanding	**Listening:** points to pictures, words, or phrases to answer questions **Speaking:** answers *yes/no* questions **Reading:** matches symbols to math terms and concepts **Writing:** draws a visual representation of a problem	**Listening:** matches, categorizes, or sequences information based on visuals **Speaking:** begins to explain reasoning, asks math questions, repeats explanations from peers **Reading:** identifies important information to solve a problem **Writing:** uses simple sentences and visual representations	**Listening:** draws conclusions and makes connections based on what they heard **Speaking:** explains and justifies concepts and solutions **Reading:** understands information in math contexts **Writing:** completes sentences using some academic vocabulary

* For more information on WIDA Standards, visit their website at:
https://wida.wisc.edu/.

• Look for strategies throughout the lesson to support multilingual learners.
• Log on to ED to find additional multilingual activities and Vocabulary Cards.

In This Chapter

Key Academic Vocabulary

Current Development • Vocabulary

Using Language Routines to Develop Understanding

 Language routines provide opportunities for children to develop an understanding of mathematical language and concepts by listening, speaking, reading, and writing. More information on these language routines can be found on the Language Support Cards.

Three Reads

Children read a problem three times with a specific focus each time.

1st Read What is the problem about?

2nd Read What do each of the numbers describe?

3rd Read What math questions could you ask about the problem?

Language Support	Substantial (WIDA Level 1)*	Moderate (WIDA Levels 2 & 3)*	Light (WIDA Levels 4 & 5)*
Language Routine Differentiation	Children listen to a problem three times with scaffolded questions. **1st Listen** What happens in the problem? **2nd Listen** What numbers do you hear? **3rd Listen** What math questions could you ask?	Children read a problem three times with a proficient partner with scaffolded questions. **1st Read** What happens in the problem? **2nd Read** What numbers do you hear? **3rd Read** What math questions could you ask?	Children engage in the language routine with proficient peers. Monitor to provide additional support if required (*example: clarify meaning of vocabulary within the guiding questions*).
Possible Student Work	**Draw to model.** $4 + 3 = 7$ **How many apples in all?** 7	**Draw to model.** $4 + 3 = 7$ **How many apples in all?** 7 🍎 in all	**Draw to model.** $4 + 3 = 7$ **How many** 🍎**?** 4 **How many** 🍎**?** 3 **How many** 🍎 **in all?** 7 **What does your number sentence mean?** 4 plus 3 is 7.

* For more information on WIDA Standards, visit their website at:
https://wida.wisc.edu/.

Assessing Prior Knowledge

Have children complete **Show What You Know** on their own. Items tested are the prerequisite skills for this chapter.

Diagnostic Interview Task

The alternative interview tasks below evaluate children's understanding of each **Show What You Know** skill. The diagnostic chart may be used for intervention on prerequisite skills.

MATERIALS red and blue connecting cubes

Allow children to use connecting cubes to model the problems.

- Show 3 red cubes and 1 blue cube. Ask children to write an addition equation to show how many cubes they have in all.
  3 + 1 = 4

- Tell the following story. **Henry sees 5 red birds and 4 blue birds in the tree. How many birds does Henry see?** Have children show how they put the numbers together.
  9, 5 + 4

Name _____

✓ Show What You Know

Addition Up to 5

1

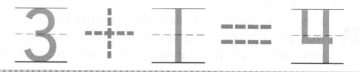

Put Together Numbers to 10

2

This page checks understanding of important skills needed for success in Chapter 11.

DIRECTIONS 1. Three rabbits are in a garden. One rabbit joins them. What is the total number of rabbits? Write the addition equation. 2. Catie sees some dogs at a park. She sees 5 dogs with spots and 4 dogs without spots. How many dogs does Catie see? Use the picture to solve the problem. Write the numbers and trace the symbols.

© Houghton Mifflin Harcourt Publishing Company

Chapter 11 • Addition Up to 10   **409**

✓ Show What You Know • Diagnostic Assessment

Use to determine if children need intervention for the chapter's prerequisite skills.

If NO...then
INTERVENE

If YES...then use
INDEPENDENT ACTIVITIES

Were children successful with Show What You Know?

	Skill	Missed More Than	Intervene With
TIER 3	Addition Up to 5	0	*Intensive Intervention* Skill E28
TIER 2	Put Together Numbers to 10	0	*Strategic Intervention* Skill S28

Version 2.0

Differentiated Centers Kit

Use the Reteach or Enrich Activities online or the independent activities in the *Grab-and-Go 2.0™ Differentiated Centers Kit*.

Vocabulary Builder

add

DIRECTIONS Add the set of bees and the set of butterflies. Write how many insects altogether.

410 Go Math! Grade K

© Houghton Mifflin Harcourt Publishing Company

Vocabulary Builder

Children use multiple strategies to develop grade-appropriate vocabulary.

Have children complete the activities on the page by working alone or with partners.

Look at the page with children. Discuss the sets of animals.

- **Look at the sets of animals. What animals do you see?** bees and butterflies

Guide children to count the animals in each set by asking questions such as the following:

- **How many bees are in the picture?** 5
- **How many butterflies do you see?** 5
- **How many insects are there?** 10

Then have children circle the sets with the same number of animals. Finally, ask children to write the number of insects in the picture.

School-Home Letter is available in English and Spanish online, and in multiple other languages.

Intervention Options MTSS RtI Response to Intervention

Use Show What You Know, Lesson Quick Check, and Assessments to diagnose children's intervention levels.

TIER 1	TIER 2	TIER 3	ENRICHMENT
On-Level Intervention	**Strategic Intervention**	**Intensive Intervention**	**Independent Activities**
For children who are generally at grade level but need early intervention with the lesson concepts, use:	For children who need small-group instruction to review concepts and skills needed for the chapter, use:	For children who need one-on-one instruction to build foundational skills for the chapter, use:	For children who successfully complete lessons, use:
			• Waggle Practice and Games
• Reteach			**Grab and Go!**
• Tabletop Flipchart Mini Lesson	▲ Prerequisite Skills Activities	▲ Prerequisite Skills Activities	Version 2.0
• Waggle	▲ Tier 2 Activity	▲ Tier 3 Activity	Differentiated Centers Kit
▲ Tier 1 Activity			• Ready for More Activity for every lesson
			• Enrich

Lesson at a Glance
One More and One Less

SNAPSHOT

Mathematical Standards
- Represent addition and subtraction with objects, fingers, mental images, drawings, sounds (e.g., claps), acting out situations, verbal explanations, expressions, or equations.

Mathematical Practices and Processes
- Model with mathematics.
- Reason abstractly and quantitatively.
- Look for and make use of structure.

(I Can) Objective
I can use addition and subtraction to find one more and one less.

Learning Goal
Add 1 and subtract 1.

Language Objective
Children explain how to find one more and one less.

MATERIALS
- MathBoard
- connecting cubes

ACROSS THE GRADES

Grade K
Add two one-digit whole numbers with sums from 0 to 10 and subtract using related facts with procedural reliability.

After
Add two whole numbers with sums from 0 to 20, and subtract using related facts with procedural reliability.

ABOUT THE MATH

Children have explored the concept of adding 1 to find one more and subtracting 1 to find one less as they counted and found the number before and after a given number. They were able to find the number that was *one more* and *one less* by counting forward and backward, respectively. They have used the terms *one more* and *one less* before with numbers to 20 without associating them with addition and subtraction. The idea that addition finds more and subtraction finds less is a critical conceptual understanding.

For more professional learning, go online to Teacher's Corner.

LESSON 11.1

DAILY ROUTINES

 **Problem of the Day 11.1**

Write the numbers from 3 to 8. 3, 4, 5, 6, 7, 8

 **Vocabulary**

- Interactive Student Edition
- Multilingual Glossary

Fluency Builder

Count Backward Write the next 3 numbers.

8 7, 6, 5,

5 4, 3, 2,

FOCUSING ON THE WHOLE STUDENT

Access Prior Knowledge

- Have children work together to make a list of five things that they might see at a petting zoo or a park.
- Have children act out a scene about flying kites.

① Engage

with the Interactive Student Edition

I Can Objective

I can use addition and subtraction to find one more and one less.

Making Connections

Invite children to tell you what they know about the phrases *one more* and *one less*.

Ask a volunteer to draw 4 kites on the left side of the board. Ask a second volunteer to draw 5 kites on the right side of the board. **Which group has more kites in it? How do you know?** the group to the right; because 5 is one more than 4

Learning Activity

Guide children toward recognizing a number that shows one more than another number.

- **You see 3 kites. What is one more than 3?**
- **You see 1 kite. What is one more than 1?**

② Explore

Listen and Draw

Materials connecting cubes

Read the story problem as children listen.

Cole has 5 cars. Meehan gives one more toy car to Cole. How many cars does Cole have now?

Have children use cubes to show Cole's five cars.

- **Meehan gives one more car to Cole. How can you show that number with cubes?** add one more cube

Explain to children that *one more* means there is one more than five. Have children add one cube to the five cubes and count cubes.

- **How many cubes are there?** 6

Help children trace and write the numbers and symbols to complete the addition equation. Remind children that six is one more than five.

- **Let's put five cubes back on the page. How can we find what number is one less than 5?** take one cube away

Explain to children that *one less* means there is one less than five. Have children take away one cube and then count how many are left.

- **How many cubes are there now?** 4 **So one less than five is four. Trace and write the subtraction equation.**

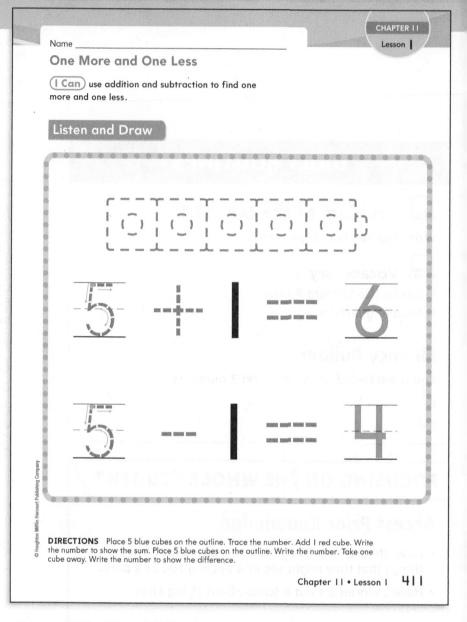

Name _____

One More and One Less

(**I Can**) use addition and subtraction to find one more and one less.

Listen and Draw

$$5 + 1 = 6$$

$$5 - 1 = 4$$

DIRECTIONS Place 5 blue cubes on the outline. Trace the number. Add 1 red cube. Write the number to show the sum. Place 5 blue cubes on the outline. Write the number. Take one cube away. Write the number to show the difference.

Chapter 11 • Lesson 1   **411**

© Houghton Mifflin Harcourt Publishing Company

 Multilingual Support

STRATEGY: Cooperative Grouping

Materials paper, marker

- Divide children into groups of 5 with mixed English language abilities. Have children sit in a circle and then count off and write their number on paper.

  My number is ___.
  It is one more than ____.
  It is one less than ____.

- Write the sentence frames on the board.

- Have children go around the circle and tell about their number by using the sentence frames. Model an example with the class.

1

$$6 + 1 = \underline{7}$$

2

$$\underline{8} = 7 + 1$$

3

$$8 + 1 = \underline{9}$$

4

$$\underline{10} = 9 + 1$$

DIRECTIONS 1–4. Use two colors of cubes to show the sum. Write the number.

© Houghton Mifflin Harcourt Publishing Company

③ Explain

Share and Show

Have children find Problem 1. Tell children that they will use cubes on their desk or table to show the addition equation.

- **Use two colors of cubes to show the addition equation. Count the cubes. How many cubes are there altogether?** 7 **Write the number.**

Guide children to look at the addition equations in Problems 2, 3, and 4. Then have them complete the problems in a similar way.

Use the checked problem for Quick Check.

✓ Quick Check MTSS (RtI)

If → a child misses the checked problem

Then → **Differentiate Instruction with**
- Reteach 11.1
- Waggle

⚠ Common Errors

Error A child finds one less instead of one more.

Springboard to Learning Have the child show a set with cubes, and then coach the child to add one more. Then count the objects. Say "__ and one more is __".

Ready for More   🕐 | Logical / Mathematical Partners

Materials two-color counters

- Ask children to complete the sentences. Encourage pairs of children to use counters if needed.

  7 is 1 more than ___. 6
  3 is 1 less than ___. 4
  9 = 1 + ___ 8
  5 = ___ minus 1 6

- If children have trouble with the equations, show that they can be rewritten as
  1 + ___ = 9 and ___ minus 1 = 5.

④ Elaborate

Share and Show

Guide children to Problem 5.

- **Use two colors of cubes to show the subtraction equation. Count the cubes. How many cubes are left?** 9 **Write the number.**

Guide children to look at the subtraction equations in Problems 6, 7, and 8. Then have them complete the problem in a similar way.

Use the checked problem for *Quick Check*.

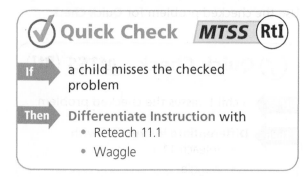

If	a child misses the checked problem
Then	**Differentiate Instruction** with • Reteach 11.1 • Waggle

Higher-Order Thinking

Evan has one fewer block than Owen. Owen has 8 blocks. How many blocks does Evan have? 7

MP **Reason abstractly and quantitatively.**

Present the problem and have children decide how to find the answer. Children will have to reverse their thinking to solve.

Let a child represent with cubes as you repeat parts of the problem. **Owen has 8 blocks.** Child shows 8 blocks. **This is one more than Evan has.**

Explain that if Evan has one fewer than Owen, then Owen has one more than Evan. Evan has 7 blocks.

Math on the Spot Use this video to help children model and solve this type of problem.

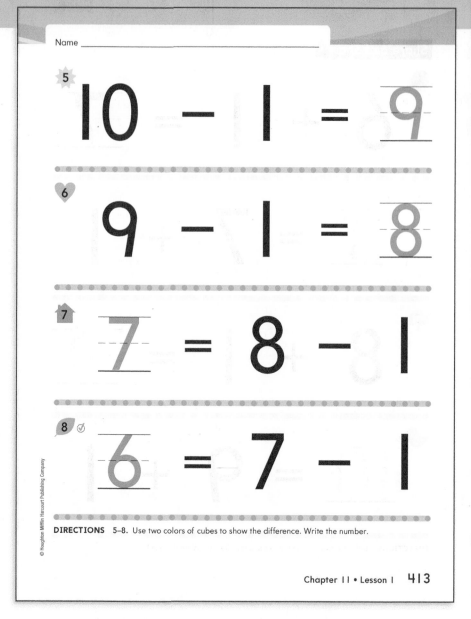

Name _____

5. $10 - 1 = \underline{9}$

6. $9 - 1 = \underline{8}$

7. $\underline{7} = 8 - 1$

8. $\underline{6} = 7 - 1$

© Houghton Mifflin Harcourt Publishing Company

DIRECTIONS 5–8. Use two colors of cubes to show the difference. Write the number.

Chapter 11 • Lesson 1   413

Meeting Individual Needs

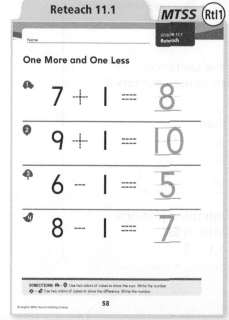

Reteach 11.1   *MTSS* (RtI1)

Name _____

One More and One Less

1. $7 + 1 = \underline{8}$
2. $9 + 1 = \underline{10}$
3. $6 - 1 = \underline{5}$
4. $8 - 1 = \underline{7}$

DIRECTIONS 1–2. Use two colors of cubes to show the sum. Write the number.
3–4. Use two colors of cubes to show the difference. Write the number.

58

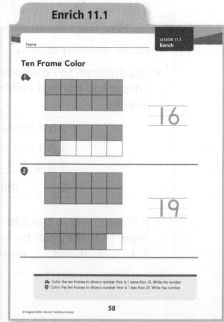

Enrich 11.1

Name _____

Ten Frame Color

1. $\underline{16}$

2. $\underline{19}$

1. Color the ten frames to show a number that is 1 more than 15. Write the number.
2. Color the ten frames to show a number that is 1 less than 20. Write the number.

58

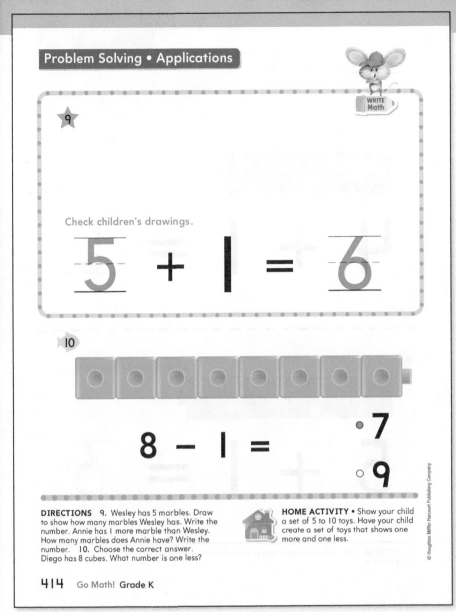

★ 9

Check children's drawings.

$$5 + 1 = 6$$

10

$$8 - 1 = \quad \cdot 7$$
$$ \circ 9$$

DIRECTIONS 9. Wesley has 5 marbles. Draw to show how many marbles Wesley has. Write the number. Annie has 1 more marble than Wesley. How many marbles does Annie have? Write the number. **10.** Choose the correct answer. Diego has 8 cubes. What number is one less?

HOME ACTIVITY • Show your child a set of 5 to 10 toys. Have your child create a set of toys that shows one more and one less.

414   Go Math! Grade K

© Houghton Mifflin Harcourt Publishing Company

DIFFERENTIATED INSTRUCTION • Independent Activities

Grab-and-Go!™
Version 2.0
Differentiated Centers Kit

Tabletop Flipchart
Mini-lessons for reteaching to targeted small groups

Readers
Supports key math skills and concepts in real-world situations.

Games
Reinforce math content and vocabulary

Activities
Meaningful and fun math practice

Problem Solving Applications WRITE Math

(MP) **Model with mathematics.**

Problem 9 Read the problem to children and have them explain how they will find the answer.

• **Wesley has 5 marbles. Draw to show how many marbles Wesley has. Write the number. Annie has 1 more marble than Wesley. How many marbles does Annie have?** 6

Guide children to draw their answer. Then restate the problem for them to check.

(MP) **Look for and make use of structure.**

Read **Problem 10** aloud to children. Direct children to fill in the bubble for the correct answer.

⑤ Evaluate | Formative Assessment

I Can

Have pairs of children write, draw, or model an example to demonstrate the skill for the I Can statement.

I can use addition and subtraction to find one more and one less by . . . using cubes and equations. I can subtract 1 to find one less or add 1 to find one more.

Exit Ticket

Draw to show how you would solve 6 and one more. Draw to show how you would solve 6 and one less.

Practice and Homework

One More and One Less

Use the Practice and Homework pages to provide children with more practice of the concepts and skills presented in this lesson. Children master their understanding as they complete practice items.

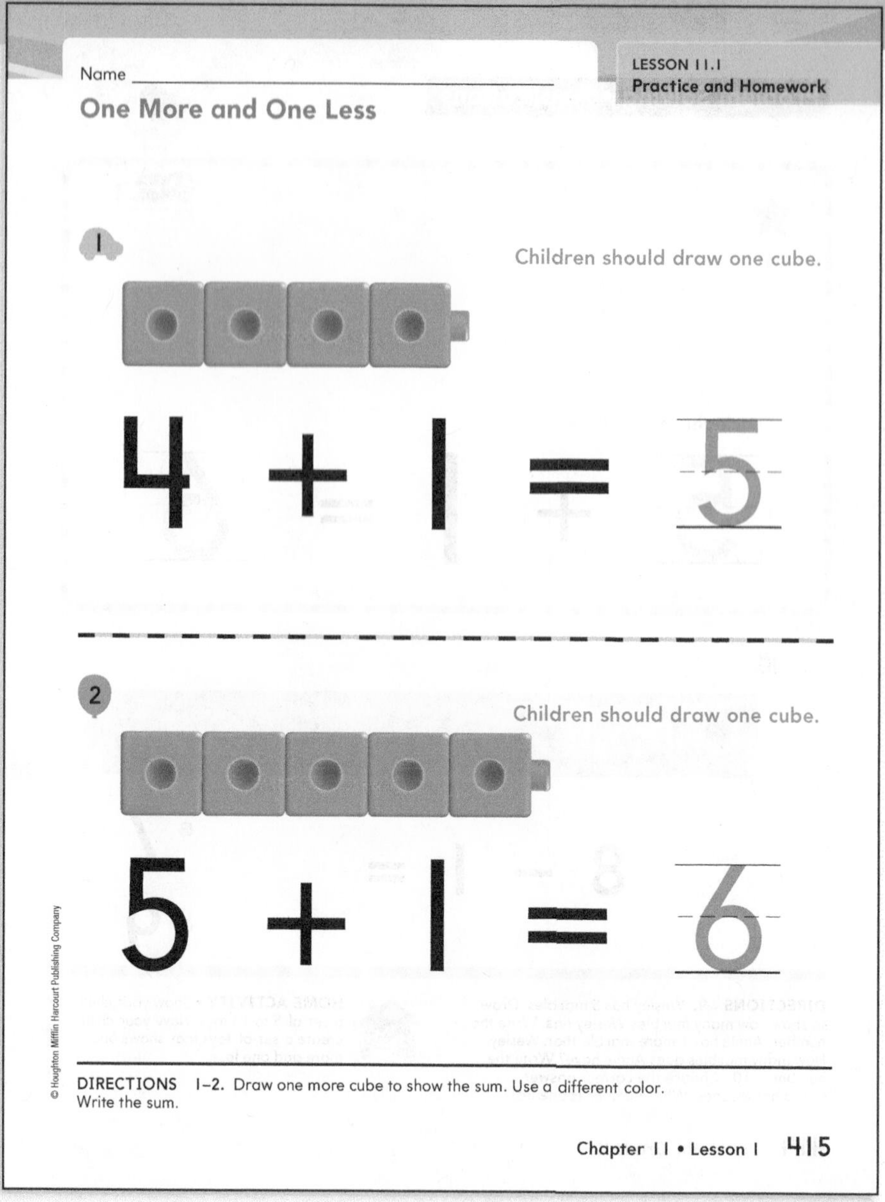

Name ________________

LESSON 11.1
Practice and Homework

One More and One Less

1. Children should draw one cube.

$4 + 1 = 5$

2. Children should draw one cube.

$5 + 1 = 6$

DIRECTIONS 1–2. Draw one more cube to show the sum. Use a different color. Write the sum.

Chapter 11 • Lesson 1 415

Lesson Check

$$3 - 1 = $$

○ 2

○ 3

Spiral Review

○ 8

● 7

DIRECTIONS Choose the correct answer. **3.** Selena has 3 brown toy bears. What number is one less? **4.** How many crayons are there?

416 Go Math! Grade K

Lesson at a Glance
Sums Up to 7

SNAPSHOT

Mathematical Standards
- Represent addition and subtraction with objects, fingers, mental images, drawings, sounds (e.g., claps), acting out situations, verbal explanations, expressions, or equations.

Mathematical Practices and Processes
- Model with mathematics.
- Construct arguments and critique reasoning of others.
- Look for and make use of structure.
- Reason abstractly and quantitatively.
- Attend to precision.

(I Can) Objective
I can write and solve addition equations with sums up to 7.

Learning Goal
Solve problems with sums to 7.

Language Objective
Children represent word problems symbolically and explain how to solve the problem.

MATERIALS
- MathBoard

ACROSS THE GRADES

Grade K
Explore addition of two whole numbers from 0 to 10, and related subtraction facts.

After
Recall addition facts with sums to 10 and related subtraction facts with automaticity.

ABOUT THE MATH

Expanding on previous learning, children will now use equations with sums to 7 to solve problems. A new tool is introduced, however, where they are using a number line to help them. Take time to explain how the number line shows addition. Explain that the first number is plotted on the number line. Then show how the arrows indicate the number that is being added. Count the total number of arrows, ignoring the numbers to which they point, to draw this connection. Then highlight the number where the arrows end, explaining that this is the sum. Another emphasis should be placed on the fact that the arrows go to the right because when added the numbers increase.

For more professional learning, go online to Teacher's Corner.

DAILY ROUTINES

 **Problem of the Day 11.2**

What number, when paired with 2, makes 10? 8

 **Vocabulary**

- Interactive Student Edition
- Multilingual Glossary

Fluency Builder

Put the following numbers in order from least to greatest.
5, 2, 8 2, 5, 8

Put the following numbers in order from greatest to least.
9, 3, 6 9, 6, 3

FOCUSING ON THE WHOLE STUDENT

Access Prior Knowledge

Choose one or more of the following activities.

- Ask children to work together to make a list of things you might find at a picnic. Write the list on the board.

- Display a stack of up to 15 plastic cups or similar objects. Ask a few volunteers to guess how many cups are in the stack. Then, remove cups one by one and count them out loud with children.

---

① Engage

with the Interactive Student Edition

I Can Objective

I can write and solve addition equations with sums up to 7.

Making Connections

Invite children to share what they know about finding sums and differences to 5.

If I have 2 boxes of crayons and my friend gives me 1 more, how many boxes of crayons do I have now? 3

Ask a volunteer to come to the board and write an equation that shows the problem. **What if I gave away 2 of my 3 boxes? How many would I have then?** 1

Learning Activity

Direct children toward understanding the different parts of an addition equation.

Show 4 green cups and 2 yellow cups.

- **How many green cups are there?** 4
- **How many yellow cups are there?** 2
- **What question could you ask?** How many cups are there altogether?

② Explore

Listen and Draw

Read the story problem as children listen.

Leslie has red flowers and blue flowers in her garden. Write how many red flowers she has. Write how many blue flowers she has. How many flowers does she have in all?

(MP) Attend to precision.

- **What information do you know?** Leslie grows red and blue flowers.
- **What do you need to find?** how many flowers in all
- **When two groups are put together, how do you find how many there are in all?** add

(MP) Look for and make use of structure.

- **How many flowers are red?** 6 **Trace the** *plus* **symbol and write the number.**
- **How many flowers are blue?** 1 **Trace the** *is equal to* **symbol and write the number.**
- **How many flowers are there in all?** 7

Read the addition equation with children.

Name _____

Sums Up to 7

(I Can) write and solve addition equations with sums up to 7.

Listen and Draw

$$6 + 1 = 7$$

DIRECTIONS Listen to the addition word problem. Write the numbers to complete the addition equation. Trace the symbols.

Chapter 11 • Lesson 2 **417**

(ML) Multilingual Support

STRATEGY: Model Concepts

Materials red and blue crayons

Children make connections between language and meaning when concepts are modeled.

- Draw six cubes in a row. Color four cubes red and write **4** under the cubes. Color two cubes blue and write **2** under the cubes. Write **6 = 4 + 2** under the cubes to show the addition equation.

- Read the addition equation. Have children count the 4 red cubes and then the 2 blue cubes. Have children repeat the addition equation and point to the cubes that represent each part of the equation.

Share and Show

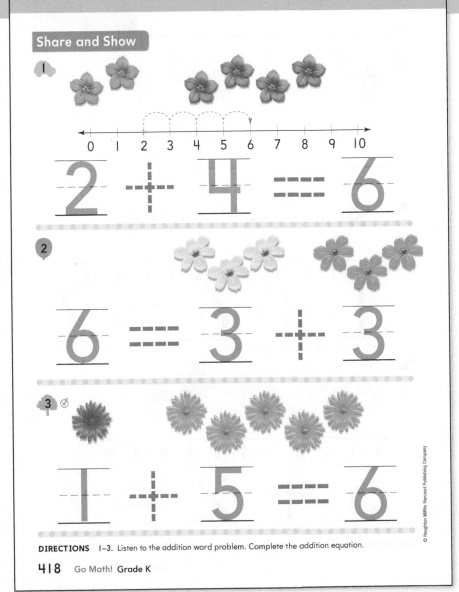

1

0 1 2 3 4 5 6 7 8 9 10

2 + 4 === 6

2

6 === 3 + 3

3

1 + 5 === 6

DIRECTIONS 1–3. Listen to the addition word problem. Complete the addition equation.

418 Go Math! Grade K

Ready for More 🕐 | Kinesthetic Partners

Materials seven red and seven blue connecting cubes

- Children will use a pattern to find all the number pairs for 6 and 7.
- Have partners start with six red cubes and write the matching addition equation. 6 = 6 + 0.
- Have children take away one red and add one blue cube to make a new number pair. Have them continue in the same way for each pair and write the addition equation each time.
- Repeat for a sum of 7.

---

③ Explain

Share and Show Math Board

Work through Problem 1 with children.

Sadie has orange and purple flowers. How many flowers does Sadie have in all?

- **How many orange flowers does Sadie have?** 2 Trace the *plus* and the *is equal to* symbols and write the number.
- **How many purple flowers does Sadie have?** 4 Trace the *plus* and the *is equal to* symbols and write the number.
- **How does the number line help you solve this problem?** The arrow lands on the sum.
- **How many flowers does Sadie have in all?** 6

Have children complete Problems 2 and 3 in the same way using the addition word problems below. Direct children to look at the pictures to count the flowers. Have children complete the equation.

- **There are three yellow flowers. There are three red flowers. How many flowers are there in all?** 6
- **One flower is purple. Five flowers are pink. How many flowers are there?** 6

Use the checked problem for Quick Check.

✓ Quick Check MTSS RtI

If ➤ a child misses the checked problem

Then ➤ **Differentiate Instruction** with
- Reteach 11.2
- Waggle

⚠ Common Errors

Error Children may write the total number of flowers instead of the number in each set.

Springboard to Learning Help children count the first group and then write the number. Repeat with the second group making sure children write the number after counting the set.

4 Elaborate

Share and Show

 Model with mathematics.

For Problems 4 through 6, read the following addition word problems aloud and have children write the addition equations.

- **There are blue and pink flowers. Write the number of flowers of each color and trace the symbols.** 4; 3 **Write how many flowers there are.** 7

- **There is one purple flower growing in a garden. There are six orange flowers growing in the garden. How many flowers are growing in the garden?** 7

- **There are five yellow flowers and two red flowers. How many flowers are there?** 7

Use the checked problem for Quick Check.

 Quick Check **MTSS** **RtI**

If → a child misses the checked problem

Then → Differentiate Instruction with
  - Reteach 11.2
  - Waggle

Higher-Order Thinking

 Construct arguments and critique reasoning of others.

Two children are asked to find a number pair that makes 7. They get two different answers. Can they both be correct? Explain.

- **Say the number pairs that make 7.** 0 and 7, 1 and 6, 2 and 5, 3 and 4

Children should be able to explain that there are many number pairs for 7. One child may show $7 = 5 + 2$ and another child may show $7 = 3 + 4$. Both answers are correct because they both make 7.

Math on the Spot Use this video to help children model and solve this type of problem.

Name _____

DIRECTIONS 4–6. Listen to the addition word problem. Complete the addition equation.

Meeting Individual Needs

Reteach 11.2   **MTSS** **RtI1**

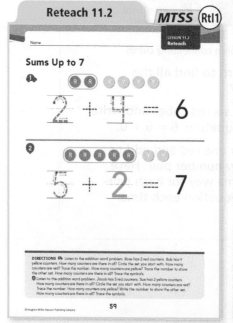

Enrich 11.2

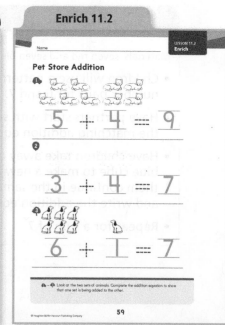

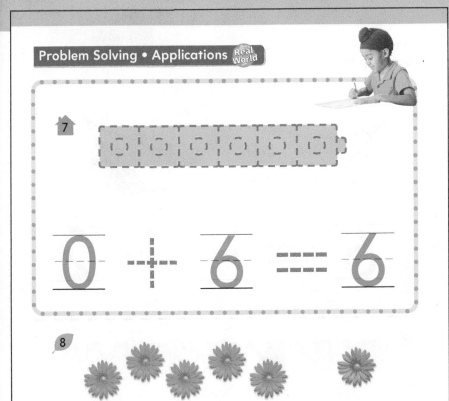

7

$$0 + 6 = 6$$

8

• $5 + 1 = 6$ ○ $5 + 2 = 7$

DIRECTIONS 7. Rohaan and Grant have six flowers in their garden. Rohaan has no flowers. How many flowers does Grant have? Color the cube train to show the number pair. Complete the addition equation. 8. Choose the correct answer. Lian has five red flowers. She gets one more purple flower. What does the picture show?

HOME ACTIVITY • Have your child use his or her fingers on two hands to show two numbers and tell how many in all.

420   Go Math! **Grade K**

© Houghton Mifflin Harcourt Publishing Company • Image Credit: ©HMH

Problem Solving Applications

Read **Problem 7** aloud.

Rohaan and Grant have six flowers in their garden. Rohaan has no flowers. How many flowers does Grant have?

(MP) **Reason abstractly and quantitatively.**

• How many flowers does Rohaan have? 0 Write the number.

• If Rohaan has no flowers and they have six flowers in all, how many flowers does Grant have? 6 Write the number.

Have children color the cube train to model the problem and find the answer. Discuss how they knew that Grant has six flowers.

Read **Problem 8** aloud to children. Direct children to fill in the bubble for the correct answer.

DIFFERENTIATED INSTRUCTION • Independent Activities

Grab and Go!
Version 2.0
Differentiated Centers Kit

Tabletop Flipchart
Mini-lessons for reteaching to targeted small groups

Readers
Supports key math skills and concepts in real-world situations.

Games
Reinforce math content and vocabulary

Activities
Meaningful and fun math practice

---

5 Evaluate | Formative Assessment

I Can

Have pairs of children write, draw, or model an example to demonstrate the skill for the I Can statement.

I can write and solve addition equations with sums up to 7 by . . . using drawings, number lines, counters, or blocks to represent the story. Then I can complete the addition equation to find the sum.

Exit Ticket

Draw to show 4 + 3. Tell a friend about your drawing.

Practice and Homework

Sums Up to 7

Use the Practice and Homework pages to provide children with more practice of the concepts and skills presented in this lesson. Children master their understanding as they complete practice items.

1

6 = 4 + 2

2

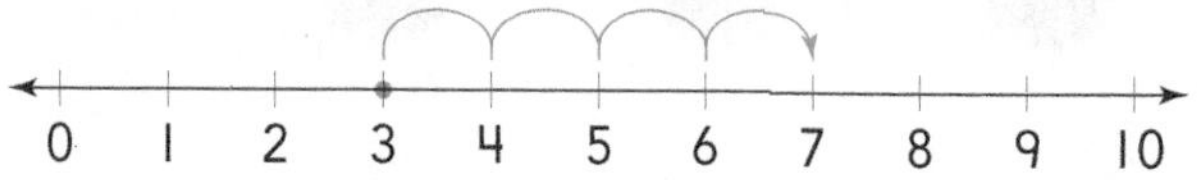

0 1 2 3 4 5 6 7 8 9 10

3 + 4 = 7

DIRECTIONS Listen to the addition word problem. Complete the addition equation.
1. There are 4 orange leaves on a branch. There are 2 red leaves on another branch. How many leaves are there? 2. The flower nursery has three green watering cans. It also has four yellow cans. How many watering cans are there?

© Houghton Mifflin Harcourt Publishing Company

Chapter 11 • Lesson 2   **421**

Lesson Check

• $4 + 2 = 6$

○ $3 + 4 = 7$

- -

Spiral Review

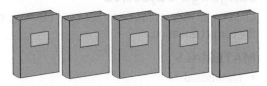

○ 7

• 6

DIRECTIONS What does the picture show? Choose the correct answer. **3.** Jackie has 4 pink shells. She gets two brown shells. **4.** There are 5 red books on a shelf. What number is one more?

422 Go Math! **Grade K**

© Houghton Mifflin Harcourt Publishing Company

Lesson at a Glance
Sums Up to 9

SNAPSHOT

Mathematical Standards
- Represent addition and subtraction with objects, fingers, mental images, drawings, sounds (e.g., claps), acting out situations, verbal explanations, expressions, or equations.

Mathematical Practices and Processes
- Model with mathematics.
- Construct arguments and critique reasoning of others.
- Look for and make use of structure.
- Attend to precision.
- Reason abstractly and quantitatively.

(I Can) Objective
I can write and solve addition equations for sums up to 9.

Learning Goal
Solve problems with sums to 9.

Language Objective
Children identify words in the scenario that help them write the correct equation.

MATERIALS
- MathBoard

ACROSS THE GRADES

Grade K
Explore addition of two whole numbers from 0 to 10, and related subtraction facts.

After
Recall addition facts with sums to 10 and related subtraction facts with automaticity.

ABOUT THE MATH

If children struggle to go from the word problem to the mathematical symbols in the equation, they might need the opportunity to act out the scenario and/or model the equation. Assess whether the lack of understanding is with the context or the mathematics. If it is with the context, clarify words or phrases children might not know. Allow them to literally act out the story or draw a picture that shows it. If they understand the story but cannot determine which equation to write, allow them to use connecting cubes, one color for each number in the story, and then put them together to count and find the sum.

For more professional learning, go online to Teacher's Corner.

🖥 Problem of the Day 11.3

What is one more than 13? 14

🖥 Vocabulary

- Interactive Student Edition
- Multilingual Glossary

Fluency Builder

Count by Ones Give children a starting number from below. Have them work in pairs to count together to 20.

5

8

11

16

FOCUSING ON THE WHOLE STUDENT

Access Prior Knowledge

Choose one or more of the following activities.

- Ask children to illustrate some things you might find in a garden. Remind them that there are lots of different types of gardens (flower, vegetable, even rock).
- Break children into two groups. Have one group brainstorm three things that are purple. Have the second group brainstorm three things that are orange.

① Engage

with the Interactive Student Edition

I Can Objective

I can write and solve addition equations for sums up to 9.

Making Connections

Invite children to tell you what they know about finding sums up to 7.

What number shows 5 and 2 more? 7 **Can you use your fingers to show me what 7 looks like?** Children will hold up 7 fingers.

Ask a volunteer to come to the board and write a number sentence showing that 5 and 2 more is 7.

Learning Activity

Help children understand how to use an addition equation to find sums up to 9.

Show some orange and purple counters.

- **How many different color counters are there?** 2
- **What are we trying to figure out?** how many there are all together
- **How can we figure that out?** by writing an addition equation

② Explore

Listen and Draw

Read the addition word problem to children.

Han grows vegetables in his garden. He grows eight carrots. He grows one cucumber. How many vegetables does Han grow in all?

(MP) **Attend to precision.**

- **What information do you know?** Han grows eight carrots and one cucumber.
- **Write the number of carrots.**
- **Write the number of cucumbers.**

(MP) **Look for and make use of structure.**

- **Trace the symbols.**
- **What do you need to find?** how many vegetables Han grows in all
- **Write the number of vegetables in the garden.** 9

Name _____

Sums Up to 9

(I Can) write and solve addition equations for sums up to 9.

Listen and Draw

Check children's work.

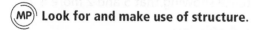

$$8 + 1 = 9$$

© Houghton Mifflin Harcourt Publishing Company

DIRECTIONS Listen to the addition word problem. Write the numbers to complete the addition equation. Trace the symbols.

Chapter 11 • Lesson 3   423

(ML) ## Multilingual Support

STRATEGY: Restate

Materials red and blue crayons

Restating key vocabulary helps children understand math problems.

- Write on the board $8 = 5 + 3$. Tell children that this addition equation says 8 is equal to 5 plus 3.

- Then say it another way. **8 is the same as 5 and 3.** Help children see the correspondence between *is equal to* and *is the same as* and between *plus* and *and*.

Share and Show

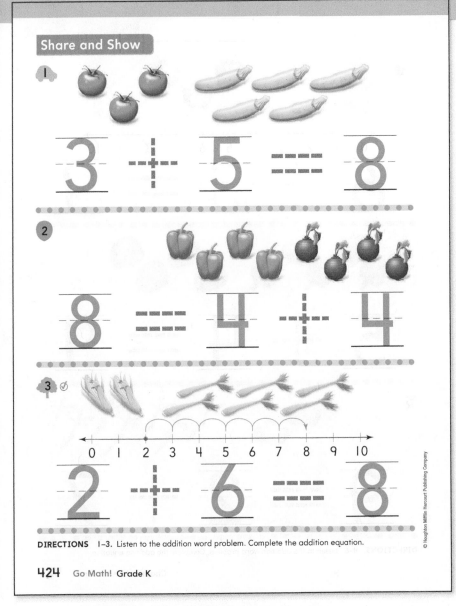

1.

$$3 + 5 = 8$$

2.

$$8 = 4 + 4$$

3. ✓

$$2 + 6 = 8$$

DIRECTIONS 1–3. Listen to the addition word problem. Complete the addition equation.

Ready for More

Kinesthetic Partners

Materials plastic cups, two-color counters

Give partners two cups and nine counters.

- Have the first child separate nine counters into two cups. Then have him or her give one cup to the second child while keeping the mystery cup.

- Have the second child count the counters in the cup and then guess the number of counters in the mystery cup.

- Have the first child reveal the counters in the mystery cup to check.

- Have both partners use that number pair that makes 9 to complete the addition equation.

---

③ Explain

Share and Show

Work through Problem 1 with children.

Ike buys vegetables at the store. Some are tomatoes and some are squash. How many vegetables does Ike buy?

- **How many tomatoes does Ike buy?** 3 Write the number.
- **How many yellow squash does Ike buy?** 5 Write the number.
- **Write how many vegetables Ike buys.** 8

Have children complete Problems 2 and 3 in the same way using these addition word problems.

- **Sima has green peppers and Clark has beets. Write the number of each kind of vegetable. How many vegetables do they have?** 8
- **Auntie buys vegetables for dinner. She buys corn on the cob and stalks of celery. Complete the addition equation. How many vegetables does she buy?** 8

Use the checked problem for Quick Check.

✓ Quick Check **MTSS** (RtI)

If ▶ a child misses the checked problem

Then ▶ **Differentiate Instruction** with
- Reteach 11.3
- Waggle

⚠ Common Errors

Error Children write the same addition equation for all problems.

Springboard to Learning Have children check each addition equation they complete to be sure that it matches the pictures and that it is different from their other equations.

④ Elaborate

Share and Show

 Reason abstractly and quantitatively.

For Problems 4 through 6, read the addition word problems aloud and have children write the numbers.

- Hazel picks zucchini from her garden. Ezra picks tomatoes from his garden. Write the number of each kind of vegetable. Write the number of vegetables they pick in all.
- How does the number line help you see the total number of vegetables? The arrows end on the sum.
- There are some artichokes and some heads of lettuce. How many vegetables are there in all? Write the numbers of each kind of vegetable. Write the answer.
- Claire buys potatoes and carrots for dinner. Write the number of each kind of vegetable. Find how many vegetables she buys.

Higher-Order Thinking

 Construct arguments and critique reasoning of others.

- How many number pairs are there for nine? Name the pairs. 0 and 9, 1 and 8, 2 and 7, 3 and 6, 4 and 5, 5 and 4, 6 and 3, 7 and 2, 8 and 1, 9 and 0
- How do you know you have counted all of the number pairs for 9?

List the numbers 0 to 9 on the board. For each number in order, ask what number pairs with it to make 9.

- 0 and what number make 9? 9

Math on the Spot Use this video to help children model and solve this type of problem.

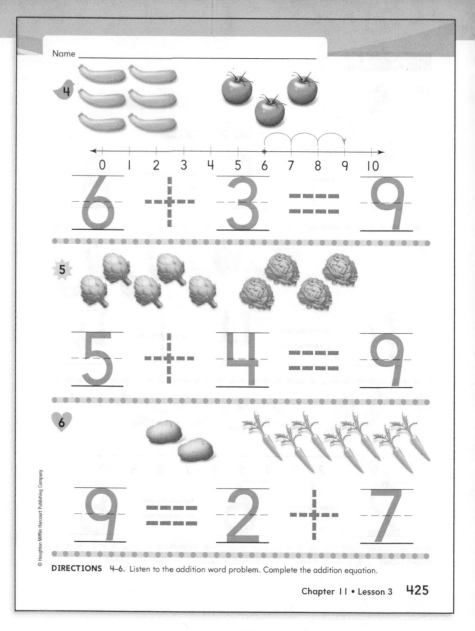

DIRECTIONS 4–6. Listen to the addition word problem. Complete the addition equation.

Chapter 11 • Lesson 3   425

Meeting Individual Needs

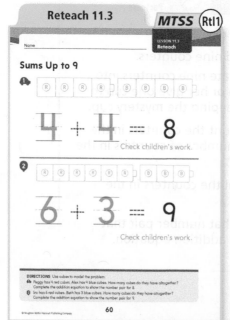

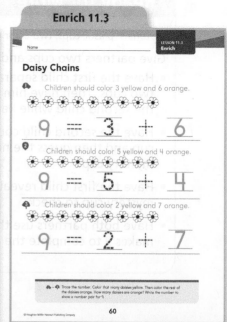

7

Check children's drawings.

$$0 + 9 = 9$$

8

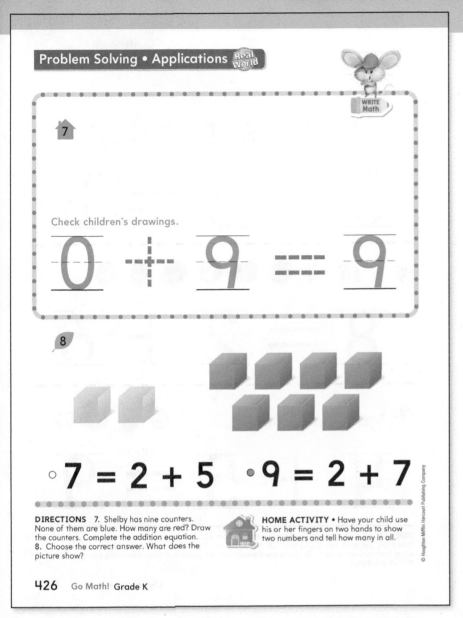

○ $7 = 2 + 5$ ● $9 = 2 + 7$

© Houghton Mifflin Harcourt Publishing Company

DIRECTIONS 7. Shelby has nine counters. None of them are blue. How many are red? Draw the counters. Complete the addition equation. 8. Choose the correct answer. What does the picture show?

HOME ACTIVITY • Have your child use his or her fingers on two hands to show two numbers and tell how many in all.

DIFFERENTIATED INSTRUCTION • Independent Activities

Grab and Go!™
Version 2.0
Differentiated Centers Kit

Tabletop Flipchart

Mini-lessons for reteaching to targeted small groups

Readers

Supports key math skills and concepts in real-world situations.

Games

Reinforce math content and vocabulary

Activities

Meaningful and fun math practice

Problem Solving Applications
Real World

(MP) **Model with mathematics.**

For **Problem 7**, ask children to listen carefully as you read the following problem aloud. Have them model with two-color counters.

Shelby has nine counters. None of them are blue. How many are red?

- **How many counters does Shelby have in all?** 9 **How many are blue?** none
- **What number do you know stands for none?** 0

Have children complete the addition equation to solve the problem.

Let children show and explain their work and the reasoning they used.

Direct children to look at the blocks in **Problem 8**. Have children fill in the bubble for the correct answer.

- **What does the picture show?**

5 Evaluate | Formative Assessment

I Can

Have pairs of children write, draw, or model an example to demonstrate the skill for the I Can statement.

I can write and solve addition equations for sums up to 9 by . . . using drawings, number lines, counters, or blocks to represent the story. Then I can complete the addition equation to find the sum.

Exit Ticket

Draw to show $5 + 4$.

Practice and Homework

Sums Up to 9

Use the Practice and Homework pages to provide children with more practice of the concepts and skills presented in this lesson. Children master their understanding as they complete practice items.

Name ______________________

LESSON 11.3
Practice and Homework

Sums Up to 9

1 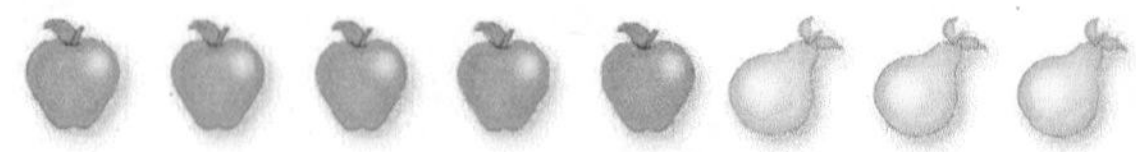

$5 + 3 = 8$

2 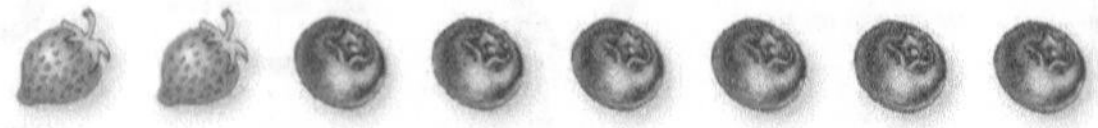

$8 = 2 + 6$

3 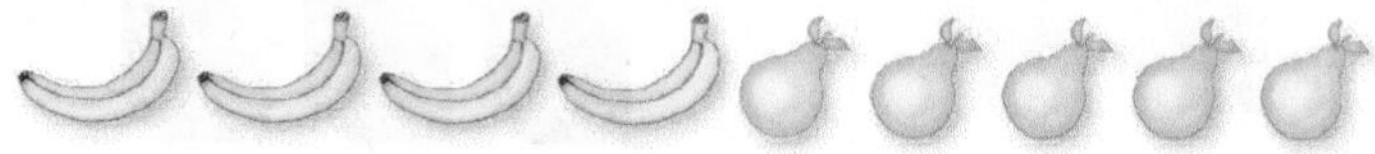

$4 + 5 = 9$

DIRECTIONS Complete the addition equation. 1. Mr. Obi bought 5 apples and 3 pears. How many pieces of fruit did he buy? 2. Mr. Jones eats 2 strawberries and 6 blueberries. How many berries does he eat? 3. There are 4 bananas and 5 pears in a bowl. How many pieces of fruit are there?

Continue to practice concepts and skills with Lesson Check. Use Spiral Review to engage children in previously taught concepts and to promote content retention.

Lesson Check

● $6 + 2 = 8$ ○ $7 + 2 = 9$

Spiral Review

$$5 + 4 = 9$$

DIRECTIONS 4. Choose the correct answer. What does the picture show? **5.** Write an addition equation about the picture.

© Houghton Mifflin Harcourt Publishing Company

Lesson at a Glance
Sums Up to 10

SNAPSHOT

Mathematical Standards

- Represent addition and subtraction with objects, fingers, mental images, drawings, sounds (e.g., claps), acting out situations, verbal explanations, expressions, or equations.

Mathematical Practices and Processes

- Model with mathematics.
- Construct arguments and critique reasoning of others.
- Reason abstractly and quantitatively.
- Use appropriate tools strategically.

(I Can) Objective

I can write and solve addition equations with sums up to 10.

Learning Goal

Solve problems with sums to 10.

Language Objective

Children explain how to use an addition equation to solve a word problem.

MATERIALS

- MathBoard

ACROSS THE GRADES

Grade K

Explore addition of two whole numbers from 0 to 10, and related subtraction facts.

After

Recall addition facts with sums to 10 and related subtraction facts with automaticity.

ABOUT THE MATH

If Children Ask

Children continue to practice using addition equations to solve problems—by now a familiar concept. The process of combining groups and also expressing that combination symbolically allows children to engage in mathematical reasoning as it applies to a real-world scenario. They also can demonstrate their understanding in multiple ways if provided the opportunity to model the addition equation with connecting cubes or to use a number line to find the sum.

For more professional learning, go online to Teacher's Corner.

DAILY ROUTINES

🖥 Problem of the Day 11.4

Write numbers from 11 to 15. 11, 12, 13, 14, 15

🖥 Vocabulary

- Interactive Student Edition
- Multilingual Glossary

Fluency Builder

Addition Facts Write the following addition problems on the board. Have children practice their addition facts by solving each problem. Then have children write a related subtraction fact.

$3 + 4$ 7; $7 - 3 = 4$ or $7 - 4 = 3$

$2 + 8$ 10; $10 - 2 = 8$ or $10 - 8 = 2$

$1 + 6$ 7; $7 - 1 = 6$ or $7 - 6 = 1$

$4 + 5$ 9; $9 - 4 = 5$ or $9 - 5 = 4$

FOCUSING ON THE WHOLE STUDENT

Access Prior Knowledge

Choose one or more of the following activities.

- Ask children to tell you about a time when they used a tool or watched someone else using tools.
- Working as a class, brainstorm a list of three places where you might use a shovel or rake.

---

① Engage

with the Interactive Student Edition

I Can Objective

I can write and solve addition equations with sums up to 10.

Making Connections

Ask children to tell you what they know about using addition equations to find sums up to 9.

Ask a volunteer to write an addition equation showing 6 and 3 more. $6 + 3 = 9$ Ask a volunteer to write an addition equation showing 5 and 4 more. $5 + 4 = 9$ **What is the same about these equations? What is different?** Answers may vary; The answer is the same, but the numbers I add are different, etc.

Learning Activity

Guide children toward using addition equations to find sums up to 10. Show children 4 counters and 5 color tiles.

- **How many counters do you see?** 4
- **How many color tiles do you see?** 5
- **How can you figure out how many counters and color tiles there are altogether?** I can count them to see how many there are.

② Explore

Listen and Draw

Read the addition word problem to children.

Abe has toy cars. Nine of his cars are blue. One car is green. How many toy cars does Abe have?

(MP) **Reason abstractly and quantitatively.**

- **What information is given in the problem?** Abe has nine blue cars and one green car.

- **What do you need to find to solve the problem?** how many cars Abe has

- **What do you know that will help you answer the problem?** I know that 9 and 1 is a number pair that makes 10.

- **Look at the picture. Write the number of cars that are blue.** 9

- **How many cars are green?** 1 **Write the number.**

- **How many cars does Abe have?** 10

Read the addition equation aloud with children. Have children trace the *plus and is equal to* symbols as they read them.

Culturally Responsive Education

As children are given progressively larger numbers to add, they may begin to doubt their ability to succeed. As an culturally responsive educator, express developmentally appropriate high expectations and a positive attitude. Be sure children know you believe in their ability to add, and remind them of past success with addition. Pay attention to students who struggle as the lesson progresses. Provide encouragement and appropriate scaffolding without lowering your expectations.

Name _____

Sums Up to 10

(I Can) write and solve addition equations with sums up to 10.

Listen and Draw

$$9 + 1 = 10$$

Check children's work.

© Houghton Mifflin Harcourt Publishing Company

DIRECTIONS Listen to the addition word problem. Write the numbers to complete the addition equation. Trace the symbols.

Chapter 11 • Lesson 4 **429**

(ML) ## Multilingual Support

STRATEGY: Define
Materials connecting cubes

Children can practice their understanding by defining words.

- Write $6 + 4 = 10$ on the board and help children read the addition equation as **six plus four is equal to ten.**

- Write *plus* underneath the plus sign and ask, **What does *plus* mean?** add, join Give children connecting cubes and have them show what *plus* means.

- Write *is equal to* underneath the equal sign and ask, **What does *is equal to* mean?** is the same as Have children use the connecting cubes to show equal sets of 10.

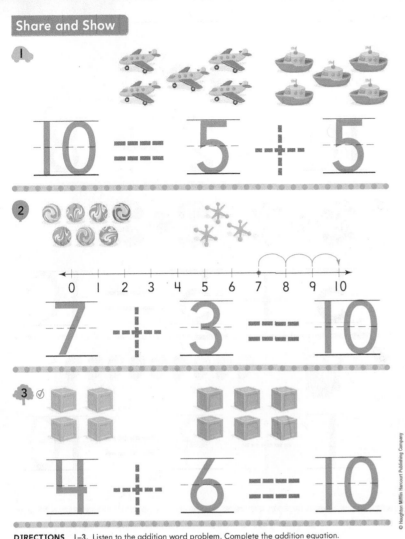

1.

$10 = 5 + 5$

2.

$7 + 3 = 10$

3.

$4 + 6 = 10$

DIRECTIONS 1–3. Listen to the addition word problem. Complete the addition equation.

430 Go Math! Grade K

© Houghton Mifflin Harcourt Publishing Company

Ready for More

 Visual
Individual / Partners

Materials ten frame, stapler

Give partners multiple copies of ten frames.

- Have partners work together to color in each ten frame to show a different number pair for 10.

- Have them record the matching addition equation beneath each ten frame.

- Have children put the pages in an order that makes sense.

- Help children bind their pages to make a book.

---

③ Explain

Share and Show

Work through Problem 1 with children.

Lula has five toy planes. Her friend August brings over five toy boats. How many toys do they have altogether?

- **How many toy planes does Lula have?** 5 **Write the number.**
- **How many toy boats did August bring?** 5 **Write the number.**
- **How many toys do they have in all?** 10

Have children complete Problems 2 and 3 in the same way, using the addition word problems below. Have children complete the addition equations.

- **Juanita has seven bouncy balls. Hector has three jacks. How many toys do they have?** 10
- **How does the number line help you solve this problem?** I can use the arrows to find how many toys in all.
- **Four blocks are orange. Write the number of blue blocks.** 6 **How many blocks are there in all?** 10

Use the checked problem for Quick Check.

✓ Quick Check   *MTSS* (RtI)

If → a child misses the checked problem

Then → **Differentiate Instruction** with
- Reteach 11.4
- Waggle

! Common Errors

Error Children may write the wrong numbers for addends.

Springboard to Learning Have children count to check the number of objects in each picture. Then have them count the number in each set twice before writing the addition equation.

④ Elaborate

Share and Show

For Problems 4 through 6, read the addition word problems aloud and have children write the addition equations.

- Gus has toy fish and ducks. Write the number of each kind of toy. Trace the symbols and complete the addition equation. How many toys does Gus have? 10

- There are red and green cars. Write the number of each color car. Complete the addition equation. How many cars are there? 10

- There is one drum. There are nine maracas. How many instruments are there? 10

Higher-Order Thinking

(MP) Construct arguments and critique reasoning of others.

- What happens if you put the numbers you are adding in a different order? Do you get another way to make the same number? **Explain your thinking.** Possible answer: Yes. When I put the numbers in a different order, I show another way to make the same number.

(MP) Model with mathematics.

Have children use two colors of cubes to make a 10-cube train and write the number pair they use. Then ask them to flip the train (from left to right) and write the equation. Discuss why this number pair makes 10.

Math on the Spot Use this video to help children model and solve this type of problem.

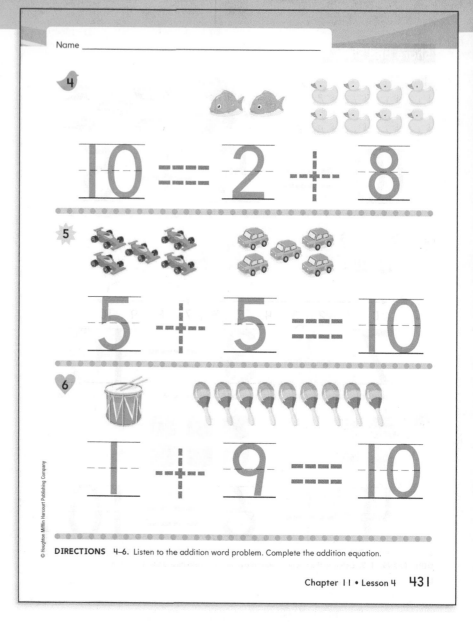

DIRECTIONS 4–6. Listen to the addition word problem. Complete the addition equation.

Chapter 11 • Lesson 4   431

Meeting Individual Needs

Reteach 11.4   MTSS (RtI1)

Sums Up to 10

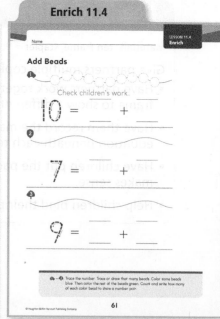

Enrich 11.4

Add Beads

Check children's drawings.

$$10 + 0 = 10$$

• $10 = 4 + 6$

○ $10 = 5 + 5$

DIRECTIONS 7. There are ten children in the cafeteria. Ten of them are drinking water. How many children are drinking milk? Draw counters to show the children drinking milk. Complete the addition equation. 8. Choose the correct answer. Nate has 4 dolls. Ollie has 6 dolls. What does the picture show?

HOME ACTIVITY • Have your child tell you an addition sentence with a sum of ten.

DIFFERENTIATED INSTRUCTION • Independent Activities

Grab and Go!
Version 2.0
Differentiated Centers Kit

Tabletop Flipchart

Mini-lessons for reteaching to targeted small groups

Readers

Supports key math skills and concepts in real-world situations.

Games

Reinforce math content and vocabulary

Activities

Meaningful and fun math practice

Problem Solving Applications *Real World*

Problem 7 Ask children to listen carefully as you read aloud the following problem.

There are ten children in the cafeteria. Ten of them are drinking water. How many children are drinking milk? 0

(MP) **Use appropriate tools strategically.**

Let children work independently on the problem. Suggest that they use counters or draw pictures to help them solve the problem. Have them complete the addition equation when they solve the problem.

Let children show and explain their work and the reasoning they used.

Read Problem 8 aloud to children. Direct children to fill in the bubble for the correct answer.

• **Nate has 4 dolls. Ollie has 6 dolls. What does the picture show?**

---

⑤ Evaluate | Formative Assessment

I Can

Have pairs of children write, draw, or model an example to demonstrate the skill for the I Can statement.

I can write and solve addition equations with sums up to 10 by . . . using drawings, number lines, counters, or blocks to represent the story. Then I can complete the addition equation to find the sum.

Exit Ticket

Write an equation to solve. There are 7 blue cubes and 3 red cubes. How many cubes in all?

Practice and Homework

Sums Up to 10

Use the Practice and Homework pages to provide children with more practice of the concepts and skills presented in this lesson. Children master their understanding as they complete practice items.

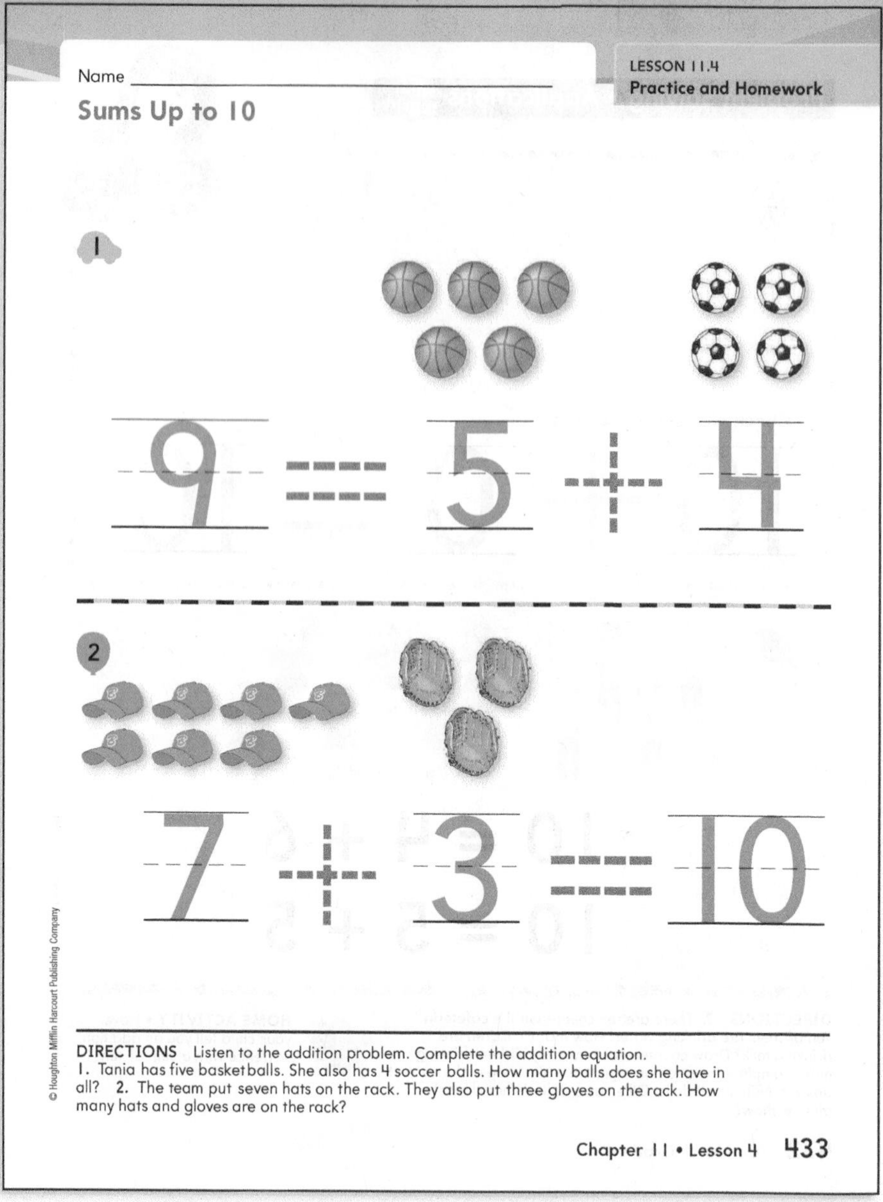

Name ____________________

LESSON 11.4
Practice and Homework

Sums Up to 10

1

9 = 5 + 4

2

7 + 3 = 10

DIRECTIONS Listen to the addition problem. Complete the addition equation. 1. Tania has five basketballs. She also has 4 soccer balls. How many balls does she have in all? 2. The team put seven hats on the rack. They also put three gloves on the rack. How many hats and gloves are on the rack?

Lesson Check

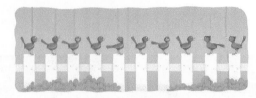

- ○ $6 + 4 = 10$
- ● $8 + 2 = 10$

Spiral Review

- ● 9
- ○ 8

DIRECTIONS Choose the correct answer. **3.** There are eight blue birds sitting on a fence. There are two red birds on the fence. What does the picture show? **4.** There are ten cats. What number is one less?

434 Go Math! Grade K

Continue to practice concepts and skills with Lesson Check. Use Spiral Review to engage children in previously taught concepts and to promote content retention.

© Houghton Mifflin Harcourt Publishing Company

Lesson at a Glance
Doubles

SNAPSHOT

Mathematical Standards
- Represent addition and subtraction with objects, fingers, mental images, drawings, sounds (e.g., claps), acting out situations, verbal explanations, expressions, or equations.

Mathematical Practices and Processes
- Model with mathematics.
- Construct arguments and critique reasoning of others.
- Look for and make use of structure.
- Attend to precision.

(I Can) Objective
I can add doubles.

Learning Goal
Find the sum of doubles.

Language Objective
Children explain how the starting number and the number of jumps on the number line are similar.

MATERIALS
- MathBoard
- connecting cubes

ACROSS THE GRADES

Grade K
Explore addition of two whole numbers from 0 to 10, and related subtraction facts.

After
Recall addition facts with sums to 10 and related subtraction facts with automaticity.

ABOUT THE MATH

The pattern of adding doubles is often exciting to children, making the recall of the facts easier. However, the purpose of knowing doubles reaches beyond such appeal. Throughout mathematics, recognizing patterns is critical to conceptual understand and ease of mathematical manipulations. Procedural fluency with doubles facts leads children to be able to use them when adding three digits or to recall other facts that are based off the doubles plus one or doubles minus one strategies. Confidence with the doubles facts carries over to confidence with other facts, thus providing more tools that children can apply in the future.

For more professional learning, go online to Teacher's Corner.

💻 Problem of the Day 11.5

Is 15 greater than or less than 17? Use drawings or a number line to show the comparison. Circle the greater number. Check children's work.

💻 Vocabulary

- Interactive Student Edition
- Multilingual Glossary

Vocabulary Builder

Addition Ask children to define the term and give several examples. Accept reasonable definitions. Possible examples given.

Term	Example(s)
doubles	$8 + 8 = 16$; $2 + 2 = 4$

FOCUSING ON THE WHOLE STUDENT

Culturally Responsive Education

Culturally responsive educators seek to close the achievement gap for culturally and linguistically diverse children by providing engaging, relatable strategies that make math more accessible. At first glance, adding doubles does not seem very engaging or relatable, but with the addition of rhyme, it can become both. Take time to allow pairs or groups of children to come up with rhymes for doubles facts. Rhymes can be short, long, silly, or witty. Here are a couple of examples.

- When it's time for math, I say, "Yipee!"
  Six is equal to three plus three!

- I can tell you math is fun.
  Math has taught me one plus one.

  You will know when I am throug
  One plus one is equal to two!

Encourage multilingual students to utilize their native language to write rhymes or to use a mix of English and their native language.

Allow children to share their rhymes if they are comfortable doing so.

Tip: Make a list of words that rhyme with number words so you can help children if they get stuck, but don't make up the rhymes for them.

① Engage

with the Interactive Student Edition

I Can Objective

I can add doubles.

Making Connections

Review what children have learned about using equations to find sums up to 10.

Using your fingers, can you show me what 4 looks like? Children will hold up 4 fingers. **Can you use your other hand to show me what 3 looks like?** Children will hold up 3 fingers. Ask a volunteer to come to the board and write an addition equation to find the total number of fingers each child held up.

Learning Activity

Guide children towards understanding doubles. Create an imaginary road. Set up 3 cones on each side.

- **How many cones are on the left side of the road?** 3

- **Are there the same number of cones on the other side of the road?** yes

- **How do you know?** I know because for each cone on the left side of the road, there is a cone on the right side of the road.

② Explore

Listen and Draw

 Look for and make use of structure.

Materials connecting cubes

Read the addition word problem to children.

Rhia has five green cubes. Casey has five blue cubes. How many cubes do Rhia and Casey have together?

- **How many cubes does Rhia have?** 5 **Place green cubes on Rhia's cubes. Trace the number.**
- **How many cubes does Casey have?** 5 **Place blue cubes on Casey's cubes. Trace the number.**
- **How many cubes do Rhia and Casey have together?** 10 **Write the number.**

Doubles are among the easiest facts for children to learn. They are especially important because they are used with strategies to build fluency in future grades.

- **When the two numbers that are added are the same, it is called a doubles problem.**

Doubles

I Can add doubles.

Listen and Draw

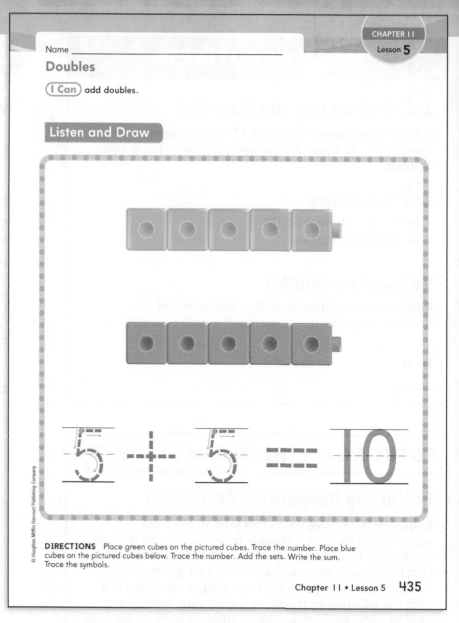

DIRECTIONS Place green cubes on the pictured cubes. Trace the number. Place blue cubes on the pictured cubes below. Trace the number. Add the sets. Write the sum. Trace the symbols.

Chapter 11 • Lesson 5 **435**

 **Multilingual Support**

STRATEGY: Model Concepts

Materials paper, markers

- Have children count off up to 5 and write their number. Children then find another child with the same number.
- Have the pairs choose an object to draw to represent their numbers. Then have them draw the total number of objects and write the equation.
- Have each pair hold up their drawing and read the equation. Beginning and intermediate English learners should repeat each modeled sentence to gain familiarity with pronunciation, meaning, and language structures.

Share and Show

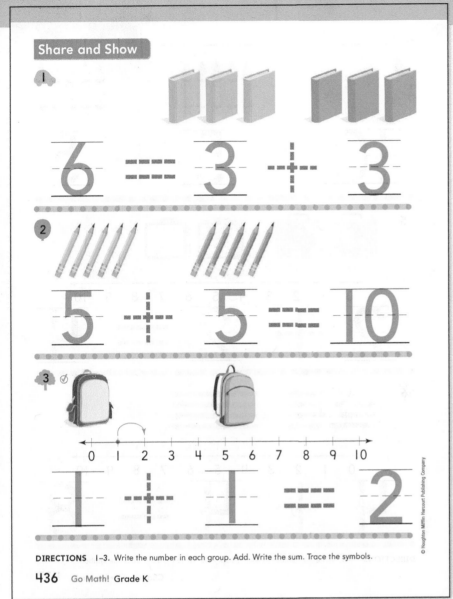

① $6 = 3 + 3$

② $5 + 5 = 10$

③ $1 + 1 = 2$

DIRECTIONS 1–3. Write the number in each group. Add. Write the sum. Trace the symbols.

© Houghton Mifflin Harcourt Publishing Company

Share and Show

Direct children's attention to Problem 1. Point to the first set of 3 books.

- **How many books are in the first set?** 3
  Write the number.
- **How many books are in the next set?** 3
  Write the number.
- **How many books are there in all?** 6
  Write the number.

Repeat in a similar way for Problems 2 and 3, helping children count each set and write the addition equation to solve.

(MP) Attend to precision.

- **How can you use the number line to find the answer?** The sum is where the arrow ends.

Use the checked problem for Quick Check.

✓ Quick Check

If → a child misses the checked problem

Then → **Differentiate Instruction** with
- Reteach 11.5
- Waggle

⚠ Common Errors

Error Children may write the total number of objects as one of the addends.

Springboard to Learning Have children count each set carefully and guide them to write the number before moving on to count the next set.

Ready for More 🕐 Logical / Mathematical Partners

- Encourage children to work with a partner.
- **What doubles fact has a sum of 8?** $4 + 4 = 8$
- **What doubles fact has a sum of 7?** Children should have trouble answering this question, since no whole number plus itself equals 7. Lead a class discussion about this question.
- **What other sums are not part of a doubles fact?** 1, 3, 5, 9

4 Elaborate

Share and Show

For Problems 4 through 6, explain that children will continue their work with doubles. Tell children to write the number for each set. Then add to find the sum.

Higher-Order Thinking

- Kyra has 5 marbles. Jill has the same number of marbles. How many marbles do they have in all? What numbers did you add? 10; 5; 5

(MP) **Construct arguments and critique reasoning of others.**

Invite volunteers to share their descriptions with the class and explain why their doubles addition word problems are shown by 5 + 5. By explaining why the problem can be represented by 5 + 5, children show that they understand its meaning.

Math on the Spot Use this video to help children model and solve this type of problem.

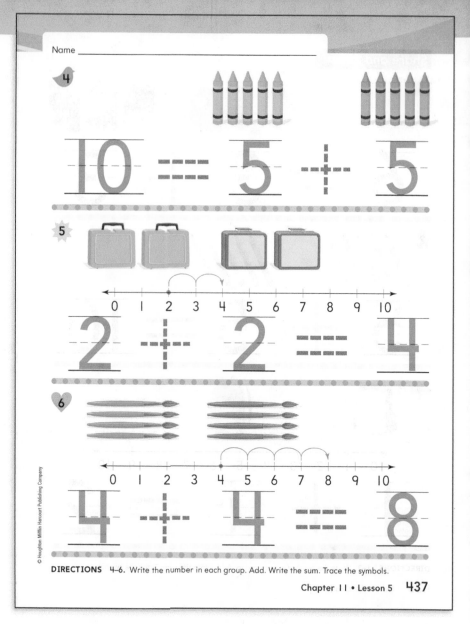

Name _____

DIRECTIONS 4–6. Write the number in each group. Add. Write the sum. Trace the symbols.

Chapter 11 • Lesson 5 437

Meeting Individual Needs

Reteach 11.5 MTSS (RtI1) **Enrich 11.5**

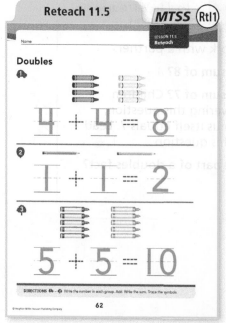

Reteach

Doubles

4 + 4 = 8

1 + 1 = 2

5 + 5 = 10

DIRECTIONS 1–3. Write the number in each group. Add. Write the sum. Trace the symbols.

62

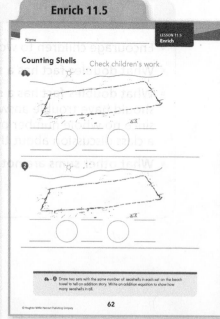

Enrich

Counting Shells Check children's work.

Draw two sets with the same number of seashells in each set on the beach towel to tell an addition story. Write an addition equation to show how many seashells in all.

62

 7

Check children's drawings.

$$2 + 2 = 4$$

8

• 4 + 4 = 8   ○ 2 + 2 = 4

DIRECTIONS 7. Simon brought two snacks to school. Draw the snacks. Write the number. Valentina brought two snacks to school. Draw the snacks. Write the number. How many snacks do they have together? Write the number. Trace the symbols.   8. Choose the correct answer. What doubles addition does the picture show?

HOME ACTIVITY • Show your child a set of 1 to 5 objects such as crayons. Have your child create a set of objects that shows the same number of objects and find the sum.

DIFFERENTIATED INSTRUCTION • Independent Activities

Grab-and-Go!™
Version 2.0
Differentiated Centers Kit

Tabletop Flipchart
Mini-lessons for reteaching to targeted small groups

Readers
Supports key math skills and concepts in real-world situations.

Games
Reinforce math content and vocabulary

Activities
Meaningful and fun math practice

Problem Solving Applications

(MP) **Model with mathematics.**

For **Problem 7**, ask children to listen carefully as you read aloud the following problem.

Simon brought two snacks to school. Valentina brought two snacks to school. How many snacks do they have together?

- **Draw the snacks that Simon brought. Write the number.** 2
- **Draw the snacks that Valentina brought. Write the number.** 2
- **Write the number of snacks in all.** 4
- **Could you use a number line to solve the problem?** Yes, a number line could help me show the addition.

Direct children to look at the pictures in **Problem 8**. Have children fill in the bubble for the correct answer.

- **What doubles addition does the picture show?**

⑤ Evaluate | Formative Assessment

I Can

Have pairs of children write, draw, or model an example to demonstrate the skill for the I Can statement.

I can add doubles by . . . drawing, using a number line, or writing an addition equation.

Exit Ticket

Use a strategy to solve 3 + 3.

Practice and Homework

Doubles

Use the Practice and Homework pages to provide children with more practice of the concepts and skills presented in this lesson. Children master their understanding as they complete practice items.

Doubles

1 $3 + 3 = 6$

2 $4 + 4 = 8$

3 $4 = 2 + 2$

DIRECTIONS 1–3. Write the number in each group. Add. Write the sum.

Chapter 11 • Lesson 5 **439**

Lesson Check

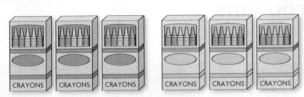

○ $4 + 4 = 8$

● $3 + 3 = 6$

- -

Spiral Review

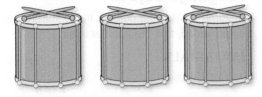

I and 2 = 3

© Houghton Mifflin Harcourt Publishing Company

DIRECTIONS 4. Choose the correct answer. What doubles addition fact does the picture show? 5. Show how to combine to make 3.

Lesson at a Glance
Addition Word Problems

SNAPSHOT

Mathematical Standards

- Represent addition and subtraction with objects, fingers, mental images, drawings, sounds (e.g., claps), acting out situations, verbal explanations, expressions, or equations.

Mathematical Practices and Processes

- Model with mathematics.
- Use appropriate tools strategically
- Look for and make use of structure.
- Reason abstractly and quantitatively.

(I Can) Objective

I can use an addition sentence to solve an addition word problem.

Learning Goal

Compete addition equation(s) to solve word problems.

Language Objective

Children identify the number in the starting set, the number being added, and the number in all.

MATERIALS

- MathBoard

ACROSS THE GRADES

Grade K

Solve addition and subtraction real-world problems using objects, drawings or equations to represent the problem.

After

Solve addition and subtraction real-world problems using objects, drawings or equations to represent the problem.

ABOUT THE MATH

Children continue their learning about addition equations as they now apply these skills to solve real-world problems. What increases the challenge here is that sometimes children must draw their own pictures from which they will write the addition equation. Each problem has three distinct parts: the number in the set to start with, how many are being added, and then the number in all. Identifying these parts draws further connections between the word problems and the mathematical symbols. It gives meaning to the location of the numbers in the equation. Allow children some creativity in how their drawings reflect this as long as the fundamental pieces are accurately depicted.

For more professional learning, go online to Teacher's Corner.

DAILY ROUTINES

 **Problem of the Day 11.6**

Draw 13 objects. Check children's drawings.

 **Vocabulary**

- Interactive Student Edition
- Multilingual Glossary

Fluency Builder

Doubles Have children write three doubles facts using numbers to 10. $1 + 1 = 2$, $2 + 2 = 4$, $3 + 3 = 6$, etc

FOCUSING ON THE WHOLE STUDENT

Access Prior Knowledge

Choose one or more of the following activities.

- Have children work together to come up with some things you could carry around in a bucket.
- Work with children to brainstorm three responsibilities you have when you're taking care of an animal.

 Social & Emotional Learning

Self-Management Help children approach learning new concepts with curiosity by recognizing and modulating their emotions. *How do you feel when you solve a challenging problem? When you start, do you feel excited, nervous, or something else entirely? Your brain works better when you are not experiencing big feelings. If solving a new type of problem makes you feel nervous or otherwise upset, try taking a deep breath or drinking a sip of water. Then focus on using what you already know to solve the problem. If you still have big feelings, talk to someone who can help you calm down and solve the problem.*

I Can Objective

I can use an addition equation to solve an addition word problem.

Making Connections

Invite children to tell you what they know about doubles.

Use your fingers to show me what 4 looks like. Children will hold up 4 fingers. **Use your other hand to hold up 4 more fingers.** Children will hold up 4 fingers on the opposite hand. **Write an equation that helps you figure out how many fingers you are holding up all together.** $4 + 4 = 8$

Learning Activity

Guide children towards learning how to solve addition word problems. Show a picture with some empty buckets and a different number of full buckets.

- **Are there the same number of full buckets as empty buckets?** no
- **How do you know?** Possible answer: the rows of buckets don't match up
- **What could you find out?** how many buckets there are all together

Explore

Unlock the Problem

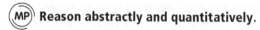 **Model with mathematics.**

Read the addition word problem to children.

Four birds were sitting in a tree. One more bird flew to the tree. How many birds are in the tree now?

- **What information do you know?** Four birds were sitting in a tree. One bird flew to the tree.
- **What do you need to find?** how many birds are in the tree now
- **How many birds were in the tree?** 4
- **How many birds fly over?** 1
- **How many birds are there now?** 5
- **Trace the symbols.**

 Reason abstractly and quantitatively.

- **How can you check your answer?** I can count all the birds in the picture.

Name _____

Addition Word Problems

(I Can) use an addition sentence to solve an addition word problem.

UNLOCK the Problem Real World

© Houghton Mifflin Harcourt Publishing Company

DIRECTIONS Listen to the addition word problem about the birds. How many birds are on the tree? Write the number. How many birds join them? Write the number. Write the number of birds in all. Trace the symbols.

Chapter 11 • Lesson 6 **441**

ML ## Multilingual Support

STRATEGY: Identify Relationships
Materials connecting cubes

Children can learn the concept of missing addends by relating common objects to addition word problems.

- **I have a blue cube train. I add five red cubes to the blue cubes.** Display a 5-cube red train.
- **Now my train has eight cubes in all. Write ___ + 5 = 8** on the board.
- **How many blue cubes did I start with?** 3 Attach a 3-cube blue train to the red train.
- **Write 3 + 5 = 8.** Have children say this addition equation aloud.

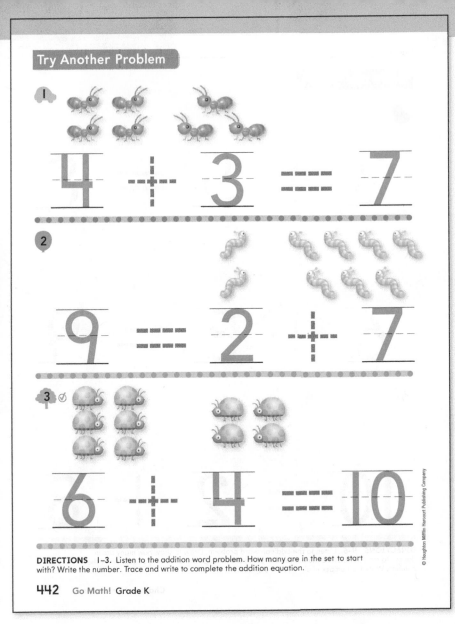

Try Another Problem

1

$$4 + 3 = 7$$

2

$$9 = 2 + 7$$

3

$$6 + 4 = 10$$

DIRECTIONS 1–3. Listen to the addition word problem. How many are in the set to start with? Write the number. Trace and write to complete the addition equation.

442 Go Math! Grade K

© Houghton Mifflin Harcourt Publishing Company

Ready for More
🕐 Kinesthetic Partners

Materials numeral cards (0–15)

Each set of partners should have two sets of numeral cards, 1 to 5 and 6 to 10.

- Have partners play a game of, "What Number Did You Start With?"
- Have one partner select a card from the 1–5 set of cards and write the number as the second addend in the addition equation.
- Have the other partner select a card from the 6–10 set and write the number as the sum in the addition equation.
- Then have partners work together to complete the addition equation that tells what number should be the first addend in the addition equation.

---

③ Explain

Try Another Problem

Work through Problem 1 with children.

There are four ants. Three more ants come to visit. How many ants are there now?

- **Look at the first group of ants. How many ants are there?** 4
- **How many ants come to visit?** 3
- **How many ants are there now?** 7 **Write the equation.**

Have children complete Problems 2 and 3 in the same way, using these addition word problems.

- **There are two worms. Seven more worms wiggle over. How many worms are there now?** 9
- **Six bugs are playing. Four more bugs come to play. How many bugs are there now?** 10

Use the checked problem for Quick Check.

✓ Quick Check MTSS RtI

If	a child misses the checked problem
Then	**Differentiate Instruction** with • Reteach 11.6 • Waggle

⚠ Common Errors

Error Children may put the sum in the place of an addend.

Springboard to Learning Help children understand what each number represents. Talk about each number before writing it in the addition equation.

Chapter 11 • Lesson 6   **442**

4 Elaborate

Share and Show

For Problems 4 through 6, ask children to listen to each addition word problem. Have them draw pictures to show the addends. Then have them write the numbers to complete the addition equation. Remind children to trace the symbols. Read the completed addition equation together.

- **There are three orange butterflies. There are five red butterflies. How many butterflies are there?** 8 butterflies

- **There is a set of six bugs and a set of three bugs. How many bugs are there altogether?** 9 bugs

- **There are two worms wiggling in the dirt. Eight worms come in. How many worms are there now?** 10 worms

Higher-Order Thinking

 Look for and make use of structure.

Draw a picture of nine bugs in a group of three and a group of six on the board and tell an addition word problem. Write the addition equation ____ + 6 = 9

- **How many bugs do you see in all?** 9

- **What addition equation could you write to match this picture?** 3 + 6 = 9

Have children compare related addition equations. Write the addition equation 6 + 3 = 9 from Problem 5 on the board. Under it, write 3 + 6 = 9.

Ask children to suggest reasons why the answer to both addition equations is 9. Elicit that there is a set of 6 and a set of 3 in both addition equations, but that the sets are in a different order.

Math on the Spot Use this video to help children model and solve this type of problem.

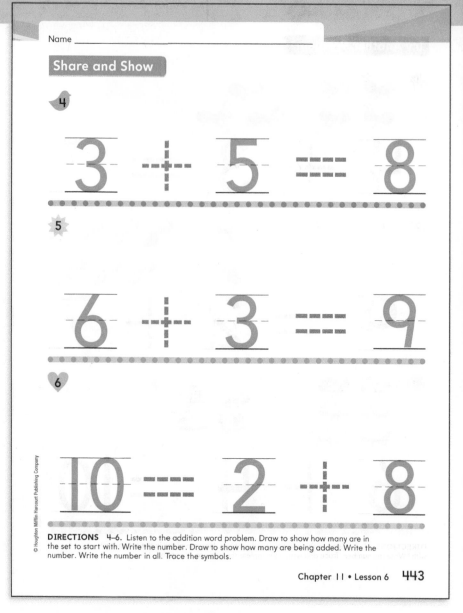

Share and Show

4

$$3 + 5 = 8$$

5

$$6 + 3 = 9$$

6

$$10 = 2 + 8$$

DIRECTIONS 4–6. Listen to the addition word problem. Draw to show how many are in the set to start with. Write the number. Draw to show how many are being added. Write the number. Write the number in all. Trace the symbols.

Chapter 11 • Lesson 6   443

Meeting Individual Needs

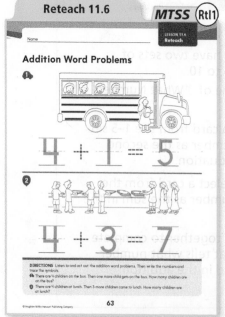

Reteach 11.6   **MTSS** (RtI1)

Name

LESSON 11.6
Reteach

Addition Word Problems

1

$$4 + 1 = 5$$

2

$$4 + 3 = 7$$

DIRECTIONS Listen to and act out the addition word problems. Then write the numbers and trace the symbols. 1. There are 4 children on the bus. Then one more child gets on the bus. How many children are on the bus? 2. There are 4 children at lunch. Then 3 more come to lunch. How many children are at lunch?

63

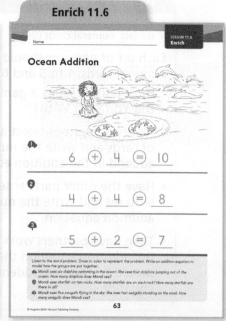

Enrich 11.6

Name

LESSON 11.6
Enrich

Ocean Addition

1

$$6 + 4 = 10$$

2

$$4 + 4 = 8$$

3

$$5 + 2 = 7$$

Listen to the word problem. Draw or color to represent the problem. Write an addition equation to model how the groups are put together. 1. Mandi sees six dolphins swimming in the ocean. She sees four dolphins jumping out of the ocean. How many dolphins does Mandi see? 2. Mandi sees starfish on two rocks. How many starfish are on each rock? How many starfish are there in all? 3. Mandi sees five seagulls flying in the sky. She sees two seagulls standing on the sand. How many seagulls does Mandi see?

63

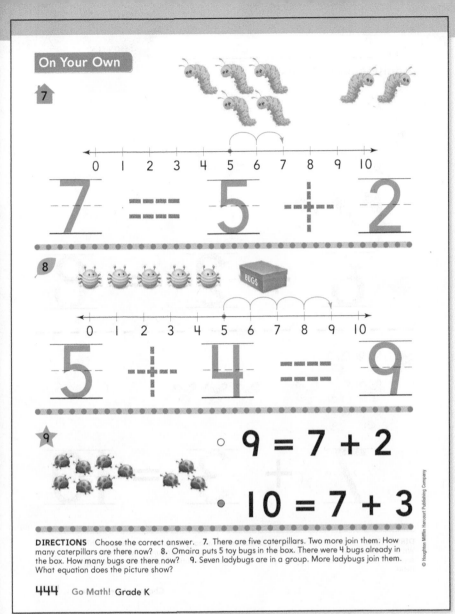

7

$$7 = 5 + 2$$

8

$$5 + 4 = 9$$

9

○ $9 = 7 + 2$

● $10 = 7 + 3$

DIRECTIONS Choose the correct answer. **7.** There are five caterpillars. Two more join them. How many caterpillars are there now? **8.** Omaira puts 5 toy bugs in the box. There were 4 bugs already in the box. How many bugs are there now? **9.** Seven ladybugs are in a group. More ladybugs join them. What equation does the picture show?

© Houghton Mifflin Harcourt Publishing Company

444 Go Math! **Grade K**

On Your Own

Read **Problem 7** to children. Ask them to describe how the picture matches the word problem.

(MP) **Use appropriate tools strategically.**

• **How can you use the number line to help you write an equation and solve the problem?** The starting number is at the point. Then the number of arrows is how much you are adding. The final arrow points to the answer.

(MP) **Model with mathematics.**

Read **Problem 8** aloud.

• **Omaira puts 5 toy bugs in the box. There were 4 bugs already in the box. How many bugs are there now?**

• **How does the equation show the word problem?** The first number is the amount in the original group. The second number is how many more. The number that they are equal to when I add is the total number, or how many in all.

Read **Problem 9** to the class. Direct children to fill in the bubble for the correct answer.

DIFFERENTIATED INSTRUCTION • Independent Activities

Grab-and-Go!™

Version 2.0

Differentiated Centers Kit

Tabletop Flipchart

Mini-lessons for reteaching to targeted small groups

Readers

Supports key math skills and concepts in real-world situations.

Games

Reinforce math content and vocabulary

Activities

Meaningful and fun math practice

⑤ Evaluate | Formative Assessment

I Can

Have pairs of children write, draw, or model an example to demonstrate the skill for the I Can statement.

I can use an addition sentence to solve an addition word problem by . . . writing an addition sentence to represent the story. Then I can add to find the answer.

Exit Ticket

Luis collected 4 big rocks and 6 small rocks. Draw to show how many rocks Luis collected in all.

Practice and Homework

Addition Word Problems

Use the Practice and Homework pages to provide children with more practice of the concepts and skills presented in this lesson. Children master their understanding as they complete practice items.

Addition Word Problems

1

$$6 + 2 = 8$$

2

$$7 + 3 = 10$$

DIRECTIONS Listen to the addition word problem. How many are in the set to start with? Write the number. Write to complete the addition sentence. **1.** There are six kites flying in the sky. Then two more kites come flying by. **2.** There are seven butterflies. Then three more join them.

Chapter 11 • Lesson 6   **445**

Lesson Check

 3

● 6

○ 4

 4

○ 8

● 5

Spiral Review

 5

● 5 + 2 = 7

○ 3 + 4 = 7

DIRECTIONS Choose the correct answer. **3.** Raul's mom buys 4 red apples. Then she buys 2 more. How many apples does she buy? **4.** Alan picks 2 ears of corn. Then he picks 3 more ears of corn. How many ears of corn does Alan pick? **5.** What does the picture show?

446 Go Math! Grade K

Continue to practice concepts and skills with Lesson Check. Use Spiral Review to engage children in previously taught concepts and to promote content retention.

Chapter Review

Summative Assessment

Use the **Chapter Review** to assess children's progress in Chapter 11.

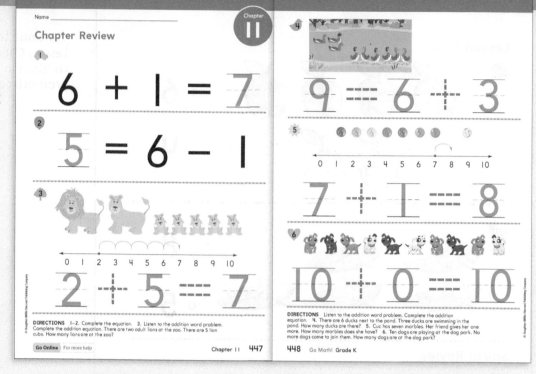

Name _____

Chapter Review

$$6 + 1 = 7$$

$$5 = 6 - 1$$

$$2 + 5 = 7$$

$$9 = 6 + 3$$

$$7 + 1 = 8$$

$$10 + 0 = 10$$

DIRECTIONS 1–2. Complete the equation. 3. Listen to the addition word problem. Complete the addition equation. There are two adult lions at the zoo. There are 5 lion cubs. How many lions are at the zoo?

DIRECTIONS Listen to the addition word problem. Complete the addition equation. 4. There are 6 ducks next to the pond. Three ducks are swimming in the pond. How many ducks are there? 5. Cuc has seven marbles. Her friend gives her one more. How many marbles does she have? 6. Ten dogs are playing at the dog park. No more dogs come to join them. How many dogs are at the dog park?

Go Online For more help

Chapter 11 447

448 Go Math! Grade K

Online, Data-Driven Decision Making

MTSS **RtI**   HMH | **Waggle**®

Based on the results of the Chapter Review, use the following resources to review skills.

Item	Lesson	Content Focus	Intervene With
1, 2	11.1	Add 1 and subtract 1.	Reteach 11.1, Waggle
3	11.2	Solve problems with sums to 7.	Reteach 11.2, Waggle
4, 5	11.3	Solve problems with sums to 9.	Reteach 11.3, Waggle
6	11.4	Solve problems with sums to 10.	Reteach 11.4, Waggle
7, 8	11.5	Find the sum of doubles.	Reteach 11.5, Waggle
9, 10, 11, 12	11.6	Complete addition sentences to solve word problems.	Reteach 11.6, Waggle

Name _____

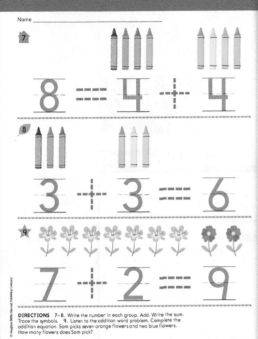

7

$$8 = 4 + 4$$

8

$$3 + 3 = 6$$

9

$$7 + 2 = 9$$

10

$$10 = 6 + 4$$

11

$$3 + 7 = 10$$

12

$$4 + 5 = 9$$

DIRECTIONS 7–8. Write the number in each group. Add. Write the sum. Trace the symbols. 9. Listen to the addition word problem. Complete the addition equation. Sam picks seven orange flowers and two blue flowers. How many flowers does Sam pick?

DIRECTIONS Listen to the addition word problem. Draw to show how many. Complete the addition equation. 10. Miguel finds six rocks by a pond. Anita finds four rocks. How many rocks do they find together? 11. Hai sees three squirrels. Seven squirrels join them. How many squirrels are there now? 12. Niko has four toy cars. Annabelle has five toy cars. How many toy cars do they have together?

Performance Assessment Task

See the Performance Tasks to assess children's understanding of the content. For each task, you will find sample student work for each of the response levels in the task scoring rubric.

Portfolio Performance Assessment Tasks may be used for portfolios.

Summative Assessment

Use the **Chapter Test** to assess children's progress in Chapter 11.

Chapter Tests are found in the *Assessment Guide*. Test items are presented in formats consistent with high-stakes assessments.

data
checkpoint

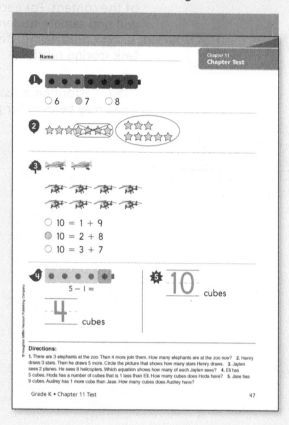

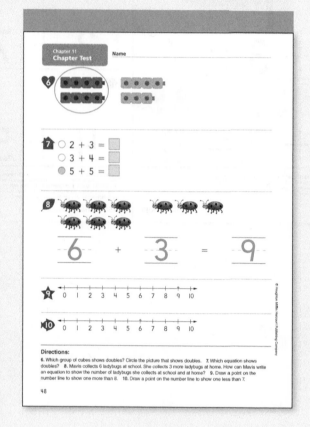

Teacher Notes

Chapter at a Glance
Subtraction Within 10

	LESSON 12.1 • 1 Day	LESSON 12.2 • 1 Day	LESSON 12.3 • 1 Day
Lesson at a Glance	Differences Within 7 . . . . 453A	Differences Within 9 . . . . 459A	Differences Within 10 . . . . 465A
I Can	I can write and solve subtraction equations within 7.	I can write and solve subtraction equations within 9.	I can write and solve subtraction equations within 10.
Learning Goal	Write and solve subtraction equations within 7.	Write and solve subtraction equations within 9.	Write and solve subtraction equations within 10.
Vocabulary			
Multilingual Support	**Strategy:** Rephrase	**Strategy:** Draw	**Strategy:** Model Concepts

Practice and Fluency	LESSON 12.1 ◆ ■ Practice and Homework ■ Waggle ◆ Achieving Facts Fluency*	LESSON 12.2 ◆ ■ Practice and Homework ■ Waggle ◆ Achieving Facts Fluency*	LESSON 12.3 ◆ ■ Practice and Homework ■ Waggle ◆ Achieving Facts Fluency*
***MTSS* RtI** **Intervention and Enrichment**	■ Waggle ◆ ■ Reteach 12.1 ◆ ■ Tier 2 Intervention Skill S31 ◆ ■ Tier 3 Intervention Skill E31 ◆ Enrich 12.1	■ Waggle ◆ ■ Reteach 12.2 ◆ ■ Tier 2 Intervention Skill S31 ◆ ■ Tier 3 Intervention Skill E31 ◆ Enrich 12.2	■ Waggle ◆ ■ Reteach 12.3 ◆ ■ Tier 2 Intervention Skill S31 ◆ ■ Tier 3 Intervention Skill E31 ◆ Enrich 12.3

See the Grab-and-Go!™ Centers Kit for more small-group activities.

Grab-and-Go!™
Version 2.0
Differentiated Centers Kit

The kit provides literature, games, and activities for small-group learning.

◆ Print/Printable Resource
■ Interactive Resource

LESSON 12.4 • 1 Day

Lesson at a Glance	Subtraction Word Problems 471A
I Can	I can solve subtraction word problems within 10.
Learning Goal	Solve subtraction word problems within 10.
Vocabulary	
Multilingual Support	**Strategy:** Model Concepts

Practice and Fluency	LESSON 12.4 ◆ ■ **Practice and Homework** ■ **Waggle** ◆ **Achieving Facts Fluency***
MTSS RtI **Intervention and Enrichment**	■ **Waggle** ◆ ■ **Reteach 12.4** ◆ ■ **Tier 2 Intervention Skill S31** ◆ ■ **Tier 3 Intervention Skill E31** ◆ **Tabletop Flipchart** ◆ **Enrich 12.4**

Consider the active and participatory communication styles of linguistically diverse children and how they engage in Math Talk.

Image Credit: ©HMH

SUPPORTING ALL LEARNERS

Embrace and honor the linguistic diversity of children by engaging them in relevant mathematics tasks with multiple paths for success.

*For individual and class practice with counting automaticity and operational fluency, go to *Achieving Facts Fluency* pages located online.

◆ Print/Printable Resource
■ Interactive Resource

Teaching for Depth
Subtraction Within 10

Acting Out Subtraction Problems

Many children can benefit from acting out the subtraction stories shown on the pages of this chapter. Consider this problem:

There are 7 raccoons. Three of the raccoons walk away. How many raccoons are left?

For this problem, have 7 children volunteer to be the "raccoons" and come to the front of the class. Choose 3 of the children to walk away from the group. Ask the other children in the class to answer the question of how many are left.

The subtraction on the number line can also be acted out by using a giant number line and having a child begin at 7 and take 3 steps backward.

From the Research

❝[W]orking with number lines may help students develop a mental representation of the order and magnitude of numbers that can then be used to make comparisons, understand place value, and model mathematical operations. . . . Purposefully targeting these concepts during early mathematics instruction may support students' conceptual understanding of more advanced topics as early as kindergarten.❞

(Woods, D. et al., 2007, p. 2)

Drawing a Subtraction Story

Some children may have difficulty getting started writing a story for a subtraction equation.

If this is the case, it might be because they are unable to think of a topic for their story. You can provide children with a list of topics to use. For example: pencils, desks, cats, chairs, and so on.

If drawing objects presents problems for some children, suggest they look at the pages in their math book and choose objects that are shown.

Mathematical Practices and Processes

Construct arguments and critique reasoning of others.

In this chapter, children draw to show what they know about subtraction equations and then tell a friend about their drawing. This provides an opportunity for children to communicate mathematical ideas, vocabulary, and methods. In listening to classmates' stories, children analyze the mathematical thinking of others.

For more professional learning, go online to Teacher's Corner.

Instructional Journey

While every classroom may look a little different, this instructional model provides a framework to organize small-group and whole-group learning for meaningful student learning.

Whole Group
Engage

5 minutes

Readiness
- Problem of the Day
- Fluency Builder or Vocabulary Builder
- Access Prior Knowledge

Engagement
- I Can
- Making Connections
- Learning Activity

Small and Whole Group
Explore

15–20 minutes

Exploration
- Listen and Draw, Unlock the Problem
- Multilingual Support and Strategy
- Common Errors

Small Group
Explain

15–20 minutes

Quick Check
- ✓ Share and Show

Differentiated Instruction

Version 2.0

Intervention
- Waggle
- Reteach
- Tier 2 and Tier 3 MTSS
- Tabletop Flipchart Mini Lessons

Language Support
- Vocabulary Activities
- Language Routines
- Multilingual Glossary

Enrichment
- Waggle Games
- Ready for More
- Enrich

Whole Group
Elaborate

5 minutes

- Math on the Spot Videos
- Higher-Order Thinking Problems

Evaluate

- I Can Reflection
- Exit Ticket
- Practice and Homework
- Fluency Practice
- Waggle

Assessment

Diagnostic	Formative	Summative
• Show What You Know	• Lesson Quick Check	• Chapter Review • Chapter Test • Performance Assessment Task

Version 2.0

Differentiated Centers Kit

The kit provides literature, games, and activities for small-group learning.

Strategies for
Multilingual Learners

Understanding a child's language development is helpful in differentiating teaching and assessment. Assessing a child's understanding of mathematical concepts can be done by listening, speaking, reading, and writing. The level of support a child needs determines how best to assess that child's understanding of mathematical concepts.

Planning for Instruction

Language Support	Substantial (WIDA Level 1)*	Moderate (WIDA Levels 2 & 3)*	Light (WIDA Levels 4 & 5)*
Child's Use of Language	• uses single words • uses common short phrases • heavily relies on visual supports and use of manipulatives	• uses simple sentences • uses some academic vocabulary • relies on visual supports and use of manipulatives	• uses a variety of sentences • uses academic vocabulary • benefits from visual supports and manipulatives
Ways to Assess Understanding	**Listening:** points to pictures, words, or phrases to answer questions **Speaking:** answers *yes/no* questions **Reading:** matches symbols to math terms and concepts **Writing:** draws a visual representation of a problem	**Listening:** matches, categorizes, or sequences information based on visuals **Speaking:** begins to explain reasoning, asks math questions, repeats explanations from peers **Reading:** identifies important information to solve a problem **Writing:** uses simple sentences and visual representations	**Listening:** draws conclusions and makes connections based on what they heard **Speaking:** explains and justifies concepts and solutions **Reading:** understands information in math contexts **Writing:** completes sentences using some academic vocabulary

* For more information on WIDA Standards, visit their website at:
https://wida.wisc.edu/.

- Look for strategies throughout the lesson to support multilingual learners.
- Log on to ED to find additional multilingual activities and Vocabulary Cards.

In This Chapter

Key Academic Vocabulary

Current Development • Vocabulary

Using Language Routines to Develop Understanding

 Language routines provide opportunities for children to develop an understanding of mathematical language and concepts by listening, speaking, reading, and writing. More information on these language routines can be found on the Language Support Cards.

Three Reads

Children read a problem three times with a specific focus each time.

1st Read What is the problem about?

2nd Read What do each of the numbers describe?

3rd Read What math questions could you ask about the problem?

Language Support	Substantial (WIDA Level 1)*	Moderate (WIDA Levels 2 & 3)*	Light (WIDA Levels 4 & 5)*
Language Routine Differentiation	Children listen to a problem three times with scaffolded questions. **1st Listen** What happens in the problem? **2nd Listen** What numbers do you hear? **3rd Listen** What math questions could you ask?	Children read a problem three times with a proficient partner with scaffolded questions. **1st Read** What happens in the problem? **2nd Read** What numbers do you hear? **3rd Read** What math questions could you ask?	Children engage in the language routine with proficient peers. Monitor to provide additional support if required (*example: clarify meaning of vocabulary within the guiding questions*).
Possible Student Work	6	9 − 3 = 6	6 = 9 − 3

* For more information on WIDA Standards, visit their website at: https://wida.wisc.edu/.

Assessing Prior Knowledge

Have children complete **Show What You Know** on their own. Items tested are the prerequisite skills for this chapter.

Diagnostic Interview Task

The alternative interview tasks below evaluate children's understanding of each **Show What You Know** skill. The diagnostic chart may be used for intervention on prerequisite skills.

MATERIALS connecting cubes, crayons, paper

Tell the story.

- **There are four birds. Three birds fly away. How many birds are left?**

Have the child use cubes to model the problem and find the answer.

Tell the story.

- **Paul has 7 stamps. He gives 5 stamps to his sister. How many stamps does he have now?**

Have the child draw a picture and solve the problem.

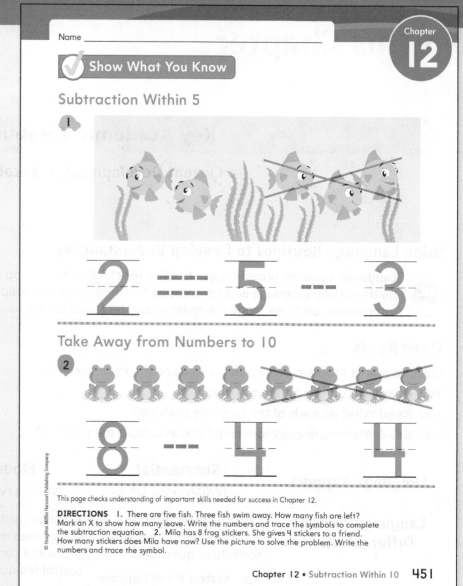

Name _____

✓ Show What You Know

Subtraction Within 5

1.

$$2 === 5 -- 3$$

Take Away from Numbers to 10

2.

$$8 --- 4 \quad 4$$

This page checks understanding of important skills needed for success in Chapter 12.

DIRECTIONS 1. There are five fish. Three fish swim away. How many fish are left? Mark an X to show how many leave. Write the numbers and trace the symbols to complete the subtraction equation. 2. Mila has 8 frog stickers. She gives 4 stickers to a friend. How many stickers does Mila have now? Use the picture to solve the problem. Write the numbers and trace the symbol.

Chapter 12 • Subtraction Within 10   451

✓ Show What You Know • Diagnostic Assessment

Use to determine if children need intervention for the chapter's prerequisite skills.

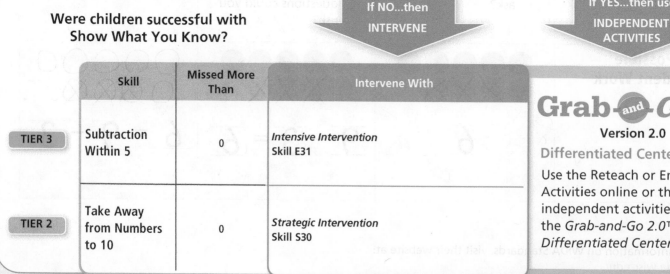

Were children successful with Show What You Know?

	Skill	Missed More Than	Intervene With
TIER 3	Subtraction Within 5	0	*Intensive Intervention* Skill E31
TIER 2	Take Away from Numbers to 10	0	*Strategic Intervention* Skill S30

If NO...then INTERVENE

If YES...then use INDEPENDENT ACTIVITIES

Grab-and-Go!™
Version 2.0
Differentiated Centers Kit

Use the Reteach or Enrich Activities online or the independent activities in the *Grab-and-Go 2.0™ Differentiated Centers Kit.*

Vocabulary Builder

Check children's work.

DIRECTIONS Tell an addition or subtraction word problem. Circle the groups and write an equation to model the problem.

452 Go Math! Grade K

© Houghton Mifflin Harcourt Publishing Company

Vocabulary Builder

Children use multiple strategies to develop grade-appropriate vocabulary.

Have children complete the activities on the page by working alone or with partners.

Look at the page with children.

- Tell an addition word problem.
- Tell a subtraction word problem.

Have children circle the groups and write an equation to model one of the word problems.

School-Home Letter is available in English and Spanish online, and in multiple other languages.

Intervention Options *MTSS* (RtI) Response to Intervention

Use Show What You Know, Lesson Quick Check, and Assessments to diagnose children's intervention levels.

TIER 1	TIER 2	TIER 3	ENRICHMENT
On-Level Intervention	**Strategic Intervention**	**Intensive Intervention**	**Independent Activities**
For children who are generally at grade level but need early intervention with the lesson concepts, use:	For children who need small-group instruction to review concepts and skills needed for the chapter, use:	For children who need one-on-one instruction to build foundational skills for the chapter, use:	For children who successfully complete lessons, use: • Waggle Practice and Games
• Reteach • Tabletop Flipchart Mini Lesson • Waggle ▲ Tier 1 Activity	▲ Prerequisite Skills Activities ▲ Tier 2 Activity	▲ Prerequisite Skills Activities ▲ Tier 3 Activity	**Grab and Go!**™ Version 2.0 Differentiated Centers Kit • Ready for More Activity for every lesson • Enrich

Lesson at a Glance
Differences Within 7

SNAPSHOT

Mathematical Standards
● Represent addition and subtraction with objects, fingers, mental images, drawings, sounds (e.g., claps), acting out situations, verbal explanations, expressions, or equations.

Mathematical Practices and Processes
● Model with mathematics.
● Attend to precision.
● Construct arguments and critique reasoning of others.
● Look for and make use of structure.

(I Can) Objective
I can write and solve subtraction equations within 7.

Learning Goal
Write and solve subtraction equations within 7.

Language Objective
Children will explain to a partner how to use subtraction equations within 7 to solve problems.

MATERIALS
• MathBoard

ACROSS THE GRADES

Grade K
Solve addition and subtraction real-world problems using objects, drawings or equations to represent the problem.

After
Solve addition and subtraction real-world problems using objects, drawings or equations to represent the problem.

ABOUT THE MATH

As children continue to develop their understanding of subtraction, they begin to see the relationship between a story, a picture, a number line, and an equation. In all of these word problems, children are looking to find how many are left. That structure should indicate to them that subtraction will be used. When subtracting, the first number always represents the original number, and then the number that leaves is taken away from it. The difference is how many are left.

For more professional learning, go online to Teacher's Corner.

DAILY ROUTINES

🖥 Problem of the Day 12.1

Write three ways to make 5.
Sample answer: 0 + 5, 1 + 4, 2 + 3

🖥 Vocabulary

- Interactive Student Edition
- Multilingual Glossary

Fluency Builder

Count forward from 1 to 20 aloud with a partner.

FOCUSING ON THE WHOLE STUDENT

Access Prior Knowledge

Choose one or more of the following activities.

- Have children tell you about a time they saw a group of things in the sky.
- Ask children to illustrate the hot-air balloons that Scout sees in the Learning Activity.

Culturally Responsive Education

As culturally responsive educators, we know children have different needs, but that can be difficult for other children to understand. Sometimes children notice appropriate accommodations being made for others and view that as unfair. It is, of course, inappropriate to share the reasons for any accommodations you are making, but it can be a learning opportunity if a child asks why someone is taking a test in a different room or why they leave with a different teacher for part of the day. Explain to children that everyone is different, and different people need different things. Use something like hair as an example. People who wear their hair short don't need the same tools to care for their hair as people who wear their hair long. Neither choice is better than the other; they are just different. Explain that as a teacher, part of your job is to be sure each child in the class is getting what they need to learn.

---

① Engage

with the Interactive Student Edition

I Can Objective

I can write and solve subtraction equations within 7.

Making Connections

Invite children to tell you what they know about finding differences within 5.

- **Hold up all of the fingers on one hand. Let's count them out loud together.** 1, 2, 3, 4, 5
- **Put down 2 of your fingers. Are you holding up more fingers or fewer fingers than you were before?** fewer
- **How many fingers are you holding up now?** 3

Learning Activity

Draw 6 balloons on the board. Tell children that these are the balloons Scout sees.

Then cross out 2 and say that they floated away. Guide children toward knowing how to find differences within 7.

- **How many balloons does Scout see at first?** 6
- **How many balloons float away?** 2
- **What kind of equation will help Scout figure out how many balloons are left?** a subtraction equation

② Explore

Listen and Draw

Read the problem aloud as children listen.

There are six butterflies. Two butterflies fly away. How many butterflies are left?

- **How many butterflies are there?** 6 **Trace that number in the subtraction equation.**
- **How many butterflies fly away?** 2 **Trace the circle and X on those butterflies. Trace the subtraction symbol and that number in the subtraction equation.**
- **How many butterflies are left?** 4 **Trace the *is equal* to sign and write that number in the subtraction equation.**

 Attend to precision.

Have children trace the complete subtraction equation as they explain each number.

- **What does the 6 mean?** 6 is the starting number.
- **What number shows how many butterflies fly away?** 2
- **How do you know how many butterflies are left?** I can count the butterflies outside the circle and X. I can read the number after the *is equal to* sign.

Name _____

Differences Within 7

(I Can) write and solve subtraction equations within 7.

Listen and Draw

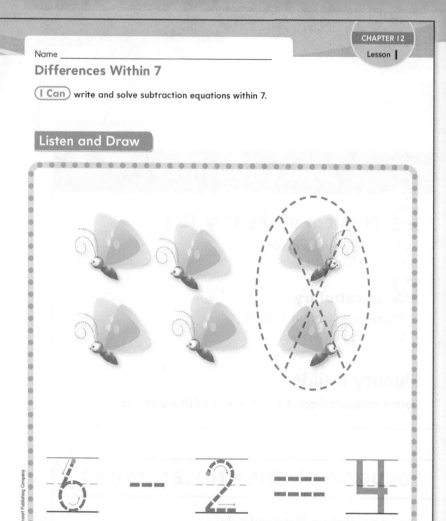

DIRECTIONS There are six butterflies. Two butterflies fly away. Trace the circle around and the X over those butterflies. How many butterflies are left? Trace and write to complete the subtraction equation.

Chapter 12 • Lesson 1   **453**

Multilingual Support

STRATEGY: Rephrase

Materials index cards, marker

- Children can demonstrate understanding of subtraction by rephrasing number equations.

- Separate children into small groups with mixed English language abilities. Give them 9 cards. Have children write one number from 0 to 8 on each card and put the cards face down in the center of a circle.

- Have children take turns selecting a card. Display the sentence frames. Then have them say equations by subtracting the number from 8 and again from 9.

My number is ____.
8 take away ____ is ____.
9 minus ____ is ____.

Share and Show

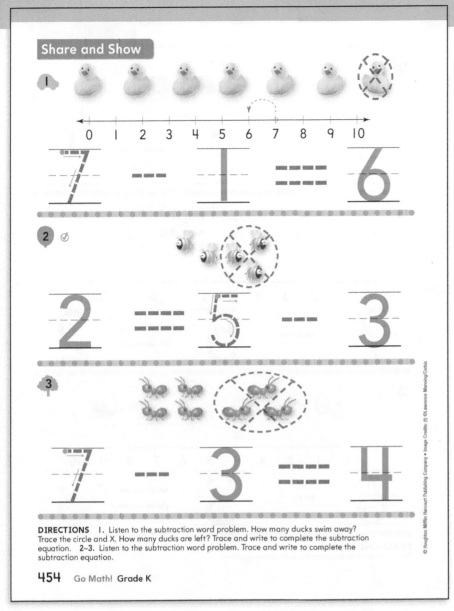

1.

$$7 - 1 = 6$$

2. ✓

$$2 = 5 - 3$$

3.

$$7 - 3 = 4$$

DIRECTIONS 1. Listen to the subtraction word problem. How many ducks swim away? Trace the circle and X. How many ducks are left? Trace and write to complete the subtraction equation. 2–3. Listen to the subtraction word problem. Trace and write to complete the subtraction equation.

Ready for More
🕐 Logical / Mathematical Partners

Materials: paper bag, 10 two-color counters

Have partners place up to ten two-color counters in the paper bag, shake it, and dump out the counters. Tell partners that the total number of counters is the number in all. The yellow counters are the ones taken away.

- One child counts the total counters and the yellow counters and then records the subtraction expression with numbers and the subtraction symbol.

- The other child then records the number of red counters that are left below the expression.

- Partners reverse roles and repeat the activity.

---

③ Explain

Share and Show Math Board

For Problem 1, have children listen as you read the subtraction word problem aloud.

There are seven ducks in the pond. One duck swims away. How many ducks are left?

- **How many ducks are in the pond?** 7 **Trace that number in the subtraction equation.**

- **How many ducks swim away?** 1 **Trace the subtraction symbol and write that number in the subtraction equation.**

Trace the circle and X on that duck. How many ducks are left? 6 **Trace the *is equal to* sign and write that number.** Have children trace the complete subtraction equation.

Guide children through Problems 2 and 3 in the same way. Have children trace and write to complete the subtraction equation.

- **In Problem 2, there are five bees. Three bees fly away. How many are left?** 2

- **In Problem 3, there are seven ants. Three ants walk away. How many are left?** 4

Use the checked problem for Quick Check.

✓ **Quick Check** **MTSS** **RtI**

If → a child misses the checked problem

Then → Differentiate Instruction with
- Reteach 12.1
- Waggle

⚠ **Common Errors**

Error Children may not understand which number tells how many are left.

Springboard to Learning Remind children that the animals that leave are circled and crossed out. The animals that are not circled and crossed out are the ones that are left.

Share and Show

 Look for and make use of structure.

Have children listen as you read the word problems for Problems 4, 5, and 6. Have them tell the number of animals that walk, fly, or crawl away. Have children trace the circle and X to show those animals. Then have them trace the subtraction symbol and write that number. Next, ask children to tell the number left. Have them trace the *is equal to* sign and write the number left to complete the subtraction equation.

- **In Problem 4,** there are four turtles. Three turtles walk away. How many are left? 1
- **In Problem 5,** there are seven ladybugs. Five fly away. How many ladybugs are left? 2
- **In Problem 6,** there are six snails. Three snails crawl away. How many are left? 3

Higher-Order Thinking

 Model with mathematics.

Write **7 – _____ = 4** on the board. Ask children to draw pictures to find the number to take away. Have them complete the subtraction equation.

Children begin by drawing objects to represent the number they start with. They count four objects to show how many are left. Then they cross out the rest of the objects, count them to show how many are taken away, and complete the subtraction equation. $7 - 3 = 4$

 Construct arguments and critique reasoning of others.

Ask children to explain what they knew, what they needed to find out, and how they found the answer. You may want to discuss with children that, like the other problems in the lesson, they know how many there are in all, and they know about one part of the whole group. They need to find the other part.

Math on the Spot Use this video to help children model and solve this type of problem.

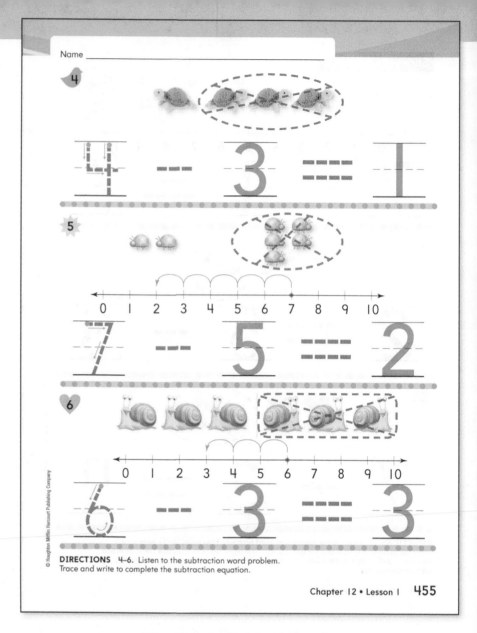

Name _____

4

$4 - 3 = 1$

5

$7 - 5 = 2$

6

$6 - 3 = 3$

DIRECTIONS 4–6. Listen to the subtraction word problem. Trace and write to complete the subtraction equation.

Chapter 12 • Lesson 1   455

Meeting Individual Needs

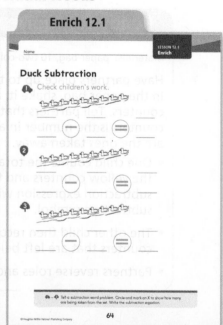

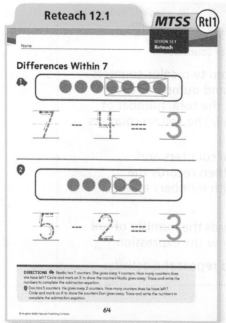

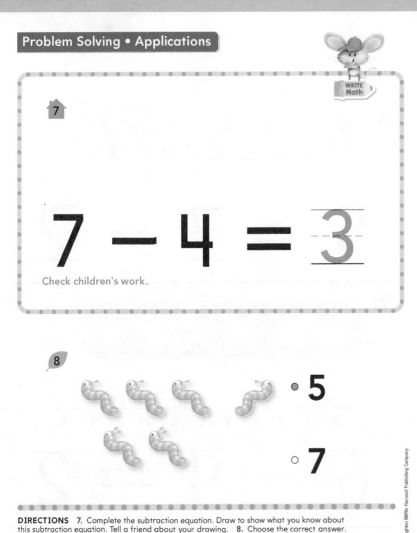

7

$$7 - 4 = \underline{3}$$

Check children's work.

8

• 5

○ 7

DIRECTIONS 7. Complete the subtraction equation. Draw to show what you know about this subtraction equation. Tell a friend about your drawing. 8. Choose the correct answer. There are six worms. One worm crawls away. What is 6 – 1?

DIFFERENTIATED INSTRUCTION • Independent Activities

Grab-and-Go!™
Version 2.0
Differentiated Centers Kit

Tabletop Flipchart

Mini-lessons for reteaching to targeted small groups

Readers

Supports key math skills and concepts in real-world situations.

Games

Reinforce math content and vocabulary

Activities

Meaningful and fun math practice

④ Elaborate

Problem Solving Applications   WRITE ▸ Math

(MP) **Model with mathematics.**

Problem 7 Children draw a real-world situation that is modeled by the subtraction equation.

(MP) **Look for and make use of structure.**

Problem 8 Compare this problem to finding the number that is one less than another number. Draw parallels between subtracting one and finding the number that is one less.

⑤ Evaluate | Formative Assessment

I Can

Have children explain to a partner how to demonstrate the skill for the I Can statement.

I can write and solve subtraction equations within 7 by . . . drawing the ones I start with and then circling and crossing out the ones being taken away. The ones not circled show how many are left, or the difference.

Exit Ticket

Draw a picture of a subtraction word problem. Write the equation that goes with it.

Practice and Homework

Differences Within 7

Use the Practice and Homework pages to provide children with more practice of the concepts and skills presented in this lesson. Children master their understanding as they complete practice items.

Name ______________________________

LESSON 12.1
Practice and Homework

Differences Within 7

1

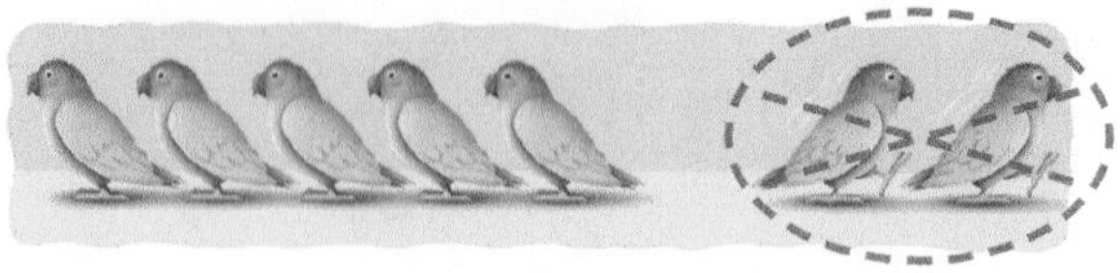

5 = 7 − 2

2

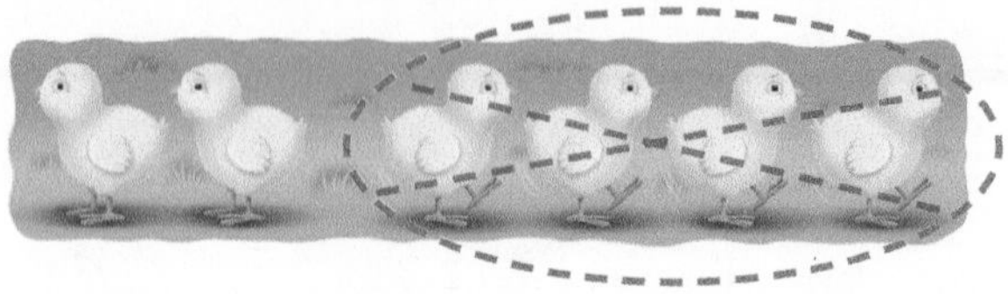

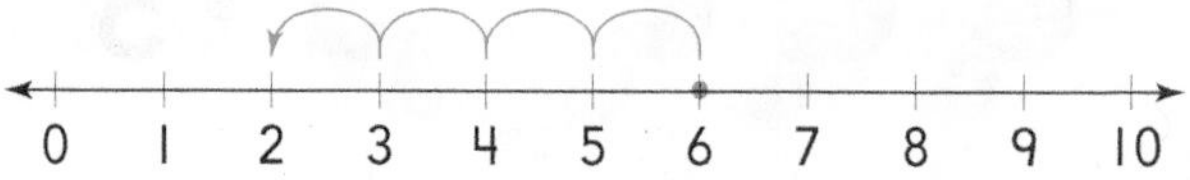

6 − 4 = 2

DIRECTIONS Trace and write to complete the subtraction equation. 1. There are seven parrots. Two parrots walk away. 2. There are six baby chicks. Four chicks go to the coop.

Lesson Check

   ○ **4**

   ● **3**

   ● **4**

   ○ **5**

Spiral Review

 5

YELLOW	BLUE
YELLOW	BLUE
YELLOW	BLUE

$$3 + 3 = 6$$

DIRECTIONS 3. Choose the correct answer. There are seven rabbits. Four rabbits hop away. What is 7 – 4? 4. Choose the correct answer. There are five kittens. One kitten scampers off. What is 5 – 1? 5. There are 3 yellow crayons and 3 blue crayons. How many crayons are there in all?

458 Go Math! Grade K

Continue to practice concepts and skills with Lesson Check. Use Spiral Review to engage children in previously taught concepts and to promote content retention.

© Houghton Mifflin Harcourt Publishing Company

Lesson at a Glance
Differences Within 9

SNAPSHOT

Mathematical Standards

● Represent addition and subtraction with objects, fingers, mental images, drawings, sounds (e.g., claps), acting out situations, verbal explanations, expressions, or equations.

Mathematical Practices and Processes

● Model with mathematics.
● Attend to precision.
● Reason abstractly and quantitatively.
● Look for and make use of structure.

(I Can) Objective

I can write and solve subtraction equations within 9.

Learning Goal

Write and solve subtraction equations within 9.

Language Objective

Children will explain to a partner how a drawing relates to a subtraction equation.

MATERIALS

• MathBoard

ACROSS THE GRADES

Grade K

Solve addition and subtraction real-world problems using objects, drawings or equations to represent the problem.

After

Solve addition and subtraction real-world problems using objects, drawings or equations to represent the problem.

ABOUT THE MATH

In this lesson, children continue to work with subtraction equations, which are sometimes called number sentences. While *equation* is the preferable term, children should be able to understand and even use each term interchangeably. Literally, if an equation is read, it is a sentence with numbers. It is important for children to learn to use precise mathematical language. They will reach a point in their mathematical careers where *number sentence* will no longer be used. Encourage children to use *equation* frequently in their mathematical discussions so that they become familiar and comfortable with the term.

For more professional learning, go online to Teacher's Corner.

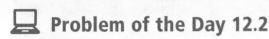

DAILY ROUTINES

🖥 Problem of the Day 12.2

Write three ways to make 10.
Sample answer: 0 + 10, 1 + 9, 2 + 8

🖥 Vocabulary

• Interactive Student Edition
• Multilingual Glossary

Fluency Builder

Count backward from 20 to 1 aloud with a partner.

FOCUSING ON THE WHOLE STUDENT

Social & Emotional Learning

Responsible Decision-Making Help foster curiosity in learning new concepts. *Are you curious about subtraction problems and how they are similar to and different from addition problems? In this lesson you were able to take what you learned in the last lesson and build on your learning. What do you want to learn about next?*

Access Prior Knowledge

Choose one or more of the following activities.

• Have each child draw and decorate a kite.

• As a class, write a story about seeing a group of kites where something happens to a few of the kites.

---

1 Engage

with the Interactive Student Edition

I Can Objective

I can write and solve subtraction equations within 9.

Making Connections

Ask children to practice finding differences.

If I have 7 boxes of juice and I give 2 to my friend, how many do I have left? 5 **Is 5 more or less than 7?** less **When you subtract, do you always end up with a number that is less than the one you started with?** yes

Learning Activity

Draw 9 kites on the board. Tell children that these are the kites Scout sees. Then cross out 2 and say that they floated away.

Have children begin thinking about how to find differences within 9.

• **What does Scout see in the sky?** kites

• **How many of the kites float away?** 2

• **What is Scout trying to find out?** how many kites are left

② Explore

Listen and Draw

Read the problem aloud as children listen.

There are nine cars. Two cars drive away.
How many cars are left?

- **How many cars are there?** 9 **Trace that number in the subtraction equation.**
- **How many cars drive away?** 2 **Trace the circle and X around those cars. Trace the subtraction symbol and that number in the subtraction equation.**
- **How many cars are left?** 7 **Trace the *is equal to* sign and write that number in the subtraction equation.**

(MP) **Look for and make use of structure.**

Have children trace the subtraction equation as they explain what each number means.

- **What does the 9 mean?** 9 is the number of cars I start with.
- **What number shows how many cars drive away?** 2
- **How do you know how many cars are left?** I can count the cars that are not inside the circle and marked with an X. I can read the number that tells how many are left.

Name _____

Differences Within 9

(I Can) write and solve subtraction equations within 9.

Listen and Draw

DIRECTIONS There are nine cars. Two cars drive away. Trace the circle around and the X over those cars. How many cars are left? Trace and write to complete the subtraction equation.

Chapter 12 • Lesson 2 459

(ML) ## Multilingual Support

STRATEGY: Draw

Materials paper, color pencils

- Children can demonstrate their prior knowledge and understanding by drawing.

- Draw a *minus* sign and an *is equal to* sign for the children to copy. Read aloud and have the children illustrate the following problem: **Bella has 10 library books. She returns 3 books to the library. How many does she have left?** 7

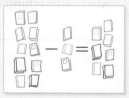

- Repeat with other objects and combinations to subtract from 10.

1

8 -- 3 === 5

2

4 == 9 -- 5

3

$$\leftarrow \quad 0 \quad 1 \quad 2 \quad 3 \quad 4 \quad 5 \quad 6 \quad 7 \quad 8 \quad 9 \quad 10 \quad \rightarrow$$

6 -- 2 === 4

DIRECTIONS 1. Listen to the subtraction word problem. How many buses drive away? Trace the circle and X. How many buses are left? Trace and write to complete the subtraction equation. 2-3. Listen to the subtraction word problem. Trace and write to complete the subtraction equation.

Ready for More

Logical / Mathematical Partners

Materials: two-color counters, 0–5 number cube (0–5 dots)

Have a small group of children sit in a circle. Place a number cube and five counters in the middle.

- Have one child toss the cube and take that many counters. Then have the child describe what he or she did as a subtraction word problem. Example: *There are five counters. I rolled a 2 and took 2 away from the set. Now there are 3 left.* Continue play in this manner around the circle. Change the number of counters in the middle up to 9 as play continues.

---

③ Explain

Share and Show   Math Board

For Problem 1, have children listen as you read the subtraction word problem aloud.

There are eight buses. Three buses drive away. How many buses are left?

- **How many buses are there?** 8 **Trace that number in the subtraction equation.**
- **How many buses drive away?** 3 **Trace the subtraction symbol and write that number in the subtraction equation.**

Trace the circle and X on those buses. How many buses are left? 5 **Trace the *is equal to* sign and write that number in the subtraction equation.** Have children trace the complete subtraction equation.

Guide children through Problems 2 and 3 in the same way. Have children trace and write to complete the subtraction equation.

- **In Problem 2, there are nine cars. Five cars drive away. How many are left?** 4
- **In Problem 3, there are six trucks. Two trucks drive away. How many are left?** 4

Use the checked problem for Quick Check.

✓ Quick Check   MTSS   RtI

If ▶ a child misses the checked problem

Then ▶ **Differentiate Instruction with**
- Reteach 12.2
- Waggle

! Common Errors

Error Children may not understand which number to subtract.

Springboard to Learning Remind children that the cars and trucks that drive away are circled and crossed out in the pictures. That number is subtracted from the cars and trucks at the beginning to find how many are left.

Share and Show

 Reason abstractly and quantitatively.

Have children listen as you read the word problems for Problems 4, 5, and 6. Have them trace the circle and X on the vehicles that drive away. Then, ask children to tell the number of vehicles there were at the beginning and have them trace that number. Ask children how many vehicles drove away and have them trace the subtraction symbol and write the number. Then, ask how many vehicles are left and have them trace the *is equal to* sign and write the number left. Have them read the subtraction equations.

- In Problem 4, there are five fire trucks. Three fire trucks drive away. How many are left? 2

- In Problem 5, there are nine tractors. Three tractors drive away. How many tractors are left? 6

- In Problem 6, there are eight cars. One car drives away. How many are left? 7

Higher-Order Thinking

 Attend to precision.

Write 9 – _____ = 5 on the board. Ask children to draw pictures to help them find the number to take away. Have them complete the subtraction equation.

Children begin by drawing objects to represent the number they start with. They count five objects to show how many are left. Then they cross out the rest of the objects and count them to show how many are taken away. 9 – 4 = 5

Supporting All Learners

This higher-order thinking activity gives children an opportunity to stretch their problem-solving muscles as well as better understand subtraction. When we give students opportunities to problem solve, we enable them to become more independent learners.

Math on the Spot Use this video to help children model and solve this type of problem.

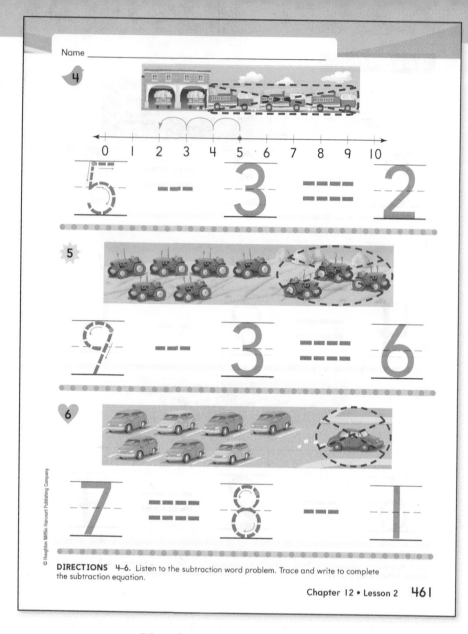

Name _____

4

$$5 - 3 = 2$$

5

$$9 - 3 = 6$$

6

$$7 = 8 - 1$$

DIRECTIONS 4–6. Listen to the subtraction word problem. Trace and write to complete the subtraction equation.

Chapter 12 • Lesson 2 461

Meeting Individual Needs

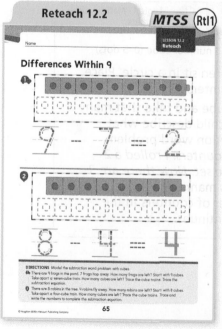

Reteach 12.2   MTSS Rtl1

Name _____

LESSON 12.2 Reteach

Differences Within 9

1

$$9 - 7 = 2$$

2

$$8 - 5 = 4$$

DIRECTIONS Model the subtraction word problem with cubes.
1. There are 9 frogs in the pond. 7 frogs hop away. How many frogs are left? Start with 9 cubes. Take apart a seven-cube train. How many cubes are left? Trace the cube trains. Trace the subtraction equation.
2. There are 8 robins in the tree. 4 robins fly away. How many robins are left? Start with 8 cubes. Take apart a four-cube train. How many cubes are left? Trace the cube trains. Trace and write the numbers to complete the subtraction equation.

65

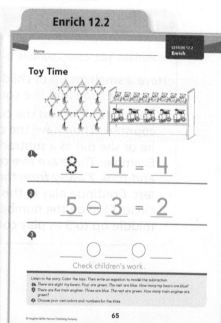

Enrich 12.2

Name _____

LESSON 12.2 Enrich

Toy Time

1

$$8 - 4 = 4$$

2

$$5 - 3 = 2$$

3

$$\bigcirc - \bigcirc$$

Check children's work.

Listen to the story. Color the toys. Then write an equation to model the subtraction.
1. There are eight toy bears. Four are green. The rest are blue. How many toy bears are blue?
2. There are five train engines. Three are blue. The rest are green. How many train engines are green?
3. Choose your own colors and numbers for the kites.

65

7

$$8 - 6 = \underline{2}$$

Check children's work.

8

○ **7**

● **8**

DIRECTIONS 7. Complete the subtraction equation. Draw to show what you know about this subtraction equation. Tell a friend about your drawing. 8. Choose the correct answer. There are nine mail trucks. One mail truck drives away. What is 9−1?

DIFFERENTIATED INSTRUCTION • Independent Activities

Grab-and-Go!™

Version 2.0

Differentiated Centers Kit

Tabletop Flipchart

Mini-lessons for reteaching to targeted small groups

Readers

Supports key math skills and concepts in real-world situations.

Games

Reinforce math content and vocabulary

Activities

Meaningful and fun math practice

④ Elaborate

Problem Solving Applications

(MP) Model with mathematics.

Problem 7 Direct children's attention to the subtraction equation. Have them complete the subtraction equation and draw a picture that shows or represents it. Have them describe how their picture represents the subtraction equation.

Read **Problem 8** aloud to children. Have children fill in the bubble for the correct answer.

• **There are nine mail trucks. One mail truck drives away. What is 9 – 1?** 8

⑤ Evaluate | Formative Assessment

I Can

Have children demonstrate for a partner the skill for the I Can statement.

I can write and solve subtraction equations within 9 by . . . drawing a picture and telling how many there are at the beginning of the problem. Then I can circle the ones being subtracted. The ones I do not circle show the difference.

Exit Ticket

Show how to use a number line to find the difference.

Differences Within 9

Use the Practice and Homework pages to provide children with more practice of the concepts and skills presented in this lesson. Children master their understanding as they complete practice items.

Differences Within 9

1

$$5 = 9 - 4$$

2

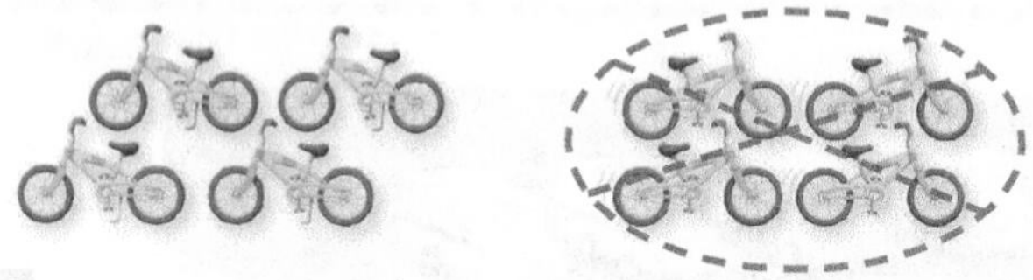

$$8 - 4 = 4$$

DIRECTIONS Trace and write to complete the subtraction equation. **1.** There are nine motorcycles. Four motorcycles drive away. Trace the circle and X. How many motorcycles are left? **2.** There are eight bicycles. Four bicycles ride away. How many bicycles are left?

Chapter 12 • Lesson 2   463

© Houghton Mifflin Harcourt Publishing Company

Lesson Check

○ **8**

● **6**

Spiral Review

$$3 + 6 = 9$$

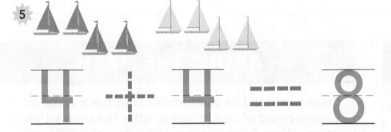

$$4 + 4 = 8$$

DIRECTIONS 3. Choose the correct answer. There are seven dump trucks. One dump truck drives away. What is 7 – 1? **4.** There are 3 green cars and 6 blue cars. How many cars are there? **5.** There are 4 purple boats and 4 yellow boats. How many boats are there?

© Houghton Mifflin Harcourt Publishing Company

Continue to practice concepts and skills with Lesson Check. Use Spiral Review to engage children in previously taught concepts and to promote content retention.

Lesson at a Glance
Differences Within 10

SNAPSHOT

Mathematical Standards
- Represent addition and subtraction with objects, fingers, mental images, drawings, sounds (e.g., claps), acting out situations, verbal explanations, expressions, or equations.

Mathematical Practices and Processes
- Reason abstractly and quantitatively.
- Model with mathematics.
- Construct arguments and critique reasoning of others.
- Look for and make use of structure.

(I Can) Objective
I can write and solve subtraction equations within 10.

Learning Goal
Write and solve subtraction equations within 10.

Language Objective
Children will draw an example to show how to use a subtraction equation to solve a problem.

MATERIALS
- MathBoard

ACROSS THE GRADES

Grade K
Solve addition and subtraction real-world problems using objects, drawings or equations to represent the problem.

After
Solve addition and subtraction real-world problems using objects, drawings or equations to represent the problem.

ABOUT THE MATH

Children should be comfortable with the *is equal to* symbol being placed before or after the subtraction in an equation. Point out that sometimes the difference will be before the symbol and sometimes it will be after. Children more naturally will want to put it after the subtraction, for example, *5 minus 3 is equal to 2*. However, practice reading it the other way with them, for example, *2 is equal to 5 minus 3*. Either way is correct.

For more professional learning, go online to Teacher's Corner.

DAILY ROUTINES

 Problem of the Day 12.3

What is one less?

10 9
5 4
2 1

🖥 Vocabulary

- Interactive Student Edition
- Multilingual Glossary

Fluency Builder

Say a number between 1 and 20. Have a partner tell you the number that is 1 less than that number. Then switch roles.

FOCUSING ON THE WHOLE STUDENT

Access Prior Knowledge

Choose one or more of the following activities.

- Working as a class, write a list of 10 different types of fruit on the board.
- Ask children to draw a bunch of bananas. Have them count and write down the number of bananas in the bunch.

① Engage

with the Interactive Student Edition

I Can Objective

I can write and solve subtraction equations within 10.

Making Connections

Invite children to tell you what they know about finding differences between two groups.

- **What does it mean to find the difference between two things?** Answers may vary; I find what is not the same about them, I find how many more or fewer there are of one thing than of another, etc. Have children work together to make a subtraction equation that tells about the difference between two things.

Learning Activity

Tell a story about Scout seeing a bucket of 10 red apples at the zoo. Seven of the apples are red. Explain that the zoo workers will feed them to the animals.

Direct children toward using a subtraction equation to find differences within 10.

- **How many apples does Scout see?** 10
- **What are the zoo workers going to do with the apples?** use them to feed the animals
- **How can Scout figure out how many green apples there are?** by writing a subtraction equation

② Explore

Listen and Draw

 Model with mathematics.

Read the problem aloud as children listen.

Tim has nine flowers for sale. Four flowers are purple. The rest of the flowers are yellow. How many flowers are yellow?

Explain to children that in the previous lessons, objects were taken away or left the group. In this lesson, subtraction is used when the group is taken apart. The number of objects in one part of the group is known. By subtracting, the number in the other part of the group can be found. Reinforce this concept as each problem is discussed.

- **How many flowers are purple?** 4 **Trace the circle and X around those flowers.**
- **How many flowers are yellow?** 5

Have children trace and write to complete the subtraction equation as they explain each number.

- **What does the 9 mean?** 9 is the number of flowers there are.
- **What number shows how many flowers are in the group that is separated?** 4
- **How do you know how many flowers are in the other group?** I can count the flowers outside the circle and X.

Name _____

Differences Within 10

(I Can) write and solve subtraction equations within 10.

Listen and Draw

$$9 - 4 = 5$$

DIRECTIONS There are nine flowers. Four flowers are purple. Trace the circle around and the X over those flowers. The rest of the flowers are yellow. How many flowers are yellow? Trace and write to complete the subtraction equation.

© Houghton Mifflin Harcourt Publishing Company

Chapter 12 • Lesson 3 **465**

 Multilingual Support

STRATEGY: Model Concepts

Materials two-color counters

- Children understand problems when they are modeled.
- Read the problem chorally with children. Draw the problem as you read it.

  There are 4 flowers. 2 flowers are red. The rest are yellow. How many flowers are yellow? 2

- Make sure children understand the events in the story by asking questions or by having them rephrase the story.
- Have children act out the story with counters as you repeat it.
- Repeat the activity using another story problem.

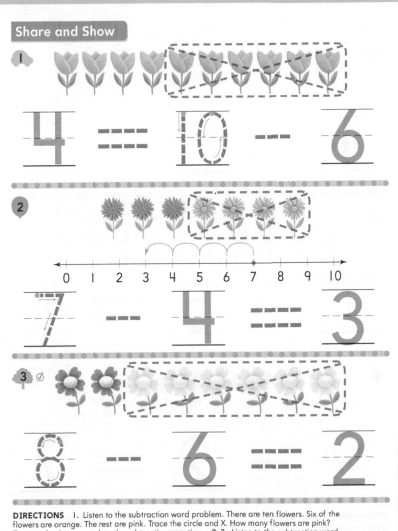

Share and Show

1.
$$4 = 10 - 6$$

2.

0 1 2 3 4 5 6 7 8 9 10
$$7 - 4 = 3$$

3.
$$8 - 6 = 2$$

DIRECTIONS 1. Listen to the subtraction word problem. There are ten flowers. Six of the flowers are orange. The rest are pink. Trace the circle and X. How many flowers are pink? Trace and write to complete the subtraction equation. 2–3. Listen to the subtraction word problem. Trace and write to complete the subtraction equation.

466 Go Math! Grade K

© Houghton Mifflin Harcourt Publishing Company

---

③ Explain

Share and Show

For Problem 1, have children listen as you read the subtraction word problem aloud.

There are ten flowers. Six flowers are orange. The rest are pink. How many flowers are pink?

- **One part of the group of flowers has orange flowers. Trace the circle and X on those flowers. How many flowers are orange?** 6
- **The other part of the group of flowers has pink flowers. How can you find how many flowers are pink?** I can subtract the number of orange flowers. What is left is the number of pink flowers. **How many flowers are pink?** 4

Have children trace and write to complete the subtraction equation.

Guide children through Problems 2 and 3 in the same way. Have children trace and write to complete the subtraction equation.

- **In Problem 2, there are seven flowers. Four flowers are blue. The rest are red. How many flowers are red?** 3
- **In Problem 3, there are eight flowers. Six flowers are yellow. The rest are purple. How many flowers are purple?** 2

Use the checked problem for Quick Check.

✓ Quick Check *MTSS* RtI

If	a child misses the checked problem
Then	**Differentiate Instruction** with • Reteach 12.3 • Waggle

⚠ Common Errors

Error Children may confuse which number is the separated group and needs to be subtracted.

Springboard to Learning Guide children to see that the number of circled objects is the number that is separated. They are asked to find how many are in the other group.

Ready for More 🕐 Logical / Mathematical Partners

Materials: 10 blue and 10 red connecting cubes

Children make a 10-cube train using blue and red cubes until they have shown and recorded eight different ways to subtract from 10. The red cubes show the number in the part that is subtracted.

- Have children begin with a 10-cube train using only blue cubes. Have them determine and write the subtraction equation shown by the cube train. $10 - 0 = 10$
- One child removes a number of blue cubes from the 10-cube train. The other child replaces the blue cubes with the same number of red cubes and writes the subtraction equation.
- Children trade roles. As each 10-cube train is made, partners check to see that the subtraction equation for that train has not been recorded yet.

Share and Show

 Reason abstractly and quantitatively.

Have children listen as you read the word problems for Problems 4, 5, and 6. Have them tell the number of flowers in the whole group. Have them trace the circle and X to show the part they know about. Then have them trace and write the number in the other part to complete the subtraction equation.

- **In Problem 4, there are six flowers. Five flowers are yellow. The rest are pink. How many are pink?** 1

- **In Problem 5, Moesha has ten flowers. Five of her flowers are blue. The rest are orange. How many flowers are orange?** 5

- **In Problem 6, there are nine flowers. Two flowers are yellow. The rest are red. How many flowers are red?** 7

Higher-Order Thinking

 Look for and make use of structure.

Write _____ – 4 = 6 on the board. Ask children to draw pictures to find the number to begin with. Have them complete the subtraction equation.

Children begin by drawing and circling a group of four objects to represent the number separated. They may draw a group of six objects to show the other group. Then they count the objects in both groups to find how many they begin with. 10 – 4 = 6

Some children may begin to see the relationship between addition and subtraction as activities like this are repeated.

Math on the Spot Use this video to help children model and solve this type of problem.

Name _____

4

$1 = 6 - 5$

5

$10 - 5 = 5$

6

$9 - 2 = 7$

DIRECTIONS 4–6. Listen to the subtraction word problem. Trace and write to complete the subtraction equation.

Chapter 12 • Lesson 3 **467**

Meeting Individual Needs

Reteach 12.3   **MTSS** Rtl1   Enrich 12.3

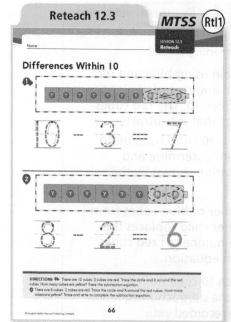

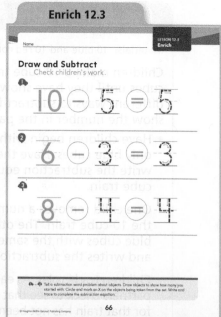

467 **Go Math! Grade K**

7

$$10 - 1 = 9$$

Check children's work.

8

● **2**

○ **3**

DIRECTIONS 7. Complete the subtraction equation. Draw to show what you know about this subtraction equation. Tell a friend about your drawing. 8. Choose the correct answer. There are nine flowers. Seven flowers are pink. The rest are yellow. What is 9 – 7?

© Houghton Mifflin Harcourt Publishing Company

468 Go Math! Grade K

DIFFERENTIATED INSTRUCTION • Independent Activities

Grab and Go!™
Version 2.0
Differentiated Centers Kit

Tabletop Flipchart

Mini-lessons for reteaching to targeted small groups

Readers

Supports key math skills and concepts in real-world situations.

Games

Reinforce math content and vocabulary

Activities

Meaningful and fun math practice

---

④ Elaborate

Problem Solving Applications

(MP) **Construct arguments and critique reasoning of others.**

Problem 7 Direct children's attention to the subtraction equation. Have them complete the subtraction equation and draw a picture that shows or represents it. Have them tell how many are in the part they know about and how many are in the other part. 1; 9

Have children complete the subtraction equation.

Read **Problem 8** aloud to children. Direct children to fill in the bubble for the correct answer.

⑤ Evaluate | Formative Assessment

I Can

Have children describe to a partner how to use a drawing to demonstrate the skill for the I Can statement.

I can write and solve subtraction equations within 10 by . . . telling how many I start with. Then I draw a circle around the part I know. The ones not circled show how many are in the other part.

Exit Ticket

Write a subtraction equation with the subtraction first and then write an equation with the difference first.

Differences Within 10

Use the Practice and Homework pages to provide children with more practice of the concepts and skills presented in this lesson. Children master their understanding as they complete practice items.

Differences Within 10

1

$$6 = 10 - 4$$

2

$$7 - 5 = 2$$

DIRECTIONS Trace and write to complete the subtraction equation. 1. There are 10 flowerpots. 4 are yellow. How many are green? 2. There are 7 birdhouses. 5 are blue. How many are red?

© Houghton Mifflin Harcourt Publishing Company

Chapter 12 • Lesson 3   469

Lesson Check

🌳 **3**

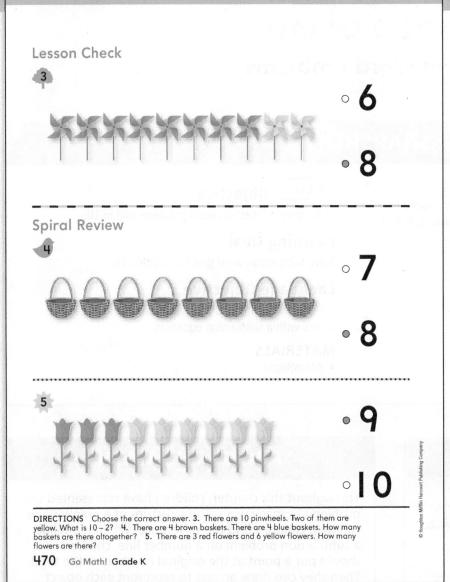

○ **6**

● **8**

Spiral Review

🐦 **4**

○ **7**

● **8**

········

⭐ **5**

● **9**

○ **10**

DIRECTIONS Choose the correct answer. **3.** There are 10 pinwheels. Two of them are yellow. What is 10 – 2? **4.** There are 4 brown baskets. There are 4 blue baskets. How many baskets are there altogether? **5.** There are 3 red flowers and 6 yellow flowers. How many flowers are there?

Continue to practice concepts and skills with Lesson Check. Use Spiral Review to engage children in previously taught concepts and to promote content retention.

Lesson at a Glance
Subtraction Word Problems

SNAPSHOT

Mathematical Standards
● Represent addition and subtraction with objects, fingers, mental images, drawings, sounds (e.g., claps), acting out situations, verbal explanations, expressions, or equations.

Mathematical Practices and Processes
● Attend to precision.
● Model with mathematics.
● Use appropriate tools strategically.
● Look for and make use of structure.

(I Can) Objective
I can solve subtraction word problems within 10.

Learning Goal
Solve subtraction word problems within 10.

Language Objective
Children will write their own word problem that can be solved with a subtraction equation.

MATERIALS
• MathBoard

ACROSS THE GRADES

Grade K
Solve addition and subtraction real-world problems using objects, drawings or equations to represent the problem.

After
Solve addition and subtraction real-world problems using objects, drawings or equations to represent the problem.

ABOUT THE MATH
Throughout this chapter, children have represented the problems in many ways. The structure of a number line can help children find the difference. When modeling a subtraction problem on a number line, children should put a point at the original number, or the total. Then they can draw arrows to represent each object that is taken away. Where the last arrow lands is the difference. It is important that children understand that they are counting the spaces, not the numbers, and that the arrows help them avoid that mistake.

For more professional learning, go online to Teacher's Corner.

 **Problem of the Day 12.4**

What is one more?

7 8
5 6
3 4

 **Vocabulary**

- Interactive Student Edition
- Multilingual Glossary

Fluency Builder

Say a number from 1 to 20. Have your partner say a number that is greater. Then switch roles and repeat.

FOCUSING ON THE WHOLE STUDENT

Access Prior Knowledge

Choose one or more of the following activities.

- Working as a class, come up with a list of things, other than flowers, that grow from the ground.
- Working as a class, come up with a story about what might happen if the animals at the petting zoo found a flower garden.

① Engage

with the Interactive Student Edition

I Can Objective

I can solve subtraction word problems within 10.

Making Connections

Invite children to tell you what they know about finding differences within 10.

Draw 10 bowling pins on the board. Have children count the pins out loud.

- **If I knock down 5 of the pins, what kind of equation can I use to figure out how many pins are left standing?** subtraction
- **What subtraction equation will show me how many pins are left standing?** $10 - 5 = 5$

Learning Activity

Draw a picture with 6 yellow flowers and 3 pink flowers. Help children understand the steps of writing a subtraction equation.

- **How many yellow flowers do you see?** 6
- **How many flowers do you see all together?** 9
- **What subtraction problem will show how many pink flowers there are?** $10 - 5 = 5$

⚠ Common Errors

Error Children may not know how to find the number to start with.

Springboard to Learning Help children recognize that the number to start with is the total number in all. Have children count all of the foxes aloud and write the number on the first line of the equation.

② Explore

Unlock the Problem

(MP) **Model with mathematics.**

Read the problem aloud to children.

There are 7 squirrels in a tree. Two of the squirrels climb out of the tree. How many squirrels are left in the tree?

- **What information do you know?** There are seven squirrels in a tree and two of them climb out of the tree.

- **Write 7 on the first line to show the total number of squirrels that you are starting with.**

- **Circle and mark an X on the squirrels that climb out of the tree. Write 2 on the second line to show the number of squirrels that leave.**

- **What do you need to find?** how many squirrels are left in the tree

Point out that this is an example of a take away subtraction problem. Explain that circling and crossing out the squirrels shows that those squirrels are leaving the tree.

- **How many squirrels are left?** 5 **The number left is called the *difference*. Write 5 on the last line.**

Read the subtraction equation with children. Review what each number in the subtraction equation represents.

- **Trace the *minus* sign and the *is equal to* sign to complete the subtraction equation.**

Name _____

Subtraction Word Problems

(I Can) solve subtraction word problems within 10.

⊞ UNLOCK the Problem *Real World*

$$7 - 2 = 5$$

DIRECTIONS Listen to the subtraction word problem about the squirrels. Circle and mark an X on the squirrels that are leaving. How many squirrels are left in the tree? Write and trace the subtraction equation.

Chapter 12 • Lesson 4   **471**

(ML) ## Multilingual Support

STRATEGY: Model Concepts

- Children may understand the concept of *taking from* if it is illustrated.

- On the left side of the board, draw three stick figures. To the right of these figures, draw two more stick figures that appear to be walking away. Count each stick figure. **There are 5 people.**

- Circle and cross out the two stick figures walking away. **Two people walk away. How many people are there now?** Guide children to count the stick figures on the left. **There are 3 people now.**

- Repeat the activity by drawing a different picture and having children model your language to solve.

Try Another Problem

1

$2 = 8 - 6$

2

$9 - 4 = 5$

3

$10 - 3 = 7$

DIRECTIONS 1–2. Listen to the subtraction word problem. Write and trace to complete the subtraction equation. 3. Listen to the subtraction word problem. Circle and mark an X on the chipmunks that run away. Write and trace to complete the subtraction equation.

© Houghton Mifflin Harcourt Publishing Company

472 Go Math! Grade K

---

③ Explain

Try Another Problem

For Problem 1, have children listen as you read the subtraction word problem aloud.

There are 8 bunnies. Six of the bunnies are brown. The rest of the bunnies are white. How many white bunnies are there?

Explain to children that this type of subtraction problem is about taking apart a group rather than taking away from a group. Point out that no bunnies are leaving. Instead, children need to find out how many white bunnies there are.

- **How many bunnies are there in all?** 8 **Write the number on the first line.**
- **How many of the bunnies are brown?** 6 **Write the number on the second line.**
- **What do you need to find?** how many bunnies are white **How can you find the number of white bunnies?** Possible answers: subtract; count
- **What is 8 − 6?** 2 **How many white bunnies are there?** 2 **Write and trace to complete the subtraction equation.**

Have children read the subtraction equation. Have them explain what the different numbers mean.

Have children complete Problems 2 and 3. Have children use the number line to help them solve Problem 3.

- **In Problem 2, there are 9 foxes. Four of the foxes are red. The rest of the foxes are gray. How many gray foxes are there?** 5
- **In Problem 3, there are 10 chipmunks in the grass. Three of the chipmunks run away. Circle and cross out the chipmunks that run away. How many chipmunks are left?** 7

Use the checked problem for Quick Check.

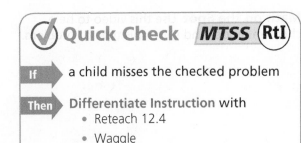

✓ **Quick Check** MTSS RtI

If a child misses the checked problem

Then Differentiate Instruction with
- Reteach 12.4
- Waggle

Ready for More ⏰ Visual Partners

Tell the following subtraction word problem. Have children draw a picture to solve the problem.

Some apples were on the tree. Two apples were taken from the tree. Draw five more apples on the tree to show how many you started with.

- Have children complete a subtraction equation to show and solve this word problem.
- Challenge children to make up a problem of their own and have their partner draw to solve and then complete the subtraction equation to match.

Share and Show

 Attend to precision.

For Problems 4 through 6, read the subtraction word problem aloud.

- **In Problem 4, there are 7 owls. One of the owls leaves the group. How many owls are left?**
- **How many owls are there in all?** 7
- **How many owls leave?** 1 **Circle and mark an X on the owl that leaves.**
- **How many owls are left?** 6

Guide children through Problem 5 in a similar way.

In Problem 6, there are 10 squirrels. Four of the squirrels are gray. The rest are black. How many black squirrels are there?

- **How many squirrels are there in all?** 10
- **How many squirrels are gray?** 4
- **How can you find the number of black squirrels?** subtract
- **What is 10 – 4?** 6 **How many black squirrels are there?** 6

As children complete each problem, have them write and trace to complete the subtraction equation.

Higher-Order Thinking

 Look for and make use of structure.

Write equation 7 + 2 = 9 on the board. **How does knowing this addition fact help you solve 9 – 2 = ____?** I know that when I add 2 to 7 I am adding 2 of something and 7 of something and the answer is 9. So if I subtract 2 from 9, my answer will be 7. **How are the equations alike?** They have the same numbers in them. **How are the equations different?** The numbers are in a different order. One equation has a plus sign, and the other has a minus sign.

Math on the Spot Use this video to help children model and solve this type of problem.

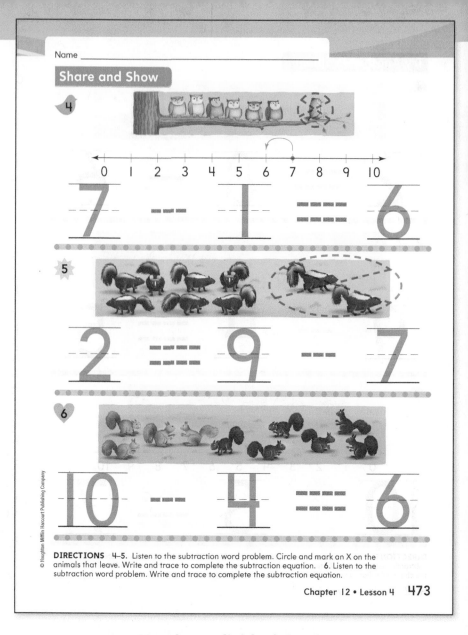

DIRECTIONS 4–5. Listen to the subtraction word problem. Circle and mark an X on the animals that leave. Write and trace to complete the subtraction equation. 6. Listen to the subtraction word problem. Write and trace to complete the subtraction equation.

Chapter 12 • Lesson 4 473

Meeting Individual Needs

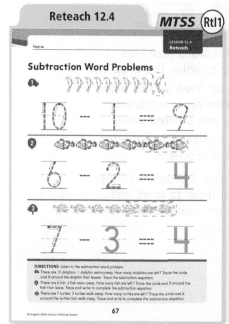

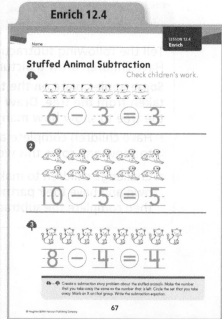

7

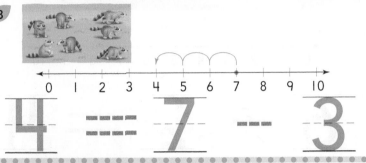

○ $5 - 3 = 2$

● $8 - 5 = 3$

8

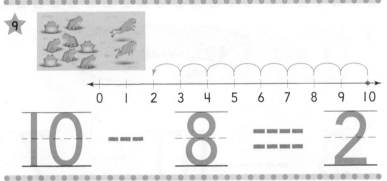

0 1 2 3 4 5 6 7 8 9 10

$4 = 7 - 3$

9

0 1 2 3 4 5 6 7 8 9 10

$10 - 8 = 2$

DIRECTIONS Choose the correct answer. **7.** There are 8 birds. Five of the birds are yellow. The rest of the birds are red. Which equation shows how to find the number of red birds? **8.** There are 7 raccoons. Three of the raccoons walk away. How many raccoons are left? **9.** There are 10 frogs. Some of the frogs hop away. Now there are 8 frogs left. How many frogs hopped away?

HOME ACTIVITY • Tell your child a subtraction word problem. Have your child write a subtraction equation to match the story.

© Houghton Mifflin Harcourt Publishing Company

474 Go Math! **Grade K**

On Your Own

Problem 7 Direct children to fill in the bubble for the correct answer.

(MP) Use appropriate tools strategically.

Problems 8 and 9 Children will model the problem using a number line as well as a subtraction equation.

I Can

Have children write their own subtraction word problem to demonstrate the skill for the I Can statement.

I can solve subtraction word problems within 10 by . . . using the pictures to help me subtract and solve the take away and take apart problems. I can use numbers in the problem to complete the subtraction equation.

Exit Ticket

Draw to show the difference between an addition word problem and a subtraction word problem.

DIFFERENTIATED INSTRUCTION • Independent Activities

 **Grab-and-Go!** ™

Version 2.0

Differentiated Centers Kit

Tabletop Flipchart

Mini-lessons for reteaching to targeted small groups

Readers

Supports key math skills and concepts in real-world situations.

Games

Reinforce math content and vocabulary

Activities

Meaningful and fun math practice

Practice and Homework

Subtraction Word Problems

Use the Practice and Homework pages to provide children with more practice of the concepts and skills presented in this lesson. Children master their understanding as they complete practice items.

1

0 1 2 3 4 5 6 7 8 9 10

6 -- 2 === 4

2

3 === 10 -- 7

DIRECTIONS Write and trace to complete the subtraction equation. 1. There are six bears. Two bears run away. Circle and mark an X on the bears that leave. 2. There are ten turkeys. Seven turkeys run away. Circle and mark an X on the turkeys that leave.

© Houghton Mifflin Harcourt Publishing Company

Chapter 12 • Lesson 4 **475**

Lesson Check

3

○ $5 - 2 = 3$

● $7 - 2 = 5$

4

○ 4

● 3

Spiral Review

5

$5 + 4 = 9$

DIRECTIONS **3.** Choose the correct answer. There are 7 cats. Two of them run away. What is 7 – 2? **4.** Choose the correct answer. There are 6 eagles. Three fly away. What is 6 – 3? **5.** There are 5 big dogs and 4 little dogs. How many dogs are there?

Summative Assessment

Use the **Chapter Review** to assess children's progress in Chapter 12.

Name _____

Chapter Review

1.

$$6 - 2 = 4$$

2.

0 1 2 3 4 5 6 7 8 9 10

$$8 - 3 = 5$$

DIRECTIONS Listen to the subtraction word problem. Complete the subtraction equation. 1. Six children are playing in the sandbox. Two leave to play on the slide. How many children are in the sandbox now? 2. Eight squirrels are looking for acorns. Three squirrels leave. How many squirrels are left?

Go Online For more help

Chapter 12   477

3.

$$3 = 6 - 3$$

4.

$$7 - 4 = 3$$

DIRECTIONS Listen to the subtraction word problem. Complete the subtraction equation. 3. Six children are playing together. Three leave to go to soccer practice. How many children are still playing? 4. Seven children are on a hike at camp. Four children go back to the tents. How many children are still hiking?

478   Go Math! Grade K

Online, Data-Driven Decision Making   MTSS RtI   HMH | Waggle®

Based on the results of the Chapter Review, use the following resources to review skills.

Item	Lesson	Content Focus	Intervene With
2, 7, 8	12.2	Write and solve subtraction equations within 9.	Reteach 12.2, Waggle
1, 3, 4	12.1	Write and solve subtraction equations within 7.	Reteach 12.1, Waggle
9	12.3	Write and solve subtraction equations within 10.	Reteach 12.3, Waggle
5, 6	12.4	Solve subtraction word problems within 10.	Reteach 12.4, Waggle

Name _____

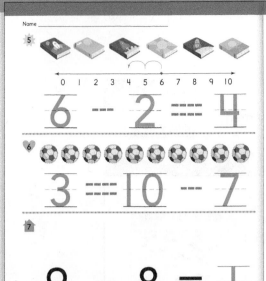

5

$$6 - 2 = 4$$

6

$$3 = 10 - 7$$

7

$$9 - 8 = 1$$

8

$$6 = 9 - 3$$

9

$$10 - 4 = 6$$

DIRECTIONS 5. Listen to the subtraction word problem. Complete the subtraction equation. Jamal borrowed six books from the library. He read and returned two. How many library books does he still have? 6. Listen to the subtraction word problem. Complete the subtraction equation. There are ten soccer balls in the school gym. Seven of them are borrowed by students during gym class. How many soccer balls are still in the gym? 7. Complete the subtraction equation. Draw to show what you know about the subtraction equation.

Chapter 12 479

480 Go Math! Grade K

DIRECTIONS 8-9. Complete the subtraction equation. Draw to show what you know about the subtraction equation.

Performance Assessment Task

See the Performance Tasks to assess children's understanding of the content. For each task, you will find sample student work for each of the response levels in the task scoring rubric.

Portfolio Performance Assessment Tasks may be used for portfolios.

Chapter Test

Summative Assessment

Use the **Chapter Test** to assess children's progress in Chapter 12.

Chapter Tests are found in the *Assessment Guide*. Test items are presented in formats consistent with high-stakes assessments.

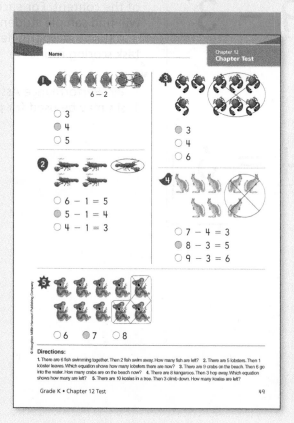

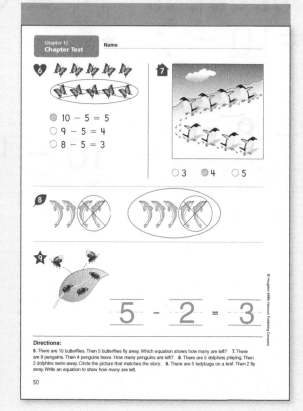

Teacher Notes

Chapter at a Glance

Count, Represent, and Compare Numbers Through 15

	LESSON 13.1 • 1 Day	**LESSON 13.2 • 1 Day**	**LESSON 13.3 • 1 Day**
Lesson at a Glance	Model and Count 11 and 12 . . . . 483A	Count and Represent 11 and 12 . . . . 489A	Model and Count 13 and 14 . . . . 495A
I Can	I can count out 11 or 12 objects.	I can write 11 or 12 to represent a group of objects.	I can count out 13 or 14 objects.
Learning Goal	Count out 11 or 12 objects.	Write 11 or 12 to represent a group of objects.	Count out 13 or 14 objects.
Vocabulary	eleven, twelve		thirteen, fourteen
Multilingual Support	**Strategy:** Model Concepts	**Strategy:** Model Language	**Strategy:** Describe
Practice and Fluency	LESSON 13.1 ◆ ■ Practice and Homework ■ Waggle ◆ Achieving Facts Fluency*	LESSON 13.2 ◆ ■ Practice and Homework ■ Waggle ◆ Achieving Facts Fluency*	LESSON 13.3 ◆ ■ Practice and Homework ■ Waggle ◆ Achieving Facts Fluency*
MTSS RtI Intervention and Enrichment	■ Waggle MA.K.NSO.1.2 ◆ ■ Reteach 13.1 ◆ ■ Tier 2 Intervention Skill S14 ◆ ■ Tier 3 Intervention Skill E14 ◆ Tabletop Flipchart ◆ Enrich 13.1	■ Waggle ◆ ■ Reteach 13.2 ◆ ■ Tier 2 Intervention Skill S14 ◆ ■ Tier 3 Intervention Skill E14 ◆ Tabletop Flipchart ◆ Enrich 13.2	■ Waggle ◆ ■ Reteach 13.3 ◆ ■ Tier 2 Intervention Skill S16 ◆ ■ Tier 3 Intervention Skill E16 ◆ Tabletop Flipchart ◆ Enrich 13.3

See the Grab-and-Go!™ Centers Kit for more small-group activities.

Grab and Go!™
Version 2.0
Differentiated Centers Kit

The kit provides literature, games, and activities for small-group learning.

◆ Print/Printable Resource
■ Interactive Resource

	LESSON 13.4 • 1 Day	**LESSON 13.5 • 1 Day**	**LESSON 13.6 • 1 Day**
Lesson at a Glance	Count and Represent 13 and 14 . . . . 501A	Model, Count, and Represent 15 . . . . . . 507A	One More and One Less to 15 . . . . 513A
I Can	I can write 13 and 14 to represent a group of objects.	I can count and represent 15 with objects or a written numeral.	I can find one more and one less to 15.
Learning Goal	Write 13 or 14 to represent a group of objects.	Count and represent 15 with objects or a written numeral.	Find one more and one less than a number to 15.
Vocabulary		fifteen	
Multilingual Support	**Strategy:** Define	**Strategy:** Rephrase	**Strategy:** Identify Patterns
Practice and Fluency	LESSON 13.4 ◆ ■ Practice and Homework ■ Waggle ◆ Achieving Facts Fluency*	LESSON 13.5 ◆ ■ Practice and Homework ■ Waggle ◆ Achieving Facts Fluency*	LESSON 13.6 ◆ ■ Practice and Homework ■ Waggle ◆ Achieving Facts Fluency*
MTSS (RtI) Intervention and Enrichment	■ Waggle ◆ ■ Reteach 13.4 ◆ ■ Tier 2 Intervention Skill S16 ◆ ■ Tier 3 Intervention Skill E16 ◆ Tabletop Flipchart ◆ Enrich 13.4	■ Waggle ◆ ■ Reteach 13.5 ◆ ■ Tier 2 Intervention Skill S16 ◆ ■ Tier 3 Intervention Skill E16 ◆ Tabletop Flipchart ◆ Enrich 13.5	■ Waggle ◆ ■ Reteach 13.6 ◆ ■ Tier 2 Intervention Skill S16 ◆ ■ Tier 3 Intervention Skill E16 ◆ Enrich 13.6

*For individual and class practice with counting automaticity and operational fluency, go to *Achieving Facts Fluency* pages located online.

◆ Print/Printable Resource
■ Interactive Resource

Teaching for Depth

Count, Represent, and Compare Numbers Through 15

Numbers 11 to 15

Children build on their understanding of numbers 0 to 10 to conceptualize the numbers 11 to 15 and beyond.

- Children practice the numbers 11 to 15, expressing each number as 10 and more and saying the number words aloud.

- Placing counters in two ten frames to show a number as 10 and some more is one way children can model numbers 11 to 15.

- Saying the number name and writing the numeral also contributes to the understanding of numbers 11 to 15.

The Numeration System

Early experiences with number concepts are foundational to more advanced ideas in our numeration system.

From the Research

66The Hindu-Arabic numeration system has four important characteristics:

1 Place value: The position of a digit represents its value...

2. Base of ten: The term base simply means a collection. Thus, in our system 10 is the value that determines a new collection, and the system has 10 digits, 0 through 9.

3. Use of zero: A symbol for zero exists and allows us to represent the absence of something...

4. Additive property: Numbers can be summed with respect to place value...99
(Reys et al., 2004, p. 169)

Compare Numbers 11 to 15

Children use their prior knowledge of the numbers 1 to 10 to compare numbers and use precise language when communicating their reasoning to others.

When talking about a teen number, children use *how many more* to describe the amount of ones more than ten.

They use *fewer than* to describe number of fewer objects in one group than than another group.

They use *is equal to* to describe numbers that represent groups that have the same amount of objects as another group.

Finding more and less than a number develops better fluency with counting and conceptual understanding of the value of numbers.

Mathematical Practices and Processes

Look for and make use of structure.

Children learn about teen numbers by placing counters in ten frames so that they can see one set of ten and some more. They also model teen numbers by making sets of 10 counters and some more counters. These experiences help children to focus on the importance of 10 in our number system as they practice seeing structure.

For more professional learning, go online to Teacher's Corner.

Instructional Journey

While every classroom may look a little different, this instructional model provides a framework to organize small-group and whole-group learning for meaningful student learning.

Whole Group
Engage

5 minutes

Readiness
- Problem of the Day
- Fluency Builder or Vocabulary Builder
- Access Prior Knowledge

Engagement
- I Can
- Making Connections
- Learning Activity

Small and Whole Group
Explore

15–20 minutes

Exploration
- Listen and Draw, Unlock the Problem
- Multilingual Support and Strategy
- Common Errors

Small Group
Explain

15–20 minutes

Quick Check
- ✓ Share and Show

Differentiated Instruction

Version 2.0

Intervention
- Waggle
- Reteach
- Tier 2 and Tier 3 MTSS
- Tabletop Flipchart Mini Lessons

Language Support
- Vocabulary Activities
- Language Routines
- Multilingual Glossary

Enrichment
- Waggle Games
- Ready for More
- Enrich

Whole Group
Elaborate

5 minutes

- Math on the Spot Videos
- Higher-Order Thinking Problems

Evaluate

- I Can Reflection
- Exit Ticket
- Practice and Homework
- Fluency Practice
- Waggle

Assessment

Diagnostic	Formative	Summative
• Show What You Know	• Lesson Quick Check	• Chapter Review • Chapter Test • Performance Assessment Task

Version 2.0
Differentiated Centers Kit
The kit provides literature, games, and activities for small-group learning.

Strategies for
Multilingual Learners

Understanding a child's language development is helpful in differentiating teaching and assessment. Assessing a child's understanding of mathematical concepts can be done by listening, speaking, reading, and writing. The level of support a child needs determines how best to assess that child's understanding of mathematical concepts.

Planning for Instruction			
Language Support	**Substantial** (WIDA Level 1)*	**Moderate** (WIDA Levels 2 & 3)*	**Light** (WIDA Levels 4 & 5)*
Child's Use of Language	• uses single words • uses common short phrases • heavily relies on visual supports and use of manipulatives	• uses simple sentences • uses some academic vocabulary • relies on visual supports and use of manipulatives	• uses a variety of sentences • uses academic vocabulary • benefits from visual supports and manipulatives
Ways to Assess Understanding	**Listening:** points to pictures, words, or phrases to answer questions **Speaking:** answers *yes/no* questions **Reading:** matches symbols to math terms and concepts **Writing:** draws a visual representation of a problem	**Listening:** matches, categorizes, or sequences information based on visuals **Speaking:** begins to explain reasoning, asks math questions, repeats explanations from peers **Reading:** identifies important information to solve a problem **Writing:** uses simple sentences and visual representations	**Listening:** draws conclusions and makes connections based on what they heard **Speaking:** explains and justifies concepts and solutions **Reading:** understands information in math contexts **Writing:** completes sentences using some academic vocabulary

* For more information on WIDA Standards, visit their website at: https://wida.wisc.edu/.

• Look for strategies throughout the lesson to support multilingual learners.
• Log on to ED to find additional multilingual activities and Vocabulary Cards.

In This Chapter

Key Academic Vocabulary

Current Development • Vocabulary

eleven, twelve, thirteen, fourteen, fifteen

Using Language Routines to Develop Understanding

 Language routines provide opportunities for children to develop an understanding of mathematical language and concepts by listening, speaking, reading, and writing. More information on these language routines can be found on the Language Support Cards.

Stronger and Clearer Each Time

1 Children show their thinking with math tools and visuals.

2 Children share their thinking and receive feedback with a partner or a group.

3 Children revoice feedback and revise their work.

Language Support	Substantial (WIDA Level 1)*	Moderate (WIDA Levels 2 & 3)*	Light (WIDA Levels 4 & 5)*
Language Routine Differentiation	**1** Children can show their thinking using visuals and/or manipulatives. **2** Children can answer yes/no or single-word-answer questions about their reasoning. Allow children to rely heavily on their visual representations. **3** Children revise their work based on feedback.	**1** Children can show their thinking using words and/or visuals. **2** Children can verbally communicate with their partner or group using visual representations to support their reasoning. **3** Children repeat feedback and revise their work.	**1** Children can show their thinking using words and visuals. **2** Children can use academic vocabulary to verbally communicate with their partner or group. **3** Children revoice feedback and revise their work.
Possible Student Work		13	13 10 and 3

* For more information on WIDA Standards, visit their website at: https://wida.wisc.edu/.

Assessing Prior Knowledge

Have children complete **Show What You Know** on their own. Items tested are the prerequisite skills for this chapter.

Diagnostic Interview Task

The alternative interview tasks below evaluate children's understanding of each **Show What You Know** skill. The diagnostic chart may be used for intervention on prerequisite skills.

MATERIALS two-color counters, connecting cubes

- Show the child a set with up to 10 counters. Have the child count them and write the number that shows how many counters there are. Then ask the child to use connecting cubes to make another set with that many cubes. Repeat with two more numbers.

- Show the child a number line from 0 to 10. Have the child point to a number. Then have the child move their finger to the number that is one more. Repeat with a different number and finding the number that is one less.

Name _____

✓ Show What You Know

Count and Represent Numbers to 10

1.

2.

One More and One Less to 10

3.

4.

This page checks understanding of important skills needed for success in Chapter 13.

DIRECTIONS 1. Circle the groups that show 7. Write the number. 2. Circle the groups that show 10. Write the number. 3–4. Look at the number. Use the number line to find one more and one less than each number. Write the numbers.

Chapter 13 • Count, Represent, and Compare Numbers Through 15 **481**

✓ Show What You Know • Diagnostic Assessment

Use to determine if children need intervention for the chapter's prerequisite skills.

	Skill	Missed More Than	Intervene With
TIER 3	Count and Represent Numbers to 10	0	*Intensive Intervention* Skill E15
TIER 2	One More and One Less to 10	0	*Strategic Intervention* Skill S1, S23, S24

If NO...then
INTERVENE

If YES...then use
INDEPENDENT ACTIVITIES

Grab and Go!™
Version 2.0
Differentiated Centers Kit
Use the Reteach or Enrich Activities online or as independent activities in the *Grab-and-Go 2.0™ Differentiated Centers Kit*.

Vocabulary Builder

one more   one less

FINISH

CABBAGE
PARK
RUN

DIRECTIONS Circle the number that is one more than 9.
Mark an X on the number that is one less than 9.

482 Go Math! Grade K

© Houghton Mifflin Harcourt Publishing Company

Vocabulary Builder

Children use multiple strategies to develop grade-appropriate vocabulary. Have children complete the activities on the page by working alone or with partners.

Look at the page with children.

Have children point to each number as they say it aloud, starting with 1 and ending at 10. Tell children that the rabbits are numbered in counting order.

Have children circle the number that is one more than 9. Then have them put an X on the number that is one less than 9.

 **School-Home Letter** is available in English and Spanish online, and in multiple other languages.

Intervention Options MTSS (RtI) Response to Intervention

Use Show What You Know, Lesson Quick Check, and Assessments to diagnose children's intervention levels.

TIER 1
On-Level Intervention

For children who are generally at grade level but need early intervention with the lesson concepts, use:

- Reteach
- Tabletop Flipchart Mini Lesson
- Waggle
- ▲ **Tier 1 Activity**

TIER 2
Strategic Intervention

For children who need small group instruction to review concepts and skills needed for the chapter, use:

- ▲ **Prerequisite Skills Activities**
- ▲ **Tier 2 Activity**

TIER 3
Intensive Intervention

For children who need one-on-one instruction to build foundational skills for the chapter, use:

- ▲ **Prerequisite Skills Activities**
- ▲ **Tier 3 Activity**

ENRICHMENT
Independent Activities

For children who successfully complete lessons, use:

- Waggle Practice and Games

Grab and Go!
Version 2.0
Differentiated Centers Kit

- Ready for More Activity for every lesson
- Enrich

Chapter 13   482

Lesson at a Glance
Model and Count 11 and 12

SNAPSHOT

Mathematical Standards
- Write numbers from 0 to 20. Represent a number of objects with a written numeral 0-20 (with 0 representing a count of no objects).
- When counting objects, say the number names in the standard order, pairing each object with one and only one number name and each number name with one and only one object.

Mathematical Practices and Processes
- Reason abstractly and quantitatively.
- Use appropriate tools strategically.
- Attend to precision.
- Construct arguments and critique reasoning of others.
- Look for and make use of structure.

(I Can) Objective
I can count out 11 or 12 objects.

Learning Goal
Count out 11 or 12 objects.

Language Objective
Children will explain to a partner how to count out 11 or 12 objects.

MATERIALS
- MathBoard
- two-color counters

ACROSS THE GRADES

Grade K
Given a number from 0 to 20, count out that many objects.

After
Starting at a given number, count forward and backwards within 120 by ones. Skip count by 2s to 20 and by 5s to 100.

ABOUT THE MATH

While working with the numbers 11 and 12, children will count objects and tell how many. They will identify the numeral that represents how many. They also will use counters to represent a number and write the number as 10 and some more. The use of ten frames allows children to see a number greater than 10 as 10 and some more. A full frame shows 10, and any other objects outside the frame tell how many more. For 11, there is always 1 more, and for 12, there is always 2 more.

For more professional learning, go online to Teacher's Corner.

DAILY ROUTINES

🖥 Problem of the Day 13.1

Which number is more, 2 or 1? 2

🖥 Vocabulary eleven, twelve
- Interactive Student Edition
- Multilingual Glossary

Vocabulary Builder

Ask children to define each term and give several examples. Accept reasonable definitions. Possible examples given.

Term	Example(s)
eleven	11; 10 and 1
twelve	12; 10 and 2

FOCUSING ON THE WHOLE STUDENT

Culturally Responsive Education

In this lesson and throughout this chapter, children begin to explore place value as they see teen numbers as ten and some more ones. The concept of place value is critical and often confusing for children. Culturally and linguistically diverse children are at a higher risk for moving forward with gaps in their understanding due to systemic issues in our education system. As such, culturally responsive educators in the primary grades are tasked with laying a foundation of knowledge that prepares children for more complex mathematics concepts in the future. Pay close attention to the ways children represent teen numbers and question children who seem to be off track. For example, if a child makes the common error of drawing more than one circle in a single square on a ten frame, instead of simply telling them that only one counter can go in each square, ask them, "How could you represent this number if you were not going to draw?" Guide the child to use the counters to discover for themselves that there can only be one counter in each square. Ask, "How can you represent this number once you take the counters off of the ten frame?" Using questions to guide children helps them build problem-solving skills that will benefit them as they grow.

❶ Engage

with the Interactive Student Edition

I Can Objective
I can count out 11 or 12 objects.

Making Connections
Invite children to tell you what they know about counting to ten.

- **What number is one more than five?** 6
- **What number is one less than ten?** 9 Show children a model of ten with counters and a ten frame.
- **How do you know without counting that there are ten counters in this ten frame?** Possible answer: The ten frame has ten squares and each square has a counter. So if the ten frame is full, then there must be ten counters.

Learning Activity
Tell children a story about Scout finding 10 and one more flowers outside. Guide children toward analyzing the question presented in the story by asking about the flowers Scout counted.

- **What did Scout find outside?** flowers
- **How many flowers did Scout count?** 10 and one more
- **What are you trying to find out?** how many flowers there are in all

Explore

Listen and Draw

Materials two-color counters

Read aloud this problem as children listen.

Valerie has 11 apples. Rachel has one more apple than Valerie. How can you use counters to model each set of apples?

(MP) **Use appropriate tools strategically.**

Review how to use a ten frame by placing objects to model the number and counting the sections from left to right and from top to bottom.

Give children counters to model each number.

* **Look at the ten frame.**
* **How many counters fill a ten frame?** 10 **Use counters to fill the ten frame.**
* **How many more counters do you need to model 11?** 1 **Where can you place that counter?** below the ten frame **Count the counters.**
* **When a ten frame is full, you know there are 10. How many is 10 and 1?** 11
* **11 is made up of a filled ten frame and one more.**

Introduce 12 in a similar way.

* **How do you think you can show 12 with counters and a ten frame?** I can show 10 counters in a ten frame and 2 counters below.

Have children draw to show 12 counters.

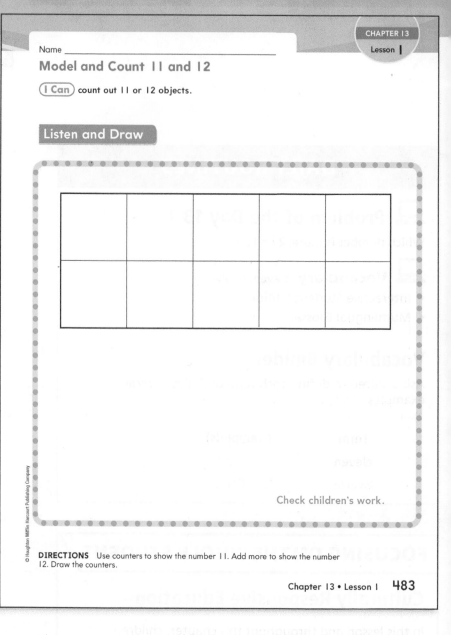

Name _____

CHAPTER 13
Lesson 1

Model and Count 11 and 12

(I Can) count out 11 or 12 objects.

Listen and Draw

Check children's work.

DIRECTIONS Use counters to show the number 11. Add more to show the number 12. Draw the counters.

Chapter 13 • Lesson 1 483

(ML) ## Multilingual Support

STRATEGY: Model Concepts

Materials connecting cubes

Modeling may help children understand concepts.

* Show a row of 10 connecting cubes and one below. Count the 11 cubes. Write the number. Repeat using 12 connecting cubes.
* Give children connecting cubes. Have them show 11 cubes and count them. Then have children write the number.

Have children show 12 connecting cubes and write the number.

1  12

2 ☑

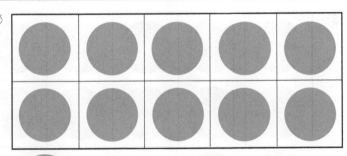

Check children's work.

3 🌳 10 and I

DIRECTIONS 1. Count and tell how many. Circle the number. 2. Use counters to show the number 11. Draw the counters. 3. Look at the counters you drew. How many are in the ten frame? Write the number. How many more are there? Write the number.

Ready for More
🕐 Auditory Individual/Partners

Have pairs of children tell each other stories about more than 10 items. For example: *I bought 12 apples.*

• Have each child draw a picture of a set of 10 and some more to go with his or her story and then write the number that goes with the picture. Then have children share and compare stories.

③ Explain

Share and Show

• Look at Problem 1. How many apples do you see? 11

(MP) **Look for and make use of structure.**

• Did the arrangement of the apples help you? How? I can see 10 apples and 1 more, so I know that there are 11 apples.

• Look at the numbers next to the apples. Circle 11.

• Look at Problem 2. How can you show the number 11 with counters? I can put 10 counters in the ten frame to model 10 and 1 counter below to model 1 more. **Draw the counters.**

(MP) **Attend to precision.**

For Problem 3, have children count and write how many are in the ten frame. Then have them count and write how many more. 10; 1

Use the checked problem for Quick Check.

✓ **Quick Check** MTSS RtI

If → a child misses the checked problem

Then → Differentiate Instruction with
• Reteach 13.1
• Waggle

! **Common Errors**

Error Children may draw more than one counter in a space in the ten frame.

Springboard to Learning Guide children to place one counter in each space of the ten frame and the eleventh counter below the ten frame. Then ask children how they could represent the counters once the counters have been removed.

Share and Show

 Reason abstractly and quantitatively.

- **Look at Problem 4. How many limes are there?** 12

- **Find 12 and circle it.**

- **Look at Problem 5. How can you show the number 12 with counters?** I can show 10 counters in the ten frame to model 10 and 2 counters below to model 2 more. **Draw the counters.**

For Problem 6, have children count and write how many counters are in the ten frame. Then have them count and write how many more.

- **How many do you have if you have 10 and 2 more?** 12

Higher-Order Thinking

Tell children to think about how they would show 11 and 12 using five frames instead of ten frames.

 Construct arguments and critique reasoning of others.

Begin a discussion about how a five frame and a ten frame are alike and different. Children should come to realize that a ten frame is made of, or equal to, 2 five frames, so if 1 ten frame is filled, 2 five frames would also be filled. Then have children tell how they would show 11 and 12 using five frames. Eleven would be 2 filled five frames and 1 more and 12 would be 2 filled five frames and 2 more.

Math on the Spot Use this video to help children model and solve this type of problem.

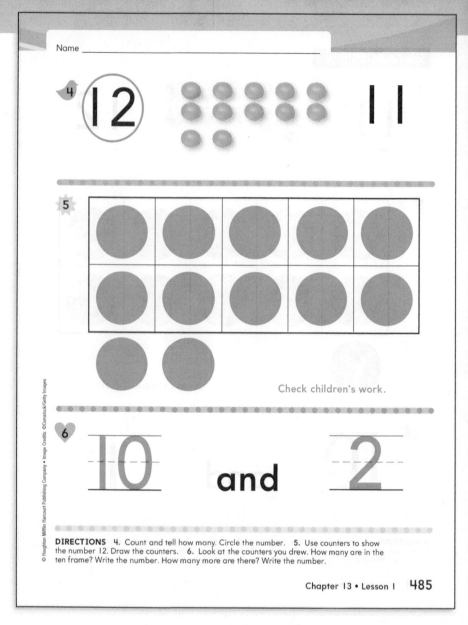

Name _____

4 12   11

5 Check children's work.

6 10 and 2

DIRECTIONS 4. Count and tell how many. Circle the number. **5.** Use counters to show the number 12. Draw the counters. **6.** Look at the counters you drew. How many are in the ten frame? Write the number. How many more are there? Write the number.

Chapter 13 • Lesson 1   485

Meeting Individual Needs

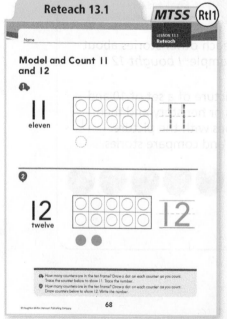

Reteach 13.1

MTSS Rtl1

Enrich 13.1

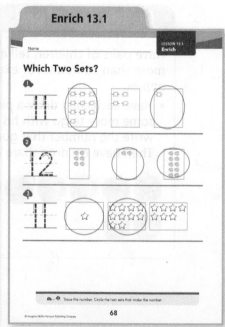

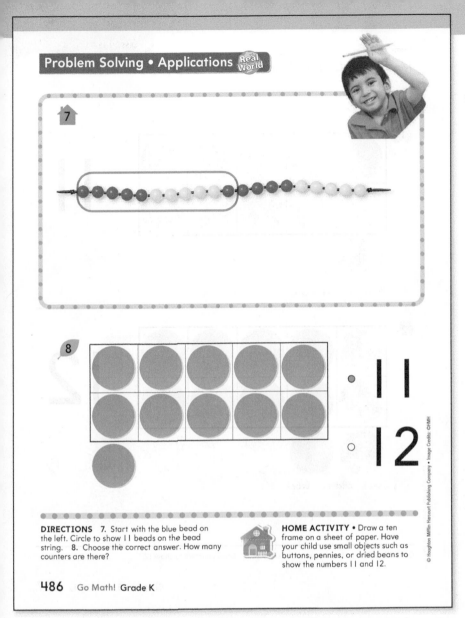

DIRECTIONS 7. Start with the blue bead on the left. Circle to show 11 beads on the bead string. 8. Choose the correct answer. How many counters are there?

HOME ACTIVITY • Draw a ten frame on a sheet of paper. Have your child use small objects such as buttons, pennies, or dried beans to show the numbers 11 and 12.

© Houghton Mifflin Harcourt Publishing Company • Image Credits: CHMH

DIFFERENTIATED INSTRUCTION • Independent Activities

Grab and Go!
Version 2.0
Differentiated Centers Kit

Tabletop Flipchart

Mini-lessons for reteaching to targeted small groups

Readers

Supports key math skills and concepts in real-world situations.

Games

Reinforce math content and vocabulary

Activities

Meaningful and fun math practice

---

④ Elaborate

Problem Solving Applications Real World

(MP) Attend to precision.

Read **Problem 7**. Ask children to explain how they will solve the problem.

- Count the first set of five blue beads and the first set of five yellow beads. How many beads do you have? 10
- How many more beads than 10 do you need to make 11? 1 Circle 11 beads.

Guide children to **Problem 8**.

- How many counters are there? Fill in the bubble next to the correct answer.

⑤ Evaluate | Formative Assessment

I Can

Have pairs of children write, draw, or model an example to demonstrate the skill for the I Can statement.

I can count out 11 or 12 objects by . . . using counters to fill a ten frame and show 1 or 2 more.

Exit Ticket

Allow time for children to communicate about what their drawings show and discuss other possible methods for showing the numbers 11 or 12.

Practice and Homework

Model and Count 11 and 12

Use Practice and Homework pages to provide children with more practice of the concepts and skills presented in this lesson. Children master their understanding as they complete practice items.

Name ______________________________

LESSON 13.1
Practice and Homework

Model and Count 11 and 12

1

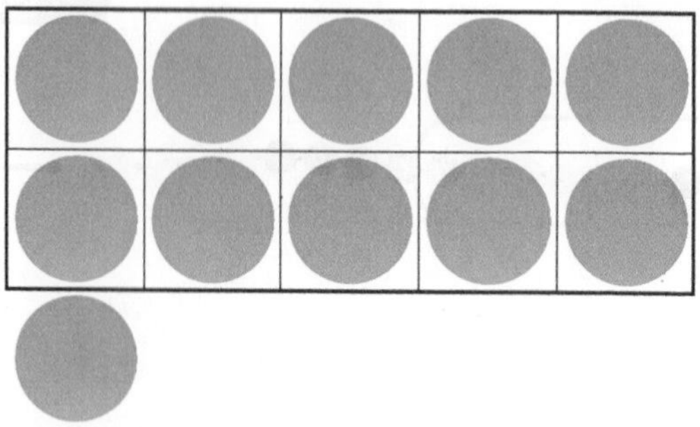

11

Check children's work.

2

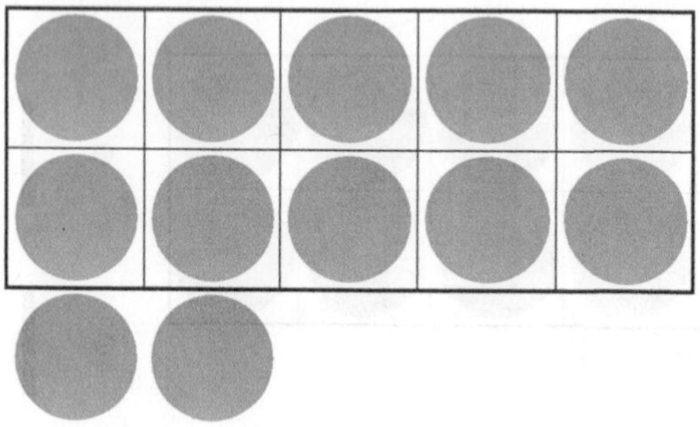

12

Check children's work.

DIRECTIONS 1. Draw counters to show 11. 2. Draw counters to show 12.

Lesson Check

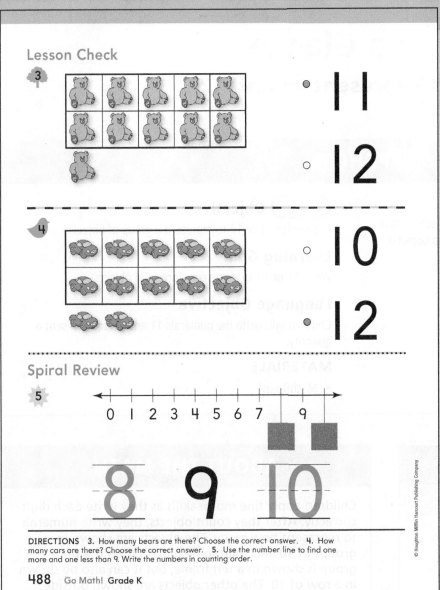

DIRECTIONS 3. How many bears are there? Choose the correct answer. 4. How many cars are there? Choose the correct answer. 5. Use the number line to find one more and one less than 9. Write the numbers in counting order.

488 Go Math! Grade K

© Houghton Mifflin Harcourt Publishing Company

Continue to practice concepts and skills with Lesson Check. Use Spiral Review to engage children in previously taught concepts and to promote content retention.

Lesson at a Glance
Count and Represent 11 and 12

SNAPSHOT

Mathematical Standards
- Write numbers from 0 to 20. Represent a number of objects with a written numeral 0–20 (with 0 representing a count of no objects).

Mathematical Practices and Processes
- Reason abstractly and quantitatively.
- Model with mathematics.
- Attend to precision.
- Construct arguments and critique reasoning of others.
- Look for and make use of structure.
- Express regularity in repeated reasoning.

(I Can) Objective
I can write 11 or 12 to represent a group of objects.

Learning Goal
Write 11 or 12 to represent a group of objects.

Language Objective
Children will write the numerals 11 and 12 to represent a quantity.

MATERIALS
- MathBoard

ACROSS THE GRADES

Grade K
Given a group of up to 20 objects, count the number of objects in that group and represent the number of objects with a written numeral. State the number of objects in a rearrangement of that group without recounting.

After
Starting at a given number, count forward and backwards within 120 by ones. Skip count by 2s to 20 and by 5s to 100.

ABOUT THE MATH
Children apply fine motor skills as they write each digit correctly. After they count objects, they write numerals to represent how many. The objects are shown in groups of 10 and then some more. Often the first group is shown in a ten frame, but it can also be shown in a row of 10. The other objects are shown outside the ten frame or in a row below the row of 10. This allows children to begin seeing 11 as 10 and 1, and 12 as 10 and 2, which is the beginning of the development of the concept of place value.

For more professional learning, go online to Teacher's Corner.

DAILY ROUTINES

🖥 Problem of the Day 13.2

Use counters to show 1.

Use counters to show 2.

Check children's representations.

🖥 Vocabulary

- Interactive Student Edition
- Multilingual Glossary

Fluency Builder

Count from 1 to 12. Which number is missing?

1, 2, 3, 4, 5, 6, 7, 8, 9, 10, ?, 12   11

FOCUSING ON THE WHOLE STUDENT

Access Prior Knowledge

Choose one or more of the following activities.

- Create a short story with children about counting objects in a hen house.
- Have children draw simple pictures of a row of nests and tell you about them.

① Engage

with the Interactive Student Edition

I Can Objective

I can write 11 or 12 to represent a group of objects.

Making Connections

Invite children to tell you what they know about how to write numbers that are greater than 10.

- **Display 10 objects or draw them on the board. How many do we see?** 10
- **Do you see anything in the classroom that we can count 10 of?** Answers will vary; sneakers, books, etc.
- **How can we show the number 10 using numbers and words?** 10; ten

Learning Activity

Draw 12 nests on the board. Label the first ten nests 1 through 10. Leave the labels off for 11 and 12. Guide children toward thinking about numbers greater than 10.

- **How many nests have numbers on them?** 10
- **How many nests are missing a number label?** 2
- **What do we need to find out?** what is 10 and 1 more, and what is 10 and 2 more

2 Explore

Listen and Draw

(MP) **Look for and make use of structure.**

Point to the red cubes at the top of the page.

- **How many cubes are in the top row?** 10
- **How many cubes are in the bottom row?** 1
- **How many cubes is 10 and 1 more?** 11

Review the purpose of the blue dots and the guide arrows on the numbers. Have children write the numbers in the air before writing them on paper.

- **Trace, then write eleven three more times.**

  Read aloud the problem as children listen.

  Kerri buys 12 bagels. Kerri writes the number of bagels on the box. What does the number look like?

Have children point to the blue cubes.

(MP) **Attend to precision.**

- **What can you tell about the number 12?** It is two greater than 10. It is one greater than 11.
- **How would you explain to a classmate how to write the number 12?** Possible answer: First write a 1 and then write a 2 right next to it.
- **What does the number 12 look like?** a 1 with a 2 right next to it

---

Name _____

Count and Represent 11 and 12

(I Can) write 11 or 12 to represent a group of objects.

Listen and Draw

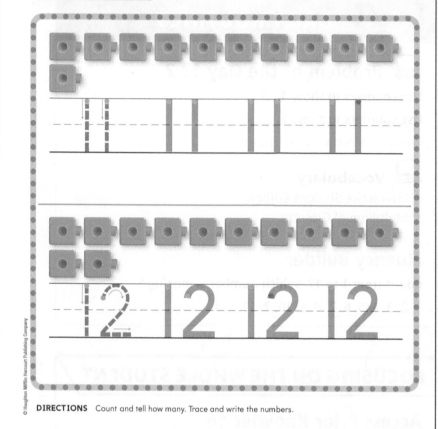

© Houghton Mifflin Harcourt Publishing Company

DIRECTIONS Count and tell how many. Trace and write the numbers.

Chapter 13 • Lesson 2   **489**

Multilingual Support

STRATEGY: Model Language

Children can learn correct pronunciation and sentence structure by repeating sentences that are modeled by proficient speakers.

- Draw a large butterfly with 11 dots on one wing.
- Have children draw 11 dots on the other wing.
- Have children echo sentences. **There is one butterfly. It has two wings. There are 11 dots on each wing.**

Repeat using a new butterfly and 12 dots.

- Draw other shapes or animals. Repeat drawing dots and saying sentences for different numbers.

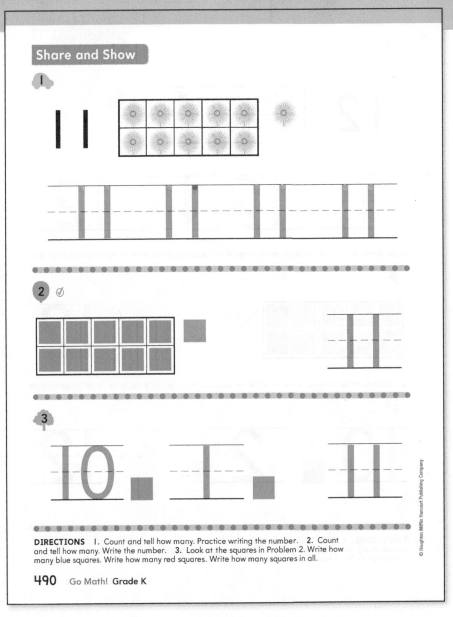

DIRECTIONS 1. Count and tell how many. Practice writing the number. 2. Count and tell how many. Write the number. 3. Look at the squares in Problem 2. Write how many blue squares. Write how many red squares. Write how many squares in all.

490 Go Math! Grade K

3 Explain

Share and Show

 Reason abstractly and quantitatively.

- In Problem 1, what number do you see? 11
- How many flowers are in the ten frame? 10 How many more are there? 1 How many is 10 and 1 more? 11
- Write the number 11 four times, and say the number quietly to yourself.
- Look at Problem 2. How many blue squares are in the ten frame? 10 How many more red squares are there? 1 How many is 10 and 1 more? 11
- Write the number.

Have children look at the blue squares and the red square in Problem 2. Have them complete Problem 3 by writing how many blue squares there are. 10 Then have children write how many red squares there are. 1 Then have them write how many squares in all. 11

Use the checked problem for Quick Check.

✓ Quick Check   *MTSS* RtI

If ➤ a child misses the checked problem

Then ➤ Differentiate Instruction with
  - Reteach 13.2
  - Waggle

! Common Errors

Error Children may not be able to count past 10.

Springboard to Learning Model counting to 11 using cubes or counters. Have children count along with you. Then model counting to 12 using cubes or counters and have them count with you.

Ready for More 🕐 | Kinesthetic Individual / Partners

Materials 12 cubes, chart paper

Have children take turns using 11 cubes to make two sets, such as 3 and 8.

- Invite children to write the number pairs to show different ways to make 11 in two columns on chart paper.
- Challenge children to find as many pairs as they can.
- Repeat the activity using 12 cubes to show different ways to make 12.

Share and Show

 Construct arguments and critique reasoning of others.

- In Problem 4, what number do you see? 12
- How many red flowers are in the ten frame? 10 How many more are there? 2 How many is 10 and 2 more? 12 Write the number 12 four times and say the number quietly to yourself.
- Look at Problem 5. How many green squares are in the ten frame? 10 How many more orange squares are there? 2 How many is 10 and 2 more? 12 Write the number.
- Look at the green squares and orange squares in Problem 5. Complete Problem 6 by writing how many green squares there are. 10 Then write how many orange squares there are. 2 Then write how many squares in all. 12

Higher-Order Thinking

 Express regularity in repeated reasoning.

- Sue saw a full ten frame and some more counters. Explain how she can tell how many there are without counting all the counters.

Remind children that a full ten frame has 10 counters. Help children see that they do not need to count this 10. They can start from 10 and count on the rest to find how many.

Math on the Spot Use this video to help children model and solve this type of problem.

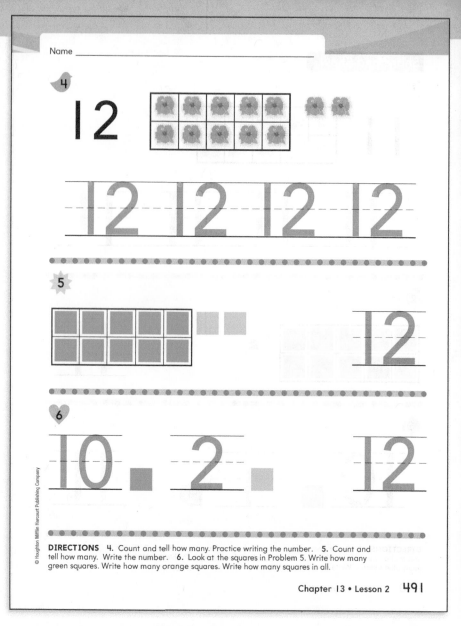

Name _____

4

12

DIRECTIONS 4. Count and tell how many. Practice writing the number. 5. Count and tell how many. Write the number. 6. Look at the squares in Problem 5. Write how many green squares. Write how many orange squares. Write how many squares in all.

Chapter 13 • Lesson 2   491

© Houghton Mifflin Harcourt Publishing Company

Meeting Individual Needs

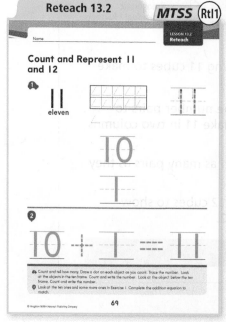

Reteach 13.2   MTSS RtI1

Count and Represent 11 and 12

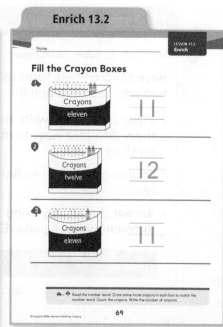

Enrich 13.2

Fill the Crayon Boxes

7 Check children's work.

| |

8 Check children's work.

| 2

9

| 2

© Houghton Mifflin Harcourt Publishing Company • Image Credits: ©HMH

DIRECTIONS 7. Look at the number. Draw more flowers to show that number. 8. Look at the number. Use drawings to represent the number. 9. Count the counters. Write the number.

HOME ACTIVITY • Ask your child to count and write the number for a set of 11 or 12 objects, such as macaroni pieces or buttons.

492 Go Math! Grade K

---

④ Elaborate

Problem Solving Applications (Real World)

For **Problems 7 and 8**, children communicate mathematical ideas by drawing the answer.

(MP) **Model with mathematics.**

Have children look at **Problem 7**.

- **Look at the number. Draw more flowers to match the number.**

Have children complete **Problem 8** by drawing the number shown.

Help children find **Problem 9**.

- **Count the counters. Write the number.**

⑤ Evaluate | Formative Assessment

I Can

Have pairs of children write, draw, or model an example to demonstrate the skill for the I Can statement.

I can write 11 or 12 to represent a group of objects by . . . counting aloud 11 objects and writing the number 11 or counting aloud 12 objects and writing the number 12.

Exit Ticket

Let children describe their drawings to the class.

DIFFERENTIATED INSTRUCTION • Independent Activities

Grab-and-Go!™
Version 2.0
Differentiated Centers Kit

Tabletop Flipchart

Mini-lessons for reteaching to targeted small groups

Readers

Supports key math skills and concepts in real-world situations.

Games

Reinforce math content and vocabulary

Activities

Meaningful and fun math practice

Count and Represent 11 and 12

Use the Practice and Homework pages to provide children with more practice of the concepts and skills presented in this lesson. Children master their understanding as they complete practice items.

Name _____

Count and Represent 11 and 12

1

11

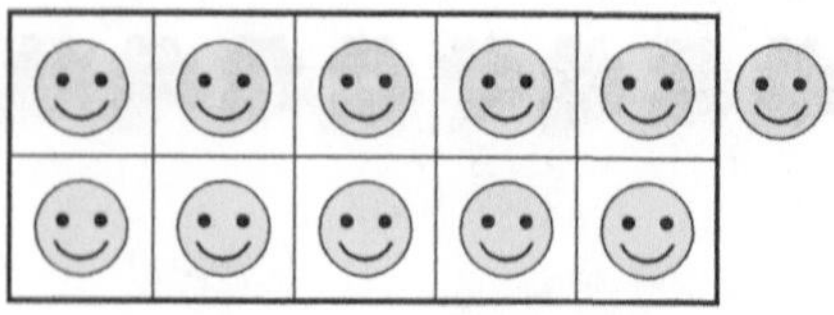

2

12

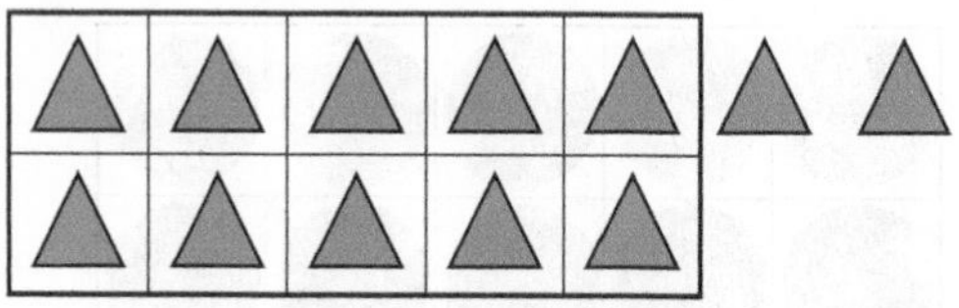

DIRECTIONS 1–2. Count and tell how many. Practice writing the number.

Chapter 13 • Lesson 2 493

Lesson Check

3 🍓🍓🍓🍓🍓🍓🍓🍓🍓🍓🍓

‖   12
   •   ○

4 🍐🍐🍐🍐🍐🍐🍐🍐🍐🍐🍐

‖   12
   ○   •

Spiral Review

5 🍎🍎🍎🍎🍎🍎🍎🍎🍎🍎

DIRECTIONS Choose the correct answer. **3.** Count the strawberries. How would you write the number? **4.** Count the pears. How would you write the number? **5.** Count the apples. How would you write the number?

494 Go Math! Grade K

Continue to practice concepts and skills with Lesson Check. Use Spiral Review to engage children in previously taught concepts and to promote content retention.

Lesson at a Glance
Model and Count 13 and 14

SNAPSHOT

Mathematical Standards
- Write numbers from 0 to 20. Represent a number of objects with a written numeral 0-20 (with 0 representing a count of no objects).
- When counting objects, say the number names in the standard order, pairing each object with one and only one number name and each number name with one and only one object.

Mathematical Practices and Processes
- Reason abstractly and quantitatively.
- Model with mathematics.
- Attend to precision.
- Construct arguments and critique reasoning of others.
- Look for and make use of structure.

(I Can) Objective
I can count out 13 or 14 objects.

Learning Goal
Count out 13 or 14 objects.

Language Objective
Children will explain to a partner how to count out 13 or 14 objects.

MATERIALS
- MathBoard
- two-color counters

ACROSS THE GRADES

Grade K
Given a number from 0 to 20, count out that many objects.

After
Starting at a given number, count forward and backwards within 120 by ones. Skip count by 2s to 20 and by 5s to 100.

ABOUT THE MATH

While working with the numbers 13 and 14, children will count objects and tell how many. They will identify the numeral that represents how many. They also will use counters to represent a number and write the number as 10 and some more. The use of ten frames allow children to see a number greater than 10 as 10 and some more. A full frame shows 10, and any other objects outside the frame tell how many more. For 13, there is always 3 more, and for 14, there is always 4 more.

For more professional learning, go online to Teacher's Corner.

DAILY ROUTINES

 Problem of the Day 13.3

Which number is more, 3 or 4? 4

 Vocabulary thirteen, fourteen

- Interactive Student Edition
- Multilingual Glossary

Vocabulary Builder

Ask children to define each term and give several examples. Accept reasonable definitions. Possible examples given.

Term	Example(s)
thirteen	13; 10 and 3
fourteen	14; 10 and 4

FOCUSING ON THE WHOLE STUDENT

Access Prior Knowledge

Choose one or more of the following activities.

- Work with children to come up with a list of things they can collect.
- Have children draw a collection of 12 items.

Social & Emotional Learning

Relationship Skills Help children recognize that their work takes place within a learning group, so that managing their own learning process often involves attention to those around them. *If you notice that someone else is having difficulty representing numbers, it is appropriate to offer help. You can talk through your strategy with the other person. If you are having difficulty, work together with someone else who is also having difficulty so you can talk through the problem together. Or you might ask someone who has completed the problem to explain their strategy to help you get started.*

❶ Engage

with the Interactive Student Edition

I Can Objective

I can count out 13 or 14 objects.

Making Connections

Ask children to tell you what they know about counting to 10 and some more.

Show children a row of 10 objects. Ask them to count each aloud with you as you go.

- **How many are in the row?** 10
- **Can you think of anything at home that you have 10 of?** Answers will vary.

Draw or make a pile of 10 acorns and a pile of 3 acorns.

Learning Activity

Help children understand how making a group of 10 can help them recognize a number that is 10 and 3 more. SHow an image of 13 acorns. Allow children to represent the acorns.

- **Are there more than 10 acorns? How do you know?** Yes; there is a pile of 10 and another pile of some more.
- **How many more than 10 are there?** 3
- **What can we find out?** What 10 and 3 more is called.

② Explore

Listen and Draw

Materials two-color counters

Read aloud this problem as children listen.

Marcell and Garrett went to the orchard to pick apples. Marcell picked 14 boxes of apples. Garrett picked one box fewer than Marcell. How can you use counters to show how many boxes of apples Garrett picked?

MP **Attend to precision.**

Distribute 13 counters to each child. Have them count the counters as they place the counters in the ten frame.

- **How many counters did you use to fill the ten frame?** 10
- **How many counters are left?** 3 **Place the counters that are left below the ten frame. Now count all the counters.**

Repeat this procedure with 14 counters. Have children draw to show the 14 counters.

MP **Reason abstractly and quantitatively.**

- **When you count, what does the next number's name always stand for?** The next number's name always stands for a set that is one larger.

Restate the above problem.

- **How can you find one less than 14?** I can say the number that is right before it; 13.
- **How can you show Garrett's boxes?** I can show a full ten frame and 3 counters below.

Name _____

Model and Count 13 and 14

(I Can) count out 13 or 14 objects.

Listen and Draw

Check children's work.

DIRECTIONS Use counters to show the number 13. Add more to show the number 14. Draw the counters.

Chapter 13 • Lesson 3 **495**

 Multilingual Support

STRATEGY: Describe

Children can improve their language skills by describing what they are seeing or hearing.

- Draw a simple picture of a train with 13 cars.
- Have children describe the train. Make sure they include that there are 13 cars on the train.
- Add one more car to the train.

Repeat the activity with 14 cars on the train.

- Have children count and describe 13 and 14 classroom objects.

1

2 ☑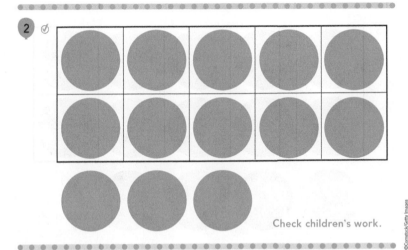

Check children's work.

3 and

DIRECTIONS **1.** Count and tell how many. Circle the number. **2.** Use counters to show the number 13. Draw the counters. **3.** Look at the counters you drew. How many are in the ten frame? Write the number. How many more are there? Write the number.

496 Go Math! Grade K

---

3 Explain

Share and Show [Math Board]

 Look for and make use of structure.

- **Look at Problem 1. How many lemons do you see?** 13
- **How did the arrangement of the lemons help you?** I can see two rows of 5 lemons, or 10 lemons, and 3 more.
- **Find the number 13 and circle it.**
- **Look at Problem 2. How can you show the number 13 with your counters?** I can put 10 counters in the ten frame to model 10 and 3 counters below to model 3 more.

 Model with mathematics.

For Problem 3, guide children in counting the counters and writing the numbers.

- **How many counters are in the ten frame?** 10 **Write the number.**
- **How many more are there?** 3 **Write the number.**

Use the checked problem for Quick Check.

✓ Quick Check *MTSS* (RtI)

If	a child misses the checked problem
Then	Differentiate Instruction with • Reteach 13.3 • Waggle

⚠ Common Errors

Error Children may not recognize a set of ten.

Springboard to Learning Have children use counters to show two rows of five. Then put together the two rows of five. Count to show that two fives are the same as ten. Explain that one set of ten is the same as two sets of five.

Ready for More Kinesthetic / Visual Small Group

Materials: numeral cards (8–15), two-dimensional shapes

Have children work in groups of four. Tell each child to choose a numeral card without showing it.

- Have each child use that number of shapes to form a geometric pattern. They should then trace the shapes on paper.
- Have children exchange papers, count the number of shapes, and write the number.

Share and Show

 Construct arguments and critique reasoning of others.

- **Look at Problem 4. How many apples do you see?** 14

Have children find the number and circle it.

- **Look at Problem 5. Use counters to show the number 14. Do you think you will fill the ten frame?** Yes.
- **How do you know?** 14 is greater than 10
- **After you fill the ten frame, how many more counters will you need?** 4

 Look for and make use of structure.

For Problem 6, guide children in counting the counters and writing the numbers.

- **If the ten frame is full, how many counters does it have?** 10 **Write the number.**
- **Count the counters below. How many more are there?** 4 **Write the number.**

Higher-Order Thinking

 Use appropriate tools strategically.

Have pairs of children use a ten frame and counters to show the numbers 14 and 11. Ask children if they can tell which is more without counting the counters. Have children explain how they found their answers.

Discuss with children how, if both numbers 11 and 14 have a filled ten frame, they only need to compare the extra counters.

Math on the Spot Use this video to help children model and solve this type of problem.

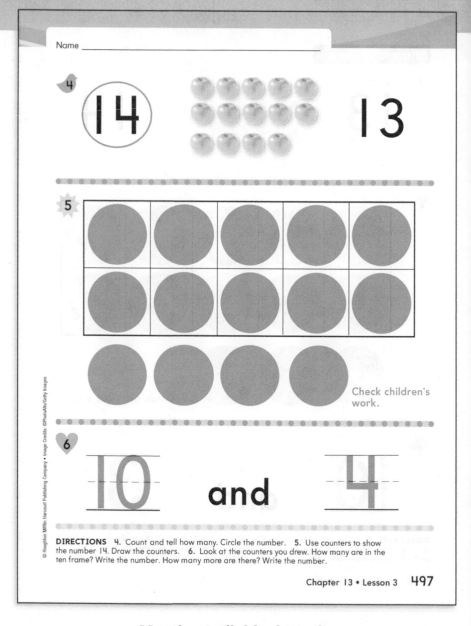

DIRECTIONS **4.** Count and tell how many. Circle the number. **5.** Use counters to show the number 14. Draw the counters. **6.** Look at the counters you drew. How many are in the ten frame? Write the number. How many more are there? Write the number.

Chapter 13 • Lesson 3   **497**

Meeting Individual Needs

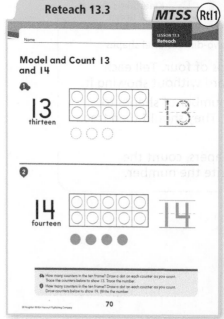

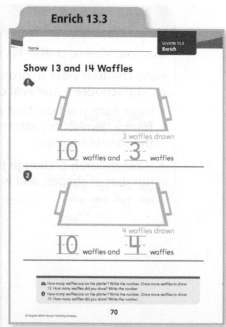

WRITE Math

7

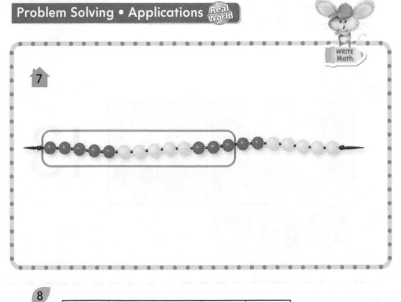

8

○ 13

● 14

DIRECTIONS 7. Start with the blue bead on the left. Circle to show 13 beads on the bead string. **8.** Choose the correct answer. How many marbles are there?

HOME ACTIVITY • Draw a ten frame on a sheet of paper. Have your child use small objects such as buttons, pennies, or dried beans to show the numbers 13 and 14.

498 Go Math! Grade K

© Houghton Mifflin Harcourt Publishing Company

---

4 Elaborate

Problem Solving Applications

Real World

(MP) **Attend to precision.**

Read **Problem 7**. Ask children to explain how they will solve the problem.

- **Count the first set of five blue beads and the first set of five yellow beads. Then count three more blue beads. How many beads did you count in all?** 13

- **How many more beads than 10 do you need to circle to make 13?** 3 **Circle 13 beads.**

Help children find **Problem 8**. Read the problem aloud.

- **How many marbles are there? Fill in the bubble next to the correct answer.**

5 Evaluate | Formative Assessment

I Can

Have pairs of children write, draw, or model an example to demonstrate the skill for the I Can statement.

I can count out 13 or 14 objects by . . . using counters to fill a ten frame and then showing 3 or 4 more.

Exit Ticket

Allow time for children to communicate about what their drawings or models show and discuss other possible methods for showing the numbers 13 or 14.

DIFFERENTIATED INSTRUCTION • Independent Activities

Grab and Go!
Version 2.0
Differentiated Centers Kit

Tabletop Flipchart

Mini-lessons for reteaching to targeted small groups

Readers

Supports key math skills and concepts in real-world situations.

Games

Reinforce math content and vocabulary

Activities

Meaningful and fun math practice

Practice and Homework

Model and Count 13 and 14

Use the Practice and Homework pages to provide children with more practice of the concepts and skills presented in this lesson. Children master their understanding as they complete practice items.

1

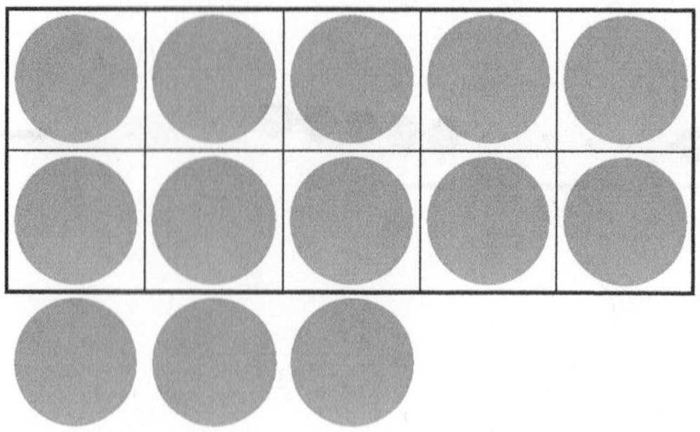

13

Check children's work.

2

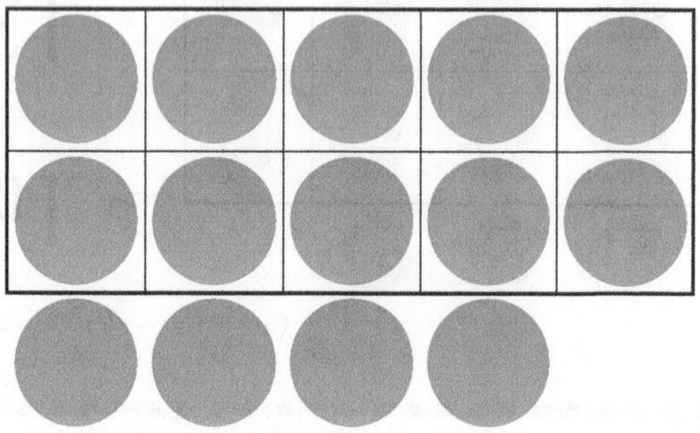

14

Check children's work.

DIRECTIONS 1. Draw counters to show 13. 2. Draw counters to show 14.

Chapter 13 • Lesson 3 **499**

© Houghton Mifflin Harcourt Publishing Company

Lesson Check

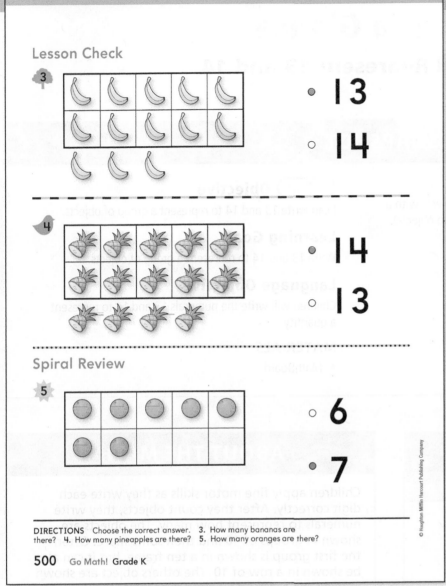

3 ● 13 ○ 14

4 ● 14 ○ 13

Spiral Review

5 ○ 6 ● 7

© Houghton Mifflin Harcourt Publishing Company

DIRECTIONS Choose the correct answer. **3.** How many bananas are there? **4.** How many pineapples are there? **5.** How many oranges are there?

Continue to practice concepts and skills with Lesson Check. Use Spiral Review to engage children in previously taught concepts and to promote content retention.

Lesson at a Glance
Count and Represent 13 and 14

SNAPSHOT

Mathematical Standards

- Write numbers from 0 to 20. Represent a number of objects with a written numeral 0–20 (with 0 representing a count of no objects).

Mathematical Practices and Processes

- Reason abstractly and quantitatively.
- Model with mathematics.
- Attend to precision.
- Construct arguments and critique reasoning of others.
- Look for and make use of structure.

(I Can) Objective

I can write 13 and 14 to represent a group of objects.

Learning Goal

Write 13 and 14 to represent a group of objects.

Language Objective

Children will write the numerals 13 and 14 to represent a quantity.

MATERIALS

- MathBoard

ACROSS THE GRADES

Grade K

Given a group of up to 20 objects, count the number of objects in that group and represent the number of objects with a written numeral. State the number of objects in a rearrangement of that group without recounting.

After

Starting at a given number, count forward and backwards within 120 by ones. Skip count by 2s to 20 and by 5s to 100.

ABOUT THE MATH

Children apply fine motor skills as they write each digit correctly. After they count objects, they write numerals to represent how many. The objects are shown in groups of 10 and then some more. Often the first group is shown in a ten frame, but it can also be shown in a row of 10. The others object are shown outside the ten frame or in a row below the row of 10. This allows children to begin seeing 13 as 10 and 3, and 14 as 10 and 4, which foreshadows upcoming concepts of place value.

For more professional learning, go online to Teacher's Corner.

DAILY ROUTINES

 **Problem of the Day 13.4**

Use counters to show 3.

Use counters to show 4.

Check children's representations.

 **Vocabulary**

- Interactive Student Edition
- Multilingual Glossary

Vocabulary Builder

Count from 1 to 19. Which number is missing?

1, 2, 3, 4, 5, 6, 7, 8, 9, 10, 11, ?, 13, 14   12

FOCUSING ON THE WHOLE STUDENT

Access Prior Knowledge

Choose one or more of the following activities.

- Ask partners to make up a story about a place that has rows of flowers. Have them describe the flowers.
- Have children draw a picture of a bunch of flowers. Then have them draw the flowers in rows.

① Engage

with the Interactive Student Edition

I Can Objective

I can write 13 and 14 to represent a group of objects.

Making Connections

Invite children to tell you what they know about counting up to 12.

Draw a row of 10 flowers on the board and another row of 2.

- **How many flowers are there altogether?** 12
- **What are some ways we can write 12?** 12; twelve

Learning Activity

Tell a story about a flower garden with 2 rows of flowers. The first row has 10 flowers and the second row has 3 flowers. Review the story with children by asking about the different numbers of flowers they see.

- **How many flowers are in the first row?** 10
- **How many flowers are in the second row?** 3
- **What do you want to know?** how many flowers there are

② Explore

Listen and Draw

Read aloud this problem as children listen.

The number on JP's jersey is thirteen. How can you write this number?

(MP) **Look for and make use of structure.**

Have children locate the yellow cubes.

- **How many cubes are in the top row?** 10
- **How many cubes are in the bottom row?** 3
- **How many cubes is 10 cubes and 3 cubes?** 13

Allow children to count if needed.

- **How do you write the number 13?** by writing a 1 with a 3 next to it
- **Trace the first 13 and then write three more after it.**
- **What number shows how many yellow cubes there are?** 13

Have children count the blue cubes and tell how many are in the first row and how many are in the second row. Have children work through the same procedure and questions for 14 as for 13.

Ask children to describe how to write 14.

Culturally Responsive Education

Discuss what kind of jersey JP could have. Take time to listen to children and learn about their interests. Building a connection with children is one of the cornerstones of culturally responsive teaching. As an enrichment activity, have children design their own jerseys with their names and any of the two-digit numbers learned thus far. Ask that they include a pictorial representation of their chosen number on their jerseys as well.

Name _____

Count and Represent 13 and 14

(I Can) write 13 and 14 to represent a group of objects.

Listen and Draw

13 13 13 13

14 14 14 14

DIRECTIONS Count and tell how many. Trace and write the numbers.

(ML) # Multilingual Support

STRATEGY: Define

Materials pattern blocks

Children can define words by matching words or visuals to their definitions.

- Arrange sets of 11, 12, 13, and 14 pattern blocks on the table.
- Write the numbers 11, 12, 13, and 14 on a sheet of paper.
- Have children count each set of pattern blocks and point to the number that matches.
- Then have children name and write the number.

Repeat the activity with other numbers if time permits.

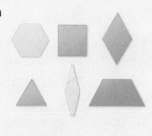

1 ✓

13

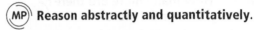

13   13   13   13

2

13

3

10   3   13

DIRECTIONS 1. Count and tell how many. Practice writing the number. 2. Count and tell how many. Write the number. 3. Look at the squares in Problem 2. Write how many blue squares. Write how many red squares. Write how many squares in all.

502   Go Math! Grade K

© Houghton Mifflin Harcourt Publishing Company

Ready for More

🕐 Vebal/Linguistic Partners

Materials numeral cards (8–15), index cards

Label each index card **10 ones and _____ ones.**

- Have children complete the "10 ones and _____ ones" phrases and match them to the numeral cards.

| 11 | 12 | 13 | 14 |

---

③ Explain

Share and Show Math Board

- In Problem 1, what number do you see? 13

(MP) **Reason abstractly and quantitatively.**

- **Without counting, how many red flowers are in the ten frame?** 10 **How do you know?** The ten frame is full. **How many more are there?** 3
- **How can you find how many 10 and 3 more is?** I can start at 10 and count 3 more: 11, 12, 13. **Write the number 13 four times and say the number quietly to yourself.**

(MP) **Model with mathematics.**

- **Look at Problem 2. How many blue squares are in the ten frame?** 10 **How many more red squares are there?** 3 **How many is 10 and 3 more?** 13
- **Write the number.**

Have children look at the blue squares and the red squares in Problem 2. Have them complete Problem 3 by writing how many blue squares there are. 10 Then have children write how many red squares there are. 3 Then have them write how many squares in all. 13

Use the checked problem for Quick Check.

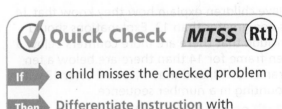

✓ Quick Check   MTSS RtI

| If | a child misses the checked problem |
| Then | Differentiate Instruction with |

- Reteach 13.4
- Waggle

! Common Errors

Error Children may not recognize a two-digit number as a whole and instead may refer to each digit in the number.

Springboard to Learning Explain that when children see the digits 1 and 3 together as in this lesson, the digits form the number thirteen (13).

Share and Show

- In Problem 4, what number do you see? 14

 Attend to precision.

- How many pink flowers are in the ten frame? 10 **How many more are there?** 4 **How many is 10 and 4 more?** 14

- Write the number 14 four times and say the number quietly to yourself.

- Look at Problem 5. How many red squares are in the ten frame? 10 **How many more blue squares are there?** 4 **How many is 10 and 4 more?** 14

- Write the number.

 Model with mathematics.

Have children look at the red squares and the blue squares in Problem 5. Have them complete Problem 6 by writing how many red squares there are. 10 Then have children write how many blue squares there are. 4 Then have them write how many squares in all. 14

Higher-Order Thinking

Ask children to tell whether 13 is greater than 10 or less than 10. Then have children tell if 14 is greater than 10 or less than 10.

- **Which of the two numbers is one greater than the other?** 14 is one greater than 13.

 Construct arguments and critique reasoning of others.

Have children explain how they know that 14 is one greater than 13. Explanations should include that there are more counters below a ten frame for 14 than there are below a ten frame for 13, and that 14 is said after 13 when counting in a number sequence.

Math on the Spot Use this video to help children model and solve this type of problem.

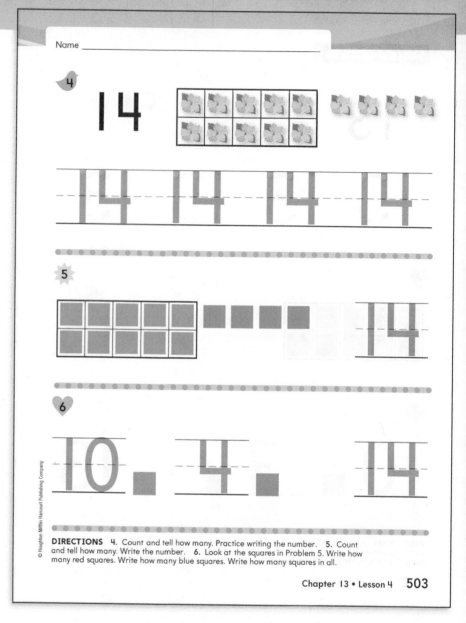

DIRECTIONS 4. Count and tell how many. Practice writing the number. 5. Count and tell how many. Write the number. 6. Look at the squares in Problem 5. Write how many red squares. Write how many blue squares. Write how many squares in all.

Chapter 13 • Lesson 4 **503**

Meeting Individual Needs

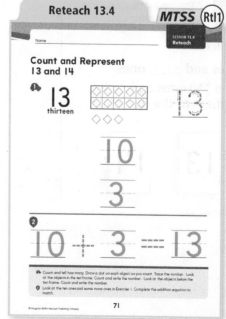

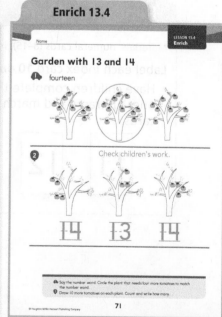

7 Check children's work.

13

8 Check children's work.

14

9

14

DIRECTIONS 7. Tia picked 13 purple flowers. Draw more purple flowers to show how many she picked. **8.** Look at the number. Use drawings to represent the number. **9.** Count the cubes. Write the number.

HOME ACTIVITY • Ask your child to count and write the number for a set of 13 or 14 objects, such as macaroni pieces or buttons.

---

④ Elaborate

Problem Solving Applications Real World

(MP) Model with mathematics.

For **Problems 7 and 8,** children communicate mathematical ideas by drawing the answer.

• **Tia picked 13 purple flowers. Draw to show how many she picked.**

Children will draw to represent the number 14 for **Problem 8.**

• **Look at the number. Use drawings to represent the number.**

(MP) Reason abstractly and quantitatively.

Guide children to Problem 9.

• **Count the cubes. Write the number.**

⑤ Evaluate | Formative Assessment

I Can

Have pairs of children write, draw, or model an example to demonstrate the skill for the I Can statement.

I can write 13 and 14 to represent a group of objects by . . . counting aloud 13 objects and writing the number 13 or counting aloud 14 objects and writing the number 14.

Exit Ticket

Let children describe their drawings to the class.

DIFFERENTIATED INSTRUCTION • Independent Activities

Grab and Go!™
Version 2.0
Differentiated Centers Kit

Tabletop Flipchart

Mini-lessons for reteaching to targeted small groups

Readers

Supports key math skills and concepts in real-world situations.

Games

Reinforce math content and vocabulary

Activities

Meaningful and fun math practice

Practice and Homework

Count and Represent 13 and 14

Use the Practice and Homework pages to provide children with more practice of the concepts and skills presented in this lesson. Children master their understanding as they complete practice items.

Name ______________________

LESSON 13.4
Practice and Homework

Count and Represent 13 and 14

1 13

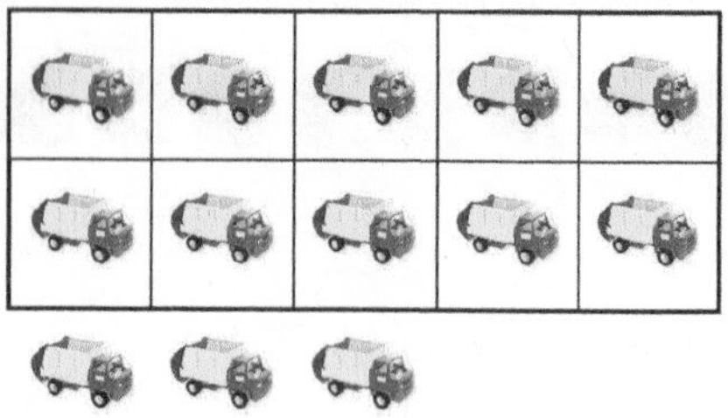

13 13 13 13

2 14

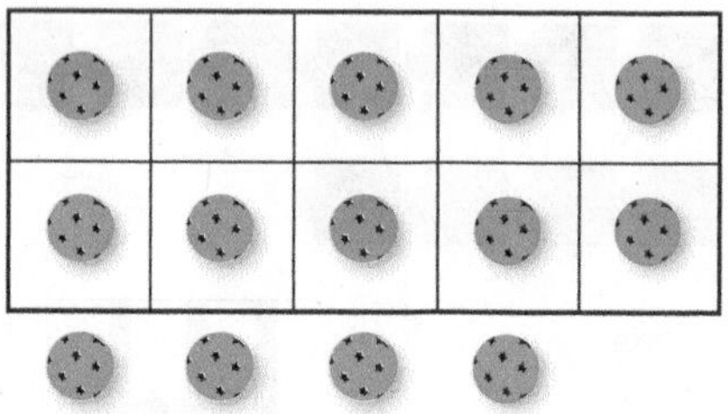

14 14 14 14

DIRECTIONS 1–2. Count and tell how many. Practice writing the number.

Lesson Check

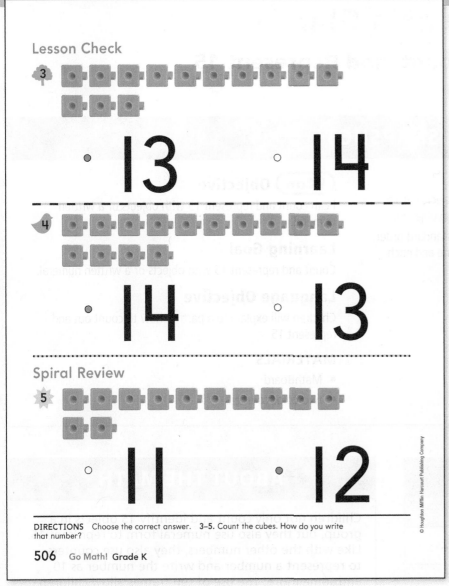

3 ● 13   ○ 14

4 ● 14   ○ 13

Spiral Review

5 ○ 11   ● 12

DIRECTIONS Choose the correct answer. 3–5. Count the cubes. How do you write that number?

506   Go Math! Grade K

Continue to practice concepts and skills with Lesson Check. Use Spiral Review to engage children in previously taught concepts and to promote content retention.

Lesson at a Glance
Model, Count, and Represent 15

SNAPSHOT

Mathematical Standards

- Write numbers from 0 to 20. Represent a number of objects with a written numeral 0-20 (with 0 representing a count of no objects).
- When counting objects, say the number names in the standard order, pairing each object with one and only one number name and each number name with one and only one object.

Mathematical Practices and Processes

- Model with mathematics.
- Attend to precision.
- Construct arguments and critique reasoning of others.
- Look for and make use of structure.
- Reason abstractly and quantitatively.

(I Can) Objective

I can count and represent 15 with objects or a written numeral.

Learning Goal

Count and represent 15 with objects or a written numeral.

Language Objective

Children will explain to a partner how to count out and represent 15.

MATERIALS

- MathBoard
- two-color counters

ACROSS THE GRADES

Grade K

Given a number from 0 to 20, count out that many objects.

After

Starting at a given number, count forward and backward within 120 by ones. Skip count by 2s to 20 and by 5s to 100.

ABOUT THE MATH

Children not only count and identify 15 objects in a group, but they also use numeral form to represent 15. Like with the other numbers, they also use counters to represent a number and write the number as 10 and some more. The use of ten frames allow children to see 15 as 10 and 5, which is fundamental to their understanding of place value. The 1 in the tens place is worth 10, and the 5 in the ones place is worth 5. Later children will learn to write numbers in expanded form, such as $15 = 10 + 5$.

For more professional learning, go online to Teacher's Corner.

DAILY ROUTINES

🖥 Problem of the Day 13.5

Use counters to show 5.

Use counters to show 10.

Check children's representations.

🖥 Vocabulary fifteen

- Interactive Student Edition
- Multilingual Glossary

Vocabulary Builder

Ask children to define each term and give several examples. Accept reasonable definitions. Possible examples given.

Term	Example(s)
fifteen	15; 10 and 5

FOCUSING ON THE WHOLE STUDENT

Access Prior Knowledge

Choose one or more of the following activities.

- Have children draw up to 14 objects and count them aloud.
- Give children cards with different numbers on them. Have them find a number of objects to match their number.

① Engage

with the Interactive Student Edition

I Can Objective

I can count and represent 15 with objects or a written numeral.

Making Connections

Ask children what they know about counting up to 14.

- Count aloud slowly up to 14 with a clap at each number, inviting children to count aloud with you and clap along. **Have you ever collected anything? What did you collect?** Answers will vary.

- **Can you think of a place that may have a lot of rocks to count?** Answers will vary.

Make 3 rows of 5 rocks or counters.

Learning Activity

Describe a scenario to children in which there are three rows of rocks, with five rocks in each row. Guide children toward understanding that 15 can be shown as 10 and some more.

- **How many rocks are in the first two rows altogether?** 10

- **How many rocks are in the last row?** 5

- **What might you want to learn?** what 10 and 5 more is called

Explore

Listen and Draw

Materials two-color counters

Read aloud this problem as children listen.

Julia needs 15 strawberries for her fruit salad. Use counters to show the strawberries Julia needs.

(MP) Use appropriate tools strategically.

Distribute 15 counters to each child. Have children count the counters as they place them in the ten frame and below.

Remind children to put the first counter in the top left space and place the counters from left to right. Have them begin the second row on the left side.

- **How many counters did you use to fill the ten frame?** 10

- **How many counters are left?** 5 **Place the counters that are left below the ten frame. Now count all the counters.**

Have children draw to show the 15 counters.

(MP) Construct arguments and critique reasoning of others.

- **Tell how you showed 15 with counters.** I put 10 counters in the ten frame and 5 counters below it.

- **How do you write the number 15?** by writing a 1 and then a 5 right next to it

- **Trace the first 15 and then write the number 15 three more times.**

- **What number shows how many counters there are?** 15

Name _____

Model, Count, and Represent 15

I Can count and represent 15 with objects or a written numeral.

Listen and Draw

Check children's work.

DIRECTIONS Use counters to show the number 15. Draw the counters. Trace and write the number.

Chapter 13 • Lesson 5   **507**

 Multilingual Support

STRATEGY: Rephrase

Materials two-color counters

Children can demonstrate their understanding by rephrasing what they have heard or seen.

- Read the following addition word problem and act it out using counters. **There were 14 children eating lunch. One more child came to eat lunch with them. Now how many children are eating lunch?** 15

- Have children rephrase the problem with the same numbers and 15 as the answer. Encourage children to seek clarification if they don't understand part of the problem or a word that was used.

Repeat with other numbers if time permits.

Share and Show

1 ☑

15 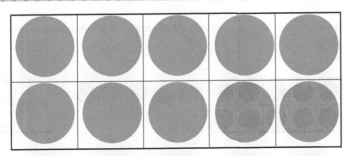 15

2

Check children's work.

3 10 and 5

DIRECTIONS 1. Count and tell how many. Write the number. 2. Use counters to show the number 15. Draw the counters. 3. Look at the counters you drew. How many are in the ten frame? Write the number. How many more? Write the number.

508 Go Math! Grade K

© Houghton Mifflin Harcourt Publishing Company

---

③ Explain

Share and Show

- In Problem 1, what number do you see? 15

 Look for and make use of structure.

- **Look at the way the kiwi slices are arranged. How can you find how many slices there are?** Possible answer: I know that there are 5 slices in each row and the first 2 rows make 10. I count 5 more; 10 and 5 more is 15.
- **Write the number.**
- **Look at Problem 2. How can you show the number 15 with counters?** I can put 10 counters in the ten frame to model 10 and 5 counters below to model 5 more.

Have children draw the counters.

For Problem 3, guide children in counting the counters and writing the numbers.

- **How many counters are in the ten frame?** 10 **Write the number.**
- **How many more are there?** 5 **Write the number.**
- **How can you show 15 with counters?** I can fill a ten frame to show 10. Then I can put 5 counters below the ten frame.

Use the checked problem for **Quick Check.**

✓ Quick Check   MTSS RtI

If ▶ a child misses the checked problem

Then ▶ **Differentiate Instruction** with
- Reteach 13.5
- Waggle

⚠ Common Errors

Error Children may miscount 15 slices.

Springboard to Learning Have children make a dot on each slice as they count the first 10. Then have them count how many more there are (5). Ask how many 10 slices and 5 slices is. Then have children recount the slices.

Ready for More   🕐 Kinesthetic Individual / Partners

Materials paper bag with 15 craft sticks, rubber band, numeral cards (11–15)

Prepare small paper bags with 15 craft sticks, a rubber band, and numeral cards 11 to 15 inside.

- Give a bag to each pair. Have one child select a numeral card. The partner then removes craft sticks from the bag to show a set of 10 ones and places a rubber band around that set. He or she then removes additional craft sticks from the bag to model the number.
- The other partner checks that the number modeled is the number shown on the card.

Partners reverse roles and continue the activity until each card has been shown.

Chapter 13 • Lesson 5   508

Share and Show

 Reason abstractly and quantitatively.

• In Problem 4, what number do you see? 15

• How many flowers are in the ten frame? 10
  How many more flowers are there? 5 How
  many is 10 flowers and 5 more flowers? 15
  Write the number.

• Look at Problem 5. How many blue circles
  are in the ten frame? 10 How many more
  red circles are there? 5 How many is 10 and
  5 more? 15

• Write the number.

 Model with mathematics.

Have children look at the blue circles and the
red circles in Problem 5. Have them complete
Problem 6 by writing how many blue circles
there are. 10 Then have children write how
many red circles there are. 5 Then have them
write how many circles in all 15

 Attend to precision.

Have children explain how they can know they
have 15 without counting every counter. I know
that when a ten frame is filled, there are 10 counters. I
know each row has 5 spaces. So if I have a filled ten frame
and a row that matches a ten frame row, it is 10 and 5
more, or 15.

• **How many five frames would you fill to
  show 15?** 3

Math on the Spot Use this video to help
children model and solve this type of problem.

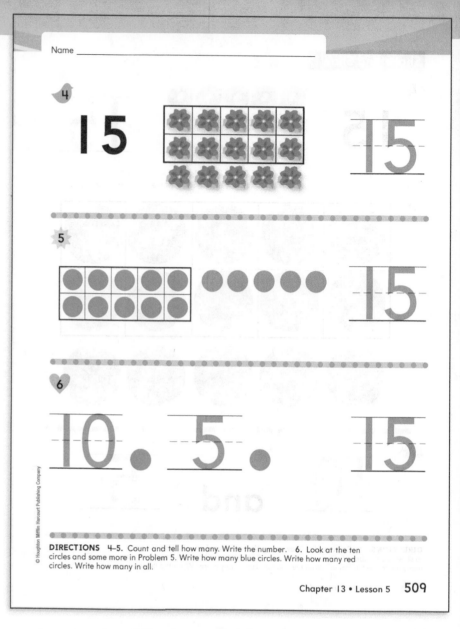

Name _____

4

15

5

6

10. 5. 15

DIRECTIONS 4–5. Count and tell how many. Write the number. **6.** Look at the ten
circles and some more in Problem 5. Write how many blue circles. Write how many red
circles. Write how many in all.

Chapter 13 • Lesson 5 **509**

Meeting Individual Needs

| Reteach 13.5 | MTSS Rtl1 | Enrich 13.5 |

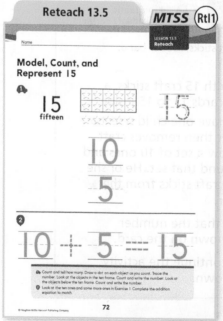

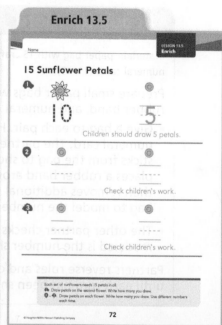

7

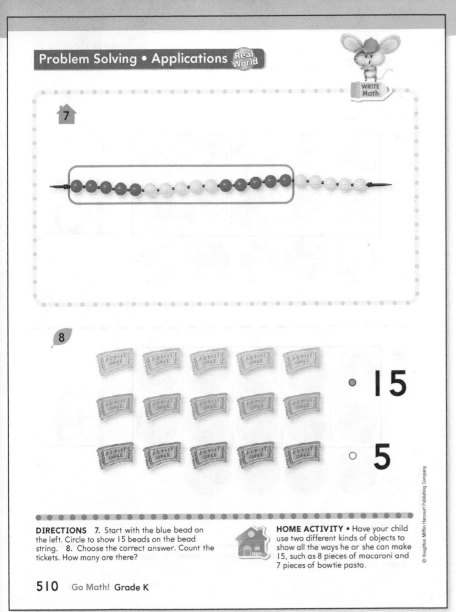

8

• 15

○ 5

DIRECTIONS 7. Start with the blue bead on the left. Circle to show 15 beads on the bead string. 8. Choose the correct answer. Count the tickets. How many are there?

HOME ACTIVITY • Have your child use two different kinds of objects to show all the ways he or she can make 15, such as 8 pieces of macaroni and 7 pieces of bowtie pasta.

DIFFERENTIATED INSTRUCTION • Independent Activities

Grab-and-Go!™
Version 2.0
Differentiated Centers Kit

Tabletop Flipchart

Mini-lessons for reteaching to targeted small groups

Readers

Supports key math skills and concepts in real-world situations.

Games

Reinforce math content and vocabulary

Activities

Meaningful and fun math practice

---

④ Elaborate

Problem Solving Applications

Read **Problem 7**. Ask children to explain how they will solve the problem.

• Count the **first set of 5 blue beads** and the **first set of 5 yellow beads. How many beads did you count in all?** 10

• **How many more beads than 10 do you need to circle to make 15?** 5 **Circle 15 beads.**

(MP) **Look for and make use of structure.**

Discuss with children how they might know without counting how to circle 15 beads. Elicit that there are 5 beads of one color in each set, so they need to circle 3 sets of 5 beads.

• **Did you circle more blue beads or more yellow beads?** blue

Guide children to **Problem 8**. Have children fill in the bubble next to the correct answer.

• **Choose the correct answer. Count the tickets. How many are there?** 15

⑤ Evaluate | Formative Assessment

I Can

Have pairs of children write, draw, or model an example to demonstrate the skill for the I Can statement.

I can count and represent 15 with objects or a written numeral by . . . filling a ten frame to show 10 and then placing 5 more below it. I can also write 15 with a 1 and a 5 next to it.

Exit Ticket

How can you use objects to show 15 as ten ones and some more ones and show 15 as a number?

Practice and Homework

Model, Count, and Represent 15

Use the Practice and Homework pages to provide children with more practice of the concepts and skills presented in this lesson. Children master their understanding as they complete practice items.

Model, Count, and Represent 15

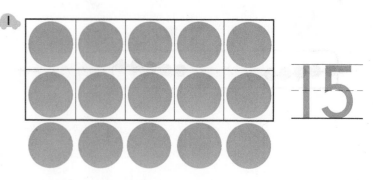

Check children's work.

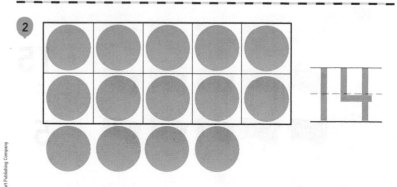

Check children's work.

DIRECTIONS 1. Draw counters to show 15. Write the number.   2. Draw counters to show 14. Write the number.

Chapter 13 • Lesson 5   511

Lesson Check

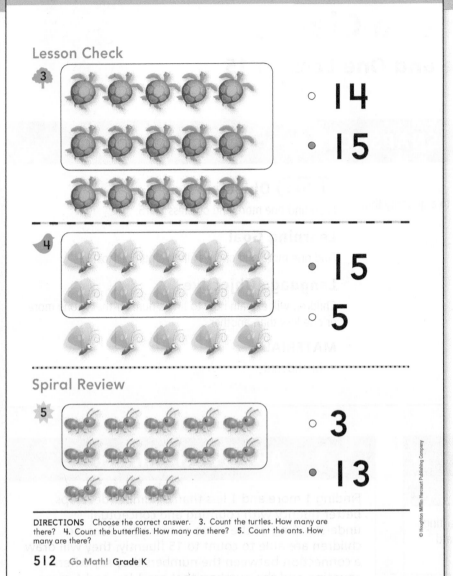

3 ○ 14

     • 15

4 • 15

     ○ 5

Spiral Review

5 ○ 3

     • 13

DIRECTIONS Choose the correct answer. **3.** Count the turtles. How many are there? **4.** Count the butterflies. How many are there? **5.** Count the ants. How many are there?

Continue to practice concepts and skills with Lesson Check. Use Spiral Review to engage children in previously taught concepts and to promote content retention.

Lesson at a Glance
One More and One Less to 15

SNAPSHOT

Mathematical Standards
- Understand that each successive number name refers to a quantity that is one larger.

Mathematical Practices and Processes
- Model with mathematics.
- Attend to precision.
- Construct arguments and critique reasoning of others.
- Look for and make use of structure.
- Reason abstractly and quantitatively.

(I Can) Objective
I can find one more and one less to 15.

Learning Goal
Find one more and one less than a number to 15.

Language Objective
Children will explain how to find a number that is one more or one less than another.

MATERIALS
- MathBoard

ACROSS THE GRADES

Grade K
Recite the number names to 100 by ones and by tens. Starting at a given number, count forward within 100 and backward within 20.

After
Starting at a given number, count forward and backward within 120 by ones. Skip count by 2s to 20 and by 5s to 100.

ABOUT THE MATH

Finding 1 more and 1 less than a number develops better fluency with counting and conceptual understanding of the value of numbers. Because children are able to count to 15 fluently, they will draw a connection between the numbers they say when counting and the numbers that are 1 less and 1 more than another. The number that is 1 less is the number they say before and the number that is 1 more is the number they say after when counting.

For more professional learning, go online to Teacher's Corner.

Problem of the Day 13.6

Complete the sentence.

___ and ___ make 10.

Sample answer: 7 and 3 make 10.

Vocabulary

- Interactive Student Edition
- Multilingual Glossary

Fluency Builder

Count backward. Which number is next?

5, 4, 3, 2

FOCUSING ON THE WHOLE STUDENT

Access Prior Knowledge

Choose one or more of the following activities.

- Discuss with children what it means to have more of something.
- Say a number from 2 to 15 to the class and have them tell you the number that comes before. Repeat with other numbers.

---

① Engage

with the Interactive Student Edition

I Can Objective

I can find one more and one less to 15.

Making Connections

Invite children to tell you what they know about the numbers 1–15.

- **What number comes right before 10?** 9
- **What number comes right after 13?** 14
- **Count the numbers 1–15 aloud with the class.**

Learning Activity

Tell a story about collecting eggs in a bucket. Model a bucket that is holding 12 eggs. Say that yesterday you gathered 1 more egg than today.

Help children to understand one more than a number.

- **How many eggs are in the bucket?** 12
- **How many more eggs were gathered yesterday than today?** 1
- **What would you like to know?** what number is one more than 12

2 Explore

Unlock the Problem

 Model with mathematics.

Read the problem aloud while children listen.

There are 14 children in the classroom. One more child walks into the classroom. How many children are in the classroom now?

- **How many children are in the classroom at first?** 14

Have children draw to model 14 children. Encourage children to draw a simple picture to model the 14 children. They can use circles with a smiley face or stick figures.

- **How many more children walk into the classroom?** 1 more

Have children add a drawing to model one more child.

Construct arguments and critique reasoning of others.

- **Explain how you can find out how many children are in the classroom.** I can count all the children I drew; I count 1 more than 14.

- **How many children are in the classroom?** 15 **Write the number.**

Name _____

One More and One Less to 15

(I Can) find one more and one less to 15.

⊞ UNLOCK the Problem

Check children's work.

I5 children

DIRECTIONS There are 14 children in the classroom. One more child walks into the classroom. How many children are in the classroom now? Draw to solve the problem. Write the number.

Chapter 13 • Lesson 6 **513**

© Houghton Mifflin Harcourt Publishing Company

 Multilingual Support

STRATEGY: Identify Patterns

Materials marbles, coins, or counters

Have children sit in a circle. Show one marble. **I have one marble.** Give the child to your right two marbles. **How many more marbles does (child) have?** One more **How many marbles does (child) have?** Two

Give another child three marbles. Ask comparison questions using the words *more* and *less*. Have children repeat the sentence, **(Child) has one more marble,** or **(Child) has one less marble.**

Check children's work.

$\underline{12}$ marbles

© Houghton Mifflin Harcourt Publishing Company

DIRECTIONS I. Avery has 13 marbles. Javier has one fewer marble than Avery. How many marbles does Javier have? Draw to solve the problem. Write the number.

Ready for More

 Visual Partners

Materials connecting cubes

• Read the problem aloud.

> Mario has 7 berries. Ben has 1 more than Mario, and Lena has 1 more than Ben. How many berries does Lena have? 9 berries

• Ask children to use cubes to help them solve the problem. They should work with a partner.

• If time allows, slightly revise the problem by changing numbers and/or changing *more* to *less*, and then ask children to solve again.

③ Explain

Try Another Problem
Use questions to guide children through Problem 1.

(MP) **Construct arguments and critique reasoning of others.**

Read the problem for children. Discuss with children the word *fewer*. Explain that it means that one set has a number of objects less than the number of objects in another set.

• **What do you need to find?** how many marbles Javier has

• **What do you know?** Possible answer: I know that Avery has 13 marbles and Javier has one fewer than Avery.

(MP) **Reason abstractly and quantitatively.**

• **What kind of picture can you draw to show Avery's marbles?** I can draw Avery's marbles, 13 in all.

• **How many marbles should you draw to model Javier's marbles?** one fewer than 13

• **Write the number to show how many marbles Javier has.** 12

 Common Errors

Error Children draw one more picture instead of one fewer.

Springboard to Learning Review the meaning of the word *fewer*. Then draw 13 circles on the board. Have children count aloud with you as you recount to make sure you have the right amount.

④ Elaborate

Share and Show

 Attend to precision.

For Problem 2, read the problem to the children. Ask them to explain how they will solve it.

- **What do you know?** I know that there are 12 children in the drink line.
- **How many children should you draw to model the snack line?** 12 children and one more
- **How many is 12 and one more?** 13 **Write the number.**

Use the checked problem for Quick Check.

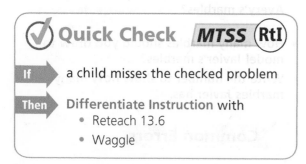

✓ **Quick Check** **MTSS** **RtI**

If → a child misses the checked problem

Then → **Differentiate Instruction with**
- Reteach 13.6
- Waggle

Higher-Order Thinking

 Look for and make use of structure.

Stella has 14 pencils. She has 1 pencil more than Joseph. How many pencils does Joseph have?

Children will need to use reverse thinking to solve this problem. They need to know that if Stella has 1 more, this also means that Joseph has 1 fewer. Have children act out or draw the problem to solve it. **How many pencils does Joseph have?** 13

Math on the Spot Use this video to help children model and solve this type of problem.

Name _____

Share and Show

② ✓   Check children's work.

$I3$ children

DIRECTIONS 2. There are 12 children in the drink line. The snack line has one more child than the drink line. How many children are in the snack line? Draw to solve the problem. Write the number.

Chapter 13 • Lesson 6   **515**

Meeting Individual Needs

Reteach 13.6   **MTSS** **RtI 1**

One More and One Less to 15

① Check children's work.

II books

② Check children's work.

$I5$ balls

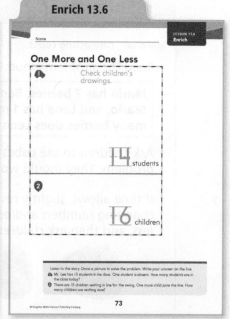

Enrich 13.6

One More and One Less

① Check children's drawings.

$I4$ students

② $I6$ children

3

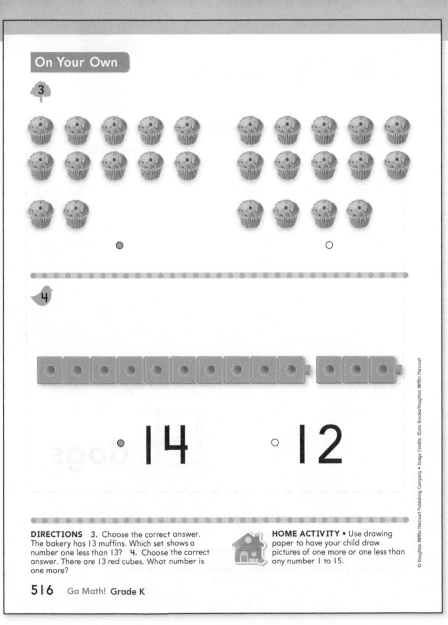

4

$\cdot$ 14 $\circ$ 12

DIRECTIONS 3. Choose the correct answer. The bakery has 13 muffins. Which set shows a number one less than 13? 4. Choose the correct answer. There are 13 red cubes. What number is one more?

HOME ACTIVITY • Use drawing paper to have your child draw pictures of one more or one less than any number 1 to 15.

516   Go Math! Grade K

On Your Own

For **Problems 3 and 4**, remind children to fill in the bubble for the correct answer.

(MP) Look for and make use of structure.

• The bakery has 13 muffins. Which set shows a number one less than 13?

• There are 13 red cubes in the train. What number is one more? Choose the correct answer.

⑤ Evaluate | Formative Assessment

I Can

Have pairs of children write, draw, or model an example to demonstrate the skill for the I Can statement.

I can find one more and one less to 15 by . . . drawing a picture to model what is happening in a problem. I count the objects I drew and add one more or draw a set that is one less.

Exit Ticket

Have children work in pairs to draw or model a number that is one more or one less than the number named by their partner.

DIFFERENTIATED INSTRUCTION • Independent Activities

Grab and Go!
Version 2.0
Differentiated Centers Kit

Tabletop Flipchart

Mini-lessons for reteaching to targeted small groups

Readers

Supports key math skills and concepts in real-world situations.

Games

Reinforce math content and vocabulary

Activities

Meaningful and fun math practice

Practice and Homework

One More and One Less to 15

Use the Practice and Homework pages to provide children with more practice of the concepts and skills presented in this lesson. Children master their understanding as they complete practice items.

Name ______________________

LESSON 13.6
Practice and Homework

One More and One Less to 15

1

Check children's work.

14 dogs

DIRECTIONS 1. There are 15 dogs playing at the dog park. One dog goes home. How many dogs are playing at the dog park now? Draw to solve the problem. Write the number.

Lesson Check

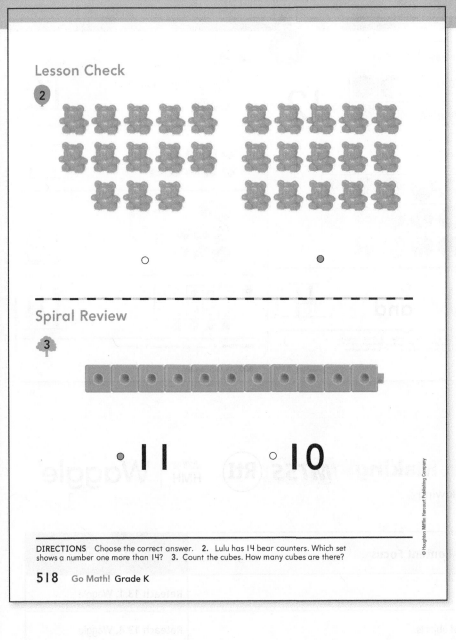

2

○   ●

- -

Spiral Review

3

• **| |**   ○ **| 0**

© Houghton Mifflin Harcourt Publishing Company

DIRECTIONS Choose the correct answer. **2.** Lulu has 14 bear counters. Which set shows a number one more than 14? **3.** Count the cubes. How many cubes are there?

Continue to practice concepts and skills with Lesson Check. Use Spiral Review to engage children in previously taught concepts and to promote content retention.

Chapter Review

Summative Assessment

Use the **Chapter Review** to assess children's progress in Chapter 13.

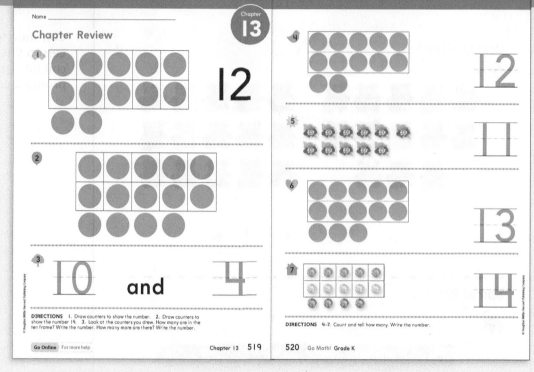

Online, Data-Driven Decision Making MTSS RtI HMH | Waggle®

Based on the results of the Chapter Review, use the following resources to review skills.

Item	Lesson	Content Focus	Intervene With
1	13.1	Count out 11 or 12 objects.	**Reteach 13.1,** Waggle
6, 7	13.4	Write 13 or 14 to represent a group of objects.	**Reteach 13.4,** Waggle
2, 3	13.3	Count out 13 or 14 objects.	**Reteach 13.3,** Waggle
11	13.6	Find one more and one less to 15.	**Reteach 13.6,** Waggle
8, 9, 10	13.5	Count and represent 15 with objects or a written numeral.	**Reteach 13.5,** Waggle
4, 5	13.2	Write 11 or 12 to represent a group of objects.	**Reteach 13.2,** Waggle

Name _____

8

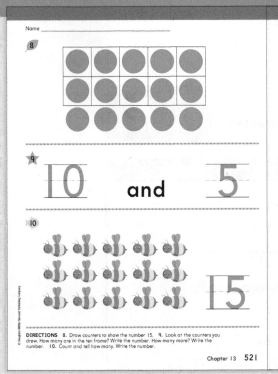

9

10 **and** 5

10

15

DIRECTIONS **8.** Draw counters to show the number 15. **9.** Look at the counters you drew. How many are in the ten frame? Write the number. How many more? Write the number. **10.** Count and tell how many. Write the number.

11

Check children's work.

13 **stickers**

DIRECTIONS **11.** Immanuel has 12 stickers in his collection. Graciela has one more sticker than Immanuel. How many stickers does Graciela have? Draw to solve the problem. Write the number.

Performance Assessment Task

See the Performance Tasks to assess children's understanding of the content. For each task, you will find sample student work for each of the response levels in the task scoring rubric.

Portfolio

Performance Assessment Tasks may be used for portfolios.

Summative Assessment

Use the **Chapter Test** to assess children's progress in Chapter 13.

Chapter Tests are found in the *Assessment Guide*. Test items are presented in formats consistent with high-stakes assessments.

data checkpoint

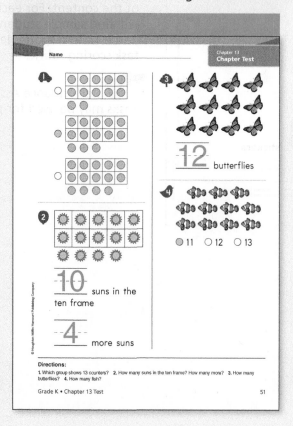

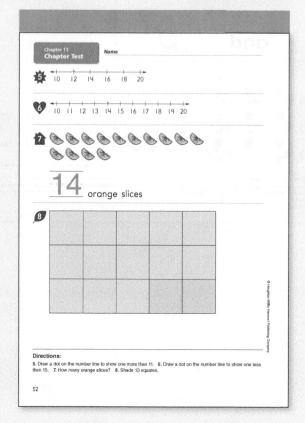

Teacher Notes

Chapter at a Glance

Count, Represent, and Compare Numbers Through 20

	LESSON 14.1 • 1 Day	LESSON 14.2 • 1 Day	LESSON 14.3 • 1 Day
Lesson at a Glance	Model and Count 16 and 17 . . . . 525A	Count and Represent 16 and 17 . . . . 531A	Model and Count 18 and 19 . . . . 537A
I Can	I can count out 16 or 17 objects.	I can write 16 or 17 to represent a group of objects.	I can count out 18 or 19 objects.
Learning Goal	Count out 16 or 17 objects.	Write 16 or 17 to represent a group of objects.	Count out 18 or 19 objects.
Vocabulary	sixteen, seventeen		eighteen, nineteen
Multilingual Support	**Strategy:** Draw	**Strategy:** Creative Grouping	**Strategy:** Model Concepts
Practice and Fluency	LESSON 14.1 ◆ ■ Practice and Homework ■ Waggle ◆ Achieving Facts Fluency*	LESSON 14.2 ◆ ■ Practice and Homework ■ Waggle ◆ Achieving Facts Fluency*	LESSON 14.3 ◆ ■ Practice and Homework ■ Waggle ◆ Achieving Facts Fluency*
MTSS RtI Intervention and Enrichment	■ Waggle ◆ ■ Reteach 14.1 ◆ ■ Tier 2 Intervention Skill S17/S19 ◆ ■ Tier 3 Intervention Skill E17/E19 ◆ Tabletop Flipchart ◆ Enrich 14.1	■ Waggle ◆ ■ Reteach 14.2 ◆ ■ Tier 2 Intervention Skill S17/S19 ◆ ■ Tier 3 Intervention Skill E17/E19 ◆ Tabletop Flipchart ◆ Enrich 14.2	■ Waggle ◆ ■ Reteach 14.3 ◆ ■ Tier 2 Intervention Skill S18/S19 ◆ ■ Tier 3 Intervention Skill E18/E19 ◆ Tabletop Flipchart ◆ Enrich 14.3

See the Grab-and-Go!™ Centers Kit for more small-group activities.

Grab-and-Go!™

Version 2.0

Differentiated Centers Kit

The kit provides literature, games, and activities for small-group learning.

◆ Print/Printable Resource
■ Interactive Resource

	LESSON 14.4 • 1 Day	LESSON 14.5 • 1 Day	LESSON 14.6 • 1 Day
Lesson at a Glance	Count and Represent 18 and 19 . . . . 543A	Model, Count, and Represent 20 . . . . . . 549A	Count and Order to 20 . . . . 555A
I Can	I can write 18 or 19 to represent a group of objects.	I can count and represent 20 with objects or a written numeral.	I can use a number line to order numbers to 20.
Learning Goal	Write 18 or 19 to represent a group of objects.	Count and represent 20 with objects or a written numeral.	Use a number line to order numbers to 20.
Vocabulary		**twenty**	
Multilingual Support	**Strategy:** Describe	**Strategy:** Draw	**Strategy:** Scaffold Language
Practice and Fluency	LESSON 14.4 ◆ ■ Practice and Homework ■ Waggle ◆ Achieving Facts Fluency*	LESSON 14.5 ◆ ■ Practice and Homework ■ Waggle ◆ Achieving Facts Fluency*	LESSON 14.6 ◆ ■ Practice and Homework ■ Waggle ◆ Achieving Facts Fluency*
MTSS RtI Intervention and Enrichment	■ Waggle ◆ ■ Reteach 14.4 ◆ ■ Tier 2 Intervention Skill S18/S19 ◆ ■ Tier 3 Intervention Skill E18/E19 ◆ Tabletop Flipchart ◆ Enrich 14.4	■ Waggle ◆ ■ Reteach 14.5 ◆ ■ Tier 2 Intervention Skill S21 ◆ ■ Tier 3 Intervention Skill E21 ◆ Tabletop Flipchart ◆ Enrich 14.5	■ Waggle ◆ ■ Reteach 14.6 ◆ ■ Tier 2 Intervention Skill S2 ◆ ■ Tier 3 Intervention Skill E2 ◆ Enrich 14.6

*For individual and class practice with counting automaticity and operational fluency, go to *Achieving Facts Fluency* pages located online.

◆ Print/Printable Resource
■ Interactive Resource

Chapter at a Glance
Count, Represent, and Compare Numbers Through 20

	LESSON 14.7 • 1 Day	LESSON 14.8 • 1 Day
Lesson at a Glance	One More and One Less to 20 . . . . 561A	Compare Numbers to 20 . . . . 567A
I Can	I can find and compare numbers to 20 using a number line.	I can compare numbers to 20.
Learning Goal	Find and compare numbers to 20 using a number line.	Compare numbers to 20 using the strategy *make a model*.
Vocabulary		
Multilingual Support	**Strategy:** Identify Patterns	**Strategy:** Restate

Practice and Fluency	LESSON 14.7 ◆ ■ Practice and Homework ■ Waggle ◆ Achieving Facts Fluency*	LESSON 14.8 ◆ ■ Practice and Homework ■ Waggle ◆ Achieving Facts Fluency*
MTSS RtI **Intervention and Enrichment**	■ Waggle ◆ ■ Reteach 14.7 ◆ ■ Tier 2 Intervention Skill S2/S19/S20 ◆ ■ Tier 3 Intervention Skill E2/E19/E20 ◆ Enrich 14.7	■ Waggle ◆ ■ Reteach 14.8 ◆ ■ Tier 2 Intervention Skill S2/S23/S24 ◆ ■ Tier 3 Intervention Skill E2/E23/E24 ◆ Enrich 14.8

◆ Print/Printable Resource
■ Interactive Resource

Teacher Notes

Teaching for Depth

Count, Represent, and Compare Numbers Through 20

Representations and Counting

It is important for children to build on their knowledge of numbers from 0 to 20 and eventually extend their number understanding to 100.

- Ten frames and connecting cubes are used to model 20. Children record the number 20 as the numeral 20 and the verbal word *twenty* to build understanding.

- Writing the missing numbers in the sequence of 1 to 20 helps reinforce children's learning.

Representations

Multiple representations for numbers promote learning. Therefore, children need a variety of experiences with representing numbers. These may include physical objects, word names, drawings, and numerals.

From the Research

"...[C]hildren need multiple experiences with not only visual representations of number and quantity, but also physical and aural representations. Pairing these representations with verbal expression--often in a descriptive dialogue of questions and statements--helps interpret and encode information so that it can be anchored with a child's knowledge framework for later retrieval.**"**
(Martinez & Martinez, 2007, p. 104)

A Foundation for Understanding Place Value

There are several activities that will help children build their understanding of place value.

Counting objects by ones and grouping them by tens reinforces the base-ten structure of the place-value system.

Similarly, counting 10 single cubes by ones and then combining them into a single tower to represent 1 ten also helps children build a foundation for understanding the place-value system.

Representing how many groups of tens and ones are in a given number will help children understand that the position of a digit in a number matters in our place-value system—the positions of the digits in the number 14 indicates that 14 is the same as 1 ten 4 ones.

Representing numbers in a variety of ways leads to the standard form.

Mathematical Practices and Processes

Look for and make use of structure.

As children begin to count, write, and identify greater numbers, they should begin to understand the structure of counting and representing numbers. For example, children have started to see that numbers 11 to 14 are always one group of ten ones plus another group of between one and four ones. Children will see that as the number of further ones increases, the number becomes greater. As children learn to count and write 15, they may begin to see that 15 is made up of not only one group of ten ones and one group of five ones, but also three groups of five ones. As children begin to understand how two-digit numbers can be made up of other numbers, encourage them to look for and note such patterns and structures.

For more professional learning, go online to Teacher's Corner.

Instructional Journey

While every classroom may look a little different, this instructional model provides a framework to organize small-group and whole-group learning for meaningful student learning.

Whole Group
Engage

5 minutes

Readiness
- Problem of the Day
- Fluency Builder or Vocabulary Builder
- Access Prior Knowledge

Engagement
- I Can
- Making Connections
- Learning Activity

Small and Whole Group
Explore

15–20 minutes

Exploration
- Listen and Draw, Unlock the Problem
- Multilingual Support and Strategy
- Common Errors

Small Group
Explain

15–20 minutes

Quick Check
- ✓ Share and Show

Differentiated Instruction
Grab and Go!
Version 2.0

Intervention
- Waggle
- Reteach
- Tier 2 and Tier 3 MTSS
- Tabletop Flipchart Mini Lessons

Language Support
- Vocabulary Activities
- Language Routines
- Multilingual Glossary

Enrichment
- Waggle Games
- Ready For More
- Enrich

Whole Group
Elaborate

5 minutes

- Math on the Spot Videos
- Higher-Order Thinking Problems

Evaluate

- I Can Reflection
- Exit Ticket
- Practice and Homework
- Fluency Practice
- Waggle

Assessment

Diagnostic	Formative	Summative
• Show What You Know	• Lesson Quick Check	• Chapter Review • Chapter Test • Performance Assessment Task

Grab and Go!
Version 2.0
Differentiated Centers Kit
The kit provides literature, games, and activities for small-group learning.

Strategies for
Multilingual Learners

Understanding a child's language development is helpful in differentiating teaching and assessment. Assessing a child's understanding of mathematical concepts can be done by listening, speaking, reading, and writing. The level of support a child needs determines how best to assess that child's understanding of mathematical concepts.

Planning for Instruction			
Language Support	**Substantial** (WIDA Level 1)*	**Moderate** (WIDA Levels 2 & 3)*	**Light** (WIDA Levels 4 & 5)*
Child's Use of Language	• uses single words • uses common short phrases • heavily relies on visual supports and use of manipulatives	• uses simple sentences • uses some academic vocabulary • relies on visual supports and use of manipulatives	• uses a variety of sentences • uses academic vocabulary • benefits from visual supports and manipulatives
Ways to Assess Understanding	**Listening:** points to pictures, words, or phrases to answer questions **Speaking:** answers *yes/no* questions **Reading:** matches symbols to math terms and concepts **Writing:** draws a visual representation of a problem	**Listening:** matches, categorizes, or sequences information based on visuals **Speaking:** begins to explain reasoning, asks math questions, repeats explanations from peers **Reading:** identifies important information to solve a problem **Writing:** uses simple sentences and visual representations	**Listening:** draws conclusions and makes connections based on what they heard **Speaking:** explains and justifies concepts and solutions **Reading:** understands information in math contexts **Writing:** completes sentences using some academic vocabulary

* For more information on WIDA Standards, visit their website at: https://wida.wisc.edu/.

- Look for strategies throughout the lesson to support multilingual learners.
- Log on to ED to find additional multilingual activities and Vocabulary Cards.

In This Chapter

Current Development • Vocabulary

sixteen, seventeen, eighteen, nineteen, twenty

Using Language Routines to Develop Understanding

 Language routines provide opportunities for children to develop an understanding of mathematical language and concepts by listening, speaking, reading, and writing. More information on these language routines can be found on the Language Support Cards.

Critique, Correct, and Clarify

1 Children analyze an incorrect explanation or solution.

2 Children work with a partner or small group to identify the error.

3 Children work together to correct the sample work.

Language Support	Substantial (WIDA Level 1)*	Moderate (WIDA Levels 2 & 3)*	Light (WIDA Levels 4 & 5)*
Language Routine Differentiation	1 Children determine that the visual representation of a provided solution is incorrect. 2 Children identify the error by circling, underlining, or pointing. 3 Children correct the visual representation of the sample.	1 Children analyze an incorrect visual representation of a provided solution. 2 Children work with a partner or small group to identify the error using simple sentences. 3 Children work together to correct the sample work.	1 Children analyze an incorrect explanation or solution. 2 Children work with a partner or small group to identify the error using some academic language. 3 Children work together to correct the sample work.
Possible Student Work	(ten frames showing 20 counters)	(ten frames showing 20 counters) 20	(ten frames showing 20 counters) 20 10 and 10

* For more information on WIDA Standards, visit their website at:
https://wida.wisc.edu/.

Assessing Prior Knowledge

Have children complete **Show What You Know** on their own. Items tested are the prerequisite skills for this chapter.

Diagnostic Interview Task

The alternative interview tasks below evaluate children's understanding of each **Show What You Know** skill. The diagnostic chart may be used for intervention on prerequisite skills.

MATERIALS two-color counters, ten frames, number lines

Have the child count out eight counters and arrange them in two rows.

• Show a ten frame filled with red counters. Then show some yellow counters under the ten frame. Ask the child to identify the number of red counters, the number of yellow counters, and the total number of counters.

• Show a number line from 0 to 10. Ask the child to draw a line under two numbers. Then ask the child to circle the number that is less.

• Show a number line from 0 to 10. Ask the child to draw a line under two numbers. Then ask the child to circle the number that is more.

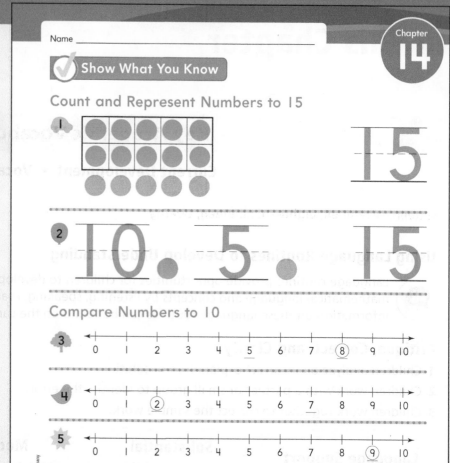

✓ Show What You Know • Diagnostic Assessment

Use to determine if children need intervention for the chapter's prerequisite skills.

If NO...then INTERVENE

If YES...then use INDEPENDENT ACTIVITIES

	Skill	Missed More Than	Intervene With
TIER 3	Count and Represent Numbers to 15	0	*Intensive Intervention* Skill E19
TIER 2	Compare Numbers to 10	1	*Strategic Intervention* Skill S23/S24

Grab-and-Go!™
Version 2.0
Differentiated Centers Kit

Use the Reteach or Enrich Activities online or the independent activities in the *Grab-and-Go 2.0™ Differentiated Centers Kit*.

Vocabulary Builder

Check children's work.

count

8
10
7
9
6

order

 6 7 8 9 10

DIRECTIONS Look at the picture. Look at the numbers next to the picture. Draw a line to match a group of objects or people to the number being represented. Write the numbers in counting order.

524 Go Math! Grade K

© Houghton Mifflin Harcourt Publishing Company

Vocabulary Builder

Children use multiple strategies to develop grade-appropriate vocabulary. Have children complete the activities on the page by working alone or with partners.

Have children point to each number as they say them aloud.

• Have children identify groups of objects or people in the picture. Ask them to count the number of objects or people in each group. Then have them match the number of objects or people to the correct number.

• Explain that to put the numbers in **order** is to write the numbers like they would when counting. Have children write the numbers in order at the bottom of the page.

 **School-Home Letter** is available in English and Spanish online, and in multiple other languages.

Intervention Options MTSS (RtI) Response to Intervention

Use Show What You Know, Lesson Quick Check, and Assessments to diagnose children's intervention levels.

TIER 1	TIER 2	TIER 3	ENRICHMENT
On-Level Intervention	**Strategic Intervention**	**Intensive Intervention**	**Independent Activities**
For children who are generally at grade level but need early intervention with the lesson concepts, use:	For children who need small-group instruction to review concepts and skills needed for the chapter, use:	For children who need one-on-one instruction to build foundational skills for the chapter, use:	For children who successfully complete lessons, use:
• Reteach • Tabletop Flipchart Mini Lesson • Waggle ▲ Tier 1 Activity	▲ Prerequisite Skills Activities ▲ Tier 2 Activity	▲ Prerequisite Skills Activities ▲ Tier 3 Activity	• Waggle Practice and Games **Grab and Go!** Version 2.0 Differentiated Centers Kit • Ready for More Activity for every lesson • Enrich

Lesson at a Glance
Model and Count 16 and 17

SNAPSHOT

Mathematical Standards
- Write numbers from 0 to 20. Represent a number of objects with a written numeral 0-20 (with 0 representing a count of no objects).
- When counting objects, say the number names in the standard order, pairing each object with one and only one number name and each number name with one and only one object.

Mathematical Practices and Processes
- Reason abstractly and quantitatively.
- Model with mathematics.
- Attend to precision.
- Construct arguments and critique reasoning of others.
- Look for and make use of structure.

(**I Can**) **Objective**
I can count out 16 or 17 objects.

Learning Goal
Count out 16 or 17 objects.

Language Objective
Children will explain to a partner how to count out 16 or 17 objects.

MATERIALS
- MathBoard
- two-color counters

ACROSS THE GRADES

Grade K
Given a number from 0 to 20, count out that many objects.

After
Starting at a given number, count forward and backwards within 120 by ones. Skip count by 2s to 20 and by 5s to 100.

ABOUT THE MATH

While working with the numbers 16 and 17, children are shown that many objects and asked to circle 10 of them. Drawing a connection between the number of objects and the written numeral, they extend this understanding as they place that number of counters in ten frames. Using 2 ten frames, children begin to visualize the values of each digit. The 1 in the tens place represents 1 ten, and the other counters represent ones. Children then apply their understanding of each number to circle that many objects.

For more professional learning, go online to Teacher's Corner.

DAILY ROUTINES

 **Problem of the Day 14.1**

Which number is less, 7 or 6? 6

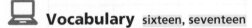 **Vocabulary** sixteen, seventeen

- Interactive Student Edition
- Multilingual Glossary

Vocabulary Builder

Ask children to define each term and give several examples. Accept reasonable definitions. Possible examples given.

Term	Example(s)
sixteen	16; 10 and 6
seventeen	17; 10 and 7

FOCUSING ON THE WHOLE STUDENT

Access Prior Knowledge

Choose one or more of the following activities.

- Have children work together to come up with a short story about finding a flower patch. Write the story on the board.
- Ask children to draw flowers with different numbers of petals. Then ask them to count the petals on each flower.

① Engage

with the Interactive Student Edition

I Can Objective

I can count out 16 or 17 objects.

Making Connections

Ask children to tell you what they know about counting to 15.

- **Hold up one hand. How many fingers do you have on that hand?** 5
- **Using your hands, can you show what 5 and 1 more looks like?** Children will hold up 6 fingers.
- **Working together, let's count the fingers you have up.** Count 1, 2, 3, 4, 5, 6 out loud with children.

Learning Activity

Help children think about 17 as "15 and 2 more." Draw a picture of 17 dandelions in 1 row of 10, 1 row of 5, and then 2 more.

- **How many dandelions are in the first group?** 10
- **How many dandelions do you see all together?** 15 and 2 more
- **What are you trying to figure out?** the number that shows 15 and 2 more

Explore

Listen and Draw

Materials two-color counters

Read this problem aloud. Tell children they will use counters to solve.

Ann has 16 peaches on Monday. On Tuesday she has 17 peaches. How can you show the numbers of peaches Ann has?

 Use appropriate tools strategically.

Give children 16 counters and ask them to fill the top ten frame.

- **How many counters fill the top ten frame?** 10

- **Put the rest of the counters in the bottom ten frame. Start in the first row of the frame.**

Count the counters together.

Continue to model the number 17.

 Reason abstractly and quantitatively.

- **How many more counters do you need to add to show 17?** one more **Why?** because 17 is one greater than 16

- **What can you tell about 17?** Possible answer: It is one greater than 16; it is two greater 15.

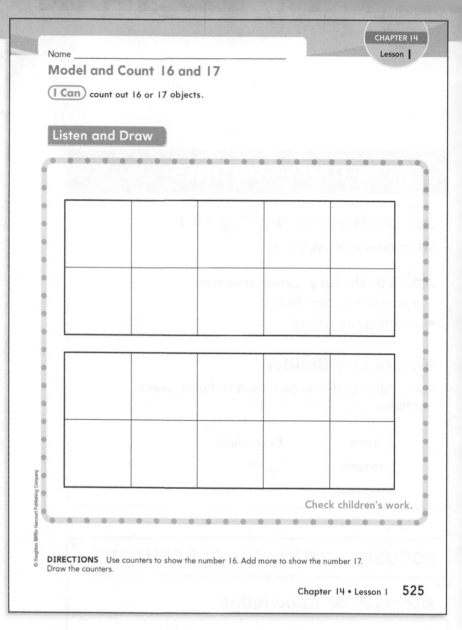

Name _____

Model and Count 16 and 17

(**I Can**) count out 16 or 17 objects.

 Listen and Draw

Check children's work.

© Houghton Mifflin Harcourt Publishing Company

DIRECTIONS Use counters to show the number 16. Add more to show the number 17. Draw the counters.

Chapter 14 • Lesson 1   **525**

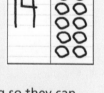

 Multilingual Support

STRATEGY: Draw

Children can demonstrate prior knowledge and understanding of concepts by drawing rather than using language.

- Fold a piece of paper in half. Write a number from 14 to 17 in the left column.

- In the right column, have children draw the corresponding number of circles for each number.

- Ask children specific questions about their drawing so they can point or give short answers. For example, **Show me 16 circles.** Child points to the column with 16 circles. **How many circles are in this column?**

Repeat with other shapes if time permits.

1

16

 2

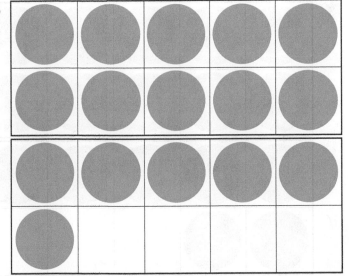

 3

 10 and 6

DIRECTIONS 1. Circle 10 peaches. Tell how many more there are. 2. Place counters in the ten frames to show the number 16. Draw the counters. 3. Look at the counters you drew in the ten frames. How many ones are in the top ten frame? Write the number. How many ones are in the bottom ten frame? Write the number.

Ready for More

 Kinesthetic Individual/Partners

Materials two-color counters

Hand each child 17 counters and paper.

- Write **16** and **17** on the board. **How many more ones than 10 ones is 17?** seven more Lead children in the chant, 10 ones and 6 ones (clap) 16; 10 ones and 7 ones (clap) 17!

- Have children place 10 counters on their paper and draw a circle around them. Ask children to add counters outside the circle to show 16 and then 17.

- **If you have 10 seashells and you want to collect 17, how many more seashells would you need? How do you know?** 7; because 17 is 10 ones and seven more

③ Explain

Share and Show Math Board

- **Look at Problem 1. What number do you see?** 16

 Look for and make use of structure.

- **Look at the way the peaches are arranged. How can you find out how many peaches there are?** Possible answer: I know that there are 10 peaches in the first two rows, and I count six more; 10 ones and 6 ones is 16.

- **Look at Problem 2. How can you show the number 16 with counters?** I can put 10 counters in the top ten frame to model 10 ones and six counters in the bottom ten frame to model 6 ones. **Count the counters. Draw the counters.**

For Problem 3, guide children in counting the counters and writing the numbers.

- **How many ones are in the top ten frame?** 10 **Write the number.**

- **How many ones are in the bottom frame?** 6 **Write the number.**

Use the checked problem for Quick Check.

✓ Quick Check MTSS RtI

| If | a child misses the checked problem |
| Then | **Differentiate Instruction** with • Reteach 14.1 • Waggle |

! Common Errors

Error Children may miscount.

Springboard to Learning Have children circle the first 10 peaches. Then have children count the remaining peaches, making a dot on each. Children should note that there are six peaches outside the circle, not five. Then recount the peaches together.

Share and Show

 **Attend to precision.**

- **Look at Problem 4. What number do you see?** 17
- **How many plums are there?** 17
- **Look at Problem 5. How can you show the number 17 with counters?** I can put 10 counters in the top ten frame and seven in the bottom frame.

For Problem 6, have children count and write how many counters they drew in each ten frame.

- **How many do you have if you have 10 and 7?** 17

Higher-Order Thinking

 **Look for and make use of structure.**

Write the following on the board:

- **10 and 1 is 11.**
- **10 and 2 is 12.**
- **10 and 3 is 13.**

Read each sentence in order with children. Ask children to describe the pattern they see and hear.

- **What number sentence would come next in this sequence?** 10 and 4 is 14.

Have children count to 17. As they count, point out that each successive number name refers to a quantity that is one larger.

Math on the Spot Use this video to help children model and solve this type of problem.

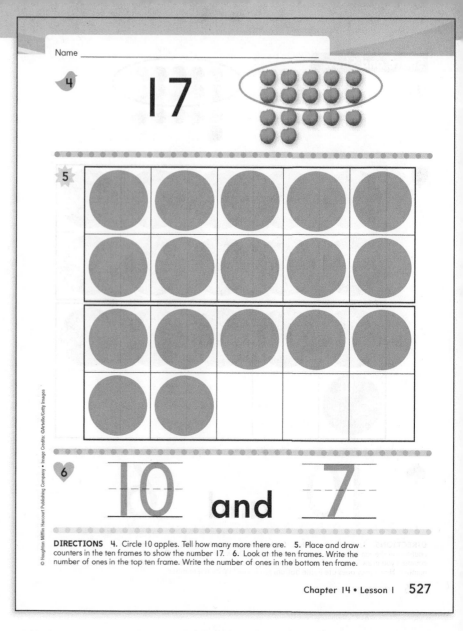

Name _____

4

17

5

6

10 and 7

DIRECTIONS 4. Circle 10 apples. Tell how many more there are. 5. Place and draw counters in the ten frames to show the number 17. 6. Look at the ten frames. Write the number of ones in the top ten frame. Write the number of ones in the bottom frame.

Chapter 14 • Lesson 1   **527**

Meeting Individual Needs

Reteach 14.1   **MTSS** **RtI1**   **Enrich 14.1**

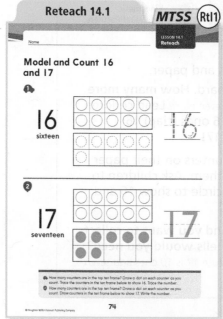

Name _____

Model and Count 16 and 17

1   16   sixteen

2   17   seventeen

How many counters are in the top ten frame? Draw a dot on each counter as you count. Trace the counters in the ten frame below to show 16. Trace the number.
How many counters are in the top ten frame? Draw a dot on each counter as you count. Draw counters in the ten frame below to show 17. Write the number.

74

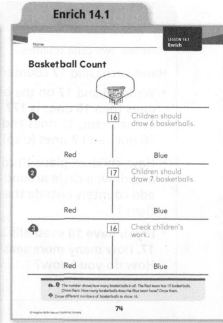

Name _____

Basketball Count

1   16   Children should draw 6 basketballs.
Red _____   Blue _____

2   17   Children should draw 7 basketballs.
Red _____   Blue _____

3   16   Check children's work.
Red _____   Blue _____

The number shows how many basketballs in all. The Red team has 10 basketballs. Draw them. How many basketballs does the Blue team have? Draw them.
Draw different numbers of basketballs to show 16.

74

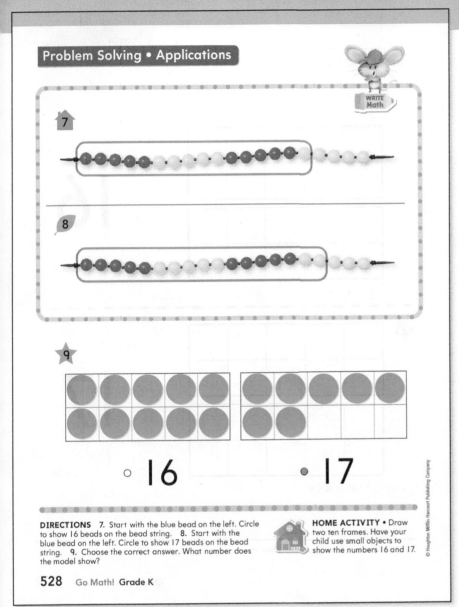

7

8

9

° 16   • 17

DIRECTIONS 7. Start with the blue bead on the left. Circle to show 16 beads on the bead string. 8. Start with the blue bead on the left. Circle to show 17 beads on the bead string. 9. Choose the correct answer. What number does the model show?

HOME ACTIVITY • Draw two ten frames. Have your child use small objects to show the numbers 16 and 17.

© Houghton Mifflin Harcourt Publishing Company

528   Go Math! Grade K

---

④ Elaborate

Problem Solving  Math
Applications

(MP) **Construct arguments and critique reasoning of others.**

Read **Problem 7**. Ask children to explain how they will solve the problem.

- **Count the first set of five blue beads and the first set of five yellow beads. How many beads did you count in all?** 10
- **How many more beads than 10 do you need to circle to make 16?** 6

(MP) **Look for and make use of structure.**

Discuss with children how they might know without counting where the sixteenth bead is. Elicit that 6 is 5 ones and one more and that after the set of 10 ones, they can circle the five blue beads and one yellow bead to make 6.

Repeat **Problem 8** in a similar way, helping children circle 17 beads on the bead string.

Read **Problem 9** aloud to children. Direct children to fill in the bubble for the correct answer.

DIFFERENTIATED INSTRUCTION • Independent Activities

Grab-and-Go!
Version 2.0
Differentiated Centers Kit

Tabletop Flipchart

Mini-lessons for reteaching to targeted small groups

Readers

Supports key math skills and concepts in real-world situations.

Games

Reinforce math content and vocabulary

Activities

Meaningful and fun math practice

---

⑤ Evaluate | Formative Assessment

I Can

Have pairs of children write, draw, or model an example to demonstrate the skill for the I Can statement.

I can count out 16 or 17 objects by . . . using counters to fill a ten frame and show 6 or 7 more.

Exit Ticket

Have children explain their drawings or models to a partner.

Practice and Homework

Model and Count 16 and 17

Use the Practice and Homework pages to provide children with more practice of the concepts and skills presented in this lesson. Children master their understanding as they complete practice items.

Model and Count 16 and 17

1

16

Check children's work.

- -

2

17

Check children's work.

© Houghton Mifflin Harcourt Publishing Company

DIRECTIONS 1. Draw counters to show 16. 2. Draw counters to show 17.

Chapter 14 • Lesson 1 **529**

Lesson Check

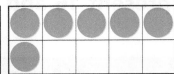

○ **17**   ● **16**

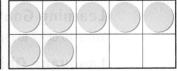

● **17**   ○ **16**

Spiral Review

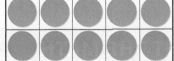

○ **12**   ● **13**

DIRECTIONS 3–5. Choose the correct answer. What number does the model show?

© Houghton Mifflin Harcourt Publishing Company

Lesson at a Glance
Count and Represent 16 and 17

SNAPSHOT

Mathematical Standards

- Write numbers from 0 to 20. Represent a number of objects with a written numeral 0-20 (with 0 representing a count of no objects).

Mathematical Practices and Processes

- Model with mathematics.
- Attend to precision.
- Reason abstractly and quantitatively.
- Look for and make use of structure.
- Construct arguments and critique reasoning of others.
- Express regularity in repeated reasoning.

(I Can) **Objective**

I can write 16 or 17 to represent a group of objects.

Learning Goal

Write 16 or 17 to represent a group of objects.

Language Objective

Children will write the numerals 16 or 17 to represent a quantity.

MATERIALS

- MathBoard

ACROSS THE GRADES

Grade K

Given a group of up to 20 objects, count the number of objects in that group and represent the number of objects with a written numeral. State the number of objects in a rearrangement of that group without recounting.

After

Starting at a given number, count forward and backwards within 120 by ones. Skip count by 2s to 20 and by 5s to 100.

ABOUT THE MATH

Children count objects and then write a numeral to represents how many. The objects are shown in groups of 10 and then some more. Often the groups are shown in two ten frames, the first one full and the next one only partially filled. After counting, children apply fine motor skills as they write each digit correctly. They also expand on the value of each number showing that 16 is 10 and 6, and 17 is 10 and 7. These expressions lay foundational work for both place value and addition.

For more professional learning, go online to Teacher's Corner.

DAILY ROUTINES

🖥 Problem of the Day 14.2

Use counters to show 6.
Use counters to show 7.

Check children's representations.

🖥 Vocabulary

- Interactive Student Edition
- Multilingual Glossary

Fluency Builder

Count from 1 to 17. Which number is missing?

1, 2, 3, 4, 5, 6, 7, 8, 9, 10, 11, 12, 13, 14, 15, 16, ? 17

FOCUSING ON THE WHOLE STUDENT

Access Prior Knowledge

Choose one or more of the following activities.

- Have children work together to come up with a story about apple picking.
- Ask children to make up sentences using the number 16.

① Engage

with the Interactive Student Edition

I Can Objective

I can write 16 or 17 to represent a group of objects.

Making Connections

Invite children to share what they know about counting and writing up to 15.

- Draw 10 apples on the board. **How many apples are there?** 10
- **Show me what the number 10 looks like when you write it.** Children will write a 10 on their papers.
- **Can you write the number that shows 10 and 1 more?** Children will write an 11 on their papers.

Learning Activity

Guide children toward knowing how to count and write 16. Draw a row of 10 apples and a row of 6 counters on the board. Tell a story about seeing apples in buckets. Explain that the first row shows how many apples are in the first bucket and the second row shows how many apples are in the second bucket.

- **What object did I see in the buckets?** apples
- **How do I figure out how many apples there are?** Count them.
- **What am I trying to learn?** how to write 16

Explore

Listen and Draw

(MP) **Model with mathematics.**

Read this problem aloud as children listen.

Josh owns racecar number 16. How can he write to show the number on his racecar? Have children count the red cubes.

- **How many cubes are in the top row?** 10
- **How many cubes are in the bottom row?** 6
- **How many cubes is 10 and six more cubes?** 16
- **How do you write 16?** First write 1, then write 6 next to it.

Have children trace and write the number 16. Repeat, helping children trace and write the number.

Culturally Responsive Education

One foundational aspect of culturally responsive teaching is ensuring that cooperation and collectivism are at least as present in your classroom as the more dominant Western ideology of individualism. Provide opportunities for children to collaborate on their learning, such as the Multilingual Support activity listed on this page or the Ready for More activity on page 532.

Name _____

Count and Represent 16 and 17

(I Can) write 16 or 17 to represent a group of objects.

Listen and Draw

16   16   16   16

17   17   17   17

Check children's work.

DIRECTIONS Count and tell how many. Trace and write the numbers.

Chapter 14 • Lesson 2   **531**

(ML) ## Multilingual Support

STRATEGY: Creative Grouping

Materials connecting cubes

Children can be grouped for language or mathematics needs to better enable language acquisition and math practice.

- Pair children who are beginning or intermediate English learners with children who are fluent in English.
- Have children make a row of 10 cubes and a row below with 6 cubes. Then have them count the two sets of cubes.
- Have children say how many by describing 10 ones and 6 ones.
- Repeat the activity using 17 cubes.

1

16

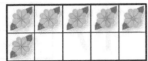 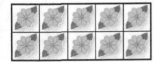

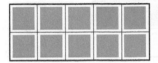 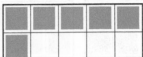

Check children's work.

2 ✓

3

10 . ☐   6 . ☐   16

DIRECTIONS 1. Count and tell how many. Practice writing the number. 2. Count and tell how many. Write the number. 3. Look at the ten frames in Problem 2. Write how many red squares. Write how many blue squares. Write how many in all.

© Houghton Mifflin Harcourt Publishing Company

③ Explain

Share and Show

- In Problem 1, which number do you see? 16

(MP) Reason abstractly and quantitatively.

- **How many orange flowers are in the first frame?** 10 **How many more flowers are in the next frame?** 6 **How many is 10 ones and 6 ones?** 16 **Write the number 16 as you say the number to yourself.**

(MP) Look for and make use of structure.

- **Look at Problem 2. How many tiles are in the first frame?** 10 **Did you have to count them? Explain.** No; the frame is full so I know there are 10.

- **How many more tiles are in the next frame?** 6 **How many is 10 and six more?** 16 **Write the number.**

Have children look at the ten frames in Problem 2. Have children write the numbers to match in Problem 3.

Use the checked problem for Quick Check.

✓ Quick Check   MTSS RtI

If	a child misses the checked problem
Then	Differentiate Instruction with

- Reteach 14.2
- Waggle

⚠ Common Errors

Error Children may write the total number of tiles instead of the number of red or the number of blue tiles.

Springboard to Learning Help children count the tiles in each ten frame. Guide them to write 10 after counting the tiles in the first frame and write 6 after counting the tiles in the next frame.

Ready for More   🕐 Kinesthetic Individual/Partners

Materials spinners (3- and 4- section), ten frames, two-color counters

Give each pair of children a spinner, counters, and two ten frames.

- Have one child spin the pointer without his or her partner seeing. Have the first child say the number as "10 ones and ____ ones."

- Have the second partner use counters to show the number on the ten frames.

- The second partner says the number, checking the spinner to see if it matches.

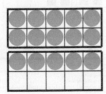

Share and Show

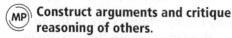

- Look at Problem 4. What number do you see? 17
- How many flowers are in the first ten frame? 10 How many more are in the next ten frame? 7 How many is 10 ones and 7 ones? 17 Trace and write the number 17.

(MP) **Construct arguments and critique reasoning of others.**

- Look at Problem 5. How many yellow tiles are in the first ten frame? 10
- How can you quickly tell how many are in the next ten frame? I know a filled top row is 5 and two more makes 7. **How many is 10 and seven more?** 17 **Write the number.**
- Look at the ten frames in Problem 5. Write the numbers to match in Problem 6. 10; 7; 17

Higher-Order Thinking

Have children suppose that they are planting flowers in rows of five or fewer.

- **How would your garden look with 17 flowers?** three rows of five and one row of two

(MP) **Express regularity in repeated reasoning.**

Read each sentence in order with children. Ask children to describe the pattern they see and hear.

- **What number of flowers would give you only two full rows of five and some more?** 11, 12, 13, 14

Discuss how children found their answers. Children should determine that two full rows is a total of 10 and that more flowers would show how many more than 10.

Math on the Spot Use this video to help children model and solve this type of problem.

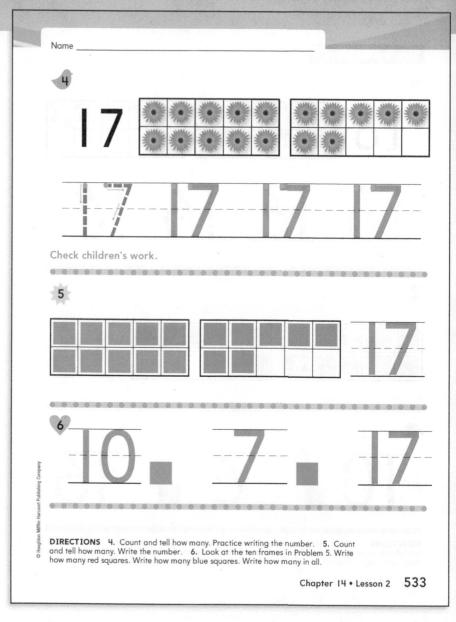

Name _____

4

17

Check children's work.

5

6

10 . 7 . 17

DIRECTIONS 4. Count and tell how many. Practice writing the number. 5. Count and tell how many. Write the number. 6. Look at the ten frames in Problem 5. Write how many red squares. Write how many blue squares. Write how many in all.

Chapter 14 • Lesson 2   533

Meeting Individual Needs

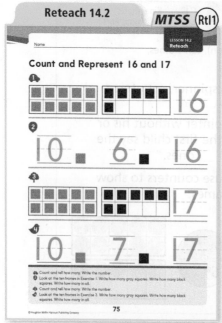

Reteach 14.2   MTSS (Rtl1)

Count and Represent 16 and 17

75

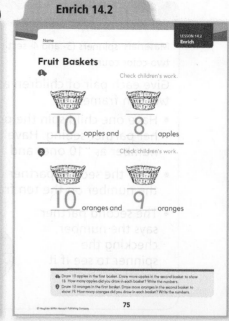

Enrich 14.2

Fruit Baskets

Check children's work.

10 apples and 8 apples

Check children's work.

10 oranges and 9 oranges

75

7 Check children's work.

17
18
19

8 Check children's drawings.

6

9

10 and ___ 17

• 7   ○ 17

DIRECTIONS 7. Circle a number. Draw more flowers to show that number. **8.** Draw a set of 16 objects. Circle 10 of the objects. How many more objects are there? Write the number. **9.** Choose the correct answer. What number goes in the blank to make 17?

HOME ACTIVITY • Ask your child to count and write the number for a set of 16 or 17 objects, such as macaroni pieces or buttons.

© Houghton Mifflin Harcourt Publishing Company • Image Credit: ©IMH

④ Elaborate

Problem Solving Applications Real World

(MP) **Attend to precision.**

Have children look at **Problem 7.** Explain to children that they may circle any of the three numbers.

- **Look at the number you circled. Draw more flowers to match your number.**

Have children look at **Problem 8.**

- **Draw a set of 16 objects. Circle 10 of the objects. How many more objects are there?** 6

Read **Problem 9** aloud to children. Direct children to fill in the bubble for the correct answer.

- **What number goes in the blank to make 17?**

⑤ Evaluate | Formative Assessment

I Can

Have pairs of children write, draw, or model an example to demonstrate the skill for the I Can statement.

I can write 16 or 17 to represent a group of objects by . . . counting aloud 16 objects and writing the number 16 or counting aloud 17 objects and writing the number 17. I can also write 10 and 6 for 16, and 10 and 7 for 17.

Exit Ticket

Call on volunteers to tell about their drawings.

DIFFERENTIATED INSTRUCTION • Independent Activities

Grab and Go!™
Version 2.0
Differentiated Centers Kit

Tabletop Flipchart

Mini-lessons for reteaching to targeted small groups

Readers

Supports key math skills and concepts in real-world situations.

Games

Reinforce math content and vocabulary

Activities

Meaningful and fun math practice

Practice and Homework

Count and Represent 16 and 17

Use the Practice and Homework pages to provide children with more practice of the concepts and skills presented in this lesson. Children master their understanding as they complete practice items.

Count and Represent 16 and 17

1 16

16 16 16 16

2 17

17 17 17 17

Check children's work.

© Houghton Mifflin Harcourt Publishing Company

DIRECTIONS 1–2. Count and tell how many. Trace and write the numbers.

Chapter 14 • Lesson 2   **535**

Lesson Check

3

10 and _____   16

○ 16   • 6

4

10 and _____   17

• 7   ○ 17

Spiral Review

5

10 and _____   15

○ 15   • 5

DIRECTIONS 3–4. Choose the correct answer. What number goes in the blank?
5. Use the counters. What number goes in the blank?

536 Go Math! Grade K

© Houghton Mifflin Harcourt Publishing Company

Lesson at a Glance
Model and Count 18 and 19

SNAPSHOT

Mathematical Standards

● Write numbers from 0 to 20. Represent a number of objects with a written numeral 0-20 (with 0 representing a count of no objects).

Mathematical Practices and Processes

● Model with mathematics.
● Attend to precision.
● Construct arguments and critique reasoning of others.
● Look for and make use of structure.
● Reason abstractly and quantitatively.

(I Can) Objective

I can count out 18 or 19 objects.

Learning Goal

Count out 18 or 19 objects.

Language Objective

Children will explain to a partner how to count out 18 or 19 objects.

MATERIALS

• MathBoard
• two-color counters

ACROSS THE GRADES

Grade K

Given a number from 0 to 20, count out that many objects.

After

Starting at a given number, count forward and backwards within 120 by ones. Skip count by 2s to 20 and by 5s to 100.

ABOUT THE MATH

While working with the numbers 18 and 19, children are shown that many objects and asked to circle 10 of them. Drawing a connection between the number of objects and the written numeral, they extend this understanding as they place that number of counters in ten frames. Using two ten frames, children begin to visualize a foundational concept of place value. They see the number 18 as 10 and 8, and 19 as 10 and 9, which is the beginning to understanding that the 1 in the tens place does not have the same value as a 1 in the ones place. Children then apply their understanding of each number to circle that many objects.

For more professional learning, go online to Teacher's Corner.

DAILY ROUTINES

💻 Problem of the Day 14.3

Which number is less, 8 or 9? 8

💻 Vocabulary eighteen, nineteen

- Interactive Student Edition
- Multilingual Glossary

Vocabulary Builder

Ask children to define each term and give several examples. Accept reasonable definitions. Possible examples given.

Term	Example(s)
eighteen	18; 10 and 8
nineteen	19; 10 and 9

FOCUSING ON THE WHOLE STUDENT

Access Prior Knowledge

Choose one or more of the following activities.

- Have children form small groups of at least 3. Ask children to act out what they think would happen if they were in a field of clovers.
- Have children work together to make up a story about finding a four-leaf clover.

---

① Engage

with the Interactive Student Edition

I Can Objective

I can count out 18 or 19 objects.

Making Connections

Invite children to share what they know about counting and writing numbers up to 17.

- **Hold up both of your hands. How many fingers do you count?** 10
- **Put down one of your fingers. How many fingers are you holding up now?** 9
- **What does that number look like when you write it?** Children will write a 9 on their papers.

Learning Activity

Guide children towards understanding how to model and count 19. Ask children to draw two groups of clovers. The first group should have 10 clovers. The second group should have 9 clovers.

- **How many clovers are in the first group that you made?** 10
- **How many clovers are in the second group that you made?** 9
- **Which group has more clovers? How do you know?** The first group has more clovers. I know this because 10 comes after 9 when I am counting.

Explore

Listen and Draw

Materials: two-color counters

 Model with mathematics.

Read this problem aloud. Tell children they will use counters to solve.

The teacher has eight oranges. She needs 18 for the class picnic. Use counters to show how many more oranges the teacher needs.

(MP) Look for and make use of structure.

Give children 18 counters and ask them to fill the top ten frame.

* **How many counters fill the top ten frame?** 10
* **How many counters are left?** 8 **Put the counters that are left in the bottom ten frame. Remember to start on the top row.**
* **How many is 10 and 8?** 18 **Count the counters.**

Read the word problem again.

* **How many more oranges does the teacher need?** 10 **How do you know?** Possible answer: I know that 10 ones and 8 ones make 18. If the teacher already has eight oranges she will need 10 more to make 18.

Repeat the pattern of questions using 19 cubes.

* **How do you use ten frames to model 19?** Fill one ten frame with 10 counters. Put nine counters in the second ten frame.

Name _____

Model and Count 18 and 19

(I Can) count out 18 or 19 objects.

Listen and Draw

Check children's work.

DIRECTIONS Use counters to show the number 18. Add more to show the number 19. Draw the counters.

 Multilingual Support

STRATEGY: Model Concepts

Materials: paper clips

Modeling may help children better understand concepts and vocabulary.

* Show children a row of 18 paper clips.
* Count the paper clips with children.
* Add one more paper clip to the row. Explain that one more than 18 is 19.
* Count the paper clips with children.

Share and Show

1

18

2 ✓

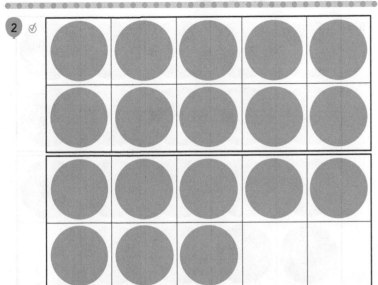

3

10 and 8

DIRECTIONS 1. Circle 10 peaches. Tell how many more there are. 2. Place counters in the ten frames to show the number 18. Draw the counters. 3. Look at the counters you drew in the ten frames. How many ones are in the top ten frame? Write the number. How many ones are in the bottom ten frame? Write the number.

Ready for More

🕐 Kinesthetic/Visual
Individual/Partners

Materials: numeral cards (8–15), (16–23)

Have children place the numeral cards 8 to 19 facedown in a stack.

- Ask each child to flip over a numeral card, say the number out loud, and draw to show the number.

16 ⭐⭐⭐⭐⭐⭐⭐⭐⭐⭐
⭐⭐⭐⭐⭐⭐

---

③ Explain

Share and Show 🔲 Math Board

MP **Attend to precision.**

- **Look at Problem 1. What number do you see?** 18

Have children circle the top set of 10 nectarines.

- **How many nectarines did you circle?** 10
  How many more nectarines do you see? 8
  What number do 10 and 8 make? 18

MP **Reason abstractly and quantitatively.**

- **Look at Problem 2. How can you show the number 18 with counters?** I can put 10 counters in the top ten frame and eight counters in the bottom.

- **How many spaces are empty?** 2

- **What do those two empty spaces mean?** They mean 18 is two less than 20.

For Problem 3, have children count and write how many counters are in each ten frame. 10; 8

Use the checked problem for Quick Check.

✓ Quick Check MTSS RtI

If → a child misses the checked problem

Then → Differentiate Instruction with
- Reteach 14.3
- Waggle

⚠ Common Errors

Error Children may not draw the correct number of counters.

Springboard to Learning Have children count the drawings by placing a dot on each to see if there are 18. If there are not, ask children to tell how many more counters are needed to complete the drawing.

Share and Show

 **Attend to precision.**

- **Look at Problem 4. What number do you see?** 19
- **How many sets of 10 pears are there?** 1 **How many more pears do you see?** 9 **How many pears are there?** 19
- **Look at Problem 5. How can you show the number 19 with counters in the ten frames?** I can put 10 counters in the top ten frame and nine in the bottom frame.

For Problem 6, have children count and write how many counters they drew in each ten frame.

- **How many do you have if you have 10 counters and 9 counters?** 19

Higher-Order Thinking

Have children use what they know about teen numbers to solve an addition problem. Ask children to use counters or draw a picture to show the following problem.

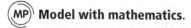 **Model with mathematics.**

- **There are 10 butterflies on a bush. There are 8 more butterflies in the grass. How many butterflies are there in all?** 18

Help children make connections between the problem and the pattern of 10 ones and more that they have been using throughout the lessons.

- **How are the 10 butterflies on one bush like a ten frame?** They show 10 ones.
- **How many is 10 and 8 more?** 18

Math on the Spot Use this video to help children model and solve this type of problem.

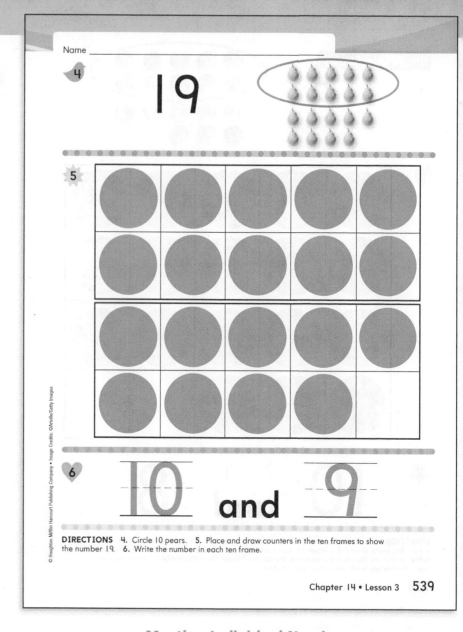

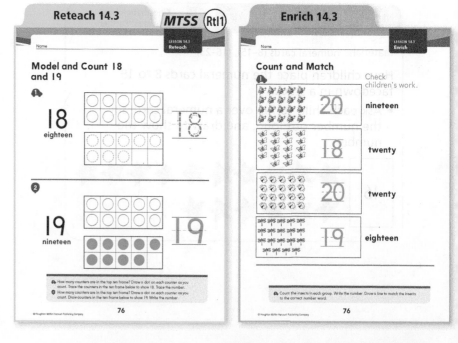

Name _____

4   **19**

5

6   **10** and **9**

DIRECTIONS 4. Circle 10 pears. 5. Place and draw counters in the ten frames to show the number 19. 6. Write the number in each ten frame.

Chapter 14 • Lesson 3   **539**

Meeting Individual Needs

Reteach 14.3   MTSS (Rtl1)   **Enrich 14.3**

Name _____

Model and Count 18 and 19

18 eighteen   **18**

19 nineteen   **19**

Name _____

Count and Match   Check children's work.

20 nineteen

18 twenty

20 twenty

19 eighteen

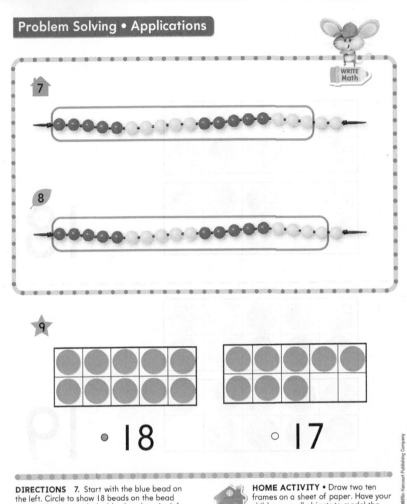

7

8

9

 18   ○ 17

DIRECTIONS 7. Start with the blue bead on the left. Circle to show 18 beads on the bead string. 8. Start with the blue bead on the left. Circle to show 19 beads on the bead string. 9. Choose the correct answer. What number does the model show?

 HOME ACTIVITY • Draw two ten frames on a sheet of paper. Have your child use small objects to model the numbers 18 and 19.

© Houghton Mifflin Harcourt Publishing Company

540   Go Math! **Grade K**

DIFFERENTIATED INSTRUCTION • Independent Activities

Grab-and-Go!™
Version 2.0
Differentiated Centers Kit

Tabletop Flipchart
Mini-lessons for reteaching to targeted small groups

Readers
Supports key math skills and concepts in real-world situations.

Games
Reinforce math content and vocabulary

Activities
Meaningful and fun math practice

---

④ Elaborate

Problem Solving Applications WRITE Math

(MP) **Construct arguments and critique reasoning of others.**

Read **Problem 7**. Ask children to explain how they will solve the problem.

Repeat in a similar way for **Problem 8**.

Read **Problem 9** aloud to children. Direct children to fill in the bubble for the correct answer.

• **What number does the model show?** 18

⑤ Evaluate | Formative Assessment

I Can

Have pairs of children write, draw, or model an example to demonstrate the skill for the I Can statement.

I can count out 18 or 19 objects by . . . using counters to fill a ten frame and then show 8 or 9 more.

Exit Ticket

Have children explain their drawings and models to classmates.

Model and Count 18 and 19

Use the Practice and Homework pages to provide children with more practice of the concepts and skills presented in this lesson. Children master their understanding as they complete practice items.

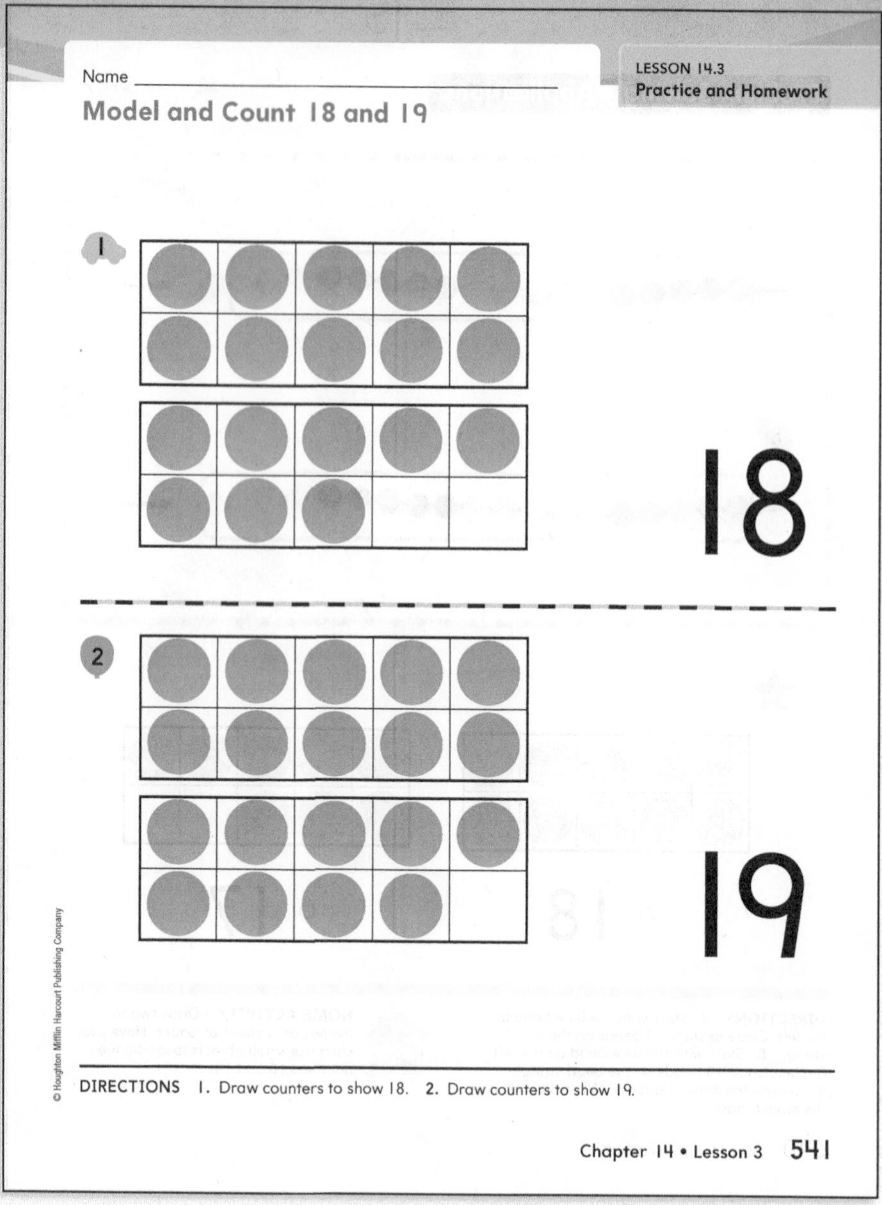

Model and Count 18 and 19

1

18

2

19

DIRECTIONS 1. Draw counters to show 18.   2. Draw counters to show 19.

Chapter 14 • Lesson 3   541

Lesson Check

3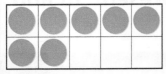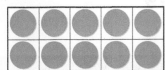

○ **17**   ○ **18**

4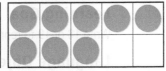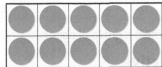

○ **16**   ● **18**

Spiral Review

5

4 5 6 7 8

DIRECTIONS 3–4. Choose the correct answer. What number do the counters represent? 5. What number does each ten frame show?

Continue to practice concepts and skills with Lesson Check. Use Spiral Review to engage children in previously taught concepts and to promote content retention.

Lesson at a Glance
Count and Represent 18 and 19

SNAPSHOT

Mathematical Standards
- Write numbers from 0 to 20. Represent a number of objects with a written numeral 0-20 (with 0 representing a count of no objects).

Mathematical Practices and Processes
- Reason abstractly and quantitatively.
- Attend to precision.
- Construct arguments and critique reasoning of others.
- Look for and make use of structure.
- Model with mathematics.
- Express regularity in repeated reasoning.

(I Can) Objective
I can write 18 or 19 to represent a group of objects.

Learning Goal
Write 18 or 19 to represent a group of objects.

Language Objective
Children will write the numerals 18 or 19 to represent a quantity.

MATERIALS
- MathBoard

ACROSS THE GRADES

Grade K
Given a group of up to 20 objects, count the number of objects in that group and represent the number of objects with a written numeral. State the number of objects in a rearrangement of that group without recounting.

After
Starting at a given number, count forward and backward within 120 by ones. Skip count by 2s to 20 and by 5s to 100.

ABOUT THE MATH

Children count objects and then write a numeral to represent how many. The objects are shown in groups of 10 and then some more. Often the groups are shown in ten frames, but they can also be shown in a row of 10 and another row that has fewer than 10. To show how many they count, children apply fine motor skills as they write each digit correctly. They also expand on the value of each number, showing that 18 is 10 and 8 and 19 is 10 and 9. These expressions lay foundational work for both place value and addition.

For more professional learning, go online to Teacher's Corner.

DAILY ROUTINES

🖥 Problem of the Day 14.4

Use counters to show 6.

Use counters to show 7.

Check children's representations.

🖥 Vocabulary

- Interactive Student Edition
- Multilingual Glossary

Fluency Builder

Count from 1 to 19. Which number is missing?

1, 2, 3, 4, 5, 6, 7, 8, 9, 10, 11, 12, 13, 14, 15, 16, 17, ?, 19   18

FOCUSING ON THE WHOLE STUDENT

Access Prior Knowledge

Choose one or more of the following activities.

- Lead children in a group discussion about parties or other events where they have seen balloons.
- Ask children to illustrate the balloons described in the Learning Activity.

I Can Objective

I can write 18 or 19 to represent a group of objects.

Making Connections

Invite children to tell you what they know about counting and writing up to 17.

Draw an octopus on the board. Have children count the number of legs out loud. Have children count all of the numbers up to 17 aloud. Start with the number 10. Ask children: **10 and what number is 11**? Repeat with numbers 12–17.

Learning Activity

Direct children toward writing 18 in number form. Tell a story about two bunches of balloons, one with 10 balloons and one with 8 balloons. Ask children how many balloons there are altogether in the two bunches.

- **How many balloons are there in the first bunch?**
  10
- **What does that number look like when you write it?** Children will write a 10.
- **What are we trying to figure out?** how many balloons there are altogether

Explore

Listen and Draw

 Model with mathematics.

Read this problem aloud as children listen.

Taryn is the same age as the last teen number. How can you write the number to show how old Taryn is?

MP Look for and make use of structure.

Have children count the yellow cubes.

* **How many cubes are in the top row?** 10
* **How many cubes are in the bottom row?** 8
* **How many cubes is 10 and eight more?** 18
* **Trace and write the number 18.**

Continue with the number 19. Ask questions in a similar pattern as above. Circulate as children write the numbers.

Reread the word problem above.

* **What number will you write to show Taryn's age?** 19

Name _____

Count and Represent 18 and 19

I Can write 18 or 19 to represent a group of objects.

Listen and Draw

© Houghton Mifflin Harcourt Publishing Company

DIRECTIONS Count and tell how many. Trace and write the numbers.

Chapter 14 • Lesson 4 **543**

 Multilingual Support

STRATEGY: Describe

Materials: 19 two-color counters

Children can practice their comprehension skills by describing what they have seen or heard.

* Draw a rectangular picture frame. Place 18 counters around the frame.
* Have children describe the frame. Make sure they include the number of counters in the description.
* Add one more counter to the frame.
* Have children describe what you did and describe the frame. There were 18 counters, and you added one more. Now there are 19 counters.

I

18

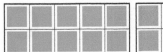

Check children's work.

2

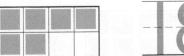 

3

10 . 8 . 18

DIRECTIONS 1. Count and tell how many. Practice writing the number. 2. Count and tell how many. Write the number. 3. Look at the ten frames in Problem 2. Write how many green squares. Write how many blue squares. Write how many in all.

544 Go Math! Grade K

© Houghton Mifflin Harcourt Publishing Company

Ready for More
Visual
Individual/Partners

Have children draw sets of ones to show the numbers 18 and 19.

• Invite children to draw a row of 10 ones and a row of some more ones. Have children label each drawing with the corresponding number.

• Have children write the numbers to go with their drawings.

• Ask children to share their drawings with classmates.

③ Explain

Share and Show

• **What number do you see?** 18

(MP) **Reason abstractly and quantitatively.**

• **How many flowers are in the first frame?** 10 **How many more are in the next frame?** 8 **How many is 10 and 8?** 18 **Trace and write the number 18.**

• **Look at Problem 2. How many tiles are in the first frame?** 10

• **How many tiles are in the next frame?** 8 **How many is 10 and eight more?** 18 **Write the number.**

• **How many empty spaces are in the frame?**
2

(MP) **Attend to precision.**

Have children look at the ten frames in Problem 2. Have children write the numbers to match in Problem 3. 10; 8; 18

Use the checked problem for Quick Check.

✓ Quick Check MTSS RtI

If	a child misses the checked problem
Then	Differentiate Instruction with

• Reteach 14.4
• Waggle

⚠ Common Errors

Error Children may reverse the order of the digits.

Springboard to Learning Review with children other teen numbers. Guide them in writing 1, 17, and 18, and explain that each of these numbers starts with 1.

Share and Show

- Look at Problem 4. What number do you see? 19
- How many flowers are in the first ten frame? 10 How many more are in the next ten frame? 9 How many is 10 ones and 9 ones? 19 Trace and write the number 19.

(MP) **Express regularity in repeated reasoning.**

- Look at Problem 5. How many spaces are empty? 1 How many spaces are filled? 19 Write the number.
- Look at the ten frames in Problem 5. Write the numbers to match in Problem 6. 10; 9; 19

Higher-Order Thinking

Have children look at the ten frames on the page as they solve the following problem.

(MP) **Look for and make use of structure.**

- One ten frame is completely full and there are eight counters in a second ten frame. How many counters are there in both ten frames? How do you know? I know that 18 is shown because a full ten frame is 10. Then I can count on from 10 to find the total.
- How can looking at the empty spaces help you know how many are in the second frame? I know that there are 10 spaces in a ten frame. So, if one space is empty, there is one less than 10, or 9. I also know that if there are two empty spaces, there are two less than 10, or 8.

Math on the Spot Use this video to help children model and solve this type of problem.

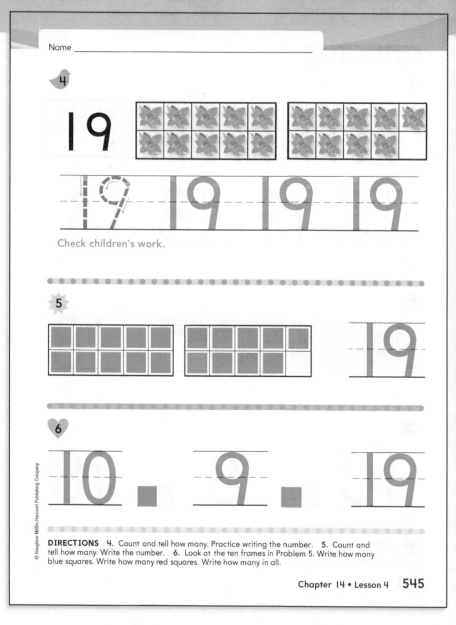

Name _____

4

19

Check children's work.

5

19

6

10 . 9 . 19

DIRECTIONS **4.** Count and tell how many. Practice writing the number. **5.** Count and tell how many. Write the number. **6.** Look at the ten frames in Problem 5. Write how many blue squares. Write how many red squares. Write how many in all.

Chapter 14 • Lesson 4   **545**

Meeting Individual Needs

Reteach 14.4   MTSS (Rtl1)

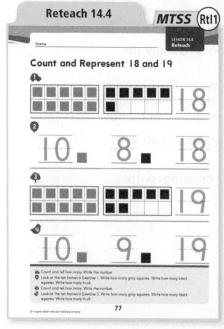

Enrich 14.4

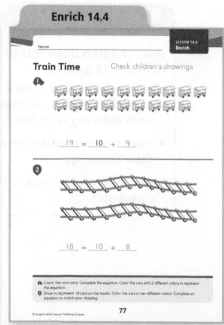

7

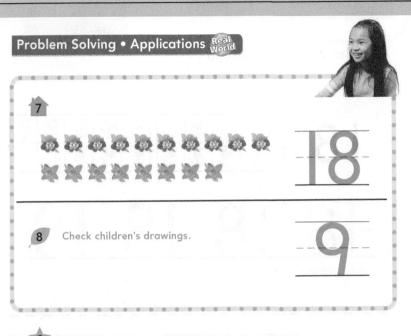

18

8 Check children's drawings.

9

9

10 and _____ 18

○ 18   • 8

DIRECTIONS 7. Jonah has 10 purple flowers. Kaiya has 8 red flowers. How many flowers do they have in all? Write the number. 8. Draw a set of 19 objects. Circle 10 of the objects. How many more objects are there? Write the number. 9. Choose the correct answer. What number goes in the blank?

 HOME ACTIVITY • Ask your child to count and write the number for a set of 18 or 19 objects, such as macaroni pieces or buttons.

DIFFERENTIATED INSTRUCTION • Independent Activities

Grab-and-Go!™
Version 2.0
Differentiated Centers Kit

Tabletop Flipchart
Mini-lessons for reteaching to targeted small groups

Readers
Supports key math skills and concepts in real-world situations.

Games
Reinforce math content and vocabulary

Activities
Meaningful and fun math practice

---

④ Elaborate

Problem Solving Applications *Real World*

(MP) Construct arguments and critique reasoning of others.

Read **Problem 7**. Ask children to explain how they will solve the problem.

For **Problem 8**, ask children to draw a set of 19 objects.

• **Circle 10 of the objects. How many more objects are there?** 9 **Write the number.**

Read **Problem 9** aloud to children. Direct children to fill in the bubble for the correct answer.

• **What number goes in the blank?** 8

⑤ Evaluate | Formative Assessment

I Can

Have pairs of children write, draw, or model an example to demonstrate the skill for the I Can statement.

I can write 18 or 19 to represent a group of objects by . . . counting aloud 18 objects and writing the number 18 or counting aloud 19 objects and writing the number 19. I can also write 10 and 8 for 18, and 10 and 9 for 19.

Exit Ticket

Have volunteers explain how to show the numbers 18 and 19 using ten and some ones.

Practice and Homework

Count and Represent 18 and 19

Use the Practice and Homework pages to provide children with more practice of the concepts and skills presented in this lesson. Children master their understanding as they complete practice items.

Name ____________________

LESSON 14.4
Practice and Homework

Count and Represent 18 and 19

1 18

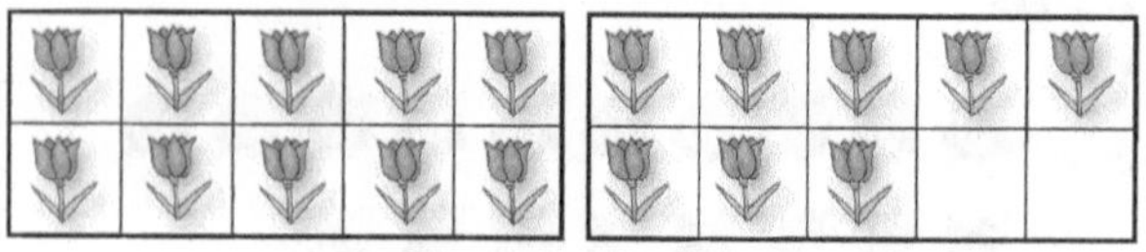

18 18 18 18

Check children's work.

2 19

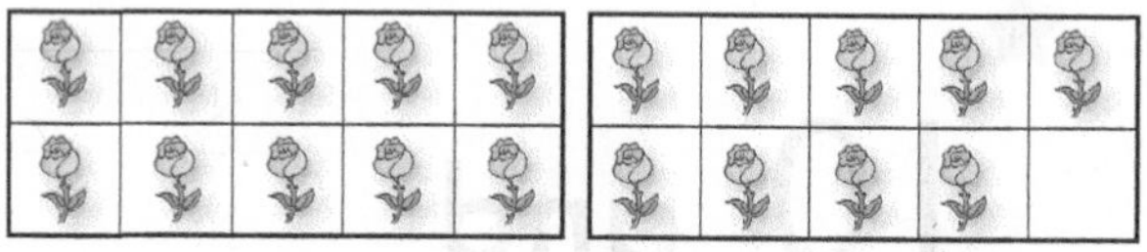

19 19 19 19

Check children's work.

DIRECTIONS 1–2. Count and tell how many. Trace and write the numbers.

Lesson Check

3

10 and ____ 19

○ 19   ● 9

4

10 and ____ 18

● 8   ○ 18

Spiral Review

5

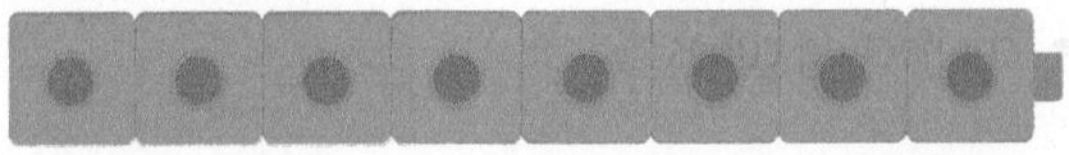

○ 9   ● 7

DIRECTIONS 3–4. Choose the correct answer. What number goes in the blank?
5. Count the cubes. How many is one less?

548 Go Math! Grade K

© Houghton Mifflin Harcourt Publishing Company

Lesson at a Glance
Model, Count, and Represent 20

SNAPSHOT

Mathematical Standards

- Write numbers from 0 to 20. Represent a number of objects with a written numeral 0-20 (with 0 representing a count of no objects).
- When counting objects, say the number names in the standard order, pairing each object with one and only one number name and each number name with one and only one object.

Mathematical Practices and Processes

- Reason abstractly and quantitatively.
- Model with mathematics.
- Attend to precision.
- Construct arguments and critique reasoning of others.
- Look for and make use of structure.

(I Can) Objective

I can count and represent 20 with objects or a written numeral.

Learning Goal

Count and represent 20 with objects or a written numeral.

Language Objective

Children will explain to a partner how to count out and represent 20.

MATERIALS

- MathBoard
- connecting cubes

ACROSS THE GRADES

Grade K

Given a number from 0 to 20, count out that many objects.

After

Starting at a given number, count forward and backwards within 120 by ones. Skip count by 2s to 20 and by 5s to 100.

ABOUT THE MATH

Children not only count and identify 20 objects in a group, but they also use numeral form to represent 20. Similar to the other numbers, they use connecting cubes to represent a number and write the number as two sets of 10. The use of ten frames allows children to see 20 as 10 and 10, which is fundamental to their understanding of place value. The 2 in the tens place is worth 20, and since there are no "extras," there is a 0 in the ones place. Later, children will express 20 as 2 tens.

For more professional learning, go online to Teacher's Corner.

DAILY ROUTINES

🖥 Problem of the Day 14.5

Use counters to show 10.

Use counters to show 20.

Check children's representations.

🖥 Vocabulary twenty

- Interactive Student Edition
- Multilingual Glossary

Vocabulary Builder

Ask children to define each term and give several examples. Accept reasonable definitions. Possible examples given.

Term	Example(s)
twenty	20; 10 and 10

FOCUSING ON THE WHOLE STUDENT

Access Prior Knowledge

Choose one or more of the following activities.

- Have small groups of children come up with a scene that shows how buckets might be used in a barn or zoo.
- Have each child pick a number from 1 to 19 and ask them to draw a picture that has something to do with their numbers.

---

① Engage

with the Interactive Student Edition

I Can Objective

I can count and represent 20 with objects or a written numeral.

Making Connections

Invite children to tell you what they know about counting and writing up to 19.

- **What number is 10 and 5 more?** 15
- **What does the number 15 look like when you write it?** Children will write a 15 on their papers.
- **What number comes right after 15?** 16

Learning Activity

Guide children toward counting up to 20. Draw a picture or model two piles of buckets, each with 10 buckets in it. Tell a story about storing these buckets in the barn.

- **What is in the barn?** buckets
- **How many buckets are in the pile on the left?** 10
- **Does the pile on the right have the same number of buckets as the one on the left? How do you know?** yes; I know because if I count them, there are the same number of buckets in each pile.

⚠ Common Errors

Error Children may not recognize that two filled ten frames are 20.

Springboard to Learning Together with children, count aloud the cubes in the first ten frame. Explain that the counting will continue even though they are moving to another ten frame. Continue counting from 11 to 20 in the second ten frame.

② Explore

Listen and Draw

Materials connecting cubes

Read this problem aloud. Tell children they will use cubes to solve.

Marla has 20 grapes. If Marla pretends that connecting cubes are grapes, how can she model 20 by using ten frames?

 Look for and make use of structure.

Count out 20 cubes with children and ask them to fill the top ten frame.

- **How many cubes fill the top ten frame?** 10
- **How many cubes are left?** 10 **Put the cubes that are left in the bottom ten frame.**
- **How many cubes fill the bottom ten frame?** 10
- **How many cubes fill two ten frames?** 20 **Count the cubes together.**
- **Trace the number.**

Name _____

Model, Count, and Represent 20

(I Can) count and represent 20 with objects or a written numeral.

Listen and Draw

DIRECTIONS Use cubes to model 20. Draw the cubes. Trace the number

Chapter 14 • Lesson 5   **549**

Ⓜ Multilingual Support

STRATEGY: Draw

Children can demonstrate their understanding by drawing rather than by using language.

- Have children draw a picture of the outdoors. Then ask them to draw grass in the picture.
- Ask children to draw 20 flowers in one line on the grass.
- Ask children to draw a dot on each flower as they count them aloud.
- Repeat this activity with a tree and 20 leaves in one line on a branch if time permits.

20  _20_

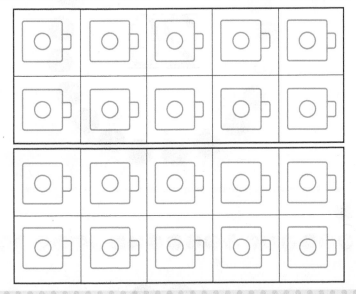

DIRECTIONS 1. Count and tell how many. Write the number. 2. Use cubes to model the number 20. Draw the cubes. 3. Use the cubes from Problem 2 to model ten-cube trains. Draw the cube trains.

© Houghton Mifflin Harcourt Publishing Company

550 Go Math! **Grade K**

---

3 Explain

Share and Show [Math Board]

(MP) **Reason abstractly and quantitatively.**

- **Look at Problem 1. What number do you see?** 20
- **How many orange parts are in the first set?** 10 **How many orange parts are in the second set?** 10 **How can you describe the two sets?** Possible answers: There are 20 in all. There are two sets of 10 orange parts.
- **Write the number 20.**
- **Look at Problem 2. How can you model the number 20 with your cubes?** I can put 10 cubes in the top ten frame and 10 cubes in the bottom ten frame. **Place and draw the cubes.**

For Problem 3, ask children to build two 10-cube trains. Count the cubes together.

(MP) **Construct arguments and critique reasoning of others.**

- **How many cubes do you have if you have two 10-cube trains?** 20
- **Explain how you know you have 20.** I have 20 because there are 2 tens and I know that 2 tens are 20.
- **How many tens are in 20?** 2

Have children locate Problem 3 and draw two 10-cube trains in the space.

Use the checked problem for Quick Check.

Ready for More   ⏱ Auditory Small Group

Have children show the number 20 by drawing and counting. Distribute three sheets of paper to each child.

- Let children choose an object to draw. Have children draw a different way to show 20 objects on each sheet of paper. Possible answers: two sets of 10 oranges; 10 sets of two oranges; one set of 20 oranges; four sets of five oranges.

- Have partners share their drawings and show how they counted to 20.

✓ Quick Check   _MTSS_ (RtI)

If ➤	a child misses the checked problem
Then ➤	**Differentiate Instruction** with • Reteach 14.5 • Waggle

Share and Show

Point to the limes in Problem 4. Guide children in counting objects placed in a circle.

 Look for and make use of structure.

- **Choose the lime to start with. Draw a dot on each lime as you count. That way, you will see when to stop counting.**
- **How many limes are there?** 20 **Write the number.**
- **Tell a friend how you counted the limes.**

Use a similar process for Problem 5. Encourage children to start counting from the beginning of the row.

- **How many plums are there?** 20 **Write the number.**

Higher-Order Thinking

 Model with mathematics.

Children use what they know about the number 20 to solve a word problem.

- **Andy has two bunches of 10 grapes. Chad has 10 bunches of two grapes. Who has more grapes?** They both have the same number of grapes.

Have children draw a picture to solve. Encourage them to find other ways to show 20 grapes. Possible answers: four bunches of five grapes; five bunches of four grapes.

Math on the Spot Use this video to help children model and solve this type of problem.

Name _____

4

20

5

20

DIRECTIONS 4–5. Count and tell how many pieces of fruit. Write the number. Tell a friend how you counted the fruit.

Meeting Individual Needs

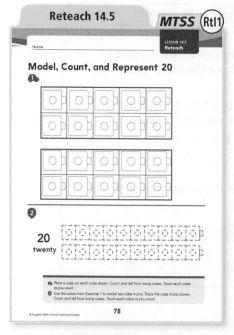

Reteach 14.5   MTSS (Rtl1)

Model, Count, and Represent 20

20
twenty

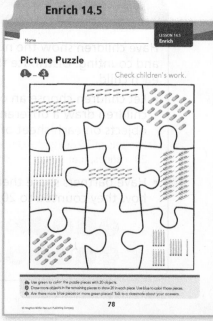

Enrich 14.5

Picture Puzzle

Check children's work.

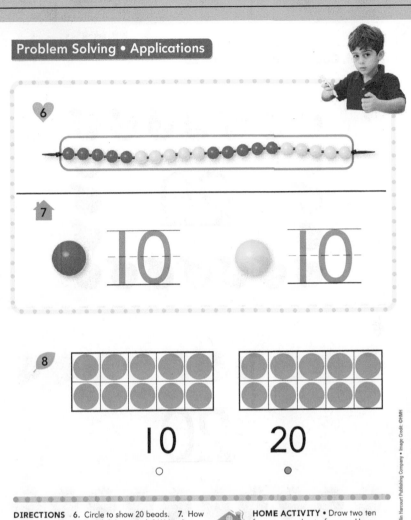

6

7

10   10

8

10   20

○   ●

DIRECTIONS 6. Circle to show 20 beads. 7. How many of each color bead did you circle? Write the numbers. Tell a friend about the number of each color bead. 8. Choose the correct answer. What number does the model show?

HOME ACTIVITY • Draw two ten frames on a sheet of paper. Have your child show the number 20 by placing small objects, such as buttons or dried beans, in the ten frames.

© Houghton Mifflin Harcourt Publishing Company • Image Credit: ©HMH

DIFFERENTIATED INSTRUCTION • Independent Activities

Grab-and-Go!™
Version 2.0
Differentiated Centers Kit

Tabletop Flipchart

Mini-lessons for reteaching to targeted small groups

Readers

Supports key math skills and concepts in real-world situations.

Games

Reinforce math content and vocabulary

Activities

Meaningful and fun math practice

---

④ Elaborate

Problem Solving Applications

Read **Problem 9**. Ask children to explain how they will solve the problem.

(MP) **Attend to precision.**

• **Look at the first set of five blue beads and the first set of five yellow beads. How many do you have?** 10

• **How many more beads than 10 do you need to circle to make 20?** 10

Discuss with children how they might know the correct number of beads to circle without counting. Children should realize that the color changes after every five beads and that 2 fives make 10, and four sets of five make 20.

For **Problem 7**, have children write how many blue beads and how many yellow beads they circled.

Read **Problem 8** aloud to children. Direct children to fill in the bubble for the correct answer.

• **What number does the model show?** 20

⑤ Evaluate | Formative Assessment

I Can

Have pairs of children write, draw, or model an example to demonstrate the skill for the I Can statement.

I can count and represent 20 with objects or a written numeral by . . . filling two ten frames or writing a 2 with a 0 next to it.

Exit Ticket

Have children discuss their models with a friend and explain how they relate to the number 20.

Practice and Homework

Model, Count, and Represent 20

Use the Practice and Homework pages to provide children with more practice of the concepts and skills presented in this lesson. Children master their understanding as they complete practice items.

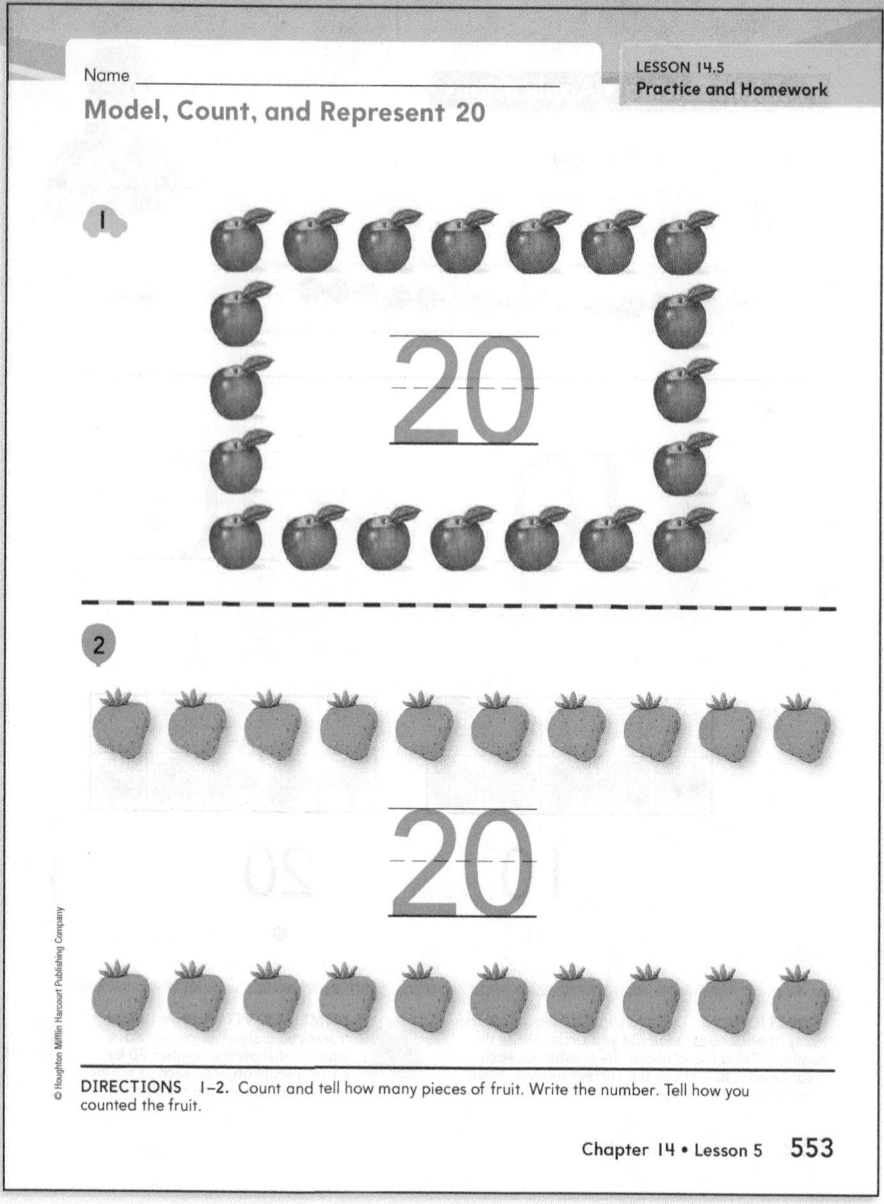
Name ______________________

LESSON 14.5
Practice and Homework

Model, Count, and Represent 20

1

20

2

20

DIRECTIONS 1–2. Count and tell how many pieces of fruit. Write the number. Tell how you counted the fruit.

© Houghton Mifflin Harcourt Publishing Company

Chapter 14 • Lesson 5 553

3

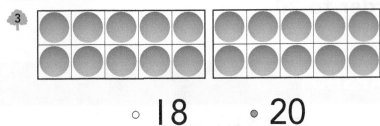

○ 18   • 20

4

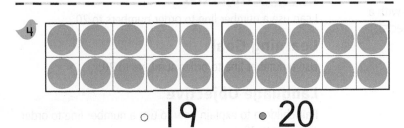

○ 19   • 20

Spiral Review

5

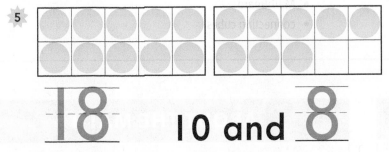

18   10 and 8

DIRECTIONS **3–4.** Choose the correct answer. What number does the model show? **5.** Look at the model. Write the numbers.

© Houghton Mifflin Harcourt Publishing Company

554   Go Math! **Grade K**

Continue to practice concepts and skills with Lesson Check. Use Spiral Review to engage children in previously taught concepts and to promote content retention.

Lesson at a Glance
Count and Order to 20

SNAPSHOT

Mathematical Standards
- Write numbers from 0 to 20. Represent a number of objects with a written numeral 0-20 (with 0 representing a count of no objects).

Mathematical Practices and Processes
- Reason abstractly and quantitatively.
- Model with mathematics.
- Attend to precision.
- Construct arguments and critique reasoning of others.
- Look for and make use of structure.
- Express regularity in repeated reasoning
- Use appropriate tools strategically.

(I Can) Objective
I can use a number line to order numbers to 20.

Learning Goal
Use a number line to order numbers to 20.

Language Objective
Pair children to explain how to use a number line to order numbers to 20.

MATERIALS
- MathBoard
- connecting cubes

ACROSS THE GRADES

Grade K
Locate, order and compare numbers from 0 to 20 using the number line and terms less than, equal to or greater than.

After
Plot, order and compare whole numbers up to 100.

ABOUT THE MATH

If Children Ask
If a child asks why we put numbers in order, ask the class to answer and make a list of the reasons they can name. Children's responses and yours might sound like the following:

- **Knowing the order of numbers can help us count. If you know the sequence of numbers, you can say them quickly and easily because you know what numbers come next.**
- **You use counting sequences in games as players count off or as you keep score.**
- **If you know numbers in order, you can tell which team is winning by looking for the greater score. If a score is 19 to 18, you know that 19 is the greater score.**
- **You use number order to tell if one person is older than another person.**

For more professional learning, go online to Teacher's Corner.

DAILY ROUTINES

🖥 Problem of the Day 14.6

What number is just before 15? What number is just after it? 14; 16

🖥 Vocabulary

- Interactive Student Edition
- Multilingual Glossary

Fluency Builder

Have children work in pairs. Ask each partner to build a train with up to 10 connecting cubes. Then ask them to determine whose train has more and whose train has less. Ask children to try again if they have the same number.

FOCUSING ON THE WHOLE STUDENT

Access Prior Knowledge

Have children use iTools: Counters to create a set of 17 counters and a set of 19 counters.

- **Which set has more counters?** the set of 19
- **Which set has fewer counters?** the set of 17
- **Which number is greater, 19 or 17?** 19
- **Which number is less?** 17

Continue with different sets to 20.

Culturally Responsive Education

As difficult as it can be to admit to ourselves as educators, culturally and linguistically diverse children often struggle in the American education system. Be inclusive of families as you teach their children. Maintain consistent, respectful communication, and have phone or in-person conferences when children are successful, not just when they are struggling. Building a positive relationship with families not only helps children grow, but also helps families see ways you are working to make your classroom a safe, equitable space for all children.

1 Engage

with the Interactive Student Edition

I Can Objective

I can use a number line to order numbers to 20.

Making Connections

Invite children to tell you what they know about ordering numbers 1 through 10.

- **When counting, what number comes right before 5?** 4
- **What number comes right after 5?** 6
- **Is 6 greater or less than 5? How do you know?** greater; because it comes after 5 in counting order

Learning Activity

Help children use number order to count forward to 20. Draw a row of 5 buckets and number them 15–19. Leave off the label for bucket 17.

- **How many buckets do you see?** 5
- **What are we trying to figure out?** the missing number on the middle bucket
- **Are the first two buckets in order? How do you know?** yes; 17 comes after 16 when I count forward

Explore

Listen and Draw

Materials connecting cubes

 Model with mathematics.

Read this problem aloud as children listen.

Izzy made cards for 6, 8, 7, and 5. He wanted to show the cards in order. How should he show them?

Have children look at the number line on the page as they count forward from 1 to 20 together. Ask questions to help them recognize the relationship between consecutive counting numbers.

(MP) **Attend to precision.**

- **Choose a number from 1 to 19. Draw a line under it.** Remind children that each number they count is one greater than the one before it.
- **What number is one greater than the one you chose? Circle that number.**
- **What number is one less than the one you chose?** Check children's answers. **How do you know?** Possible answer: When I count, it is the number I say just before I say my number.

Have children build cube trains to model the number underlined and the one circled. Remind children that the next number name they say when counting refers to a quantity that is one greater.

- **Draw the cube trains and circle the larger cube train.**

Repeat the word problem.

- **How should Izzy show his cards?** 5, 6, 7, 8

Count and Order to 20

(I Can) use a number line to order numbers to 20.

Listen and Draw

$$0\ \ 1\ \ 2\ \ 3\ \ 4\ \ 5\ \ 6\ \ 7\ \ 8\ \ 9\ \ 10\ 11\ 12\ 13\ 14\ 15\ 16\ 17\ 18\ 19\ 20$$

Check children's work.

© Houghton Mifflin Harcourt Publishing Company

DIRECTIONS Draw a line under a number. Count forward to 20 from that number. Use the terms *greater than* and *less than* to compare and describe the order of numbers. Circle the number that is one greater than the number you underlined. Build cube trains to model the numbers you marked. Draw the cube trains. Circle the larger cube train.

Chapter 14 • Lesson 6 **555**

 Multilingual Support

STRATEGY: Scaffold Language

Children can develop understanding of counting and ordering by describing what they see and hear.

Place a set of 11 cubes and a set of 17 cubes in front of children. Have children count each set together.

- **Which set has more cubes, the set with 17 cubes or the set with 11 cubes?** The set with 17 has more cubes than the set with 11. **Which set has fewer cubes?** The set of eleven has fewer. **Which is the greater number, 17 or 11?** 17 is greater than 11.

Give each child 20 connecting cubes. Have children make a set of cubes for any number. Have children compare the numbers in their sets with sentences using the terms *greater than* and *less than*.

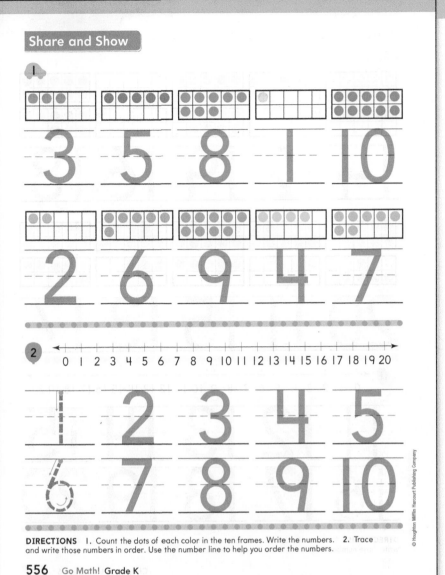

DIRECTIONS 1. Count the dots of each color in the ten frames. Write the numbers. 2. Trace and write those numbers in order. Use the number line to help you order the numbers.

© Houghton Mifflin Harcourt Publishing Company

③ Explain

Share and Show

With children, read the numbers 1 to 20. Then direct attention to Problem 1.

- **How many red counters are there in the first ten frame?** 3 **Write the number.**
- **The next frame has the top row filled. Do you know how many without counting?** Yes. 5 **Write the number.**

Ask similar questions for the rest of the ten frames.

For Problem 2, tell children that they will write the numbers from Problem 1 in counting order and that they can use the number line to help them order the numbers.

- **Of the numbers you see, which one comes first?** 1 **Trace the number.**

Have children complete the problems.

(MP) Construct arguments and critique reasoning of others.

- **How did you know what numbers to write after 6?** I counted forward from 6 to 10.

Have volunteers share what they wrote and tell how they know it is correct.

Ready for More
Visual
Small Group

Materials numeral cards (0–23)

Select a child to place the cards in order showing 1 to 10 in one row and 11 to 20 in a row below.

Ask children to point to and read the numbers.

Turn over a few cards at random and ask which numbers are missing.

- **How can you tell what numbers are missing?** by counting and seeing which numbers that I counted are not there; by knowing what comes before or after the missing numbers

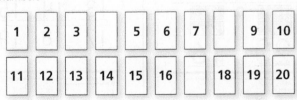

⚠ Common Errors

Error Children may have trouble counting forward from a given number.

Example Children write the incorrect number after the number 6 in Problem 2.

Springboard to Learning Have children write numbers on self-stick notes and place them in order in small sets such as 6 to 10 as they count forward aloud.

Share and Show

 Use appropriate tools strategically.

Call attention to Problem 3. Have children complete the problem by counting the counters or by using other strategies and then writing the number that tells how many.

 Look for and make use of structure.

Have children complete Problem 4 by tracing and writing the numbers from 11 to 20 in order. Point out that the number line also shows the numbers in order. Then invite children to read the numbers in order.

Use the checked problem for Quick Check.

 Quick Check **MTSS** **RtI**

If	a student misses the checked problem
Then	Differentiate Instruction with • Reteach 14.6 • Waggle

Higher-Order Thinking

Read aloud the following problem to children. Have them discuss models and strategies they can use to solve it.

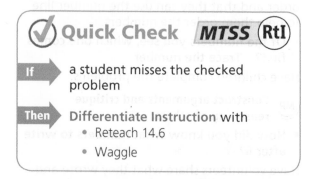 **Reason abstractly and quantitatively.**

• **Can you describe the same number using both the terms greater than and less than? Give an example.** Yes. Possible answer: 2 is greater than 1 and 2 is less than 3.

Discuss the relationship of numbers and how a number can, at the same time, be greater than one number and less than another.

• **What number is one greater than 12 and two less than 15?** 13

• **How can you use the words greater than to compare 12 and 13?** 13 is greater than 12.

Math on the Spot Use this video to help children model and solve this type of problem.

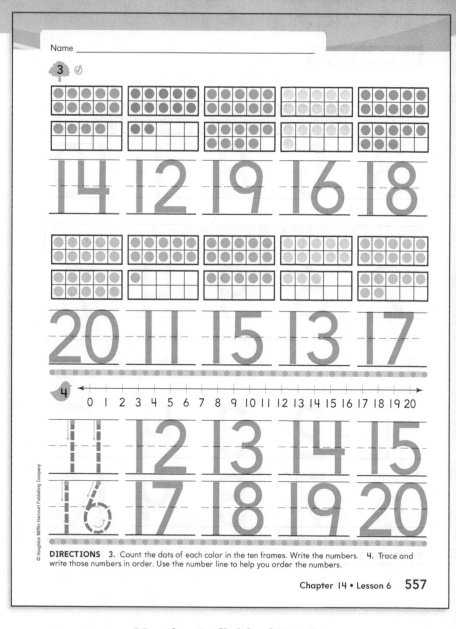

DIRECTIONS 3. Count the dots of each color in the ten frames. Write the numbers. 4. Trace and write those numbers in order. Use the number line to help you order the numbers.

Chapter 14 • Lesson 6 **557**

Meeting Individual Needs

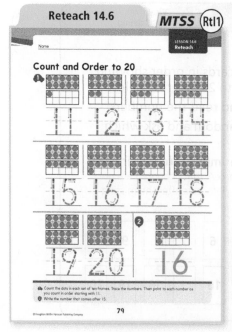

5

1	2	3	4	5
6	7	8	9	10
11	12	13	14	15
16	17	18	19	20

DIRECTIONS 5. Write to show the numbers in order. Count forward to 20 from one of the numbers you wrote.

HOME ACTIVITY • Give your child a set of 11 objects, a set of 12 objects, and a set of 13 objects. Have him or her count the objects in each set and place the sets in order from smallest amount to largest amount.

© Houghton Mifflin Harcourt Publishing Company

④ Elaborate

Problem Solving Applications Real World

MP Express regularity in repeated reasoning.

- **Look at this page. What do you see?**
  a number chart
- **What do you notice about this number chart?** The numbers are in order.
- **Write the numbers in order on the number chart.**
- **Point to one of the numbers you wrote. Count forward from that number to 20.**

Exit Ticket

Tell children to write to show what they know about the missing numbers. Have children share how they found the missing numbers.

⑤ Evaluate | Formative Assessment

I Can

Have pairs of children write, draw, or model an example to demonstrate the skill for the I Can statement.

I can use a number line to order numbers to 20 by . . . starting at any number and reading the numbers until I get to 20.

DIFFERENTIATED INSTRUCTION • Independent Activities

Grab-and-Go!™
Version 2.0
Differentiated Centers Kit

Tabletop Flipchart

Mini-lessons for reteaching to targeted small groups

Readers

Supports key math skills and concepts in real-world situations.

Games

Reinforce math content and vocabulary

Activities

Meaningful and fun math practice

Count and Order to 20

Use the Practice and Homework pages to provide children with more practice of the concepts and skills presented in this lesson. Children master their understanding as they complete practice items.

Count and Order to 20

1

14 11 13 2 15

17 16 20 18 19

2

0 1 2 3 4 5 6 7 8 9 10 11 12 13 14 15 16 17 18 19 20

11 12 13 14 15

16 17 18 19 20

DIRECTIONS 1. Count the dots in each set of ten frames. Trace or write the numbers. 2. Trace and write those numbers in order. Use the number line to help you order the numbers.

Chapter 14 • Lesson 6 **559**

Lesson Check

3

Spiral Review

4

10 and 3 13

5

ERASER ERASER ERASER ERASER 4

DIRECTIONS 3. Count forward. Trace and write the numbers in order. 4. Look at the cats. How many are in the ten frame? Write the number. How many more are there? Write the number. Write the total number of cats. 5. How many erasers are there? Write the number.

560 Go Math! Grade K

© Houghton Mifflin Harcourt Publishing Company

Lesson at a Glance
One More and One Less to 20

SNAPSHOT

Mathematical Standards
- Understand that each successive number name refers to a quantity that is one larger.

Mathematical Practices and Processes
- Model with mathematics.
- Attend to precision.
- Construct arguments and critique reasoning of others.
- Look for and make use of structure.
- Reason abstractly and quantitatively.

(I Can) **Objective**

I can find and compare numbers to 20 using a number line.

Learning Goal
Find and compare numbers to 20 using a number line.

Language Objective
Children will describe how to use a number line to find and compare numbers to 20.

MATERIALS
- MathBoard
- two-color counters

ACROSS THE GRADES

Grade K
Locate, order and compare numbers from 0 to 20 using the number line and terms less than, equal to or greater than.

After
Plot, order and compare whole numbers up to 100.

ABOUT THE MATH

Children have previously found 1 more and 1 less with numbers up to 15. Because children are able to count to 20 fluently, they will transition to finding 1 more and 1 less to greater numbers, those between 15 and 20. As they found before, the number that is 1 less is the number they say before and the number that is 1 more is the number they say after when counting. Children will incorporate the use of a number line as they did to order numbers to 20. They will visually be able to see the number before and the number after as they develop proficiency with this topic.

For more professional learning, go online to Teacher's Corner.

DAILY ROUTINES

 Problem of the Day 14.7

Circle the number that is less. Cross out the number that is more.

⑥   ̶8̶

 Vocabulary

- Interactive Student Edition
- Multilingual Glossary

Fluency Builder

Count backward. What number is next?

4, 3, 2, 1

FOCUSING ON THE WHOLE STUDENT

Access Prior Knowledge

Choose one or more of the following activities.

- Discuss the words *more* and *less*. Work with children to come up with a few sentences that use one or both of the words. Write the sentences on the board.
- Have children act out a conversation between two people about the apples that they have.

Social & Emotional Learning

Relationship Skills Encourage children to give and receive feedback as part of managing their learning process. *When you are learning to do something your teacher or someone else might try to tell you to try something new or to change the way you are doing something. This is called feedback. When you receive good feedback, you can fix a misunderstanding or adjust your thinking about a problem. Feedback helps us get better! You can give feedback to others to help them get better.*

① Engage

with the Interactive Student Edition

I Can Objective

I can find and compare numbers to 20 using a number line.

Making Connections

Ask children to share what they know about drawing pictures to find one more or one less.

Learning Activity

Work with children to help them understand how to write the number that is one less than 14. Draw 4 apples on the board.

- **How many apples are on the board? Let's count out loud together.** 1, 2, 3, 4
- **Have one child come up to the board to draw 1 more apple. How many apples are on the board now? Let's count out loud together.** 1, 2, 3, 4, 5

Tell a story about feeding animals apples. Draw or model two rows of apples, 10 in the first row and 4 in the next row. Explain that you need 13 apples to feed the animals.

- **Why do you want to count the apples?** to see if there are enough to feed all of the animals
- **How many apples are in the top row?** 10
- **How many apples are in the bottom row?** 4
- **How do you know if you have enough?** 13 is 1 less than 14, so there are enough.

② Explore

Listen and Draw

Materials two-color counters

Read the story problem as children listen.

Melissa has 10 flowers. Juan has a number of flowers that is one less than Melissa. How many flowers does Juan have?

 Look for and make use of structure.

Have children use counters to show Melissa's ten flowers in the ten frame.

- **The number of flowers Juan has is one less than what Melissa has. How can you show that number in the ten frame?** take one counter away

Explain to children that *one less* means there is one fewer than ten.

 Model with mathematics.

Have children remove one counter from the ten frame and count the remaining counters.

- **How many counters are left?** 9 **Juan has one fewer counters than Melissa, which is 9.**

Help children to write the number on the line next to 10. Remind children that nine is one less than ten.

- **Let's put 10 counters back into the ten frame. How can we find what number is one more than 10?** add one more counter

Explain to children that *one more* means there is one greater than ten. Have children add one more counter next to the ten frame and count the counters.

- **How many counters are there now?** 11 **So one more than ten is eleven. Write the number 11 after 10.**

Name _____

One More and One Less to 20

(I Can) find and compare numbers to 20 using a number line.

Listen and Draw

9   10

DIRECTIONS Place 10 counters in the ten frame. Take one counter away. Write the number that is one less than 10. Place 10 new counters in the ten frame. Add one more counter. Write the number that is one more than 10.

Chapter 14 • Lesson 7   561

 Multilingual Support

STRATEGY: Identify Patterns

- Give each pair a set of 20 small objects, such as marbles.
- Have one partner make a set of marbles. Ask children to count the marbles together.
- Have the other partner make a set that is one more and count the set aloud. **How does making a set that is one more relate to the counting sequence?** Help children see that one more means the next number in the counting sequence.
- Repeat the activity for one less.

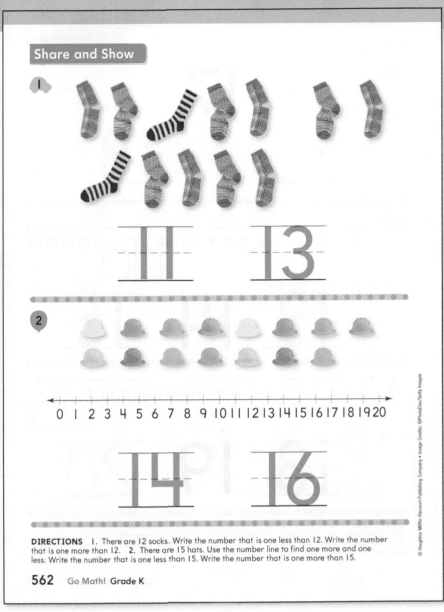

DIRECTIONS 1. There are 12 socks. Write the number that is one less than 12. Write the number that is one more than 12. 2. There are 15 hats. Use the number line to find one more and one less. Write the number that is one less than 15. Write the number that is one more than 15.

③ Explain

Share and Show

(MP) **Reason abstractly and quantitatively.**

Have children find Problem 1.

- **How many socks do you see?** 12 **What number would be one more than twelve?** 13 **Write the number.**
- **What number would be one less than twelve?** 11 **Write the number.**

Guide children to look at the hats in Problem 2. Then have them complete the problem in a similar way. Children can use the number line to help them find the numbers.

Ready for More 🕐 Bodily/Kinesthetic Small Groups

Materials: 6-sided number cubes, paper

- Organize children into groups of 3.
- One child should roll two number cubes and draw Xs to show how many he or she rolled.
- Another child should draw a set with one less and write the number.
- The third child should draw a set with one more and write the number.
- Children should play the game three times, and switch roles each time.

Share and Show

Guide children to Problem 3.

(MP) **Attend to precision.**

- **Listen to the numbers you hear just before and after seventeen. Count 15, 16, 17, 18, 19, 20**

- **What number is one less than 17?** 16 **How do you know?** Sixteen comes before seventeen in counting order.

Show children where to write the number 16.

- **What number is one more than 17?** 18 **How do you know?** Eighteen comes after seventeen in counting order. **Show children where to write the number 18.**

Complete Problems 4 and 5 in a similar way. Discuss with children how the number line can help them solve the problem.

Use the checked problem for Quick Check.

Math on the Spot Use this video to help children model and solve this type of problem.

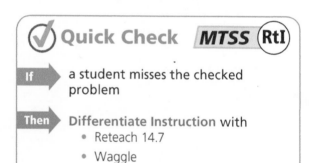

Quick Check **MTSS** (RtI)

If	a student misses the checked problem
Then	**Differentiate Instruction** with • Reteach 14.7 • Waggle

⚠ **Common Errors**

Error A child writes a number more than one less.

Springboard to Learning Have the child show a set with counters, take one away, and then count.

Higher-Order Thinking

Lucie has one more block than Eva. Lucie has 14 blocks. How many blocks does Eva have?

- **Lucie has 14 blocks. Represent them with counters.** Child shows 14 counters. **This is one** *more* **than Eva has. If Lucie has one** *more* **than Eva, then Eva has one** *less* **than Lucie.**

- **How many blocks does Eva have?** 13 blocks

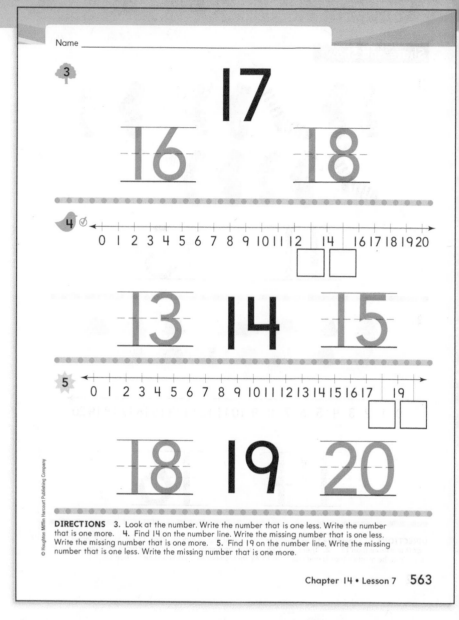

Name _____

© Houghton Mifflin Harcourt Publishing Company

DIRECTIONS **3.** Look at the number. Write the number that is one less. Write the number that is one more. **4.** Find 14 on the number line. Write the missing number that is one less. Write the missing number that is one more. **5.** Find 19 on the number line. Write the missing number that is one less. Write the missing number that is one more.

Chapter 14 • Lesson 7 **563**

Meeting Individual Needs

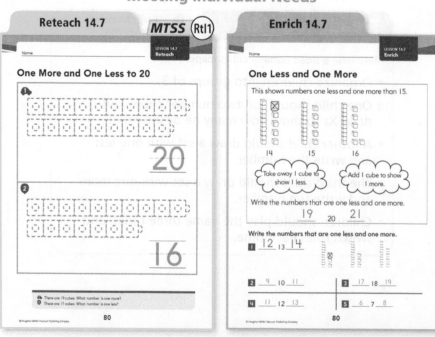

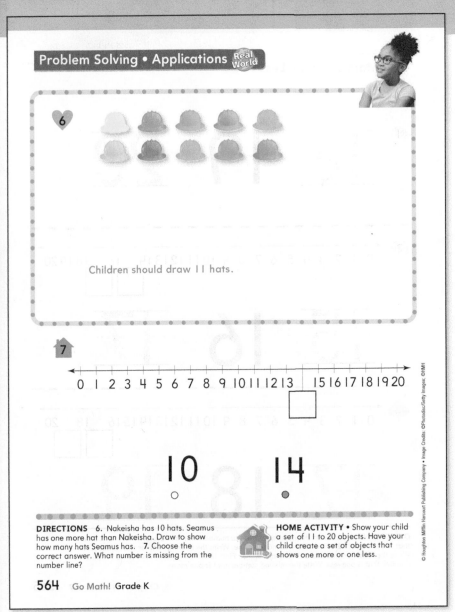

6

Children should draw 11 hats.

7

0 1 2 3 4 5 6 7 8 9 10 11 12 13 ☐ 15 16 17 18 19 20

10   14
 ○   ●

DIRECTIONS 6. Nakeisha has 10 hats. Seamus has one more hat than Nakeisha. Draw to show how many hats Seamus has. 7. Choose the correct answer. What number is missing from the number line?

HOME ACTIVITY • Show your child a set of 11 to 20 objects. Have your child create a set of objects that shows one more or one less.

DIFFERENTIATED INSTRUCTION • Independent Activities

Version 2.0

Differentiated Centers Kit

Tabletop Flipchart

Mini-lessons for reteaching to targeted small groups

Readers

Supports key math skills and concepts in real-world situations.

Games

Reinforce math content and vocabulary

Activities

Meaningful and fun math practice

---

④ Elaborate

Problem Solving Applications *Real World*

Read **Problem 6** to children.

Nakeisha has 10 hats. Seamus has one more hat than Nakeisha. Draw to show how many hats Seamus has. Explain your drawing.

Guide children to draw their answer. Then encourage children to explain their drawing by telling if they drew one more or one less.

(MP) **Construct arguments and critique reasoning of others**

Read **Problem 7** aloud to children. Direct children to fill in the bubble for the correct answer.

• **What number is missing from the number line?** 14

Have children explain how they know their answer is correct.

⑤ Evaluate | Formative Assessment

I Can

Have pairs of children write, draw, or model an example to demonstrate the skill for the I Can statement.

I can find and compare numbers to 20 using a number line by . . . finding the number that comes before or after a number both when counting and when using the number line.

Exit Ticket

Tell children to write to show what they know about finding missing numbers on a number line.

One More and One Less to 20

Use the Practice and Homework pages to provide children with more practice of the concepts and skills presented in this lesson. Children master their understanding as they complete practice items.

One More and One Less to 20

1

18   19   20

---

2 0 1 2 3 4 5 6 7 8 9 10 11 12 13 14 ⬜ 16 ⬜ 18 19 20

15   16   17

---

3 0 1 2 3 4 5 6 7 8 9 10 11 12 13 14 15 16 ⬜ 18 ⬜ 20

17   18   19

DIRECTIONS 1. Look at the number. Write the number that is one less. Write the number that is one more.   **2.** Find 16 on the number line. Write the missing number that is one less. Write the missing number that is one more.   **3.** Find 18 on the number line. Write the missing number that is one less. Write the missing number that is one more.

Chapter 14 • Lesson 7   **565**

© Houghton Mifflin Harcourt Publishing Company

Lesson Check

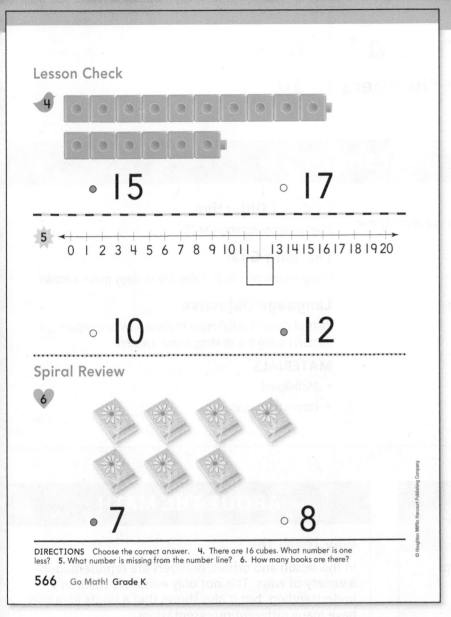

4

○ 15   ○ 17

5

0 1 2 3 4 5 6 7 8 9 10 11 ☐ 13 14 15 16 17 18 19 20

○ 10   ● 12

Spiral Review

6

● 7   ○ 8

DIRECTIONS Choose the correct answer. **4.** There are 16 cubes. What number is one less? **5.** What number is missing from the number line? **6.** How many books are there?

Lesson at a Glance
Compare Numbers to 20

SNAPSHOT

Mathematical Standards
● Understand that each successive number name refers to a quantity that is one larger.

Mathematical Practices and Processes
● Model with mathematics.
● Construct arguments and critique reasoning of others.
● Look for and make use of structure.
● Reason abstractly and quantitatively.
● Use appropriate tools strategically.

(I Can) **Objective**

I can compare numbers to 20.

Learning Goal
Compare numbers to 20 using the strategy *make a model*.

Language Objective
Pairs of children collaborate to show how to compare numbers using the strategy *make a model*.

MATERIALS
• MathBoard
• connecting cubes

ACROSS THE GRADES

Grade K
Compare the number of objects from 0 to 20 in two groups using the terms less than, equal to or greater than.

After
Plot, order and compare whole numbers up to 100.

ABOUT THE MATH

Why Teach This?

In this lesson and others, numbers are represented in a variety of ways. This not only enhances children's understanding, but it also shows that a single idea may have many different representations.

Manipulatives such as connecting cubes are used to model numbers in concrete ways. In this lesson, children use connecting cubes to help them identify whether the number of objects in one set is greater than or less than the number of objects in another set. Because the connecting cubes are sensory—they can be seen, handled, and moved about—they attract and hold children's attention. Modeling with manipulatives helps children visualize quantities and compare and contrast numbers.

For more professional learning, go online to Teacher's Corner.

DAILY ROUTINES

🖥 Problem of the Day 14.8

How can we compare the number of cubes by using *less than* and *greater than*?

4 is less than 8 and 8 is greater than 4.

Show children cubes as pictured and have them compare. Then show a set of 6 cubes and have a child display a set of cubes with the same number.

🖥 Vocabulary

• Interactive Student Edition
• Multilingual Glossary

Fluency Builder

Cube Train Counting Order

Materials numeral cards (0–9), connecting cubes

Distribute numeral cards and connecting cubes to partners. Have one child hold up a card and have the child's partner represent the number it shows using connecting cubes. If there are not enough connecting cubes to go around, children can draw instead.

Then have partners use the cube trains as a guide to put the cards in order from least to greatest.

FOCUSING ON THE WHOLE STUDENT

Access Prior Knowledge

For more practice with counting sets, use iTools: Counters. Show a set of 10 counters and a set of seven counters.

Have children describe the sets using the term *10 and 7 more*. Continue with sets of 18, 19, and 20.

❶ Engage

with the Interactive Student Edition

I Can Objective

I can compare numbers to 20.

Making Connections

Invite children to share what they know about finding one more or one fewer than a given number.

Learning Activity

Tell children a story about three piles of leaves. The first pile has 7 leaves, and the other piles have one more and one fewer leaves.

Use various colors of construction paper to represent a pile of leaves. Have a volunteer count and lay out 7 leaves. Pick another volunteer to count and lay out one fewer than 7 leaves. Child will count and lay out 6 leaves. Have a third volunteer count and lay out one more than 7 leaves. Child will count and lay out 8 leaves.

Have children think about which of the piles has more leaves in it.

• **How many leaves are in the first pile?** 7
• **How many leaves are in the second pile?** one fewer than 7, or 6
• **How many leaves are in the third pile?** one more than 7, or 8

⚠ Common Errors

Error Children may not be able to identify the greater number.

Example Children identify the number 17 as greater than 18.

Springboard to Learning Model 18 and 17 with counters using matching. Help children see that the group of 17 has a counter without a match, so 18 is greater than 17.

Explore

Unlock the Problem

Materials connecting cubes

Read aloud this problem as children listen.

Alma has a number of yellow cubes one greater than 15. Juan has a number of green cubes one less than 15. Who has more cubes?

(MP) **Use appropriate tools strategically.**

Have partners use cubes to work through the problem.

• **The problem says that Alma has a number of yellow cubes one greater than 15. How many yellow cubes should you start with for Alma?** 15 **Use cubes to show this as ten ones and some more ones. Add one more. How many does Alma have now?** 16

• **How many green cubes does Juan have?** one less than 15 **Start with 15 green cubes. Use cubes to show this as ten ones and some more ones. Now what should you do?** Take 1 away. **How many does Juan have now?** 14

Explain that there are two ways to compare the cube trains, matching and counting. Have children decide on a strategy. Explain that the ten-cube trains are the same so they will be comparing the ones.

• **Who has more cubes?** They have the same number.

(MP) **Construct arguments and critique reasoning of others.**

• **Explain how you compared the sets.** Answers should describe either matching or counting the cubes.

Name _____

Compare Numbers to 20

(I Can) compare numbers to 20.

 UNLOCK the Problem

Check children's work.

DIRECTIONS Alma has a number of yellow cubes one greater than 15. Juan has a number of green cubes one less than 15. Show the cubes. Compare the sets of cubes. Draw the cubes. Tell a friend about your drawing.

Chapter 14 • Lesson 8   **567**

 Multilingual Support

STRATEGY: Restate

Restate key vocabulary by renaming comparing terms in a more familiar way.

Show children two sets of cubes (19, 20).

Explain that when you compare numbers you say *greater than* and *less than*. When you compare objects you say *more* or *fewer*.

Have children count the cubes. Explain that the set of 20 objects has one more than the set of 19. Point to each set and have children tell how it compares to the other set.

Repeat with other sets of cubes, having children compare the numbers in each set.

Try Another Problem

1.

Check children's work.

_____   _____

‒ ‒ ‒ ‒ ‒ ‒ ‒   ‒ ‒ ‒ ‒ ‒ ‒ ‒

_____   _____

0 1 2 3 4 5 6 7 8 9 10 11 12 13 14 15 16 17 18 19 (20)

© Houghton Mifflin Harcourt Publishing Company

DIRECTIONS 1. Cristobal has 19 apples. Kiara has a number of apples one greater than Cristobal. Use cubes to model the sets of apples. Compare the sets. Which set has a larger amount? Draw the cubes. Write how many in each set. Find and draw a line under the numbers on the number line. Circle the number that is greater.

568 Go Math! **Grade K**

---

③ Explain

Try Another Problem

For Problem 1, read the problem and ask children what they need to find out.
how many apples Kiara has, and who has more apples

- **How many apples does Cristobal have?** 19
- **What do you need to find out next?** how many apples Kiara has
- **Kiara has a number of apples one greater than Cristobal. So how many apples does Kiara have?** 20

Have children use cubes to model the apples and compare the cubes.

- **Draw the cubes. Write the numbers.**
- **How many in each set?** 19 and 20

Have children underline each number on the number line.

(MP) **Reason abstractly and quantitatively.**

Clarify for children that the question "Which set has a larger amount?" means "Which set has more?"

- **Which set has a larger amount?** 20 **How do you know?** This set has more cubes.
- **Which number is greater?** 20

Have children circle the greater number.

- **Explain to a classmate how you know which number is greater.** Observe children's conversations for understanding.

Use the checked problem for Quick Check.

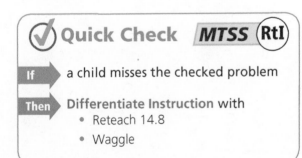

✓ Quick Check **MTSS** **RtI**

If	a child misses the checked problem

| Then | Differentiate Instruction with
• Reteach 14.8
• Waggle |

Chapter 14 • Lesson 8 568

Share and Show

Read the problem and have children use cubes to model Salome's and Zion's sets of oranges.

(MP) Model with mathematics.

- **How can you find out which set has fewer cubes?** Possible answers: I can match the cubes to see which set has fewer cubes; I can count how many are in each set of cubes.

Have children draw the cubes and write the numbers. Have children underline each number on the number line.

(MP) Reason abstractly and quantitatively.

- **Circle the number that is less. Talk to a friend about how you compared the numbers.** Observe children's conversations for understanding. Correct any misapprehensions.

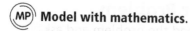

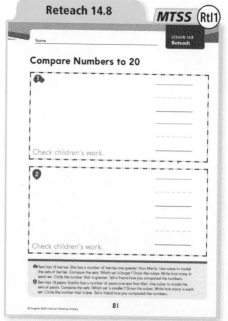

Name _____

Share and Show

2

Check children's work.

0 1 2 3 4 5 6 7 8 9 10 11 12 13 14 15 16 (17) 18 19 20

DIRECTIONS 2. Salome has 18 oranges. Zion has a number of oranges one less than Salome. Use cubes to model the sets of oranges. Compare the sets. Which set is smaller? Draw the cubes. Write how many in each set. Find and draw a line under the numbers on the number line. Circle the number that is less.

Chapter 14 • Lesson 8   **569**

Meeting Individual Needs

| Reteach 14.8 | MTSS (Rtl1) | Enrich 14.8 |

Reteach 14.8

LESSON 14.8
Reteach

Name _____

Compare Numbers to 20

1

Check children's work.

2

Check children's work.

1. Toni has 16 berries. She has a number of berries one greater than Marta. Use cubes to model the sets of berries. Compare the sets. Which set is larger? Draw the cubes. Write how many in each set. Circle the number that is greater. Tell a friend how you compared the numbers.
2. Ben has 18 pears. Sophia has a number of pears one less than Ben. Use cubes to model the sets of pears. Compare the sets. Which set is smaller? Draw the cubes. Write how many in each set. Circle the number that is less. Tell a friend how you compared the numbers.

81

Enrich 14.8

LESSON 14.8
Enrich

Name _____

Compare Numbers

1

18   drawing of 18 cubes with a line below the set

2

20   drawing of 20 cubes with a circle around the set

3

19   drawing of 19 cubes with an X on the set

1.–3. Model the number with connecting cubes. Draw the cubes. Circle the set of 20 cubes. Draw a line under the set that has a number of cubes one less than 20. Mark an X on the set that has a number of cubes one less than 20.

81

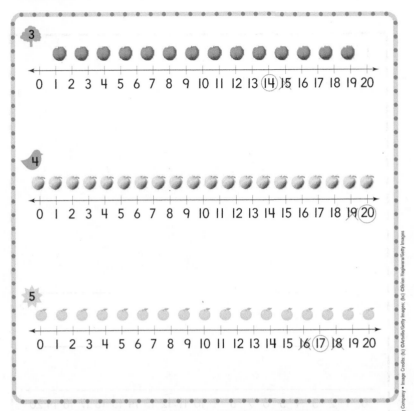

DIRECTIONS 3. Count the red apples. Circle the number of red apples on the number line. Mark an X on the number that is one greater than the number of red apples. **4.** Count the yellow apples. Circle the number of yellow apples on the number line. Mark an X on the number that is one less than the number of yellow apples. **5.** Count the oranges. Circle the number of oranges on the number line. Mark Xs on the numbers that are one greater and one less than the number of oranges.

HOME ACTIVITY • Have your child count two sets of objects in your home, and write how many are in each set. Then have your child circle the greater number. Repeat with sets of different numbers.

570 Go Math! **Grade K**

4 Elaborate

On Your Own

(MP) **Look for and make use of structure.**

Problems 3 and 4 Children use number lines to find the numbers that are one greater or one less than the number of pieces of fruit. They should know that the greater number is to the right and the lesser number is to the left on the number line.

Problem 5 Children use a number line to find the numbers that are bnoth one more and one less than the given number of fruit.

5 Evaluate | Formative Assessment

I Can

Have pairs of children write, draw, or model an example to demonstrate the skill for the I Can statement.

I can compare numbers to 20 by . . . making a model so that I can match and count objects to solve the problem.

Exit Ticket

Have children tell a friend about the two numbers using *greater than* or *less than*.

DIFFERENTIATED INSTRUCTION • Independent Activities

Grab-and-Go!™
Version 2.0
Differentiated Centers Kit

Tabletop Flipchart

Mini-lessons for reteaching to targeted small groups

Readers

Supports key math skills and concepts in real-world situations.

Games

Reinforce math content and vocabulary

Activities

Meaningful and fun math practice

Compare Numbers to 20

Use the Practice and Homework pages to provide children with more practice of the concepts and skills presented in this lesson. Children master their understanding as they complete practice items.

Compare Numbers to 20

1.

Check children's work.

_____   _____

— — — — —   — — — — —

_____   _____

0 1 2 3 4 5 6 7 8 9 10 11 12 13 14 15 (16) 17 18 19 20

DIRECTIONS 1. Teni has 16 berries. She has a number of berries one greater than Marta. Use cubes to model the sets of berries. Compare the sets. Which set has a larger amount? Draw the cubes. Write how many in each set. Find and draw a line under the numbers on the number line. Circle the number that is greater.

Chapter 14 • Lesson 8   571

© Houghton Mifflin Harcourt Publishing Company

Lesson Check

2

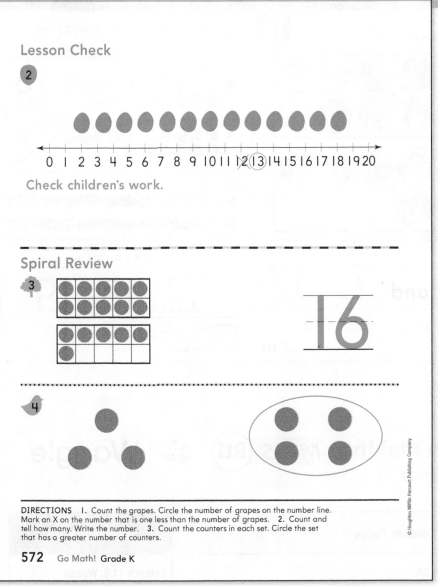

Check children's work.

- -

Spiral Review

3

16

4

© Houghton Mifflin Harcourt Publishing Company

DIRECTIONS 1. Count the grapes. Circle the number of grapes on the number line. Mark an X on the number that is one less than the number of grapes. **2.** Count and tell how many. Write the number. **3.** Count the counters in each set. Circle the set that has a greater number of counters.

572 Go Math! Grade K

Continue to practice concepts and skills with Lesson Check. Use Spiral Review to engage children in previously taught concepts and to promote content retention.

Chapter Review

Summative Assessment
Use the **Chapter Review** to assess children's progress in Chapter 14.

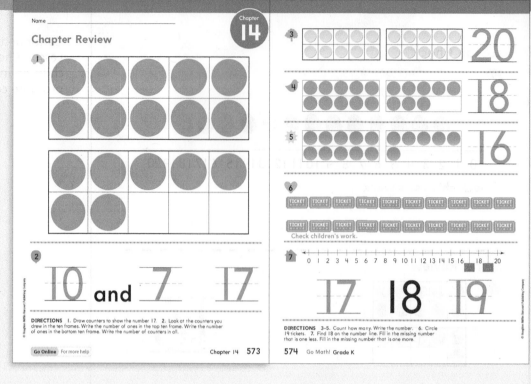

Online, Data-Driven Decision Making *MTSS* (RtI) HMH | Waggle®

Based on the results of the Chapter Review, use the following resources to review skills.

Item	Lesson	Content Focus	Intervene With
8, 9	14.6	Use a number line to order numbers to 20.	**Reteach 14.6,** Waggle
5	14.2	Write 16 or 17 to represent a group of objects.	**Reteach 14.2,** Waggle
4	14.4	Write 18 or 19 to represent a group of objects.	**Reteach 14.4,** Waggle
1, 2	14.1	Count out 16 or 17 objects.	**Reteach 14.1,** Waggle
3	14.5	Count and represent 20 with objects or a written numeral.	**Reteach 14.5,** Waggle
7	14.7	Find and compare numbers to 20 using a number line.	**Reteach 14.7,** Waggle
10	14.8	Compare numbers to 20 using the strategy *make a model*.	**Reteach 14.8,** Waggle
6	14.3	Count out 18 or 19 objects.	**Reteach 14.3,** Waggle

Name _____

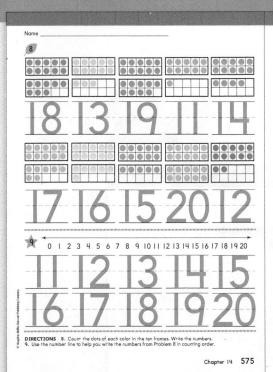

Check children's work.

DIRECTIONS 8. Count the dots of each color in the ten frames. Write the numbers.
9. Use the number line to help you write the numbers from Problem 8 in counting order.

Chapter 14 575

DIRECTIONS 10. Donta has 18 balloons. Hayley has a number of balloons two more than Donta. Draw to represent the sets of balloons. Write how many in each set. Find and draw a line under the numbers on the number line. Circle the number that is less.

576 Go Math! Grade K

Performance Assessment Task

See the Performance Tasks to assess children's understanding of the content. For each task, you will find sample student work for each of the response levels in the task scoring rubric.

Performance Assessment Tasks may be used for portfolios.

Chapter Test

Summative Assessment

Use the **Chapter Test** to assess children's progress in Chapter 14.

Chapter Tests are found in the *Assessment Guide*. Test items are presented in formats consistent with high-stakes assessments.

data
checkpoint

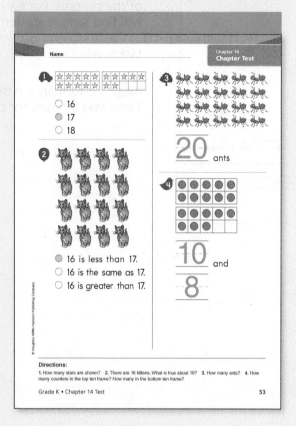

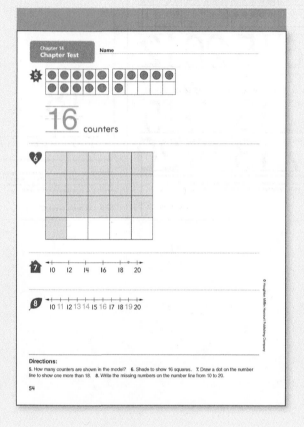

Teacher Notes

Chapter at a Glance

Explore Addition and Subtraction to 20

	LESSON 15.1 • 1 Day	LESSON 15.2 • 1 Day	LESSON 15.3 • 1 Day
Lesson at a Glance	Use a Ten to Put Together and Take Apart Numbers to 14 . . . . . 579A	Use a Ten to Put Together and Take Apart Numbers to 18 . . . . . 585A	Use Numbers to 15 . . . . 591A
I Can	I can put together and take apart numbers to 14.	I can put together and take apart numbers to 18.	I can explain why addition and subtraction equations are true using objects or drawings.
Learning Goal	Understand the numbers 11 to 14 by decomposing the numbers into 10 ones and some more ones using objects.	Understand the numbers 15 to 18 by decomposing the numbers into 10 ones and some more ones using objects.	Solve problems by using the *draw a picture* strategy and writing an equation.
Vocabulary	tens, ones		
Multilingual Support	**Strategy:** Sentence Frames	**Strategy:** Sentence Frames	**Strategy:** Illustrate Understanding

Practice and Fluency	LESSON 15.1	LESSON 15.2	LESSON 15.3
	◆ ■ Practice and Homework	◆ ■ Practice and Homework	◆ ■ Practice and Homework
	■ Waggle	■ Waggle	■ Waggle
	◆ Achieving Facts Fluency*	◆ Achieving Facts Fluency*	◆ Achieving Facts Fluency*

MTSS (RtI) **Intervention and Enrichment**	■ Waggle	■ Waggle	■ Waggle
	◆ ■ Reteach 15.1	◆ ■ Reteach 15.2	◆ ■ Reteach 15.3
	◆ ■ Tier 2 Intervention Skill S16	◆ ■ Tier 2 Intervention Skill S17/S18	◆ ■ Tier 2 Intervention Skill S19
	◆ ■ Tier 3 Intervention Skill E16	◆ ■ Tier 3 Intervention Skill E17/E18	◆ ■ Tier 3 Intervention Skill E19
	◆ Enrich 15.1	◆ Enrich 15.2	◆ Enrich 15.3

See the Grab-and-Go!™ Centers Kit **for more small-group activities.**

Version 2.0

Differentiated Centers Kit

The kit provides literature, games, and activities for small-group learning.

◆ Print/Printable Resource
■ Interactive Resource

LESSON 15.4 • 1 Day

Lesson at a Glance	Use a Ten to Put Together and Take Apart Numbers to 20 . . . . . 597A
I Can	I can put together and take apart numbers to explore addition and subtraction within 20.
Learning Goal	Understand numbers to 20 by decomposing the numbers into 10 ones and some more ones using objects.
Vocabulary	
Multilingual Support	**Strategy:** Sentence Frames

Practice and Fluency

LESSON 15.4

◆ ■ Practice and Homework
■ Waggle
◆ Achieving Facts Fluency*

***MTSS* (RtI)**

Intervention and Enrichment

■ Waggle
◆ ■ Reteach 15.4
◆ ■ Tier 2 Intervention Skill S20
◆ ■ Tier 3 Intervention Skill E20
◆ Enrich 15.4

*For individual and class practice with counting automaticity and operational fluency, go to *Achieving Facts Fluency* pages located online.

Consider how you leverage children's funds of knowledge to bridge to new mathematics learning.

Image Credit: © HMH

SUPPORTING ALL LEARNERS

Leverage children's funds of knowledge and ways of knowing, including multiple mathematical representations, to bridge to new learning and position children as mathematically competent.

◆ Print/Printable Resource
■ Interactive Resource

Meaning of Subtraction

As children learn to represent subtraction with objects and drawings, they will need reinforcement of what is happening in each situation. This is especially necessary when children are taking apart a group, rather than taking from a group. Use the vocabulary *taking apart* consistently, and consistently show one group of objects being taken apart into two smaller groups. Explain to children that subtraction can mean either taking from or taking apart. In either case, subtraction involves turning a larger group into two smaller groups.

Teacher to Teacher

My building math coach did an afterschool learning session on the pitfalls of emphasizing key words in story problems. She challenged all of us to try introducing numberless story problems. The strategy has had a profound impact on our classroom discussions about story problems and children's understanding of addition and subtraction. On chart paper, I write a problem like, "____ children were waiting for the swings on the playground. ____ children decided to go play soccer. How many children are still waiting for the swings?" I read the problem to children and ask them to tell a partner what they remember. Then I ask a volunteer to describe what they see in their mind. I encourage other children to add on or disagree. Then, we start talking about possible strategies. It is so helpful to do this before there are numbers because no one can rush ahead to finding the answer. Some children say they will draw circles on a paper and then cross out the children that go play soccer. Other children would rather make a line of counters and then take away the ones that go play soccer. After we've talked about possible strategies, I write numbers in the blanks and ask children to go back to their tables to solve the problem.

 For more professional learning, go online to Teacher's Corner.

Moving from Concrete to Symbolic Representation

As children learn to read and write equations to represent addition, their primary focus should remain on the concept of addition as putting together two groups or adding a number to a group. Give frequent opportunities to manipulate and express addition in different ways.

Draw frequent connections to children's prior learning about addition and equations as they practice addition with greater numbers. Demonstrate and encourage verbalization of addition equations by having children read the equations aloud both before and after they are written. Provide frequent practice with putting together two groups of objects and connecting these representations to their equations.

Mathematical Practices and Processes

Reason abstractly and quantitatively.

Subtraction may require a greater degree of abstract thinking than addition. When they approach addition problems with visual modeling, children can readily count the total number of objects. A similar subtraction problem may not be as straightforward; rather than counting two smaller groups and the larger group (the sum or total), children must recognize that a larger group is taken apart into two smaller groups. Encourage children to articulate that a number is being taken apart into two lesser numbers, or that one number is being taken away from a greater number. Facilitate children's reasoning by asking frequent questions about what is happening in a subtraction situation. Give children opportunities to act out subtraction by making groups of objects and taking some away, by making groups of objects and splitting them into two smaller groups, and by grouping themselves and then subtracting from their own group. As children learn about subtraction, ask them to explore different ways of expressing the same relationship; for example, $9 - 3 = 6$ and $9 - 6 = 3$ may represent the same group (9) being taken apart into smaller groups (3 and 6).

Instructional Journey

While every classroom may look a little different, this instructional model provides a framework to organize small-group and whole-group learning for meaningful student learning.

Whole Group
Engage

5 minutes

Readiness
- Problem of the Day
- Fluency Builder or Vocabulary Builder
- Access Prior Knowledge

Engagement
- I Can
- Making Connections
- Learning Activity

Small and Whole Group
Explore

15–20 minutes

Exploration
- Listen and Draw, Unlock the Problem
- Multilingual Support and Strategy
- Common Errors

Small Group
Explain

15–20 minutes

Quick Check
- ✓ Share and Show

Differentiated Instruction

Grab and Go!™
Version 2.0

Intervention
- Waggle
- Reteach
- Tier 2 and Tier 3 MTSS
- Tabletop Flipchart Mini Lessons

Language Support
- Vocabulary Activities
- Language Routines
- Multilingual Glossary

Enrichment
- Waggle Games
- Ready for More
- Enrich

Whole Group
Elaborate

5 minutes

- Math on the Spot Videos
- Higher-Order Thinking Problems

Evaluate

- I Can Reflection
- Exit Ticket
- Practice and Homework
- Fluency Practice
- Waggle

Assessment

Diagnostic	Formative	Summative
• Show What You Know	• Lesson Quick Check	• Chapter Review • Chapter Test • Performance Assessment Task

Grab and Go!™
Version 2.0
Differentiated Centers Kit

The kit provides literature, games, and activities for small-group learning.

Strategies for
Multilingual Learners

Understanding a child's language development is helpful in differentiating teaching and assessment. Assessing a child's understanding of mathematical concepts can be done by listening, speaking, reading, and writing. The level of support a child needs determines how best to assess that child's understanding of mathematical concepts.

Planning for Instruction			
Language Support	**Substantial** (WIDA Level 1)*	**Moderate** (WIDA Levels 2 & 3)*	**Light** (WIDA Levels 4 & 5)*
Child's Use of Language	• uses single words • uses common short phrases • heavily relies on visual supports and use of manipulatives	• uses simple sentences • uses some academic vocabulary • relies on visual supports and use of manipulatives	• uses a variety of sentences • uses academic vocabulary • benefits from visual supports and manipulatives
Ways to Assess Understanding	**Listening:** points to pictures, words, or phrases to answer questions **Speaking:** answers *yes/no* questions **Reading:** matches symbols to math terms and concepts **Writing:** draws a visual representation of a problem	**Listening:** matches, categorizes, or sequences information based on visuals **Speaking:** begins to explain reasoning, asks math questions, repeats explanations from peers **Reading:** identifies important information to solve a problem **Writing:** uses simple sentences and visual representations	**Listening:** draws conclusions and makes connections based on what they heard **Speaking:** explains and justifies concepts and solutions **Reading:** understands information in math contexts **Writing:** completes sentences using some academic vocabulary

* For more information on WIDA Standards, visit their website at:
https://wida.wisc.edu/.

• Look for strategies throughout the lesson to support multilingual learners.
• Log on to ED to find additional multilingual activities and Vocabulary Cards.

In This Chapter

Key Academic Vocabulary

Current Development • Vocabulary

tens, ones

Using Language Routines to Develop Understanding

 Language routines provide opportunities for children to develop an understanding of mathematical language and concepts by listening, speaking, reading, and writing. More information on these language routines can be found on the Language Support Cards.

Stronger and Clearer Each Time

1 Children show their thinking with math tools and visuals.
2 Children share their thinking and receive feedback with a partner or a group.
3 Children revoice feedback and revise their work.

Language Support	Substantial (WIDA Level 1)*	Moderate (WIDA Levels 2 & 3)*	Light (WIDA Levels 4 & 5)*
Language Routine Differentiation	1 Children can show their thinking using visuals and/or manipulatives. 2 Children can answer yes/no or single-word-answer questions about their reasoning. Allow children to rely heavily on their visual representations. 3 Children revise their work based on feedback.	1 Children can show their thinking using words and/or visuals. 2 Children can verbally communicate with their partner or group using visual representations to support their reasoning. 3 Children repeat feedback and revise their work.	1 Children can show their thinking using words and visuals. 2 Children can use academic vocabulary to verbally communicate with their partner or group. 3 Children revoice feedback and revise their work.
Possible Student Work	10 2 12	$10 + 2 = 12$	$12 = 10 + 2$

* For more information on WIDA Standards, visit their website at:
https://wida.wisc.edu/.

Assessing Prior Knowledge

Have children complete **Show What You Know** on their own. Items tested are the prerequisite skills for this chapter.

Diagnostic Interview Task

The alternative interview tasks below evaluate children's understanding of each **Show What You Know** skill. The diagnostic chart may be used for intervention on prerequisite skills.

MATERIALS two-color counters, ten frames

- Show a ten frame with 10 red counters and another 10 frame with fewer than 10 yellow counters. Have the child tell the number being represented. Then have the child write the number of red counters, yellow counters, and the total number of counters.

- Tell an addition word problem about seagulls. The total number of seagulls should be within 10. **There are __ seagulls on the beach. Then __ more seagulls land on the beach. How many seagulls are on the beach?** Guide children in using counters and writing an addition equation to represent the word problem.

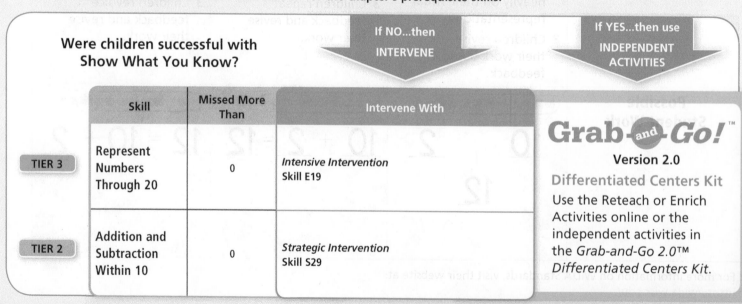

Name _____

✓ Show What You Know

Chapter 15

Represent Numbers Through 20

1

19

2

10 ■ 9   19

Addition and Subtraction Within 10

3

6 + 2 = 8

This page checks understanding of important skills needed for success in Chapter 15.

DIRECTIONS 1. Count and tell how many. Write the number. 2. Look at the ten frames in Problem 1. Write how many green squares. Write how many yellow squares. Write how many in all. 3. There are six shells on the beach. The tide brings in two more shells. How many shells are on the beach? Draw counters to show the shells. Complete the addition equation.

© Houghton Mifflin Harcourt Publishing Company

Chapter 15 • Explore Addition and Subtraction to 20   **577**

✓ Show What You Know • Diagnostic Assessment

Use to determine if children need intervention for the chapter's prerequisite skills.

If NO...then
INTERVENE

If YES...then use
INDEPENDENT
ACTIVITIES

	Skill	Missed More Than	Intervene With
TIER 3	Represent Numbers Through 20	0	*Intensive Intervention* Skill E19
TIER 2	Addition and Subtraction Within 10	0	*Strategic Intervention* Skill S29

Grab-and-Go!™
Version 2.0
Differentiated Centers Kit
Use the Reteach or Enrich Activities online or the independent activities in the *Grab-and-Go 2.0™ Differentiated Centers Kit.*

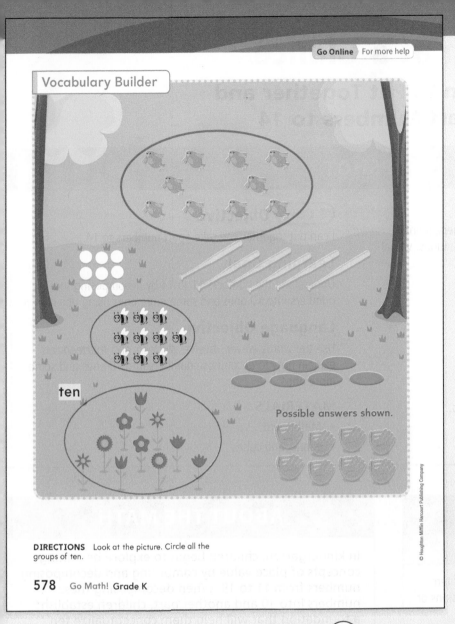

Vocabulary Builder

ten

Possible answers shown.

DIRECTIONS Look at the picture. Circle all the
groups of ten.

Vocabulary Builder

Children use multiple strategies to develop
grade-appropriate vocabulary.

Have children complete the activities on the
page by working alone or with partners.

Look at the page with children.

Read the number word with children. Then
count with children and identify the sets of
10 objects.

Have children circle the groups of ten.

School-Home Letter is available in
English and Spanish online, and in
multiple other languages.

Intervention Options MTSS RtI Response to Intervention

Use Show What You Know, Lesson Quick Check, and Assessments to diagnose children's intervention levels.

TIER 1	TIER 2	TIER 3	ENRICHMENT
On-Level Intervention	**Strategic Intervention**	**Intensive Intervention**	**Independent Activities**
For children who are generally at grade level but need early intervention with the lesson concepts, use:	For children who need small-group instruction to review concepts and skills needed for the chapter, use:	For children who need one-on-one instruction to build foundational skills for the chapter, use:	For children who successfully complete lessons, use:
• Reteach • Tabletop Flipchart Mini Lesson • Waggle ▲ Tier 1 Activity	▲ Prerequisite Skills Activities ▲ Tier 2 Activity	▲ Prerequisite Skills Activities ▲ Tier 3 Activity	• Waggle Practice and Games **Grab-and-Go!** Version 2.0 Differentiated Centers Kit • Ready for More Activity for every lesson • Enrich

Lesson at a Glance

Use a Ten to Put Together and Take Apart Numbers to 14

SNAPSHOT

Mathematical Standards

- Represent addition and subtraction with objects, fingers, mental images, drawings, sounds (e.g., claps), acting out situations, verbal explanations, expressions, or equations.

Mathematical Practices and Processes

- Model with mathematics.
- Attend to precision.
- Express regularity in repeated reasoning
- Look for and make use of structure.
- Reason abstractly and quantitatively.
- Construct arguments and critique reasoning of others.

(I Can) Objective

I can put together and take apart numbers to 14.

Learning Goal

Understand the numbers 11 to 14 by decomposing the numbers into 10 ones and some more ones using objects.

Language Objective

Use the words *eleven*, *twelve*, *thirteen*, and *fourteen* and explain how to decompose numbers into 10 ones and some more ones.

MATERIALS

- MathBoard
- connecting cubes

ACROSS THE GRADES

Grade K

Represent whole numbers from 10 to 20, using a unit of ten and a group of ones, with objects, drawings and expressions or equations.

After

Compose and decompose two-digit numbers in multiple ways using tens and ones. Demonstrate each composition or decomposition with objects, drawings and expressions or equations.

ABOUT THE MATH

In kindergarten, children begin to explore beginning concepts of place value by composing and decomposing numbers from 11 to 19. When decomposing these numbers into 10 and another part, children establish a foundation that will help them conceptualize ten as a single unit. At that time, children will begin to understand teen numbers as a ten and some ones.

Give children opportunities to decompose numbers using objects and drawings. Talk about patterns that children notice. Children might notice that when decomposing a number into ten and a part, the part is the digit in the ones place. Although children are not yet familiar with ones and tens places, they will apply this understanding when they are introduced to place-value concepts.

For more professional learning, go online to Teacher's Corner.

DAILY ROUTINES

 Problem of the Day 15.1

Find the difference.

? = 6 – 5   1

? = 4 – 1   3

? = 7 – 3   4

? = 8 – 0   8

? = 9 – 4   5

Vocabulary   tens, ones

• Interactive Student Edition
• Multilingual Glossary

Vocabulary Builder

Have children draw to represent each term.

eleven, fourteen, more, ones, thirteen, twelve
Check children's drawings.

FOCUSING ON THE WHOLE STUDENT

Social & Emotional Learning

Relationship Skills Help children recognize that their work takes place within a learning group, so that managing their own learning process often involves attention to those around them. *If you notice that someone else is having difficulty representing numbers, it is appropriate to offer help. Do not just tell your answer, though. You can talk through your strategy with the other person. If you are having difficulty, work together with someone else who is also having difficulty so you can talk through the problem together. Or you might ask someone who has completed the problem to explain their strategy to help get you started.*

---

① Engage

with the Interactive Student Edition

I Can Objective

I can put together and take apart numbers to 14.

Making Connections

Display a group of eight circles and a group of six circles arranged as shown below.

Have children count the circles and write the number in each group.

Learning Activity

Materials numbers cards 1, 2, 3, 4, and 10; groups of 11–14 counting sticks, rubber bands

Have children count the sticks in the first group. Ask them to place a rubber band around the sticks to make a bundle of ten. Then have them use the number cards to label the number of sticks in the bundle and the sticks that are not bundled. Repeat for the other groups of sticks.

⚠ Common Errors

Error Children might miscount the cubes when writing the extra ones.

Example Children start counting at 10, instead of 11, when making 12, and add 3 ones instead of 2.

Springboard to Learning Have children make a single cube train with 12 cubes and then break it into a cube train with ten ones and a cube train with 2 ones.

② Explore

Unlock the Problem Real World

(MP) **Model with mathematics.**

Read aloud this problem as children listen.

Juanita sees some ants on trees. On one tree, there are 10 ants. On another tree, there are 4 ants. Write the number of ants on each tree. How many ants are there?

- **What do you need to find out?** how many ants there are

- **What do you need to find first?** write how many ants are on each tree

(MP) **Construct arguments and critique reasoning of others.**

- **What do you need to do to solve the problem?** Possible answer: represent the number of ants on each tree and count them in all

- **How many ants are on the first tree? How can you show this?** There are 10 ants on the first tree. I can write the number 10.

- **How many ants are on the second tree? How can you show this?** There are 4 ants on the second tree. I can write the number 4.

- **How can you show that the two groups are separate?** Possible answer: I can circle each group of ants.

- **How can you represent the total number of ants?** Possible answer: as ten ones and 4 more ones, or 14

Name _____

Use a Ten to Put Together and Take Apart Numbers to 14

(I Can) put together and take apart numbers to 14.

▦ UNLOCK the Problem Real World

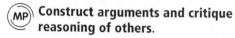

10 ones and 4 ones

14 ants

DIRECTIONS Juanita sees some ants on trees. On one tree there are ten ants. On another tree there are 4 ants. Write the number of ants on each tree. How many ants are there?

Chapter 15 • Lesson 1   **579**

(ML) ## Multilingual Support

STRATEGY: Sentence Frames

For each number 11 through 14, write the following sentence frames.

___ is 10 ones and ___ ones.

___ is 1 ten and ___ ones.

___ = ___ + ___

Have children read the sentences aloud. Explain that they all represent the same number.

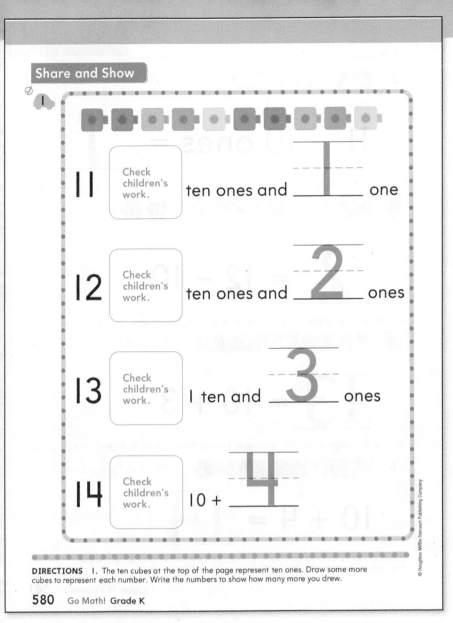

11 — Check children's work. — ten ones and _____ one

12 — Check children's work. — ten ones and _____ ones

13 — Check children's work. — 1 ten and _____ ones

14 — Check children's work. — 10 + _____

DIRECTIONS 1. The ten cubes at the top of the page represent ten ones. Draw some more cubes to represent each number. Write the numbers to show how many more you drew.

Ready for More

visual partners

Materials connecting cubes, three index cards with the following written on them: 10 ones and 3 more ones, 10 ones and 1 more one, 10 ones and 4 more ones

• Have children read each index card. Ask them to work together to show the number described on the card. Then have them write the number on the back of the index card.

③ Explain

Share and Show

(MP) Look for and make use of structure.

Tell children that the connecting cubes at the top of the page represent ten ones. Explain that they will use ten ones and some more ones to compose each number. Have them look at the ten cubes at the top of the page and then decide how many more cubes they need to draw to represent the number.

Use questions to guide children through these problems.

• **If you have ten connecting cubes, how many more cubes do you need to make eleven?** one

• **How will you represent that cube?** Possible answer: I will draw a cube and write the number 1.

• **How can you describe the number 11?** Possible answer: 10 ones and 1 more one

(MP) Reason abstractly and quantitatively.

• **Now that you have completed your drawings for 11, 12, 13, and 14, what do you notice about the numbers?** Possible answer: The number of more ones goes up by one with each number.

Read the problem to children. Ask them to explain how they will solve the problem.

Use the checked problem for Quick Check.

✓ Quick Check   *MTSS* (RtI)

If ▶ a child misses the checked problem

Then ▶ Differentiate Instruction with
• Reteach 15.1
• Waggle

Share and Show

Direct children's attention to each group of cubes on the page. Have children use the cubes and trains to help them compose or decompose the numbers 11, 12, 13, and 14.

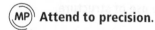 **Attend to precision.**

Problems 2 and 3 Children decompose a number to find how many ones there are after subtracting ten. Review how 10, 1 ten, and 10 ones are the same amount.

Problems 4 and 5 Children are given 10 cubes, and then they draw more cubes to show the number.

Math on the Spot Use this video to help children model and solve this type of problem.

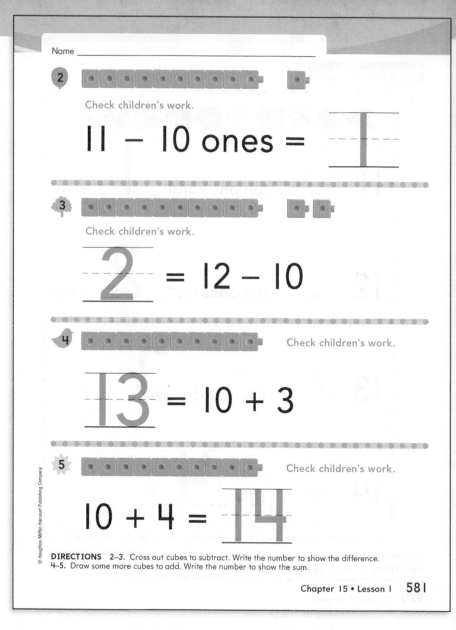

Name _____

2

Check children's work.

$$11 - 10 \text{ ones} = \underline{\quad}$$

3

Check children's work.

$$\underline{2} = 12 - 10$$

4

Check children's work.

$$\underline{13} = 10 + 3$$

5

Check children's work.

$$10 + 4 = \underline{14}$$

DIRECTIONS 2–3. Cross out cubes to subtract. Write the number to show the difference. 4–5. Draw some more cubes to add. Write the number to show the sum.

Chapter 15 • Lesson 1 **581**

Meeting Individual Needs

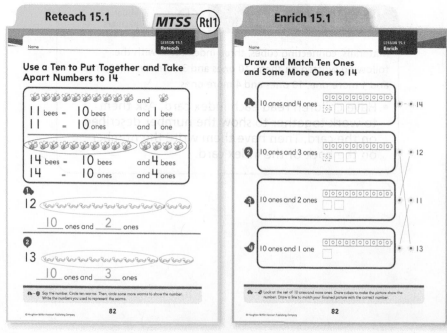

Reteach 15.1

MTSS Rtl1

Use a Ten to Put Together and Take Apart Numbers to 14

Enrich 15.1

Draw and Match Ten Ones and Some More Ones to 14

6

Check children's work.

$$10 + 3 = 13$$

7

Check children's work.

$$14 - 10 = 4$$

DIRECTIONS 6. Circle a ten. Then put together the number. 7. Cross out a ten. Then show how to use 10 to take apart the number.

HOME ACTIVITY • Ask your child to gather 14 of something. Then have them tell you how many tens and ones.

© Houghton Mifflin Harcourt Publishing Company

4 Elaborate

Problem Solving Applications

(MP) **Express regularity in repeated reasoning.**

Problem 6 Children demonstrate their understanding of composing ten ones and some more ones to 13.

Problem 7 Children demonstrate their understanding of using a ten to take apart 14.

5 Evaluate | Formative Assessment

I Can

Have children draw a picture to answer the I Can statement.

I can put together and take apart numbers to 14 by . . . making a group of ten and then adding more ones until I get to 14.

Exit Ticket

Draw to show a group of ten and 2 more. Write how many in all.

DIFFERENTIATED INSTRUCTION • Independent Activities

 **Grab and Go!**

Version 2.0

Differentiated Centers Kit

Tabletop Flipchart

Mini-lessons for reteaching to targeted small groups

Readers

Supports key math skills and concepts in real-world situations.

Games

Reinforce math content and vocabulary

Activities

Meaningful and fun math practice

Practice and Homework

Use a Ten to Put Together and Take Apart Numbers to 14

Use the Practice and Homework pages to provide children with more practice of the concepts and skills presented in this lesson. Children master their understanding as they complete practice items.

1

12   13   14

Check children's work.

_____

- - - - - - - - - -

ten ones and _____ ones

2

Check children's work.

$$14 - 10 = 4$$

DIRECTIONS 1. Choose a number from 12 to 14 and circle it. The 10 bears represent ten ones. Use those bears and draw some more ones to show the number you chose. Write the number to show how many more ones. 2. Cross out a ten. Then show how to use 10 to take apart the number.

© Houghton Mifflin Harcourt Publishing Company

Chapter 15 • Lesson 1   583

Lesson Check

3

Check children's work.

$$12 - 10 = 2$$

4

13 [●●●] ten ones and ___3___ ones

Spiral Review

 5

5, ___4___ , 3, 2, ___1___

DIRECTIONS 3. Cross out a ten. Then show how to use a 10 to take apart the number.
4. Look at the 10 counters. Draw some more ones to show 13. Then put together the number.
5. Count backwards from five. Write the missing numbers.

584 Go Math! Grade K

Continue to practice concepts and skills with Lesson Check. Use Spiral Review to engage children in previously taught concepts and to promote content retention.

Lesson at a Glance

Use a Ten to Put Together and Take Apart Numbers to 18

SNAPSHOT

Mathematical Standards

- Represent addition and subtraction with objects, fingers, mental images, drawings, sounds (e.g., claps), acting out situations, verbal explanations, expressions, or equations.

Mathematical Practices and Processes

- Model with mathematics.
- Attend to precision.
- Express regularity in repeated reasoning.
- Look for and make use of structure.
- Reason abstractly and quantitatively.

(I Can) Objective

I can put together and take apart numbers to 18.

Learning Goal

Understand the numbers 15 to 18 by decomposing the numbers into 10 ones and some more ones using objects.

Language Objective

Use the words *fifteen, sixteen, seventeen,* and *eighteen* and explain how to decompose numbers into 10 ones and some more ones.

MATERIALS

- MathBoard
- connecting cubes

ACROSS THE GRADES

Grade K

Represent whole numbers from 10 to 20, using a unit of ten and a group of ones, with objects, drawings and expressions or equations.

After

Compose and decompose two-digit numbers in multiple ways using tens and ones. Demonstrate each composition or decomposition with objects, drawings and expressions or equations.

ABOUT THE MATH

Why Teach This?

An understanding of place value lays the foundation for success in math. In this lesson, children decompose numbers to 18 into ten ones and some more ones. Later, children will begin to understand ten ones as a unit of ten. This allows them to recognize and represent a 2-digit number as a number of tens and ones.

For more professional learning, go online to Teacher's Corner.

🖥 Problem of the Day 15.2

Show three ways to make 5.

Sample answer: $2 + 3$, $4 + 1$, $0 + 5$

🖥 Vocabulary

- Interactive Student Edition
- Multilingual Glossary

Vocabulary Builder

Have children draw to represent each term.

eighteen, fifteen, seventeen, sixteen
Check children's drawings.

FOCUSING ON THE WHOLE STUDENT

Access Prior Knowledge

Ask children to represent the number 14. Children can write their responses on their MathBoards or show their representations with connecting cubes or counters and ten frames. After they have made their first representation, ask children to show 14 in a different way.

Have children share their representations. Ask them to compare the different ways to make 14. Have them tell how their representation differed from a classmate's.

Watch for children who only know how to show 14 as a group of 14 ones and not as 10 ones and 4 more ones.

Repeat for the number 12.

Supporting All Learners

This chapter explores the addition and subtraction of numbers within 20 by integrating children's understanding of addition and subtraction with place-value relationships. This concept can be very intimidating, and children may get discouraged. Remember the importance of maintaining high expectations for all students while meeting them with realistic, positive encouragement. Provide scaffolds if necessary, and take time to celebrate children's successes.

1 Engage

with the Interactive Student Edition

I Can Objective

I can put together and take apart numbers to 18.

Making Connections

Draw a row of twelve flowers on the board.

- **Maggie has some flowers. She puts ten flowers in a vase. Have a volunteer circle the flowers Maggie puts in a vase. How many flowers does Maggie have in all?** twelve

- **How can you represent 12 as ten ones and some more ones?** 10 ones and 2 more ones

Learning Activity

Provide children with sets of 14, 15, and 16 counters. Have children count the number of counters in each group. Then have children place 10 counters out of each group in a row. Next, have children identify the number of counters left over. Ask children to identify the group that has ten ones and five more ones. Have children tell how many total counters are in that group.

② Explore

Listen and Draw

 Model with mathematics.

Read aloud this problem as children listen.

Claude has some strawberries on two plates. Write the numbers to represent the number of strawberries on each plate. How many strawberries are there?

- **What do you need to find out?** how many strawberries there are

- **What do you need to find first?** how many strawberries are on each plate

- **What do you need to do to solve the problem?** Possible answer: represent the number of strawberries on each plate

- **How many strawberries are on the first plate? How can you show this?** There are 10 strawberries on the first plate. I can draw 10 circles or lines.

- **How many strawberries are on the second plate? How can you show this?** There are 8 strawberries on the second plate. I can draw 8 circles or lines.

 Reason abstractly and quantitatively.

- **How can you represent the number of strawberries in the groups?** Possible answer: as 10 ones and 8 more ones

- **How would you write a number to tell the number of strawberries?** Possible answer: I can write 18 since 10 ones and 8 more ones is 18.

Name _____

Use a Ten to Put Together and Take Apart Numbers to 18

(I Can) put together and take apart numbers to 18.

Listen and Draw Real World

10 ones   8 ones

18 strawberries

DIRECTIONS Claude has some strawberries on two plates. Write the numbers to represent the number of strawberries on each plate. How many strawberries are there?

Chapter 15 • Lesson 2   **585**

ML **Multilingual Support**

STRATEGY: Sentence Frames

For each number 15 through 18, write the following sentence frames.

__ is 10 ones and ___ ones.

__ is 1 ten and ___ ones.

__ = ___ + ___

Have children read the sentences aloud. Explain that they all represent the same number.

15   Check children's work.   ten ones and _____5_____ ones

16   Check children's work.   1 ten and _____6_____ ones

17   Check children's work.   1 ten and _____7_____ ones

18   Check children's work.   10 + _____8_____

DIRECTIONS 1. The ten cubes at the top of the page represent ten ones. Draw some more cubes to represent each number. Write the numbers to show how many more you drew.

© Houghton Mifflin Harcourt Publishing Company

③ Explain

Share and Show

Tell children that the connecting cubes at the top of the page represent ten ones. Explain that they will use ten ones and some more ones to compose each number. Have them look at the ten cubes at the top of the page and then decide how many more cubes they need to draw to represent the number.

Use questions to guide children through these problems.

(MP) Look for and make use of structure.

- **If you have ten connecting cubes, how many more cubes do you need to make fifteen?** five
- **How will you represent those cubes?** Possible answer: I will draw 5 cubes and write the number 5.
- **How can you describe the number 15?** Possible answer: 10 ones and 5 more ones

(MP) Reason abstractly and quantitatively.

- **Now that you have completed your drawings for 15, 16, 17, and 18, what do you notice about the numbers?** Possible answer: The number of more ones goes up by one with each number.

Read the problem to children. Ask them to explain how they will solve the problem.

Use the checked problem for Quick Check.

✓ Quick Check   MTSS (RtI)

If → a child misses the checked problem

Then → **Differentiate Instruction** with
- Reteach 15.2
- Waggle

! Common Errors

Error Children might omit a cube when counting.

Example Children might say 15 is ten ones and 4 cubes.

Springboard to Learning Have children draw and number the cubes as they count them.

Ready for More   🕐 visual partners

Materials connecting cubes, four index cards with one of the following written on each: 10 ones and 3 more ones, 10 ones and 1 more one, 10 ones and 4 more ones, and 10 ones and 5 more ones

- Have children read each index card. Ask children to predict the number of connecting cubes they need to show each description. Give children that number of cubes and have them use the cubes to represent the number. Discuss whether or not children's initial answers were correct.

Share and Show

Direct children's attention to each group of cubes on the page. Have children use the cubes and trains to help them compose or decompose the numbers 15, 16, 17, and 18.

 Attend to precision.

Problems 2 and 3 Children decompose a number to find how many ones there are after subtracting ten. Review how 10, 1 ten, and 10 ones are the same amount.

Problems 4 and 5 Children are given 10 cubes, and then they draw more cubes to show the number.

Math on the Spot Use this video to help children model and solve this type of problem.

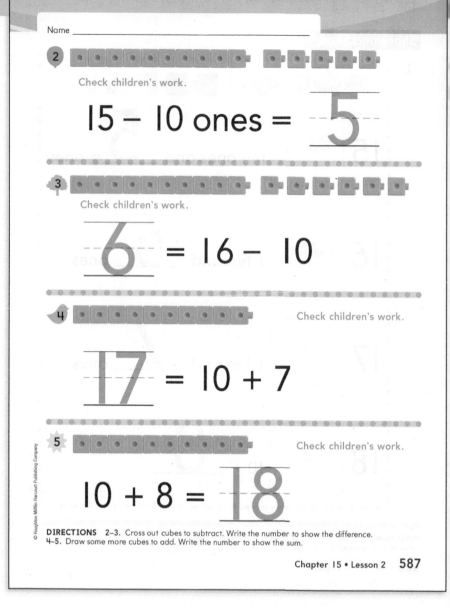

Name _____

2 Check children's work.

$$15 - 10 \text{ ones} = 5$$

3 Check children's work.

$$6 = 16 - 10$$

4 Check children's work.

$$17 = 10 + 7$$

5 Check children's work.

$$10 + 8 = 18$$

DIRECTIONS 2–3. Cross out cubes to subtract. Write the number to show the difference.
4–5. Draw some more cubes to add. Write the number to show the sum.

Chapter 15 • Lesson 2 **587**

Meeting Individual Needs

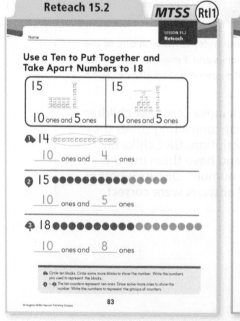

Reteach 15.2 MTSS Rtl1

Name _____

Use a Ten to Put Together and Take Apart Numbers to 18

15 — 10 ones and 5 ones
15 — 10 ones and 5 ones

1 14 — 10 ones and 4 ones

2 15 — 10 ones and 5 ones

3 18 — 10 ones and 8 ones

83

Enrich 15.2

Name _____

Shop with Ten Ones and Some More Ones to 18

18 17 16 15 14

83

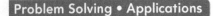

6

Check children's work.

$$10 + 5 = 15$$

7

Check children's work.

$$18 - 10 = 8$$

DIRECTIONS 6. Circle a ten. Then put together the number. 7. Cross out a ten. Then show how to use 10 to take apart the number.

HOME ACTIVITY • Ask your child to gather 18 of something. Then have them show you a ten and some ones.

© Houghton Mifflin Harcourt Publishing Company

588 Go Math! Grade K

---

④ Elaborate

Problem Solving Applications

(MP) Express regularity in repeated reasoning.

Problem 6 Children demonstrate their understanding of composing ten ones and some more ones to 15.

Problem 7 Children demonstrate their understanding of using a ten to take apart 18.

⑤ Evaluate | Formative Assessment

I Can

Have children draw a picture to answer the I Can statement.

I can put together and take apart numbers to 18 by . . . making a group of ten and then adding more ones, or taking away from groups of ten to see how many ones are left.

Exit Ticket

Find or draw 16 objects. Take away 10. How many objects are left?

DIFFERENTIATED INSTRUCTION • Independent Activities

Grab-and-Go!™
Version 2.0
Differentiated Centers Kit

Tabletop Flipchart

Mini-lessons for reteaching to targeted small groups

Readers

Supports key math skills and concepts in real-world situations.

Games

Reinforce math content and vocabulary

Activities

Meaningful and fun math practice

Practice and Homework

Use a Ten to Put Together and Take Apart Numbers to 18

Use the Practice and Homework pages to provide children with more practice of the concepts and skills presented in this lesson. Children master their understanding as they complete practice items.

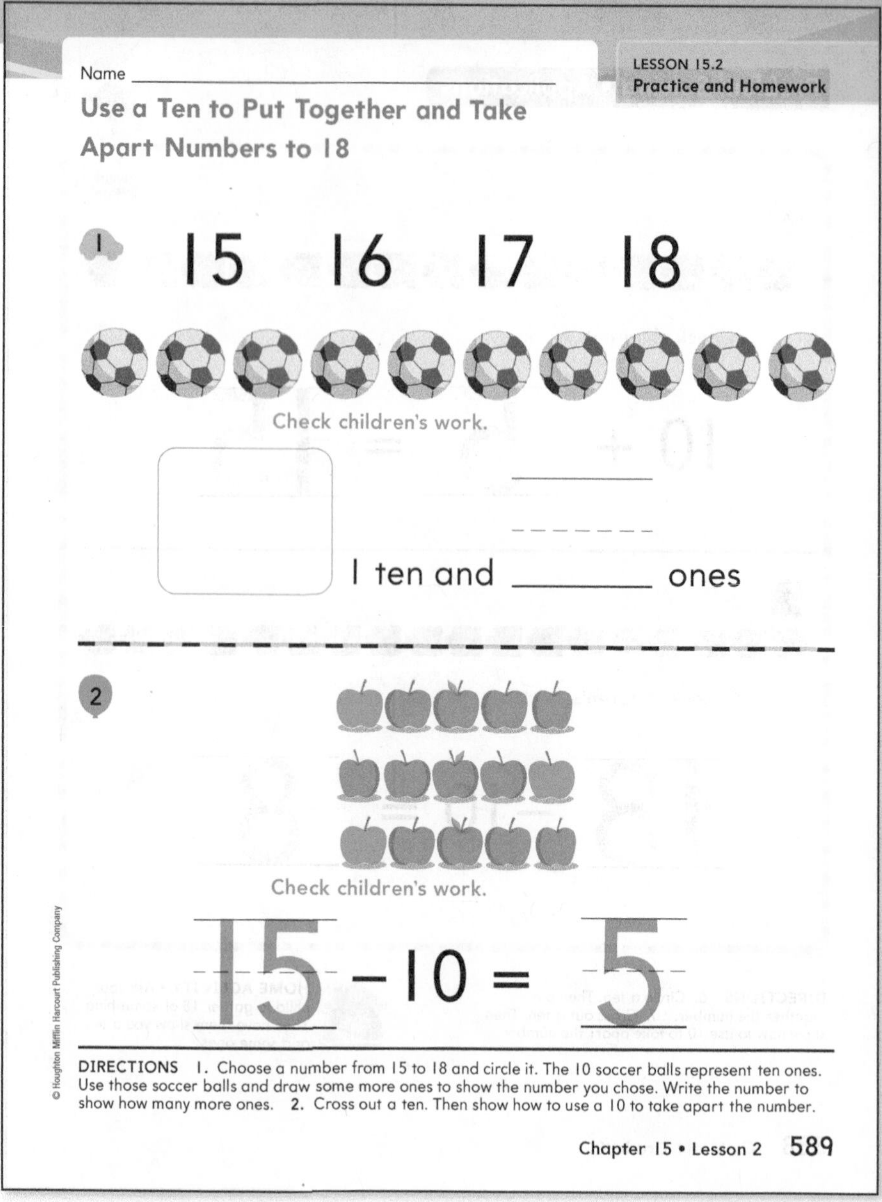

Name ____________________

LESSON 15.2
Practice and Homework

Use a Ten to Put Together and Take Apart Numbers to 18

1 15 16 17 18

Check children's work.

I ten and _______ ones

2

Check children's work.

15 − 10 = 5

DIRECTIONS 1. Choose a number from 15 to 18 and circle it. The 10 soccer balls represent ten ones. Use those soccer balls and draw some more ones to show the number you chose. Write the number to show how many more ones. 2. Cross out a ten. Then show how to use a 10 to take apart the number.

Chapter 15 • Lesson 2 589

Lesson Check

3

Check children's work.

$$17 - 10 = 7$$

4

16    I ten and **6** ones

Spiral Review

5   ○ 12   ● 19

DIRECTIONS 3. Cross out a ten. Then show how to use a 10 to take apart the number.
4. Look at the 10 counters. Draw some more ones to show 16. Then put together the number.
5. Which number is greater? Fill the bubble next to the correct answer.

Continue to practice concepts and skills with Lesson Check. Use Spiral Review to engage children in previously taught concepts and to promote content retention.

Lesson at a Glance
Use Numbers to 15

SNAPSHOT

Mathematical Standards
- Represent addition and subtraction with objects, fingers, mental images, drawings, sounds (e.g., claps), acting out situations, verbal explanations, expressions, or equations.

Mathematical Practices and Processes
- Model with mathematics.
- Construct viable arguments and critique the reasoning of others.
- Reason abstractly and quantitatively.
- Attend to precision.

(I Can) Objective
I can explain why addition and subtraction equations are true using objects or drawings.

Learning Goal
Solve problems by using the *draw a picture* strategy and writing an equation.

Language Objective
Children draw a picture and write an equation that shows the solution to a problem.

MATERIALS
- MathBoard

ACROSS THE GRADES

Grade K
Explain why addition or subtraction equations are true using objects or drawings.

After
Determine and explain if equations involving addition or subtraction are true or false.

ABOUT THE MATH

Teaching for Depth

Draw a picture is one of the problem-solving strategies that children can use to solve word problems. Representing a problem with a drawing can help a child work toward a solution. A drawing may show such things as size, quantity, or action.

It is not important that children draw a detailed picture. They can draw pictures of manipulatives, circles, lines, or other representations for the objects in the problem.

Encourage children to develop a plan to solve a problem by identifying the information needed, carrying out the plan by drawing a picture, and checking whether their answer makes sense. Have children spend time sharing how they solved the problem.

For more professional learning, go online to Teacher's Corner.

Problem of the Day 15.3

Find the sum.

? = 6 + 2 8

? = 4 + 1 5

? = 3 + 7 10

? = 1 + 8 9

? = 0 + 9 9

🖥 Vocabulary

- Interactive Student Edition
- Multilingual Glossary

Fluency Builder

Write Numerals to 10

Have one partner hold up any number of fingers on two hands. Have the other partner write the numeral that shows the number of fingers. Children can work together to check the answer. Have partners take turns.

Circulate to check their work and to ask children questions, such as:

- **How do you know how many fingers there are?**
- **If your partner wrote a number, how could you show that many fingers?**

FOCUSING ON THE WHOLE STUDENT

Access Prior Knowledge

Use iTools: Counters. Stamp a set of 10 counters and click *Line Up*. Then stamp one counter.

Have children describe the set using the pattern 10 ones 1 one.

Continue stamping counters to show 12, 13, and 14. Have children describe each set using the pattern of 10 ones and some more ones.

---

① Engage

with the Interactive Student Edition

I Can Objective

I can explain why addition and subtraction equations are true using objects or drawings.

Making Connections

Invite children to tell about problem solving strategies.

- **Tell what you know about the make a model strategy.** I make a model using objects like counters. The objects show me what is going on in the problem.

- **When do you use the act it out strategy?** Sometimes we can do what we read in a problem. Then we act it out to understand it.

Learning Activity

Introduce children to the strategy *draw a picture*.

- **You have 14 friends at a party and only 12 party hats. You want to know how many more hats you need.**

Guide children to understand that they can draw a picture to solve. Discuss why the strategies make a model and act it out would not be good ways to solve the problem.

② Explore

Unlock the Problem

Read aloud this problem as children listen.

There are 14 children sitting on chairs. There is one chair with no child on it. How many chairs are there?

 Reason abstractly and quantitatively.

- **What do you need to find out?** how many chairs there are

Ask children to draw the chairs as described in the problem and write an addition equation to find the sum.

- **Explain how you can find out how many chairs there are.** I know there are 14 children sitting on chairs. There is one chair with no child on it. So there are 14 and one more chairs.
- **How many chairs are there in all?** 15
- **Write the number of chairs.**

Ask children how the solution would be different if an adult were sitting in the chair that has no child in it instead. The number of chairs would be the same.

Culturally Responsive Education

The problem-solving skills children are using in the lesson benefit their independence as learners. Independent learners take ownership of their learning, and they take initiative to find answers when they cannot solve a problem on their own. As culturally responsive educators, we need to be cautious not to create learned helplessness in our diverse student population; allow children time to solve these problems independently, and encourage them to ask for help only when they have tried at least two or three strategies on their own.

Name _____

Use Numbers to 15

(I Can) explain why addition and subtraction equations are true using objects or drawings.

▦ UNLOCK the Problem Real World

Check children's work.

$$15 = 14 + 1$$

15 chairs

DIRECTIONS There are 14 children sitting on chairs. There is one chair with no child on it. How many chairs are there? Draw and write an addition equation to solve the problem.

Chapter 15 • Lesson 3 **591**

ML Multilingual Support

STRATEGY: Illustrate Understanding

Have children listen to the following problem: **There are 14 baseball hats and 15 children at a picnic. How many more baseball hats are needed so every child has a hat?** 1 more hat

Help children find the number of hats needed by having them draw circles to show the 15 children. They can draw a hat on 14 of the circles.

Discuss the problem. Connect the words in the problem to the picture children drew.

Check children's work.

$$15 - 10 = 5$$

5 more bees

DIRECTIONS 1. There are 15 flowers. Ten flowers have 1 bee on them. How many more bees would you need to have one bee on each flower? Draw and write a subtraction equation to solve the problem. Write how many more bees.

© Houghton Mifflin Harcourt Publishing Company

③ Explain

Try Another Problem
Use questions to guide children through this problem.

 Construct viable arguments and critique the reasoning of others.

- **What do you need to find?** how many more bees I would need to have one bee on each flower
- **What information do you have?** Possible answer: I know there are 15 flowers, and 10 flowers each have one bee on them.
- **What kind of picture could you draw?** Since there are 15 flowers, I can draw 15 flowers and draw a bee on the first 10. Then I will see which flowers do not have bees.
- **How does your picture help you find how many more bees you would need to show one bee on each flower?** I can see that there are five flowers without bees, so I will need to draw five bees to show a bee on each flower.
- **Write the number to show how many more bees.** 5
- **What subtraction equation can you write to solve the problem?** $15 - 10 = 5$
- **How do you know that your answer makes sense?** Accept reasonable answers that demonstrate children's understanding of one-to-one correspondence.

⚠ Common Errors

Error Children may focus more on drawing the flowers and bees than on matching items one-to-one to show how many more bees are needed.

Example Children's drawings do not show a bee on each flower to show one-to-one correspondence.

Springboard to Learning Model drawing 15 flowers on the board. Draw a dot on 10 flowers as children count them. Explain that the dots stand for bees. Guide children in counting the remaining flowers.

4 Elaborate

Share and Show

Read the problem to children. Ask them to explain how they will solve the problem. Use the checked problem for Quick Check.

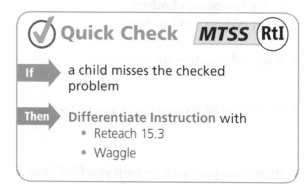

| Quick Check | **MTSS** | **RtI** |

If → a child misses the checked problem

Then → Differentiate Instruction with
- Reteach 15.3
- Waggle

Higher-Order Thinking

 (MP) Attend to precision.

Have children draw pictures to model this problem: **Stella has 14 pencils. She has 1 pencil more than Joseph. How many pencils does Joseph have?**

Children will need to use reverse thinking. They need to know that if Stella has 1 more, this also means that Joseph has 1 fewer. Have children act out the problem to solve it. How many pencils does Joseph have? 13

Math on the Spot Use this video to help children model and solve this type of problem.

Name _____

Share and Show

2 ✓

Check children's work.

$$15 - 6 = 9$$

__9__ tomato plants

DIRECTIONS 2. There are 15 plants in Miss Nazari's garden. There are 5 plants in each row. There are 3 tomato plants and 2 pepper plants in each row. How many tomato plants are in the garden? Draw and write a subtraction equation to solve the problem.

Meeting Individual Needs

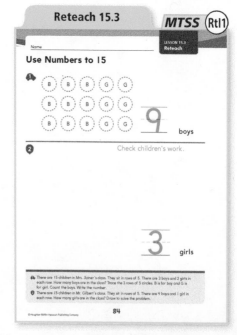

Reteach 15.3   **MTSS** **RtI1**

Name _____

Use Numbers to 15

❶ (B)(B)(B)(G)(G)
(B)(B)(B)(G)(G)
(B)(B)(B)(G)(G)   __9__ boys

❷ Check children's work.

__3__ girls

There are 15 children in Mrs. Joiner's class. They sit in rows of 5. There are 3 boys and 2 girls in each row. How many boys are in the class? Trace the 3 rows of 5 circles. B is for boy and G is for girl. Count the boys. Write the number.
There are 15 children in Mr. Gilbert's class. They sit in rows of 5. There are 4 boys and 1 girl in each row. How many girls are in the class? Draw to solve the problem.

84

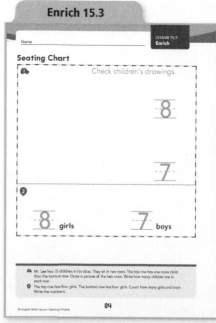

Enrich 15.3

Name _____

Seating Chart

❶ Check children's drawings.

__8__

__7__

❷ __8__ girls   __7__ boys

Mr. Lee has 15 children in his class. They sit in two rows. The top row has one more child than the bottom row. Draw a picture of the two rows. Write how many children are in each row.
The top row has four girls. The bottom row has four boys. Count how many girls and boys. Write the numbers.

84

---

3 Check children's work.

$$12 + 3 = 15$$

$$\underline{3} \text{ more books}$$

DIRECTIONS There are 15 children. Twelve children are each holding 1 book. How many more books would you need to have 1 book for each child? Draw and write a number sentence to solve the problem. Write how many more books.

 HOME ACTIVITY • Draw a ten frame on a sheet of paper. Have your child use small objects, such as buttons, pennies, or dried beans, to show the number 15.

594   Go Math! Grade K

On Your Own

 Model with mathematics.

Children will draw a picture and write an equation to represent and solve the problem. Encourage children to think about the answers to the following questions.

- **How does your picture show the problem?**
- **How can you use your picture to solve the problem?**
- **How does your picture help you write an equation?**

These types of questions will help children make a connection between the verbal, visual, and numerical representations of the problem.

5 Evaluate | Formative Assessment

I Can

Have children draw a picture to answer the I Can statement.

I can explain why addition and subtraction equations are true using objects or drawings by . . . finding out what information I have and drawing a picture to solve the problem. If both sides of the equation have the same value, the equation is true.

Exit Ticket

Draw a picture to solve 13 + 2.

DIFFERENTIATED INSTRUCTION • Independent Activities

Grab and Go!
Version 2.0
Differentiated Centers Kit

Tabletop Flipchart

Mini-lessons for reteaching to targeted small groups

Readers

Supports key math skills and concepts in real-world situations.

Games

Reinforce math content and vocabulary

Activities

Meaningful and fun math practice

Practice and Homework

Use Numbers to 15

Use the Practice and Homework pages to provide children with more practice of the concepts and skills presented in this lesson. Children master their understanding as they complete practice items.

Name ______________________

LESSON 15.3
Practice and Homework

Use Numbers to 15

1

Check children's work.

9 + 6 = 15

6 carrot plants

DIRECTIONS 1. There are 15 vegetables in the garden. They are planted in rows of 5. There are 2 carrot plants and 3 potato plants in each row. How many carrot plants are in the garden? Draw and write an addition equation to solve the problem.

Continue to practice concepts and skills with Lesson Check. Use Spiral Review to engage children in previously taught concepts and to promote content retention.

Lesson Check

2

15 === 10 + 5

5 **caps** Check children's work.

Spiral Review

3

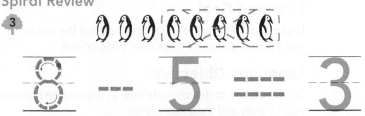

8 − 5 === 3

4

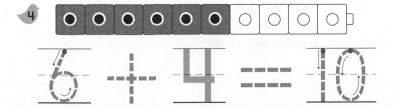

6 + 4 === 10

DIRECTIONS **2.** There are 15 children. Ten children are each wearing 1 cap. How many more caps would you need to have one cap on each child?. Draw and write an addition equation to solve the problem. Write how many more caps. **3.** Trace and write to show the subtraction sentence for the penguins. **4.** Look at the cube train. How many white cubes are added to the gray cubes to make 10? Write and trace to show this as an addition sentence.

596 Go Math! Grade K

© Houghton Mifflin Harcourt Publishing Company

Lesson at a Glance
Use a Ten to Put Together and Take Apart Numbers to 20

SNAPSHOT

Mathematical Standards

- Represent addition and subtraction with objects, fingers, mental images, drawings, sounds (e.g., claps), acting out situations, verbal explanations, expressions, or equations.

Mathematical Practices and Processes

- Express regularity in repeated reasoning.
- Model with mathematics.
- Attend to precision.
- Look for and make use of structure.
- Reason abstractly and quantitatively.

(I Can) Objective

I can put together and take apart numbers to explore addition and subtraction within 20.

Learning Goal

Understand numbers to 20 by decomposing the numbers into 10 ones and some more ones using objects.

Language Objective

Draw a picture to demonstrate how to decompose numbers into 10 ones and some more ones.

MATERIALS

- MathBoard
- connecting cubes

ACROSS THE GRADES

Grade K

Represent whole numbers from 10 to 20, using a unit of ten and a group of ones, with objects, drawings and expressions or equations.

After

Compose and decompose two-digit numbers in multiple ways using tens and ones. Demonstrate each composition or decomposition with objects, drawings and expressions or equations.

ABOUT THE MATH

In kindergarten, children begin to understand and use abstract representations of numbers. They also represent mathematical situations with numerals and symbols. As children become more comfortable representing numbers and mathematical situations, they begin to reason using these symbols and rely less on concrete representations.

In this lesson, children compose numbers through 19 using objects and drawings. Later, children will compose and decompose numbers with or without objects and will describe numbers in terms of tens and ones. Give children the opportunity to discuss the patterns they see as they work with numbers. As children work with objects and drawings and record their work, have them explore the connections between these concrete and abstract representations.

For more professional learning, go online to Teacher's Corner.

💻 Problem of the Day 15.4

Make a ten.

6 and __ 4

8 and __ 2

3 and __ 7

5 and __ 5

1 and __ 9

💻 Vocabulary

- Interactive Student Edition
- Multilingual Glossary

Vocabulary Builder

Have children draw to represent each term.

nineteen, twenty
Check children's drawings.

FOCUSING ON THE WHOLE STUDENT

Access Prior Knowledge

Write **15** on the board.

Tell children that this is the number of the day. Have children name the number. Ask how else they can represent the number of the day. Have them share their representation with a classmate and discuss how their representations are similar and different. Children can draw their representations on their MathBoards or use connecting cubes or counters and ten frames. If any children do not represent 15 as 10 ones and 5 more ones, follow up to correct any misapprehensions.

---

❶ Engage

with the Interactive Student Edition

I Can Objective

I can put together and take apart numbers to explore addition and subtraction within 20.

Making Connections

Draw a row of ten squares on the board. Below the squares write:

_____ ones and _____ ones

- Ask children to count the squares and tell how many. 10
- Explain that the 10 squares represent 10 ones. Then write **10** on the first line below the squares.
- **How many more squares do we need to draw to have 12?** 2
- Draw two more squares and write 2 on the second line below the squares.
- Read the phrase aloud with children: **10 ones and 2 ones.**
- Repeat the process with the numbers 13, 14, and 15.

Learning Activity

Materials red and blue connecting cubes

Have children work in small groups. Have them make a cube train using 10 red cubes and some more blue cubes. When each child has made a cube train, they should share their cube train with others in the group. Encourage children to share the number of cubes of each color they used to make the train.

Ask questions about their representations, such as:

- **How many red cubes did you use?**
- **How many blue cubes did you use?**
- **How many cubes long is your cube train?**

⚠️ Common Errors

Error Children might forget to include the 10 cubes at the top of page 598.

Example Children write 9 for 19.

Springboard to Learning Have children redraw a train of 10 cubes in addition to the extra cubes to make sure the picture includes all of the ones.

Explore

Listen and Draw

 Model with mathematics.

Read aloud this problem as children listen.

Shivali has some marbles in a jar. Write the numbers to represent the number of marbles in each jar. How many marbles are there?

- **What do you need to find out?** how many marbles there are

MP **Reason abstractly and quantitatively.**

- **What do you need to do to solve the problem?** Possible answer: represent the number of marbles in each jar

- **How many marbles are in the first jar? How can you show this?** There are 10 marbles in the first jar. I can draw 10 circles.

- **How many marbles are in the second jar? How can you show this?** There are 5 marbles in the second jar. I can draw 5 circles.

- **How can you represent the number of marbles in each group?** Possible answer: 10 ones and 5 more ones

- **How can you show that the two groups are separate in your representation?** Possible answer: I can circle the group of 10.

- **How can you show the number of marbles in all?** Possible answer: I write 15, since 10 ones and 5 ones is 15.

Name _____

Use a Ten to Put Together and Take Apart Numbers to 20

(I Can) put together and take apart numbers to explore addition and subtraction within 20.

Listen and Draw

10 ones   5 ones

15 marbles

DIRECTIONS Shivali has some marbles in jars. Write the numbers to represent the number of marbles in each jar. How many marbles are there?

© Houghton Mifflin Harcourt Publishing Company

Chapter 15 • Lesson 4   **597**

ML ## Multilingual Support

STRATEGY: Sentence Frames

For the number 19, write the following sentence frames.

__ is 10 ones and ___ ones.

__ is 1 ten and ___ ones.

__ = ___ + ___

Have children read the sentences aloud. Explain that they all represent the same number.

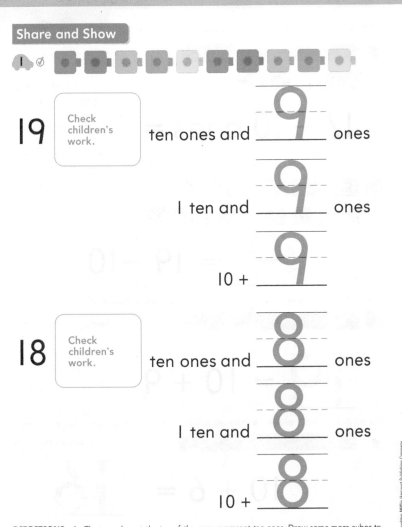

19 | Check children's work. | ten ones and ___9___ ones

1 ten and ___9___ ones

10 + ___9___

18 | Check children's work. | ten ones and ___8___ ones

1 ten and ___8___ ones

10 + ___8___

DIRECTIONS 1. The ten cubes at the top of the page represent ten ones. Draw some more cubes to represent each number. Write the number to show how many more ones. Write the numbers to show how many more you drew.

③ Explain

Share and Show Math Board

Direct children's attention to the connecting cubes at the top of the page. Explain that those cubes represent ten ones. Tell children they will use those ten ones and some more ones to compose numbers 19 and 18.

Use questions to guide children through these problems.

(MP) Look for and make use of structure.

- **If you have ten connecting cubes, how many more cubes do you need to make nineteen?** 9
- **How will you represent those cubes?** Possible answer: I will draw 9 cubes and write the number 9.
- **How can you describe the number 19?** Possible answer: 10 ones and 9 more ones
- **If you have ten connecting cubes, how many more cubes do you need to make eighteen?** 8
- **How will you represent those cubes?** Possible answer: I will draw 8 cubes and write the number 8.
- **How can you describe the number 18?** Possible answer: 10 ones and 8 more ones

Use the checked problem for Quick Check.

Ready for More | ⏱ visual partners

Materials connecting cubes

Write the numbers 19 and 20 on the board. Have children predict how to decompose each number into 10 ones and some more ones. After children make their predictions, have them use connecting cubes to check their answers. Call on children to support their ideas using the connecting cubes.

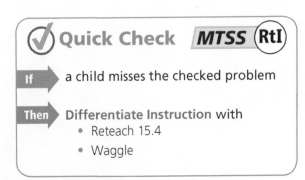

✓ Quick Check **MTSS** **(RtI)**

If → a child misses the checked problem

Then → Differentiate Instruction with
- Reteach 15.4
- Waggle

Share and Show

Direct children's attention to each group of cubes on the page. Have children use the cubes and trains to help them compose or decompose the numbers.

(MP) Attend to precision.

Problems 2 and 3 Children decompose a number to find how many ones there are after subtracting ten. Review how 10, 1 ten, and 10 ones are the same amount.

Problems 4 and 5 Children are given 10 cubes, and then they draw more cubes to show the number.

Math on the Spot Use this video to help children model and solve this type of problem.

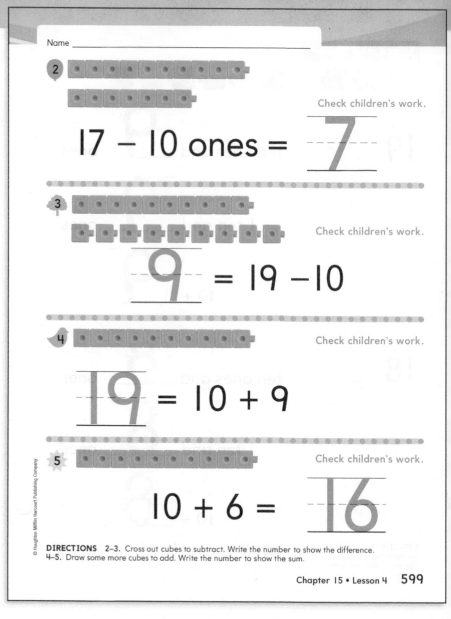

Name _____

2

$$17 - 10 \text{ ones} = 7$$

Check children's work.

3

$$9 = 19 - 10$$

Check children's work.

4

$$19 = 10 + 9$$

Check children's work.

5

$$10 + 6 = 16$$

Check children's work.

DIRECTIONS 2–3. Cross out cubes to subtract. Write the number to show the difference. 4–5. Draw some more cubes to add. Write the number to show the sum.

Chapter 15 • Lesson 4 **599**

Meeting Individual Needs

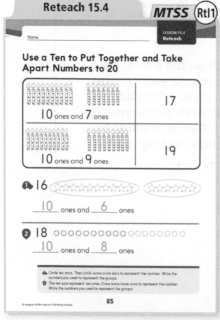

Reteach 15.4 **MTSS (Rtl1)**

LESSON 15.4
Reteach

Name _____

Use a Ten to Put Together and Take Apart Numbers to 20

	17
10 ones and 7 ones	
10 ones and 9 ones	19

1 16

_10_ ones and _6_ ones

2 18 ○○○○○○○○○○ ○○○○○○○○

_10_ ones and _8_ ones

85

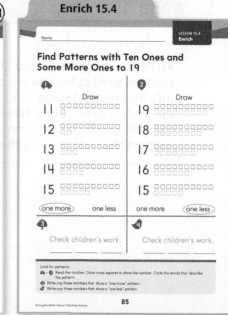

Enrich 15.4

LESSON 15.4
Enrich

Name _____

Find Patterns with Ten Ones and Some More Ones to 19

A Draw | **B** Draw
11 | 19
12 | 18
13 | 17
14 | 16
15 | 15

(one more) one less | one more (one less)

3 Check children's work. | **4** Check children's work.

Look for patterns.

85

6

Check children's work.

$$10 + 4 = 14$$

7

Check children's work.

$$19 - 10 = 9$$

© Houghton Mifflin Harcourt Publishing Company

DIRECTIONS 6. Circle a ten. Then put together the number. 7. Cross out a ten. Then show how to use 10 to take apart the number.

HOME ACTIVITY • Ask your child to gather up to 20 of something. Then have them show you how to make a group of tens and a group of some more ones.

④ Elaborate

Problem Solving Applications

Real World

(MP) Express regularity in repeated reasoning.

Problem 6 Children demonstrate their understanding of composing 10 ones and some more ones.

Problem 7 Children demonstrate their understanding of using a ten to take apart 19.

⑤ Evaluate | Formative Assessment

I Can

Have children draw a picture to answer the I Can statement.

I can put together and take apart numbers to explore addition and subtraction within 20 by . . . making a group of ten and then adding more ones, or taking away from groups of ten to see how many ones are left.

Exit Ticket

Find or draw objects to solve 18 − 10.

DIFFERENTIATED INSTRUCTION • Independent Activities

Grab and Go!™
Version 2.0
Differentiated Centers Kit

Tabletop Flipchart

Mini-lessons for reteaching to targeted small groups

Readers

Supports key math skills and concepts in real-world situations.

Games

Reinforce math content and vocabulary

Activities

Meaningful and fun math practice

Use a Ten to Put Together and Take Apart Numbers to 20

Use the Practice and Homework pages to provide children with more practice of the concepts and skills presented in this lesson. Children master their understanding as they complete practice items.

Name _____

Use a Ten to Put Together and Take Apart Numbers to 20

LESSON 15.4
Practice and Homework

1

13   18

Check children's work.

I ten and _____ ones

2

Check children's work.

$$15 - 10 = 5$$

DIRECTIONS 1. Choose number 13 or 18 and circle it. The 10 acorns represent ten ones. Use those acorns and draw some more ones to show the number you chose. Write the number to show how many more ones.   2. Cross out ten. Then show how to use 10 to take apart the number.

Chapter 15 • Lesson 4 **601**

© Houghton Mifflin Harcourt Publishing Company

Lesson Check

3

Check children's work.

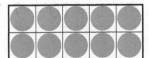 $19 - 10 = 9$

4

$10 + 7 = 17$

Spiral Review

5

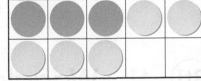

● $5 + 3$ ○ $4 + 4$

DIRECTIONS 3. Cross out a ten. Then show how to use a 10 to take apart the number.
4. Look at the 10 counters. Draw some more ones to show 17. Then put together the number.
5. Which numbers are represented by the counters? Fill the bubble next to the correct answer.

602 Go Math! Grade K

© Houghton Mifflin Harcourt Publishing Company

Summative Assessment

Use the **Chapter Review** to assess children's progress in Chapter 15.

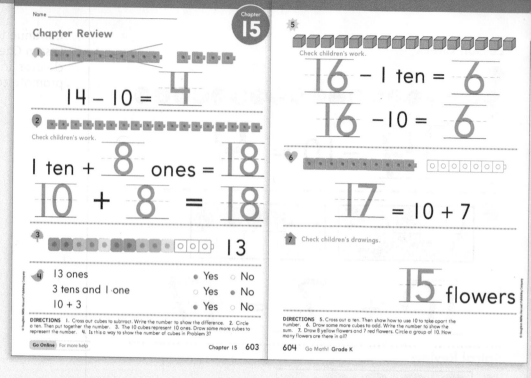

Name _____

Chapter Review

Chapter **15**

1. $14 - 10 = 4$

2. Check children's work.

   $1 \text{ ten} + 8 \text{ ones} = 18$

   $10 + 8 = 18$

3. 13

4.
13 ones	• Yes	○ No
3 tens and 1 one	○ Yes	• No
10 + 3	• Yes	○ No

DIRECTIONS 1. Cross out cubes to subtract. Write the number to show the difference. 2. Circle a ten. Then put together the number. 3. The 10 cubes represent 10 ones. Draw some more cubes to represent the number. 4. Is this a way to show the number of cubes in Problem 3?

Go Online For more help

Chapter 15   603

5. Check children's work.

   $16 - 1 \text{ ten} = 6$

   $16 - 10 = 6$

6. $17 = 10 + 7$

7. Check children's drawings.

   15 flowers

DIRECTIONS 5. Cross out a ten. Then show how to use 10 to take apart the number. 6. Draw some more cubes to add. Write the number to show the sum. 7. Draw 8 yellow flowers and 7 red flowers. Circle a group of 10. How many flowers are there in all?

604   Go Math! Grade K

Online, Data-Driven Decision Making   MTSS RtI   HMH | Waggle®

Based on the results of the Chapter Review, use the following resources to review skills.

Item	Lesson	Content Focus	Intervene With
5, 6	15.2	Understand the numbers 15 to 18 by decomposing the numbers into 10 ones and some more ones using objects.	**Reteach 15.2,** Waggle
2, 8, 10	15.4	Understand numbers to 20 by decomposing the numbers into 10 ones and some more ones using objects.	**Reteach 15.4,** Waggle
1, 3, 4, 9	15.1	Understand the numbers 11 to 14 by decomposing the numbers into 10 ones and some more ones using objects.	**Reteach 15.1,** Waggle
7, 11	15.3	Solve problems by using the *draw a picture* strategy and writing an equation.	**Reteach 15.3,** Waggle

Name _____

8

I ten and [8 / 9] ones

9

ten ones and __3__ ones

I ten and __3__ ones

10 + __3__

__13__

DIRECTIONS **8.** Circle a ten. Put together the number. **9.** Write the numbers to show how many tens and ones.

Chapter 15   605

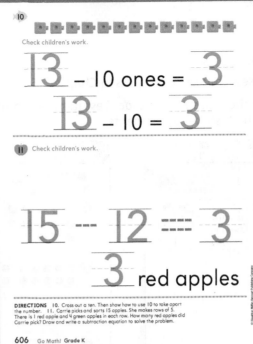

10

Check children's work.

__13__ – 10 ones = __3__

__13__ – 10 = __3__

11 Check children's work.

__15__ --- __12__ === __3__

__3__ red apples

DIRECTIONS **10.** Cross out a ten. Then show how to use 10 to take apart the number. **11.** Carrie picks and sorts 15 apples. She makes rows of 5. There is 1 red apple and 4 green apples in each row. How many red apples did Carrie pick? Draw and write a subtraction equation to solve the problem.

606   Go Math! Grade K

Performance Assessment Task

See the Performance Tasks to assess children's understanding of the content. For each task, you will find sample student work for each of the response levels in the task scoring rubric.

Portfolio   Performance Assessment Tasks may be used for portfolios.

Chapter Test

Summative Assessment

Use the **Chapter Test** to assess children's progress in Chapter 15.

Chapter Tests are found in the *Assessment Guide*. Test items are presented in formats consistent with high-stakes assessments.

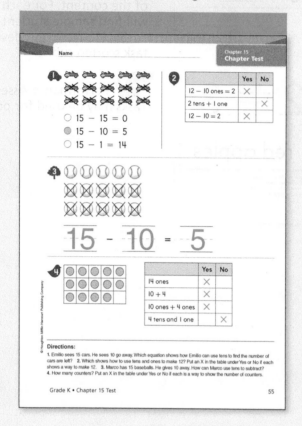

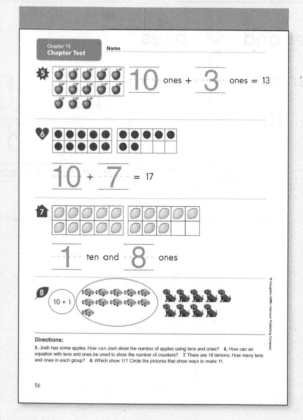

Teacher Notes

Chapter at a Glance
Count to 100

	LESSON 16.1 • 1 Day	**LESSON 16.2 • 1 Day**	**LESSON 16.3 • 1 Day**
Lesson at a Glance	Count to 50 by Ones 609A	Count to 100 by Ones 615A	Count to 100 by Tens 621A
I Can	I can count to 50 by ones.	I can count to 100 by ones.	I can count to 100 by tens.
Learning Goal	Know the count sequence when counting to 50 by ones.	Know the count sequence when counting to 100 by ones.	Know the count sequence when counting to 100 by tens.
Vocabulary	fifty	one hundred	
Multilingual Support	**Strategy:** Identify Relationships	**Strategy:** Model Concepts	**Strategy:** Scaffold Language

Practice and Fluency	LESSON 16.1 ◆ ■ **Practice and Homework** ■ **Waggle** ◆ Achieving Facts Fluency*	LESSON 16.2 ◆ ■ **Practice and Homework** ■ **Waggle** ◆ Achieving Facts Fluency*	LESSON 16.3 ◆ ■ **Practice and Homework** ■ **Waggle** ◆ Achieving Facts Fluency*
MTSS (RtI) Intervention and Enrichment	■ Waggle ◆ ■ Reteach 16.1 ◆ ■ Tier 2 Intervention Skill S32 ◆ ■ Tier 3 Intervention Skill E32 ◆ Enrich 16.1	■ Waggle ◆ ■ Reteach 16.2 ◆ ■ Tier 2 Intervention Skill S32 ◆ ■ Tier 3 Intervention Skill E32 ◆ Tabletop Flipchart ◆ Enrich 16.2	■ Waggle ◆ ■ Reteach 16.3 ◆ ■ Tier 2 Intervention Skill S14 ◆ ■ Tier 3 Intervention Skill E14 ◆ Tabletop Flipchart ◆ Enrich 16.3

See the Grab-and-Go!™ Centers Kit for more small-group activities.

Grab-and-Go!™
Version 2.0
Differentiated Centers Kit

The kit provides literature, games, and activities for small-group learning.

◆ Print/Printable Resource
■ Interactive Resource

LESSON 16.4 • 1 Day

Lesson at a Glance	Count Forward and Backward 627A
I Can	I can count and order numbers forward and backward to 20.
Learning Goal	Order numbers and recognize the number sequence to 20.
Vocabulary	
Multilingual Support	**Strategy:** Creative Grouping

Practice and Fluency

LESSON 16.4
- ◆ ■ **Practice and Homework**
- ■ **Waggle**
- ◆ **Achieving Facts Fluency***

MTSS (RtI) Intervention and Enrichment

- ■ **Waggle**
- ◆ ■ **Reteach 16.4**
- ◆ ■ **Tier 2 Intervention Skill S2**
- ◆ ■ **Tier 3 Intervention Skill E2**
- ◆ **Enrich 16.4**

*For individual and class practice with counting automaticity and operational fluency, go to *Achieving Facts Fluency* pages located online.

> Consider ways in which families can help create a shared vision for deep, meaningful mathematics learning.

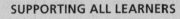

SUPPORTING ALL LEARNERS

Develop relationships with families and the local community to create a shared vision of deep, meaningful mathematics learning.

Image Credit: © HMH

◆ Print/Printable Resource
■ Interactive Resource

Teaching for Depth
Count to 100

Representations and Counting

It is important for children to build on their knowledge of numbers from 0 to 20 and extend their number understanding to 100.

- Ten frames and connecting cubes are used to model 20. Children record the number 20 as the numeral 20 and the word *twenty* to build understanding.

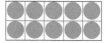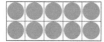

- Writing the missing numbers in the sequence of 1 to 20 helps reinforce children's learning.

Place Value and Numbers to 100

Children may be able to count to 100, but they may not be applying place value concepts (Van de Walle, 2007). Counting by ones and counting by tens sets the foundation for further exploration and learning about the base-ten structure of the place value system. To become proficient with numbers greater than 10, children will learn to group by tens and represent numbers using the place value or base-ten positional system. To attain this proficiency, they must see structure. Children engage in grouping activities with tens and ones.

From the Research

"It is absolutely essential that students develop a solid understanding of the base-ten numeration system and place value concepts ... including how numbers are written."
(NCTM, 2000, p. 81)

Count and Order Numbers to 100

A hundred chart extends children's ability to count to 100 and to identify number patterns shown on the hundred chart.

- Children should use a hundred chart to count. After counting, they compa-re the positions of numbers on the hundred chart by using the phrases *greater than* and *less than*.

- Children compare sets by counting and then recording the number of objects in each set. Then they can identify the set that has more or fewer objects.

Mathematical Practices and Processes

Use appropriate tools strategically.

Children use ten frames and the hundred chart to extend their experiences representing, counting, and writing numbers to 20 and beyond. Ten frames and counters are useful for showing 20, while the hundred chart is useful for counting to 100 by ones and tens. Using ten frames and the hundred chart helps children see how different tools can support their thinking. These experiences will help children use different methods and tools.

For more professional learning, go online to Teacher's Corner.

Instructional Journey

While every classroom may look a little different, this instructional model provides a framework to organize small-group and whole-group learning for meaningful student learning.

Whole Group
Engage

5 minutes

Readiness
- Problem of the Day
- Fluency Builder or Vocabulary Builder
- Access Prior Knowledge

Engagement
- I Can
- Making Connections
- Learning Activity

Small and Whole Group
Explore

15–20 minutes

Exploration
- Listen and Draw, Unlock the Problem
- Multilingual Support and Strategy
- Common Errors

Small Group
Explain

15–20 minutes

Quick Check

 Share and Show

Differentiated Instruction

Grab-and-Go!
Version 2.0

Intervention
- Waggle
- Reteach
- Tier 2 and Tier 3 MTSS
- Tabletop Flipchart Mini Lessons

Language Support
- Vocabulary Activities
- Language Routines
- Multilingual Glossary

Enrichment
- Waggle Games
- Ready for More
- Enrich

Whole Group
Elaborate

5 minutes

- Math on the Spot Videos
- Higher-Order Thinking Problems

Evaluate

- I Can Reflection
- Exit Ticket
- Practice and Homework
- Fluency Practice
- Waggle

Assessment

Diagnostic	Formative	Summative
• Show What You Know	• Lesson Quick Check	• Chapter Review • Chapter Test • Performance Assessment Task

Grab-and-Go!
Version 2.0
Differentiated Centers Kit
The kit provides literature, games, and activities for small-group learning.

Strategies for
Multilingual Learners

Understanding a child's language development is helpful in differentiating teaching and assessment. Assessing a child's understanding of mathematical concepts can be done by listening, speaking, reading, and writing. The level of support a child needs determines how best to assess that child's understanding of mathematical concepts.

Planning for Instruction			
Language Support	**Substantial** (WIDA Level 1)*	**Moderate** (WIDA Levels 2 & 3)*	**Light** (WIDA Levels 4 & 5)*
Child's Use of Language	• uses single words • uses common short phrases • heavily relies on visual supports and use of manipulatives	• uses simple sentences • uses some academic vocabulary • relies on visual supports and use of manipulatives	• uses a variety of sentences • uses academic vocabulary • benefits from visual supports and manipulatives
Ways to Assess Understanding	**Listening:** points to pictures, words, or phrases to answer questions **Speaking:** answers *yes/no* questions **Reading:** matches symbols to math terms and concepts **Writing:** draws a visual representation of a problem	**Listening:** matches, categorizes, or sequences information based on visuals **Speaking:** begins to explain reasoning, asks math questions, repeats explanations from peers **Reading:** identifies important information to solve a problem **Writing:** uses simple sentences and visual representations	**Listening:** draws conclusions and makes connections based on what they heard **Speaking:** explains and justifies concepts and solutions **Reading:** understands information in math contexts **Writing:** completes sentences using some academic vocabulary

* For more information on WIDA Standards, visit their website at:
https://wida.wisc.edu/.

• Look for strategies throughout the lesson to support multilingual learners.
• Log on to ED to find additional multilingual activities and Vocabulary Cards.

In This Chapter

Key Academic Vocabulary

Current Development • Vocabulary

fifty, one hundred

Using Language Routines to Develop Understanding

 Language routines provide opportunities for children to develop an understanding of mathematical language and concepts by listening, speaking, reading, and writing. More information on these language routines can be found on the Language Support Cards.

Compare and Contrast

Children share their work with a partner to compare and contrast their strategies.

Language Support	Substantial (WIDA Level 1)*	Moderate (WIDA Levels 2 & 3)*	Light (WIDA Levels 4 & 5)*
Language Routine Differentiation	Children will physically point out similarities and differences on visual representations. They may use short phrases such as "the same" and "different" to verbally compare and contrast their strategies.	Children will rely on visual representations to inform their simple-sentence discussions as they compare and contrast their strategies.	Children will be able to use some academic vocabulary to compare and contrast their strategies with a partner or small group.
Possible Student Work	Provide a hundred chart and ask, "What number is one less than 46?" Children may respond by pointing to or circling 45. Ask children to circle another number on the hundred chart. Ask, "Is the number you circled less than 45?" Children may nod or say yes or no.	Provide a hundred chart and ask, "What number is one less than 46?" children may say, "45." Ask children to circle another number on the hundred chart. Ask, "Is the number you circled less than 45? How do you know?" Children may say, "Yes. It is less because it is before 45."	Provide a hundred chart and ask, "What number is one less than 46?" children may write "45." Ask children to circle another number on the hundred chart. Ask, "Is the number you circled less than 45? How do you know?" Children may say, "Yes. The hundred chart shows that it is less because my number is before 45."

* For more information on WIDA Standards, visit their website at:
https://wida.wisc.edu/.

Assessing Prior Knowledge

Have children complete **Show What You Know** on their own. Items tested are the prerequisite skills for this chapter.

Diagnostic Interview Task

The alternative interview tasks below evaluate children's understanding of each **Show What You Know** skill. The diagnostic chart may be used for intervention on prerequisite skills.

MATERIALS two-color counters, numeral cards (9–12), ten frames

- Have the child count out 8 counters and arrange them in two rows.
- **How many counters are there?** 8

Have the child arrange the same eight counters into three rows and count. Point out that the arrangement changed, but the number of counters did not.

- Place 10 counters on a ten frame. Place 8 counters on a second ten frame.
- **Which ten frame has fewer counters?** the one with eight counters
- Display the numeral cards nonsequentially. Ask the child to order the numbers from least to greatest.

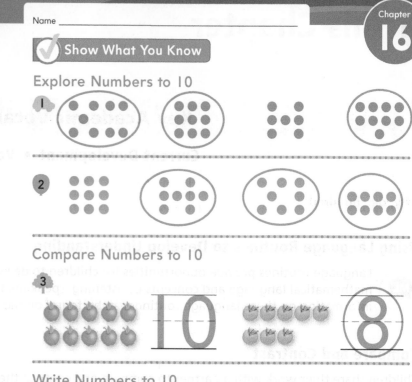

Name _____

✓ Show What You Know

Explore Numbers to 10

1

2

Compare Numbers to 10

3

Write Numbers to 10

4   3 4 5 6 7 8

This page checks understanding of important skills needed for success in Chapter 16.

DIRECTIONS 1. Circle all the sets that show 9. 2. Circle all the sets that show 8. 3. Count and tell how many. Write the number. Circle the number that is less. 4. Write the numbers in order as you count forward.

Chapter 16 • Count to 100   **607**

© Houghton Mifflin Harcourt Publishing Company

✓ Show What You Know • Diagnostic Assessment

Use to determine if children need intervention for the chapter's prerequisite skills.

	Skill	Missed More Than	Intervene With
TIER 3	Explore Numbers to 10	0	*Intensive Intervention* Skill E13
TIER 2	Compare Numbers to 10	0	*Strategic Intervention* Skills S23, S24
TIER 2	Write Numbers to 10	0	*Strategic Intervention* Skill S1

Were children successful with **Show What You Know?**

If NO...then **INTERVENE**

If YES...then use **INDEPENDENT ACTIVITIES**

Grab-and-Go!™

Version 2.0

Differentiated Centers Kit

Use the Reteach or Enrich Activities online or the independent activities in the *Grab-and-Go 2.0™ Differentiated Centers Kit*.

Vocabulary Builder

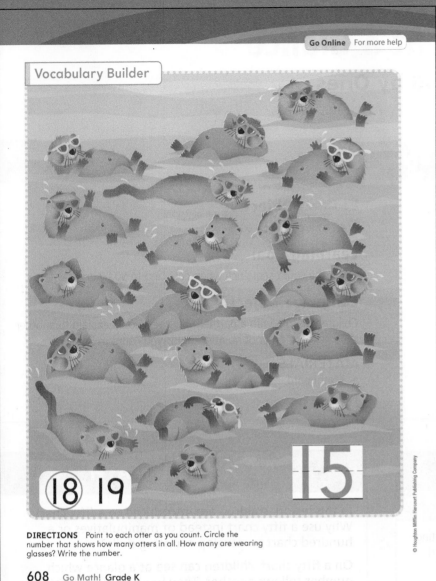

Vocabulary Builder

 18 19

15

DIRECTIONS Point to each otter as you count. Circle the number that shows how many otters in all. How many are wearing glasses? Write the number.

608 Go Math! Grade K

Vocabulary Builder

Children use multiple strategies to develop grade-appropriate vocabulary. Have children complete the activities on the page by working alone or with partners.

Look at the page with children.

Have children count aloud as they point to each sea otter.

- **How many otters are there?** 18
- **Point to the number that shows how many otters in all.**
- **How many otters are wearing sunglasses?** 15
- **Write the number.** 15
- **Are there more otters wearing sunglasses or more otters without sunglasses?** more otters with sunglasses

 School-Home Letter is available in English and Spanish online, and in multiple other languages.

Intervention Options *MTSS* (RtI) Response to Intervention

Use Show What You Know, Lesson Quick Check, and Assessments to diagnose children's intervention levels.

TIER 1	TIER 2	TIER 3	ENRICHMENT
On-Level Intervention	**Strategic Intervention**	**Intensive Intervention**	**Independent Activities**
For children who are generally at grade level but need early intervention with the lesson concepts, use:	For children who need small-group instruction to review concepts and skills needed for the chapter, use:	For children who need one-on-one instruction to build foundational skills for the chapter, use:	For children who successfully complete lessons, use:
• Reteach			• Waggle Practice and Games
• Tabletop Flipchart Mini Lesson	▲ Prerequisite Skills Activities	▲ Prerequisite Skills Activities	**Grab and Go!**
• Waggle	▲ Tier 2 Activity	▲ Tier 3 Activity	Version 2.0
▲ Tier 1 Activity			Differentiated Centers Kit
			• Ready for More Activity for every lesson
			• Enrich

Lesson at a Glance
Count to 50 by Ones

SNAPSHOT

Mathematical Standards
- Count to 100 by ones and by tens.

Mathematical Practices and Processes
- Attend to precision.
- Construct arguments and critique reasoning of others.
- Look for and make use of structure.
- Reason abstractly and quantitatively.

(I Can) **Objective**
I can count to 50 by ones.

Learning Goal
Know the count sequence when counting to 50 by ones.

Language Objective
Children discuss with a partner how they would explain to another child how the order of numbers helps you count to 50 by ones.

MATERIALS
- MathBoard

ACROSS THE GRADES

Grade K

Recite the number names to 100 by ones and by tens. Starting at a given number, count forward within 100 and backward within 20.

After

Starting at a given number, count forward and backwards within 120 by ones. Skip count by 2s to 20 and by 5s to 100.

ABOUT THE MATH

In this lesson, children are introduced to a fifty chart. Why use a fifty chart instead of manipulatives or a hundred chart to develop counting skills?

On a fifty chart, children can see at a glance which number follows another. They begin to detect patterns in numbers not as obvious as in manipulatives such as connecting cubes. Ask children questions such as the following as they study the fifty chart:

- **What do you notice about the numbers in this column?**
- **How are the numbers in this row like the ones in the next row?**

The fifty chart prepares children for using the hundred chart, a very important tool in the development of place-value concepts.

For more professional learning, go online to Teacher's Corner.

DAILY ROUTINES

 Problem of the Day 16.1

What number is two greater than 18? 20 **What number is two less than 30?** 28

Have children start counting at 20 and count forward to 28.

 Vocabulary fifty

- Interactive Student Edition
- Multilingual Glossary

Vocabulary Builder

Work as a class to model 50 objects. Encourage children to show the objects in groups of 10.

FOCUSING ON THE WHOLE STUDENT

Access Prior Knowledge

Give children more practice comparing numbers. Have them count from 1 to 20.

- **What number is one greater than 14 and one less than 16?** 15

Continue with other numbers.

Culturally Responsive Education

Use this chapter's concept as an opportunity to foster relationships with children's families. Suggest counting games that families can play with children at home, such as the child and another family member counting every other number. Ask families to help their children find 50 of something outside, whether they collect it or simply count it. Ask families if children seem to find the concept exciting or if they seem less engaged. Listen to feedback from families and use the feedback to improve your relationships with their children.

1 Engage

with the Interactive Student Edition

I Can Objective

I can count to 50 by ones.

Making Connections

Ask children what they know about counting and ordering up to 20.

- **Hold up both your hands. Count aloud how many fingers you are holding up.** 1, 2 . . . 10
- **Count aloud to 20. Start with 11 instead of 1.** 11, 12 . . . 20
- **Is 20 greater or less than 10?** greater
- **How do you know?** Possible answers: because two 10s make a 20; because 20 comes after 10 when I count

Learning Activity

Draw a row of 10 trash cans numbered 21 to 30, with the number 27 omitted.

Guide children toward understanding how counting order can help them find missing numbers in a sequence.

- **How many trash cans do you see?** 10
- **How do you know the trash cans are in the right order?** Possible answer: because 21 always comes before 22 when I count
- **What are you trying to figure out?** the missing number for one of the trash cans

② Explore

Listen and Draw

Read the problem aloud as children look at the fifty chart on the page.

Bella wants to count to 50 by reading a fifty chart. Where will she look for the first number? What number will be the last one she says?

 Construct arguments and critique reasoning of others.

- **Why do you think this chart is called a fifty chart?** It shows numbers 1 to 50.
- **How many rows does it have?** 5
- **How many numbers are in each row?** 10
- **What is the first number in the top row?** 1
- **Where should Bella look for the first number?** She should look at the first number in the top row.

 Look for and make use of structure.

- **How are the first nine numbers in the second row like the first nine numbers in the first row? How are the last numbers in the first two rows the same?** The first nine numbers in each row end with the numbers 1 to 9 in order. The last numbers in the first two rows end with zero.

Reason abstractly and quantitatively.

Review with children that when they count, each number is one greater than the number before it.

- **Point to each number in the top row. Say the number names in order.** 1, 2, 3, 4, 5, 6, 7, 8, 9, 10
- **Point to the beginning of the next row. What number do you count after 10?** 11

Have children continue to count in order to 20, pointing to each number as they count.

Reread the word problem.

- **What is the last number on the fifty chart?** 50
- **What number will be the last one Bella says?** 50

Challenge children to use the fifty chart to tell whether it is always true that a number is one greater than the number before it in the counting order.

Name _____

Count to 50 by Ones

(I Can) count to 50 by ones.

Listen and Draw

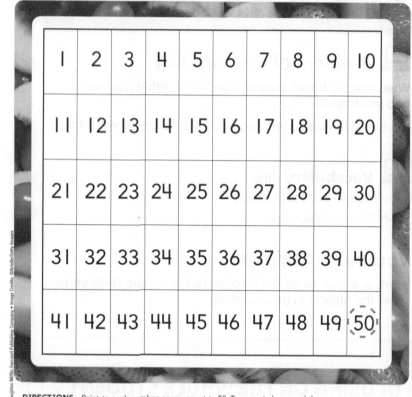

1	2	3	4	5	6	7	8	9	10
11	12	13	14	15	16	17	18	19	20
21	22	23	24	25	26	27	28	29	30
31	32	33	34	35	36	37	38	39	40
41	42	43	44	45	46	47	48	49	50

DIRECTIONS Point to each number as you count to 50. Trace a circle around the number 50. Check children's work.

Chapter 16 • Lesson 1   609

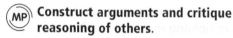 **Multilingual Support**

STRATEGY: Identify Relationships

Children can use the number patterns they are familiar with to better understand counting.

Write the following set of ordered numbers on the board: **24, 25, _____, 27, _____, 29.** Ask children to look for patterns.

- **How do you know what number goes in the first blank?** Possible answer: Since 6 comes after 5, 26 should come after 25.

Have children use number patterns to find the second missing number in the set.

Repeat with other sets of ordered numbers, having children identify missing numbers in each set and explain their answers.

1	2	3	4	5	6	7	8	9	10
11	12	13	14	(15)	16	17	18	19	20
21	22	23	24	25	26	27	28	29	30
31	32	33	34	35	36	37	38	39	40
41	42	43	44	45	46	47	48	49	50

© Houghton Mifflin Harcourt Publishing Company

DIRECTIONS 1. Point to each number as you count to 50. Circle the number 15. Begin with 15 and count forward to 50. Draw a line under the number 50.

Ready for More

 Kinesthetic
Individuals / Partners

Materials fifty chart

Have one partner hold the fifty chart so the other partner cannot see it.

The partner looking at the fifty chart asks two questions, one at a time, about the numbers on the chart. Sample questions: **What number is one greater than 39?** 40 **What number is greater than 24 and less than 26?** 25

The partner facing away from the chart answers. Partners switch roles and continue the activity.

1	2	3	4	5	6	7	8	9	10
11	12	13	14	15	16	17	18	19	20
21	22	23	24	25	26	27	28	29	30
31	32	33	34	35	36	37	38	39	40
41	42	43	44	45	46	47	48	49	50

③ Explain

Share and Show

Have children describe the chart on the page.

- **How are the numbers shown on the chart?**
  They are shown in order, 1 to 50.

(MP) Attend to precision.

Have children point to each number as you count together. 1, 2, 3, . . . 48, 49, 50

Remind children that when they finish counting a row, they move down to the next row and start counting from left to right.

- **Find the number 15. Circle it.**
- **Begin at 15 and count forward to 50.**
- **Draw a line below the number 50.**

Have children tell how they know each answer is correct.

! Common Errors

Error Children may not be able to follow the order of the numbers on the chart.

Example Children do not track correctly to the next row on the chart.

Springboard to Learning Have children cover all except the top two rows. Count from 1 to 10 and direct attention to the next row. Have children move the cover down a row and sweep their fingers to the beginning of the second row to continue counting from 11. Repeat with the remaining rows to 50.

Chapter 16 • Lesson 1   610

Share and Show

Call attention to the fifty chart. Count from 1 to 50 as a group. Remind children to point to each number as they count.

Have each child look away from the page and point to any number. Have children circle the number and count forward from that number to 50. Have them draw a line under the number 50.

Higher-Order Thinking

(MP) **Look for and make use of structure.**

Read aloud the following problem to children. Have them discuss models and strategies they can use to solve it.

- **Jobi counts forward from 25 to 39. Then Michelle continues counting forward to 50. What numbers does Michelle say?** 40, 41, 42, 43, 44, 45, 46, 47, 48, 49, 50

Children should be able to use what they know about counting to 50 to continue the counting pattern. Ask how they know what numbers follow 39 to end at 50.

Use the checked problem for Quick Check.

Math on the Spot Use this video to help children model and solve this type of problem.

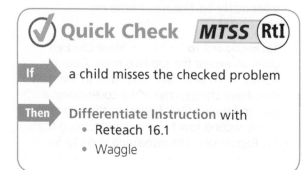

✓ Quick Check   *MTSS* (RtI)

If	a child misses the checked problem
Then	Differentiate Instruction with • Reteach 16.1 • Waggle

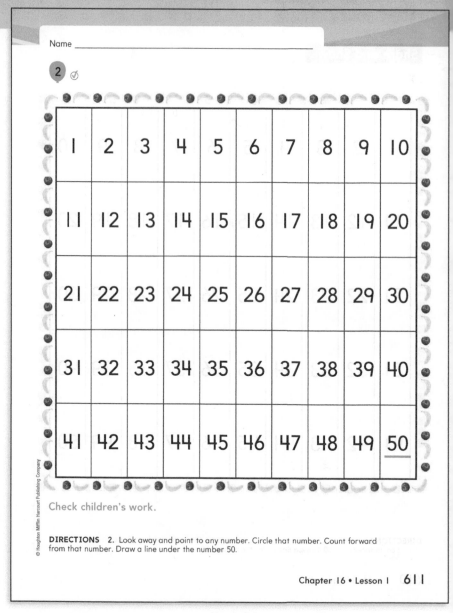

Name _____

2 ✓

1	2	3	4	5	6	7	8	9	10
11	12	13	14	15	16	17	18	19	20
21	22	23	24	25	26	27	28	29	30
31	32	33	34	35	36	37	38	39	40
41	42	43	44	45	46	47	48	49	50

Check children's work.

DIRECTIONS   2. Look away and point to any number. Circle that number. Count forward from that number. Draw a line under the number 50.

Chapter 16 • Lesson 1   **611**

Meeting Individual Needs

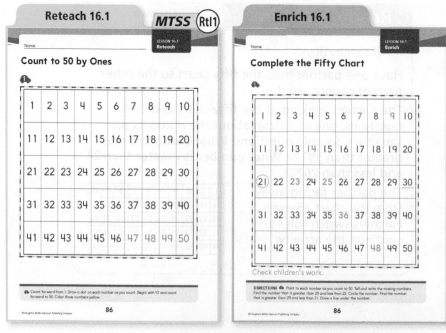

Reteach 16.1   *MTSS* (RtI1)

Name _____

LESSON 16.1 Reteach

Count to 50 by Ones

1	2	3	4	5	6	7	8	9	10
11	12	13	14	15	16	17	18	19	20
21	22	23	24	25	26	27	28	29	30
31	32	33	34	35	36	37	38	39	40
41	42	43	44	45	46	47	48	49	50

Count forward from 1. Draw a dot on each number as you count. Begin with 47 and count forward to 50. Color those numbers yellow.

86

Enrich 16.1

Name _____

LESSON 16.1 Enrich

Complete the Fifty Chart

1	2	3	4	5	6	7	8	9	10
11	12	13	14	15	16	17	18	19	20
21	22	23	24	25	26	27	28	29	30
31	32	33	34	35	36	37	38	39	40
41	42	43	44	45	46	47	48	49	50

Check children's work.

DIRECTIONS Point to each number as you count to 50. Tell and write the missing numbers. Find the number that is greater than 20 and less than 22. Circle the number. Find the number that is greater than 29 and less than 31. Draw a line under the number.

86

③ WRITE Math

1	2	3	4	5	6	7	8	9	10
11	12	13	14	15	16	17	18 (blue)	19	20
21	22	23	24	25 (red)	26	27	28	29	30
31	32	33	34	35	36	37	38	39	40
41	42	43	44	45	46	47	48	49	50

DIRECTIONS 3. I am greater than 17 and less than 19. What number am I? Use blue to color that number. I am greater than 24 and less than 26. What number am I? Use red to color that number.

 **HOME ACTIVITY** • Think of a number between 1 and 50. Say *greater than* and *less than* to describe your number. Have your child say the number.

612   Go Math! Grade K

© Houghton Mifflin Harcourt Publishing Company

---

④ Elaborate

Problem Solving Applications

Problem 3 Explain to children that they are going to use the fifty chart to solve riddles. Read the first riddle aloud.

• **What number is greater than 17 and less than 19?** 18 **Color the number blue.**

(MP) **Construct arguments and critique reasoning of others.**

• **How did you know which number to color blue?** Possible answer: I found 17 on the fifty chart. I used the counting order to see that 18 is one greater than 17 and one less than 19.

Read the next riddle aloud.

• **What number is greater than 24 and less than 26?** 25 **Use red to color the number.**

⑤ Evaluate | Formative Assessment

I Can

Have children discuss with a partner how they would finish the I Can statement.

I can count to 50 by ones by . . . following the counting order. I know what number to say after each number. If I start with 1 and say each number in counting order, I can count from 1 to 50.

Exit Ticket

Write the number 10. What are the numbers that come after? Write all of the numbers from 10 to 50.

DIFFERENTIATED INSTRUCTION • Independent Activities

Grab-and-Go!
Version 2.0
Differentiated Centers Kit

Tabletop Flipchart

Mini-lessons for reteaching to targeted small groups

Readers

Supports key math skills and concepts in real-world situations.

Games

Reinforce math content and vocabulary

Activities

Meaningful and fun math practice

Practice and Homework

Count to 50 by Ones

Use the Practice and Homework pages to provide children with more practice of the concepts and skills presented in this lesson. Children master their understanding as they complete practice items.

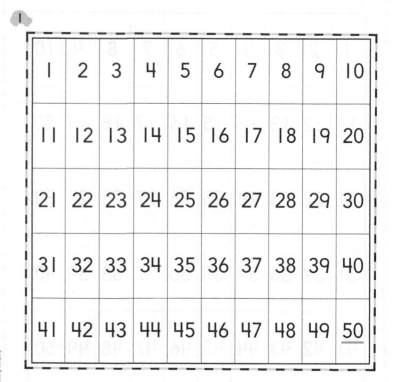

1	2	3	4	5	6	7	8	9	10
11	12	13	14	15	16	17	18	19	20
21	22	23	24	25	26	27	28	29	30
31	32	33	34	35	36	37	38	39	40
41	42	43	44	45	46	47	48	49	50

Check children's work.

DIRECTIONS 1. Look away and point to any number. Circle that number. Count forward from that number. Draw a line under the number 50.

Chapter 16 • Lesson 1 613

CROSS-CURRICULAR

SCIENCE

Materials self-stick notes, chart paper

- Draw a fifty chart on chart paper, leaving each square large enough to hold a self-stick note. Next to it, write: **day, night, day, night, day, night**. Establish that day follows night and night follows day. Refer to it as a sequence, or order, that never changes.
- Recall that numbers have sequence, or order, too.
- Write the following on self-stick notes and show them on the board in this order: 44, 35, 40, 43, 38, 36, 41, 42, 39, 37. Have children place one self-stick note at a time on the fifty chart until the numbers are in order.

| day | night | day | night | day | night |

SOCIAL STUDIES

Materials chart paper

- Discuss the difference between **needs** and **wants**. Explain that food is a **need** and that a toy is a **want**.
- Talk about basic needs that creatures have, such as shelter, food, and water.
- Make a chart with the following information:

  30 apples   27 apples   25 apples
  26 apples   28 apples   29 apples

- Read the chart with children. Have children put the numbers on the chart in order and count from the greatest number to 50.

Lesson Check

1	2	3	4	5	6	7	8	9	10
11	12	13	14	15	16	17	18	19	20
<u>21</u>	22	23	24	25	26	27	28	29	30

Spiral Review

$$7 = 2 + 5$$

$$10 - 3 = 7$$

DIRECTIONS **2.** Begin with 1 and count forward to 20. What is the next number? Draw a line under that number. **3.** Complete the addition sentence to show the numbers that match the cube train. **4.** Shelley has 10 counters. Three of her counters are white. The rest of her counters are gray. How many are gray? Complete the subtraction sentence to show the answer.

© Houghton Mifflin Harcourt Publishing Company

614 Go Math! **Grade K**

Continue to practice concepts and skills with Lesson Check. Use Spiral Review to engage children in previously taught concepts and to promote content retention.

Lesson at a Glance
Count to 100 by Ones

SNAPSHOT

Mathematical Standards
- Count to 100 by ones and by tens.

Mathematical Practices and Processes
- Express regularity in repeated reasoning.
- Reason abstractly and quantitatively.
- Attend to precision.
- Construct arguments and critique reasoning of others.
- Use appropriate tools strategically.
- Look for and make use of structure.

(I Can) Objective
I can count to 100 by ones.

Learning Goal
Know the count sequence when counting to 100 by ones.

Language Objective
Children explain to a partner how the order of numbers helps you to count to 100 by ones.

MATERIALS
- MathBoard

ACROSS THE GRADES

Grade K

Recite the number names to 100 by ones and by tens. Starting at a given number, count forward within 100 and backward within 20.

After

Starting at a given number, count forward and backwards within 120 by ones. Skip count by 2s to 20 and by 5s to 100.

ABOUT THE MATH

Teaching for Depth

John Van de Walle recommended in his book, *Elementary and Middle School Mathematics: Teaching Developmentally*, that teachers encourage children to explore counting patterns on hundred charts.

In this lesson, children are introduced to the hundred chart. They will begin to identify patterns in the sequence of numbers. They will look for relationships between "neighboring numbers."

Even though children in kindergarten may not have an understanding of place value, they can learn much about the sequence of numbers to 100 by using the hundred chart.

For more professional learning, go online to Teacher's Corner.

Problem of the Day 16.2

Name five numbers that are greater than 12 and less than 18 but are not the same number.
13, 14, 15, 16, 17

Have a volunteer write the numbers in order on the board. Have children take turns completing these sentence frames for the numbers on the board:
___ is greater than ___; ___ is less than ___

Vocabulary one hundred

- Interactive Student Edition
- Multilingual Glossary

Vocabulary Builder

Materials hundred chart

Show children a hundred chart.

- **Each square represents one. How many ones are in the first row?** 10
- **Each row represents a set of 10 ones.**

Count with children the number of rows in the chart, circling each row after you have counted it.

- **How many sets are there in all?** 10
- *One hundred* is 10 sets of 10 ones.

1	2	3	4	5	6	7	8	9	10
11	12	13	14	15	16	17	18	19	20
21	22	23	24	25	26	27	28	29	30
31	32	33	34	35	36	37	38	39	40
41	42	43	44	45	46	47	48	49	50
51	52	53	54	55	56	57	58	59	60
61	62	63	64	65	66	67	68	69	70
71	72	73	74	75	76	77	78	79	80
81	82	83	84	85	86	87	88	89	90
91	92	93	94	95	96	97	98	99	100

FOCUSING ON THE WHOLE STUDENT

💬 Social & Emotional Learning

Self-Awareness After the lesson, encourage children to recognize when they are ready for a challenge. *When you have confidence, you know you can do something. Did you believe that you could count by ones to 100? If you believe that you can do it, you are more likely to try harder until you do. It is okay if you were not sure you could do it. If you are not sure if you can count to 100, try to count farther each time you try. If you count a little farther each time, eventually you will reach your goal.*

① Engage

with the Interactive Student Edition

I Can Objective

I can count to 100 by ones.

Making Connections

Review with children what they know about counting and ordering up to 50.

- **Is 20 more or less than 30?** less **How do you know?** Possible answers: because it comes first when I'm counting by ones; because it comes first on a number chart; because 30 has one more 10 than 20

- **What are some ways you can count to 50?** Possible answers: We can count out loud together; I can use my fingers; I can use a number chart.

Learning Activity

Tell children a story about 89 people visiting a science museum. Direct children toward using a number chart to identify a specific number.

- **Do numbers go in counting order in a number chart?** yes

- **Is the number of visitors greater or less than 86?** greater

- **How do you know?** because the number comes right after 86 in a number chart

Explore

Listen and Draw

Read the problem aloud as children listen.

Ben reads the numbers on a hundred chart. What is the first number he says? What will be the last number he says?

 Look for and make use of structure.

- **Look at this chart of numbers. It is called a hundred chart.**

Explain that it is like a fifty chart because it has rows and numbers in order. It is a hundred chart because it has the numbers 1 to 100.

- **What is the first number on the chart?** 1
- **What is the first number Ben says?** 1
- **How can you use the top row to count?** Point to numbers across the row and say them in order.
- **When you reach the end of the top row, how can you continue your counting?** Go down to the beginning of the next row.

 Attend to precision.

Have children point to each number as they count to 100. Check that they move correctly from row to row. Stop at the end of each row. Discuss the new tens number and remind children that it is used to name the numbers in the next row.

- **What is the last number on the chart?** 100
- **What will be the last number Ben says?** 100
- **If Ben started counting over again from the beginning, what number would he say first?** 1

Name _____

Count to 100 by Ones

(I Can) count to 100 by ones.

Listen and Draw

1	2	3	4	5	6	7	8	9	10
11	12	13	14	15	16	17	18	19	20
21	22	23	24	25	26	27	28	29	30
31	32	33	34	35	36	37	38	39	40
41	42	43	44	45	46	47	48	49	50
51	52	53	54	55	56	57	58	59	60
61	62	63	64	65	66	67	68	69	70
71	72	73	74	75	76	77	78	79	80
81	82	83	84	85	86	87	88	89	90
91	92	93	94	95	96	97	98	99	100

© Houghton Mifflin Harcourt Publishing Company

DIRECTIONS Point to each number as you count to 100. Trace a circle around the number 100.

Check children's work.

Chapter 16 • Lesson 2 **615**

(ML) ## Multilingual Support

STRATEGY: Model Concepts

Children can count to 100 using counting patterns if they are modeled.

Have children point to each number on the hundred chart as they count to 100.

To help children identify the counting pattern, have them emphasize the digits that repeat each decade as they point to them on the hundred chart: twenty-ONE, twenty-TWO, twenty-THREE . . .

Ask children to explain how they know what comes next at least once for each decade, or ten years, on the hundred chart.

1	2	3	4	5	6	7	8	9	10
(11)	12	13	14	15	16	17	18	19	20
21	22	23	24	25	26	27	28	29	30
31	32	33	34	35	36	37	38	39	40
41	42	43	44	45	46	47	48	49	50
51	52	53	54	55	56	57	58	59	60
61	62	63	64	65	66	67	68	69	70
71	72	73	74	75	76	77	78	79	80
81	82	83	84	85	86	87	88	89	90
91	92	93	94	95	96	97	98	99	__100__

DIRECTIONS 1. Point to each number as you count to 100. Circle the number 11. Begin with 11 and count forward to 100. Draw a line under the number 100.

616 Go Math! Grade K

Ready for More

Mathematical / Visual
Individual / Small Group

Materials 10 × 10 grid

Distribute grids and let children color squares to create simple pictures or designs.

Have children count the number of colored squares and write the number. Then have them count forward from that number to 100. Display children's work.

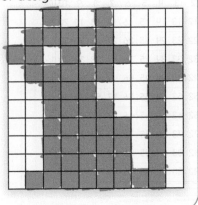

3 Explain

Share and Show

- **What do you see on this page?** a hundred chart
- **How do you know that it is a hundred chart?** It has the numbers 1 to 100 in order.

MP Use appropriate tools strategically.

Show children a hundred chart.

- **Point to each number on the chart as you count aloud to 100.**
- **Find the number 11. Circle it.**
- **Begin at 11 and count forward to 20.**
- **What is the same about all the numbers you counted except 20?** They start with 1.
- **How did the numbers change as you counted from 11 to 19?** They ended with the numbers 1 to 9 in order.
- **Now begin at 11 and count forward to 100.**
- **Draw a line below the number 100.**

Have children repeat this activity by counting forward from 61 to 70 and from 91 to 100.

- **Point to each number as we count. 1, 2, 3 . . . 98, 99, 100.**

Remind children how to move to the next row when they reach the end of each row.

MP Reason abstractly and quantitatively.

- **How did the numbers change as you counted?** The numbers went up. **How do you know?** I know because each number was one more than the one before it.

Common Errors

Error Children may not count all of the numbers as they use the chart to count.

Example Children count 61, 62, 64, 65, 66, 68, 70.

Springboard to Learning Instead of picking up their fingers after they say a number and then pointing to the next number, have children slide their fingers across each row, stopping on each successive number.

Share and Show

Explain to children that they will count the numbers on this hundred chart as they did on the previous page. Then suggest that children place one hand on the hundred chart. Ask them to look away, lift the hand slightly, and point to a number. They then circle the number, count forward from this number to 100, and draw a line under 100.

Use the checked problem for Quick Check.

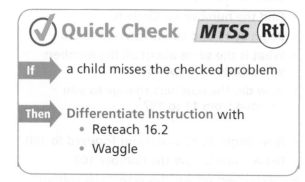

✓ **Quick Check** **MTSS** **RtI**

If → a child misses the checked problem

Then → **Differentiate Instruction** with
- Reteach 16.2
- Waggle

Higher-Order Thinking

(MP) **Express regularity in repeated reasoning.**

Read aloud the following problem to children. Discuss strategies they can use to solve it.

- **Darlene counts forward from 1 and stops at 87. The teacher asks Julio to continue counting to 100. What numbers does Julio say?** 88, 89, 90, 91, 92, 93, 94, 95, 96, 97, 98, 99, 100.

Children should be able to use what they know about counting to 100 to continue a counting pattern, starting from a given number. They should be able to explain how they know what numbers follow 87 to end at 100.

Math on the Spot Use this video to help children model and solve this type of problem.

Name _____

2 ✓

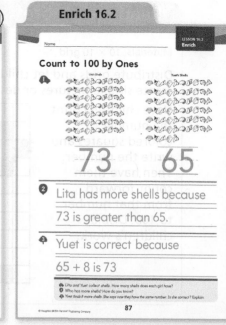

Check children's work.

DIRECTIONS 2. Point to each number as you count to 100. Look away and point to any number. Circle that number. Count forward to 100 from that number. Draw a line under the number 100.

Meeting Individual Needs

Reteach 16.2 **MTSS** **RtI1**

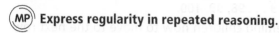

Enrich 16.2

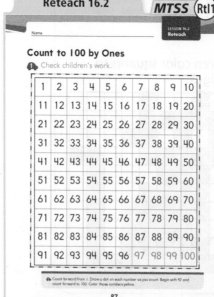

Check children's work.

DIRECTIONS 3. Place your finger on the number 15. Write or trace to show the numbers that are "neighbors" to the number 15. Say *greater than* and *less than* to describe the numbers. 4. Draw to show what you know about some other "neighbor" numbers in the chart.

HOME ACTIVITY • Show your child a calendar. Point to a number on the calendar. Have him or her tell you all the numbers that are "neighbors" to that number.

618 Go Math! Grade K

© Houghton Mifflin Harcourt Publishing Company • Image Credit: ©HMH

---

④ Elaborate

Problem Solving Applications

Problem 3 Have children point to 15.

- The numbers around 15 are called the neighbors of 15.

(MP) Construct arguments and critique reasoning of others.

- **What number would be just before 15?** 14 **Write it. Use the term *less than* to describe the numbers.** 14 is less than 15.

- **What number is just after 15?** 16 **Write it. Use the term *greater than* to describe these numbers.** 16 is greater than 15.

- **How can you find the number that is just above 15 on the chart?** I know that 5 is one greater than 4 and one less than 6. I know that 5 is 10 less than 15. **Write it.**

- **How can you find the number that is just below 15 on the chart?** I know that 25 is one greater than 24 and one less than 26. I know that 25 is 10 more than 15. **Write it.**

Problem 4 Discuss ideas about other neighbor numbers children find in the chart.

DIFFERENTIATED INSTRUCTION • Independent Activities

Grab and Go!™
Version 2.0
Differentiated Centers Kit

Tabletop Flipchart

Mini-lessons for reteaching to targeted small groups

Readers

Supports key math skills and concepts in real-world situations.

Games

Reinforce math content and vocabulary

Activities

Meaningful and fun math practice

---

⑤ Evaluate | Formative Assessment

I Can

Have children explain to partners how to answer the I Can statement.

I can count to 100 by ones by . . . knowing the order of numbers. I can start counting from any number and count by ones to 100.

Exit Ticket

Have children share their drawings with a friend. Children should describe their drawings using math vocabulary such as *greater than* and *less than*, and also explain how they decided what to draw.

Practice and Homework

Count to 100 by Ones

Use the Practice and Homework pages to provide children with more practice of the concepts and skills presented in this lesson. Children master their understanding as they complete practice items.

Count to 100 by Ones

1	2	3	4	5	6	7	8	9	10
11	12	13	14	15	16	17	18	19	20
21	22	23	24	25	26	27	28	29	30
31	32	33	34	35	36	37	38	39	40
41	42	43	44	45	46	47	48	49	50
51	52	53	54	55	56	57	58	59	60
61	62	63	64	65	66	67	68	69	70
71	72	73	74	75	76	77	78	79	80
81	82	83	84	85	86	87	88	89	90
91	92	93	94	95	96	97	98	99	100

Check children's work.

DIRECTIONS 1. Point to each number as you count to 100. Look away and point to any number. Circle that number. Count forward to 100 from that number. Draw a line under the number 100.

Chapter 16 • Lesson 2   619

© Houghton Mifflin Harcourt Publishing Company

Lesson Check

2

71	72	73	74	75	76	77	78	79	80
81	82	83	84	85	86	87	88	89	90
91	92	93	94	95	96	97	98	99	100

Spiral Review

3

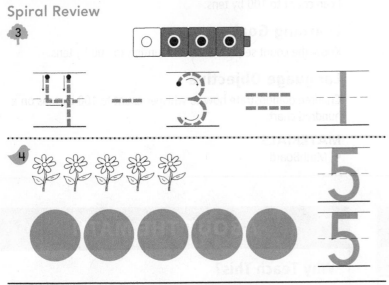

4

DIRECTIONS **2.** Begin with 71 and count forward to 80. What is the next number? Draw a line under that number. **3.** Pete makes the cube train shown. He takes the cube train apart to show how many cubes are gray. Complete the subtraction sentence to show Pete's cube train. **4.** Count how many flowers. Write the number. Draw to show a set of counters that has the same number as the set of flowers. Write the number.

Continue to practice concepts and skills with Lesson Check. Use Spiral Review to engage children in previously taught concepts and to promote content retention.

Lesson at a Glance
Count to 100 by Tens

SNAPSHOT

Mathematical Standards
● Count to 100 by ones and by tens.

Mathematical Practices and Processes
● Reason abstractly and quantitatively.
● Model with mathematics.
● Attend to precision.
● Construct arguments and critique reasoning of others.
● Look for and make use of structure.
● Use appropriate tools strategically.

(I Can) **Objective**
I can count to 100 by tens.

Learning Goal
Know the count sequence when counting to 100 by tens.

Language Objective
Children demonstrate how to whisper count to 100 by tens on a hundred chart.

MATERIALS
● MathBoard

ACROSS THE GRADES

Grade K
Recite the number names to 100 by ones and by tens. Starting at a given number, count forward within 100 and backward within 20.

After
Starting at a given number, count forward and backwards within 120 by ones. Skip count by 2s to 20 and by 5s to 100.

ABOUT THE MATH

Why Teach This?

In this lesson, children have multiple opportunities to count by tens to 100 using a hundred chart. They fill in missing numbers on a chart and continue to discuss relationships between the numbers and the numbers' neighbors on the chart.

As children work with a hundred chart, it is important that they look for patterns in the way that numbers are made. For example, each row of ten has a pattern using the 1 to 9 order. Also, each number in the last column has a pattern with the first number being in the 1 to 9 order and the second number always a 0.

As children use the hundred chart, suggest they touch or point to each number as they count. This will help them as they count forward starting with different numbers than 1 or 10.

For more professional learning, go online to Teacher's Corner.

DAILY ROUTINES

 **Problem of the Day 16.3**

I am thinking of a number that is two less than 30.
What is it? 28 I am thinking of a number that has two zeros.
You can find it on a hundred chart. What is that number?
100

Continue asking riddles about numbers to 100 for children
to solve.

Vocabulary

• Interactive Student Edition
• Multilingual Glossary

Vocabulary Builder

Materials hundred chart

Show children a hundred chart.

• **Each square represents one. How many ones
  are in the first row?** 10

• **Each row represents a ten.**

• **One hundred is 10 *tens*.**

Have children color the tens on the hundred chart.

FOCUSING ON THE WHOLE STUDENT

Access Prior Knowledge

Use a hundred chart. Explain to children that they are
going to read a hundred chart together.

• **What number do you read first when you read the
  hundred chart?** 1

Have children read aloud the numbers across the first row
of the hundred chart.

• **What number will we read next?** 11

Have children read together the rest of the chart as they
point to the numbers.

1 Engage

with the Interactive Student Edition

I Can Objective

I can count to 100 by tens.

Making Connections

Ask children to share what they know about
finding missing numbers in a sequence.

Write the numbers 71–75 and 77–79 on the board,
leaving a blank space between the number ranges.
Ask:

• **What is the same about all of these numbers?**
  Possible answers: They all start with 7; they are
  all 70-something.

• **What is the missing number? How do you know?**
  76. Possible answers: because 76 comes after
  75 and before 77; because 6 comes after 5 and
  before 7

Learning Activity

Tell a story about workers counting a number of
eggs by tens. They count by tens 6 times.

Guide children toward knowing how and why to
count by tens.

• **Why did the workers count the eggs by tens
  instead of by ones?** Possible answers: because
  it's faster; because there are so many eggs

• **Is the number of eggs greater or less than 70?**
  less

• **How do you know?** Possible answer: because
  counting 10 by 6 equals 60, and 60 comes before
  70 on the hundred chart

② Explore

Listen and Draw

Read the problem aloud as children listen.

Olivia is using a hundred chart to count to 100. She wants to find a faster way to get to 100 than counting by ones. What is another way that Olivia can count to 100?

 Use appropriate tools strategically.

- **Look at the hundred chart. Circle all the numbers that end in zero.**
- **Look at the circled numbers. What can you tell about these numbers?** They all end in zero. The first part of each numbers goes up by 1 each time.
- **What is the first number you circled?** 10
- **Start with 10 and say the numbers you circled in order.** 10, 20, 30 . . . 100

Explain that each number circled is 10 more than the circled number before. Have children count several rows to check. Point out that the circled numbers are called tens.

 Reason abstractly and quantitatively.

- **Does every ten end in a zero?** yes
- **Tell a friend how you are counting.** by tens

Reread the word problem.

- **What is a faster way for Olivia to use the hundred chart to count to 100?** by tens

---

Name _____

Count to 100 by Tens

(I Can) count to 100 by tens.

Listen and Draw

1	2	3	4	5	6	7	8	9	10
11	12	13	14	15	16	17	18	19	20
21	22	23	24	25	26	27	28	29	30
31	32	33	34	35	36	37	38	39	40
41	42	43	44	45	46	47	48	49	50
51	52	53	54	55	56	57	58	59	60
61	62	63	64	65	66	67	68	69	70
71	72	73	74	75	76	77	78	79	80
81	82	83	84	85	86	87	88	89	90
91	92	93	94	95	96	97	98	99	100

DIRECTIONS Trace the circles around the numbers that end in a 0. Beginning with 10, count those numbers in order. Tell a friend how you are counting. Check children's work.

Chapter 16 • Lesson 3 **621**

 Multilingual Support

STRATEGY: Scaffold Language

Children can demonstrate their understanding of number patterns by describing them.

Have a volunteer color the first column of a hundred chart.

- **Describe how the numbers in this column end.** They end with 1. **Describe how the numbers begin.** Possible answer: It is like counting from 1 to 9.

Have another volunteer color the last column on the chart. Ask children to use the following sentence frames to describe the numbers in the column.

- **The numbers in this column end with _____. The numbers in this column begin with _____.** Repeat for other columns on the chart.

1	2	3	4	5	6	7	8	9	10
11	12	13	14	15	16	17	18	19	20
21	22	23	24	25	26	27	28	29	30
31	32	33	34	35	36	37	38	39	40
41	42	43	44	45	46	47	48	49	50

Check children's work.

DIRECTIONS 1. Write the numbers to complete the counting order to 20. Trace the numbers to complete the counting order to 50. Count by tens as you point to the numbers you wrote and traced.

622 Go Math! Grade K

© Houghton Mifflin Harcourt Publishing Company

③ Explain

Share and Show Math Board

- **What do you see on this page?** a fifty chart with some missing numbers

 Attend to precision.

- **Start with 1. Point to each number and count until you get to the place where a number is missing.** 1, 2, 3 . . . 9
- **What is the missing number?** 10 **How do you know?** Possible answers: 10 is the next number after 9 when you count; 10 is 1 greater than 9. **Write 10.**

Have children repeat for the remaining rows, writing or tracing 20, 30, 40, and 50.

- **Look at the numbers you wrote. What is the special name for these numbers?** tens
- **Start with 10. Count by tens as you point to the numbers you wrote and traced.** 10, 20, 30, 40, 50
- **How did you just count to 50?** by tens

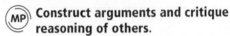 **Construct arguments and critique reasoning of others.**

- **How do you know this way is faster than counting by ones?** It is faster because you are not counting every single number, just the tens.

⚠ Common Errors

Error Children may count the full ten frame as 1 instead of 10.

Example Children count 30 after 10.

Springboard to Learning Show children the last column of a hundred chart. Point out that the first part of each number goes up by one each time.

Ready for More 🕐 Logical / Mathematical Small Group

Materials hundred chart

Suggest that children listen to clues in order to find a "secret number" on a hundred chart.

- **My secret number is between 60 and 80. It comes right after 69. What is my secret number?** 70 Have a child circle 70 on a hundred chart.
- **When you were listening to my riddle, how did you know where to look on the hundred chart?** Possible answer: I know the numbers between 60 and 80 are near the bottom of the chart and 69 is near the last column, so I looked at the end of that row.

Repeat with other numbers.

④ Elaborate

Share and Show

Have children locate Problem 2.

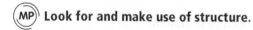 **Look for and make use of structure.**

- **Count forward from 51 to 100. Trace each missing number when you come to it.**

Have children point to the numbers they have traced and count together by tens.

Use the checked problem for Quick Check.

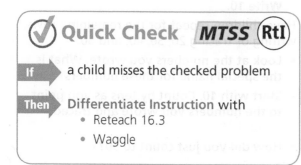

> **✓ Quick Check** **MTSS** **RtI**
>
> **If** ➡ a child misses the checked problem
>
> **Then** ➡ **Differentiate Instruction** with
> - Reteach 16.3
> - Waggle

Higher-Order Thinking

MP **Look for and make use of structure.**

Read aloud the following problem to children.

- **How would you count by tens starting at 34?** I would use a hundred chart and say all the numbers in order that are below 34 in the same column.

- **How can you tell without looking at the hundred chart what number is next?** Possible answer: I know that the first part of the number goes up by 1 and the other part of the number stays the same. So with 34, the 3 changes to 4 and the 4 stays the same. The next number is 44.

Children should be able to use what they know about the patterns in a hundred chart to solve this problem. Ask about different numbers and discuss the patterns children see in the hundred chart.

Math on the Spot Use this video to help children model and solve this type of problem.

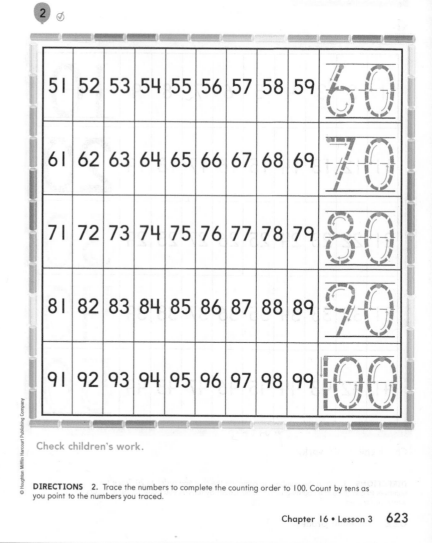

Name _____

② ⊘

51	52	53	54	55	56	57	58	59	60
61	62	63	64	65	66	67	68	69	70
71	72	73	74	75	76	77	78	79	80
81	82	83	84	85	86	87	88	89	90
91	92	93	94	95	96	97	98	99	100

Check children's work.

DIRECTIONS 2. Trace the numbers to complete the counting order to 100. Count by tens as you point to the numbers you traced.

Chapter 16 • Lesson 3   623

Meeting Individual Needs

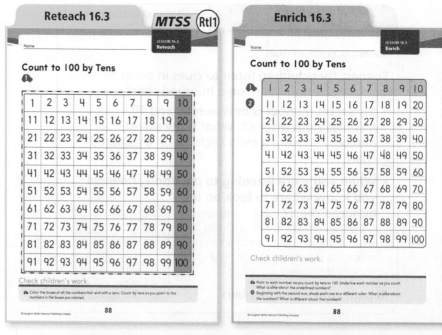

Reteach 16.3 **MTSS** **RtI**

Name _____

LESSON 16.3
Reteach

Count to 100 by Tens

1	2	3	4	5	6	7	8	9	10
11	12	13	14	15	16	17	18	19	20
21	22	23	24	25	26	27	28	29	30
31	32	33	34	35	36	37	38	39	40
41	42	43	44	45	46	47	48	49	50
51	52	53	54	55	56	57	58	59	60
61	62	63	64	65	66	67	68	69	70
71	72	73	74	75	76	77	78	79	80
81	82	83	84	85	86	87	88	89	90
91	92	93	94	95	96	97	98	99	100

Check children's work.

88

Enrich 16.3

Name _____

LESSON 16.3
Enrich

Count to 100 by Tens

1	2	3	4	5	6	7	8	9	10
11	12	13	14	15	16	17	18	19	20
21	22	23	24	25	26	27	28	29	30
31	32	33	34	35	36	37	38	39	40
41	42	43	44	45	46	47	48	49	50
51	52	53	54	55	56	57	58	59	60
61	62	63	64	65	66	67	68	69	70
71	72	73	74	75	76	77	78	79	80
81	82	83	84	85	86	87	88	89	90
91	92	93	94	95	96	97	98	99	100

Check children's work.

88

3

1	2	3	4	5	6	7	8	9	**10**
11	12	13	14	15	16	17	18	19	**20**
21	22	23	24	25	26	27	28	29	<u>30</u>
31	32	33	34	35	36	37	38	39	40
41	42	43	44	45	46	47	48	49	(50)

DIRECTIONS 3. Antonio has 10 marbles. Write the number in order. Jasmine has 10 more than Antonio. Write that number in order. Lin has 10 more marbles than Jasmine. Draw a line under the number that shows how many marbles Lin has. When counting by tens, what number comes right after 40? Circle the number.

HOME ACTIVITY • Show your child a calendar. Use pieces of paper to cover the numbers that end in 0. Ask your child to say the numbers that are covered. Then have him or her remove the pieces of paper to check.

624 Go Math! Grade K

© Houghton Mifflin Harcourt Publishing Company • CHMH

Problem Solving Applications **Real World**

Ask children what they notice about the fifty chart. Some numbers are missing.

(MP) **Model with mathematics.**

- **Antonio has 10 marbles. Where will you write 10 on the chart?** at the end of the first row
- **Jasmine has ten more marbles than Antonio. What is the fastest way to count from 10 to find out how many Jasmine has?** by tens **How many does she have?** 20 **Write the number in order on the chart.**
- **Lin has ten more marbles than Jasmine. How many does Lin have?** 30 **Draw a line under the number to show how many marbles Lin has.**
- **What number comes right after 40 when you are counting by tens?** 50 **Circle that number.**

⑤ Evaluate | Formative Assessment

I Can

Have children demonstrate how to whisper count to answer the I Can statement.

I can count to 100 by tens by . . . finding 10 on the hundred chart. Then I can look down that column and say each number to count by tens.

Exit Ticket

Have children point to the numbers on the hundred chart as they whisper count.

DIFFERENTIATED INSTRUCTION • Independent Activities

Version 2.0
Differentiated Centers Kit

Tabletop Flipchart

Mini-lessons for reteaching to targeted small groups

Readers

Supports key math skills and concepts in real-world situations.

Games

Reinforce math content and vocabulary

Activities

Meaningful and fun math practice

Practice and Homework

Count to 100 by Tens

Use the Practice and Homework pages to provide children with more practice of the concepts and skills presented in this lesson. Children master their understanding as they complete practice items.

Count to 100 by Tens

51	52	53	54	55	56	57	58	59	60
61	62	63	64	65	66	67	68	69	70
71	72	73	74	75	76	77	78	79	80
81	82	83	84	85	86	87	88	89	90
91	92	93	94	95	96	97	98	99	100

Check children's work.

DIRECTIONS   1. Trace the numbers to complete the counting order to 100. Count by tens as you point to the numbers you traced.

Chapter 16 • Lesson 3   **625**

PROFESSIONAL LEARNING

MATHEMATICAL PRACTICES AND PROCESSES

(MP) Look for and make use of structure.

Understanding relationships between numbers helps children make sense of the world in a mathematical way.

- Children who are confident in their counting abilities are more comfortable attempting to solve problems in everyday life. Children who have a firm sense of the order of numbers are better able to solve everyday problems such as counting money or following steps in a recipe.

- Children use their counting abilities to solve more complex problems, such as by writing an addition or subtraction equation to describe a situation.

- In this lesson, children count to 100 by tens using a hundred chart. The hundred chart helps them begin to understand relationships between numbers.

Children can begin to see patterns in numbering, such as counting by fives and tens.

Provide opportunities for children to describe how they use the hundred chart to learn about numbers.

- **How is counting from 91 to 100 like counting from 11 to 20 on a number chart?** You read the numbers across the row. Each number is one more than the last one. 11 and 91 end in 1, 12 and 92 end in 2, and so on across the rows.

- **How does using a hundred chart help you learn the counting sequence?** I can see all the numbers in order. I can see ways the numbers are alike and different.

Lesson Check

1	2	3	4	5	6	7	8	9	10
11	12	13	14	15	16	17	18	19	20
21	22	23	24	25	26	27	28	29	30

Spiral Review

$$9 - 2 = 7$$

DIRECTIONS 2. Count by tens as you point to the numbers in the shaded boxes. Start with the number 10. What number do you end with? Draw a line under that number. 3. How many tiles are there? Write the number. 4. Complete the subtraction sentence that matches the cube train.

© Houghton Mifflin Harcourt Publishing Company

Continue to practice concepts and skills with Lesson Check. Use Spiral Review to engage children in previously taught concepts and to promote content retention.

Lesson at a Glance
Count Forward and Backward

SNAPSHOT

Mathematical Standards
- Count to 100 by ones and by tens.

Mathematical Practices and Processes
- Model with mathematics.
- Attend to precision.
- Reason abstractly and quantitatively.
- Look for and make use of structure.

(I Can) Objective
I can count and order numbers forward and backward to 20.

Learning Goal
Order numbers and recognize the number sequence to 20.

Language Objective
Partners describe how to count forward and backward to 20.

MATERIALS
- MathBoard

ACROSS THE GRADES

Grade K
Recite the number names to 100 by ones and by tens. Starting at a given number, count forward within 100 and backward within 20.

After
Starting at a given number, count forward and backwards within 120 by ones. Skip count by 2s to 20 and by 5s to 100.

ABOUT THE MATH

If Children Ask
If a child asks why we put numbers in order, you might ask the class and see what reasons they can name.

Children's responses and yours might sound like the following:

- Knowing the order of numbers can help us count; if we know the order of numbers, we can say them quickly and easily because we know what numbers come next.
- We use counting in order in games as players count off or as we keep score. Some games have a countdown that requires us to count backward.
- If we know numbers in order, we can tell which score or price is greater and which is less. For example, if a score is 19 to 18, we know that 19 is the greater score. If price tags show 19¢ and 11¢, we know that 11¢ is the lesser price because when we count we reach 11 before 19.

For more professional learning, go online to Teacher's Corner.

DAILY ROUTINES

🖥 Problem of the Day 16.4

```
|----|----|----|----|----|----|----|----|----|
1    2    3    4    5    6    7    8    9    10
```

What number comes just before 5? 4 **What number comes just after 3?** 4

Write the numbers 1–10 in order.

Point to the numbers again and explain the following: **When you count forward, 1 comes just before 2, and 6 comes just after 5.**

🖥 Vocabulary

- Interactive Student Edition
- Multilingual Glossary

Fluency Builder

Lead children in counting forward from 1 to 20 and backward from 10 to 1.

Say aloud some counting sequences such as the ones shown below, clapping to designate a missing number. Have children listen carefully and try to tell the missing number.

10, 11, 12, 13, clap, 15, 16 14

14, 15, 16, 17, 18, 19, clap 20

20, 19, 18, 17, clap, 15, 14, 13 16

FOCUSING ON THE WHOLE STUDENT

Access Prior Knowledge

Materials numeral cards (0–23)

Hand out the cards, giving one to each child. Have the child who is holding the number 5 come up to the front of the class.

- **Which number comes next?** 6

- **If you are holding the next number, come up and stand next to the 5 with your number.**

- **Which number comes after 6?** 7

Have that child come next. Begin again, starting with another number and have children come up for the next two numbers.

① Engage

with the Interactive Student Edition

I Can Objective

I can count and order numbers forward and backward to 20.

Making Connections

Show children number cards from 1 to 5. Have a volunteer put them in order. Count forward as you read them aloud as a class. Then have another volunteer reverse the order of the numbers. Count backward as you read them aloud as a class.

Learning Activity

Materials numeral cards (1–16)

- Display a number line that shows 5, 10, and 15. Distribute a card to each child.

- Tell children that you are going to give them an "I Spy" clue, such as the following. **I spy the number that comes right before 5. Who has it?** Children can look around and help. The child whose card matches the clue should say the number and place it on the number line.

- When all the cards have been called, have children use the completed number line to count forward and backward several times.

Explore

Listen and Draw

Read aloud this problem as children listen.

Bob is making a number line for his sister. He has to fill in the numbers. Will he write 18 before or after 17?

(MP) **Look for and make use of structure.**

Call attention to the number line on the page. Count the numbers from 0 to 20 with the children.

- **Point to the number 14 on the number line. Count forward one. What number are you on?** 15 **Write the number.**

- **When counting backward, do you want the number before a given number on the number line, or after a given number?** before the number

- **Point to the number 9 on the number line. Count back one. What number are you on?** 8 **Write the number.**

Ask similar questions with other numbers.

Reread the problem. Ask:

- **Will Bob write 18 before or after 17?** He will write 18 after 17.

Have children practice counting forward and backward on the number line.

Name _____

Count Forward and Backward

(I Can) count and order numbers forward and backward to 20.

Listen and Draw

14 15 16

9 8 7

DIRECTIONS Point to the numbers on the number line and count forward to 20. Start on 14 and count forward one. What number are you on? Write the number. Now start on 9 and count back one. What number are you on? Write the number.   Check children's work.

Chapter 16 • Lesson 4   **627**

(ML) **Multilingual Support**

STRATEGY: Creative Grouping

Materials index cards

Children can be grouped according to individual needs for language support or for mathematics practice.

Partner advanced Multilingual Learners or children who are fluent in English with beginning and intermediate learners.

- Have children write the numbers 1 through 20 on index cards.

- Have them practice ordering the numbers from 1 to 20.

- Make sure children can explain the process of ordering numbers either verbally or in drawings.

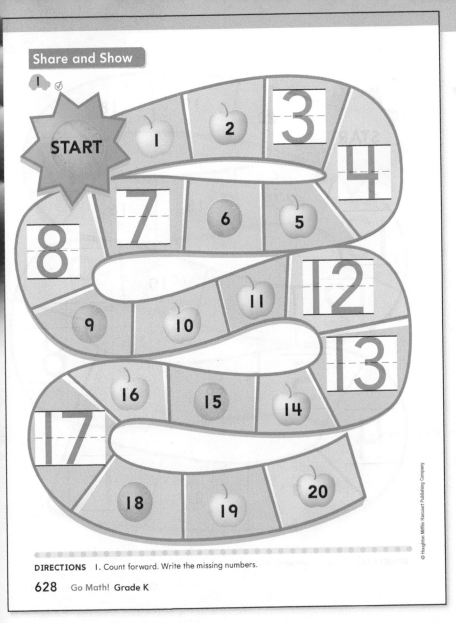

DIRECTIONS 1. Count forward. Write the missing numbers.

628 Go Math! Grade K

© Houghton Mifflin Harcourt Publishing Company

Ready for More

Visual Small Group

Materials numeral cards (0–23)

- Have a child place the cards in order from least to greatest.
- Next, have children take turns mixing up the numbers and putting them in order, this time from greatest to least.

| 23 | 22 | 21 | 20 |

---

③ Explain

Share and Show
Math Board

MP Model with mathematics.

- **Focus on the numbers that are arranged in a path that looks like a game board. Trace the path with your finger.**
- **What is missing from the path?** some numbers
- **How can you tell what numbers are missing?** by counting

On which number will you start? 1

- **Find the last number. On which number will you end?** 20

Have children complete the number sequence by writing the numbers on the lines. You can have them count quietly to themselves, or you may wish to have children take turns reading the numbers aloud.

- **What numbers does this path show?**
  the numbers from 1 to 20

Point out that the path shows numbers counted forward.

Use the checked problem for Quick Check.

 Quick Check MTSS RtI

If ▶ a child misses the checked problem

Then ▶ **Differentiate Instruction** with
- Reteach 16.4
- Waggle

Common Errors

Error The child miscounts the numbers from 1 to 20.

Example The child does not fill in the correct missing numbers in the path.

Springboard to Learning Have the child write the numbers 1 through 20 in order while counting. Then use these numbers to help the child fill in the number path. Help the child place the numbers correctly.

Chapter 16 • Lesson 4 **628**

Share and Show

 Reason abstractly and quantitatively.

Focus on the path of numbers.

- **On which number does this path start?** 20
- **If you start on 20 and end near 2, how are you counting?** backward
- **Look at the last box. The number isn't there yet. Next to it is a 2. On what number do you think the number path will end?** 1
- **How can you tell what numbers are missing?** I can count backward and see what numbers are not there.

Together, practice counting backward from 20 to 1. Then have children complete the number sequence and take turns reading it aloud.

Higher-Order Thinking

 Attend to precision.

Draw a number line from 10 to 17. Challenge children to add three numbers before 10 and three numbers after 17 to the number line.

Children now have to determine mentally which three numbers come before 10 and which three numbers come after 17. They will use what they know about number sequence to solve.

Math on the Spot Use this video to help children model and solve this type of problem.

Culturally Responsive Education

This lesson provides an excellent opportunity to utilize movement activities to help a concept become more meaningful to children during recess. You could talk to children about how to draw a hopscotch board with chalk on the sidewalk with numbers from 1–10. Challenge children to create a separate board with numbers from 11–20 or with numbers going backward. Explain the traditional rules of hopscotch, but give children the freedom to play in any way they wish. Consider alternative fun activities for children with differing physical abilities, such as board games with spinners or number cubes.

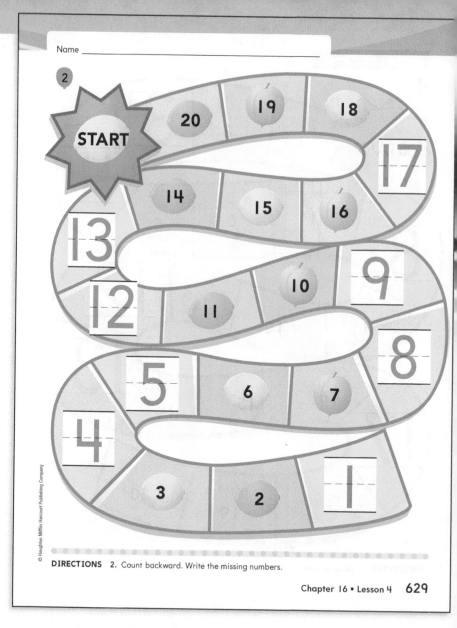

Name _____

DIRECTIONS 2. Count backward. Write the missing numbers.

Chapter 16 • Lesson 4 **629**

Meeting Individual Needs

Reteach 16.4 **MTSS** (RtI1)

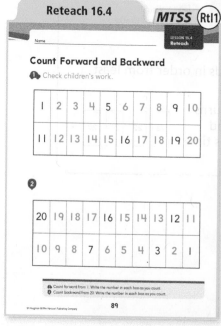

Enrich 16.4

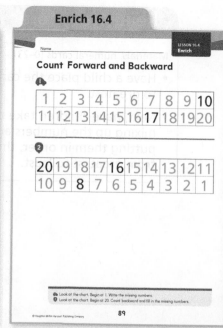

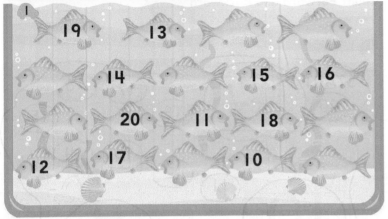

1.
19   13   14   15   16   20   11   18   12   17   10

2.

10   11   12   13
14   15   16   17
18   19   20

© Houghton Mifflin Harcourt Publishing Company

DIRECTIONS 1. Start on the fish that has the number 10. Count forward. As you say each number, point to the fish that has that number. 2. Write to show what you know about counting forward from 10.

HOME ACTIVITY • Make for your child a set of number cards with any five numbers in a row that are less than 10. Have your child place the cards in order and read them forward and backward.

---

④ Elaborate

Problem Solving Applications Real World

(MP) **Model with mathematics.**

Problem 1 Read the directions and have a volunteer read the numbers that are shown.

Start on the fish that has the number 10. Count forward. As you say each number, point to the fish that has that number.

Continue until the children have counted forward to 20.

Problem 2 Have children write to show what they know about counting forward from 10. Then ask them to take turns reading the sequence of numbers from 10 to 20.

⑤ Evaluate | Formative Assessment

I Can

Have children work with a partner to demonstrate the skill for the I Can statement.

I can count and order numbers forward and backward to 20 by . . . looking at a set of numbers and deciding which comes first. Then I can count and write the numbers in counting order.

Exit Ticket

Show how a number line can help you count forward and backward.

DIFFERENTIATED INSTRUCTION • Independent Activities

Grab-and-Go!™
Version 2.0
Differentiated Centers Kit

Tabletop Flipchart

Mini-lessons for reteaching to targeted small groups

Readers

Supports key math skills and concepts in real-world situations.

Games

Reinforce math content and vocabulary

Activities

Meaningful and fun math practice

Practice and Homework

Count Forward and Backward

Use the Practice and Homework pages to provide children with more practice of the concepts and skills presented in this lesson. Children master their understanding as they complete practice items.

DIRECTIONS 1. Count backward. Write the missing numbers.

Chapter 16 • Lesson 4 **631**

CROSS-CURRICULAR

SCIENCE

Materials numeral cards (0–23)

- Talk about the fact that children can learn if they look very carefully and think about what they see.
- Present a row of numbers and have children name them: 13, 14, 15, 16, 17, 18.
- Ask children to look very carefully at the numbers. Ask children to close their eyes while you remove one number.
- Have children open their eyes, identify the missing number, and name the numbers that come before it and after it.
- Repeat with other numbers, and do some backward sequences.

SOCIAL STUDIES

- Pass around postage stamps for children to look at.
- Talk about different images on the stamps and what they represent. For flag stamps, ask children where they have seen an American flag and what it means.
- Count out 10 stamps with children.
- Then count backward as you remove one stamp at a time.

---

631 **Go Math! Grade K**

Lesson Check

2

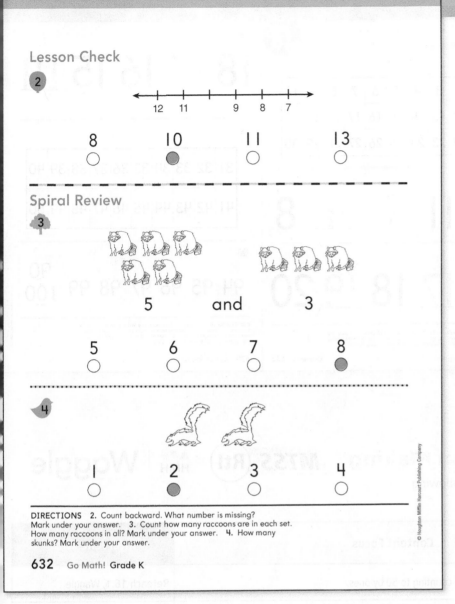

↔ | 12 | 11 | | 9 | 8 | 7 |

8 ○ 10 ● 11 ○ 13 ○

Spiral Review

3

5   and   3

5 ○   6 ○   7 ○   8 ●

....

4

1 ○   2 ●   3 ○   4 ○

DIRECTIONS 2. Count backward. What number is missing?
Mark under your answer. 3. Count how many raccoons are in each set.
How many raccoons in all? Mark under your answer. 4. How many
skunks? Mark under your answer.

Continue to practice concepts and skills with
Lesson Check. Use Spiral Review to engage
children in previously taught concepts and to
promote content retention.

Summative Assessment

Use the **Chapter Review** to assess children's progress in Chapter 16.

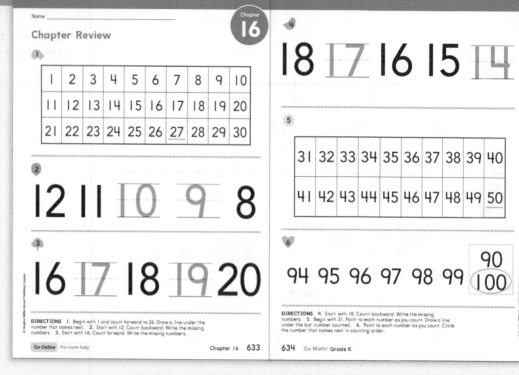

Online, Data-Driven Decision Making MTSS RtI HMH Waggle®

Based on the results of the Chapter Review, use the following resources to review skills.

Item	Lesson	Content Focus	Intervene With
1, 5	16.1	Know the count sequence when counting to 50 by ones.	**Reteach 16.1,** Waggle
6, 7, 11	16.2	Know the count sequence when counting to 100 by ones.	**Reteach 16.2,** Waggle
8, 9, 10	16.3	Know the count sequence when counting to 100 by tens.	**Reteach 16.3,** Waggle
2, 3, 4	16.4	Order numbers and recognize the number sequence to 20.	**Reteach 16.4,** Waggle

Name _____

7

81	82	83	84	85	86	(87)	88	89	90
91	92	93	94	95	96	97	98	99	100

8

10 20 30 40 50

9

60 70 80 90 100

DIRECTIONS 7. I am counting from 1 to 100. I say eighty-six. Circle the number that comes next. 8. Count by tens. Write the missing numbers. 9. Count by tens. Write the missing numbers.

10

1	2	3	4	5	6	7	8	9	(10)
11	12	13	14	15	16	17	18	19	(20)
21	22	23	24	25	26	27	28	29	(30)
31	32	33	34	35	36	37	38	39	(40)
41	42	43	44	45	46	47	48	49	(50)
51	52	53	54	55	56	57	58	59	(60)
61	62	63	64	65	66	67	68	69	(70)
71	72	73	74	75	76	77	78	79	(80)
81	82	83	84	85	86	87	88	89	(90)
91	92	93	94	95	96	97	98	99	(100)

11

DIRECTIONS 10. Start at 0. Count by tens to 100. Circle the numbers you say. 11. I am greater than 33 and less than 35. What number am I? Use blue to color that number. I am greater than 40 and less than 42. What number am I? Use red to color that number.

Performance Assessment Task

See the Performance Tasks to assess children's understanding of the content. For each task, you will find sample student work for each of the response levels in the task scoring rubric.

Portfolio   Performance Assessment Tasks may be used for portfolios.

Chapter Test

Summative Assessment

Use the **Chapter Test** to assess children's progress in Chapter 16.

Chapter Tests are found in the *Assessment Guide*. Test items are presented in formats consistent with high-stakes assessments.

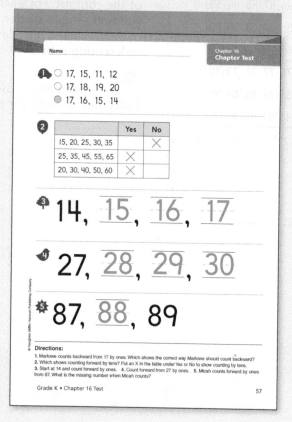

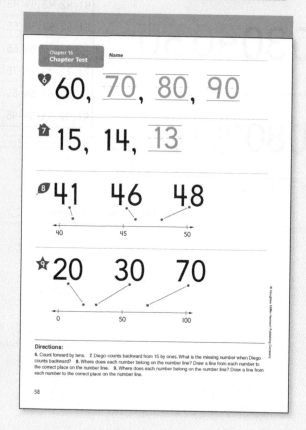

Teacher Notes

SNAPSHOT

Mathematical Standards

- Preskill: Represent whole numbers from 10 to 20, using a unit of ten and a group of ones, with objects, drawings and expressions or equations.

Mathematical Practices and Processes

- Model with mathematics.
- Construct arguments and critique reasoning of others.
- Look for and make use of structure.
- Attend to precision.

Learning Goal

Use the words *alike* and *different* to compare two-dimensional shapes by attributes.

Language Objective

Children sort pictures of two-dimensional shapes and use the sentence frame _____ *and* _____ *are alike* (or *different*) *because* _____ to compare two-dimensional shapes.

MATERIALS

- MathBoard

ACROSS THE GRADES

Grade K

- Children will compare two-dimensional figures based on their similarities, differences, and positions. Sort two-dimensional figures based on their similarities and differences. Figures are limited to circles, triangles, rectangles and squares.
- Children will find real-world objects that can be modeled by a given two- or three-dimensional figure.

After

- Children will sketch two-dimensional figures when given defining attributes. Figures are limited to triangles, rectangles, squares and hexagons.
- Given a real-world object, children will identify parts that are modeled by two- and three-dimensional figures.

Professional Learning

Go Online to Teacher's Corner

PROFESSIONAL DEVELOPMENT IN THE CLASSROOM

Formats for Classroom Discourse

Whole-Class Discussions are led by the teacher, who helps the class focus on higher-level concepts, mathematical reasoning, and making sense of new ideas. The teacher should clear up widely held misconceptions and tie past concepts to new thinking.

Small Groups of three to six children discuss ideas for solving the problem as a group and then with the teacher. This is a crucial time for the teacher to look for both conceptual and procedural errors. The teacher challenges group members to explain their strategies, whether correct or incorrect, for solving the problem.

Partners respond to each other's statements so that both partners put their thoughts into words. They practice contributing to the discussion and try to answer each other's questions. The teacher asks for clarification of their thinking and asks directional questions, focusing on identifying and helping the children resolve their own errors.

Social & Emotional Learning

Working with partners and in groups is a key component of learning mathematics. These questions are designed specifically to support learning in a collaborative math classroom.

- Why might they say that? (for children who are struggling, to help them understand correct answers)
- How can you help them out? (for children who are on-target, to help children who are struggling)
- What can you add to what they're saying? (for incomplete answers)
- Do you think their answer is reasonable?
- What can you add to help them? (for incorrect answers)
- How can you repeat what they said using your own words? (to help children consider the reasoning of others)
- Can you reread the problem out loud? (when a child is disengaged, disruptive, or both)

! Common Errors with Shapes

Within this lesson:

- Children may have difficulty deciding what shapes are alike.
- Children may have difficulty identifying different shapes by the correct name.

In other lessons with shapes:

- Children may not be able to identify the vertices of a shape.
- Children may not recognize everyday objects that are shaped like specific shapes.
- Children may not be able to tell the difference between sides and vertices.

For further information and tips on helping children understand and correct common errors, see individual lessons.

Launch Activity
Shapes

Introducing Shapes

This Launch Activity lesson challenges children to group shapes based on similarities. Children will then draw shapes that have similarities to a given shape. This lesson prepares children to name and categorize shapes based on the number of sides and vertices.

Engage Children

Begin by discussing the opening topic. Invite children to participate by asking them to talk about street signs they see every day. Children show an increased aptitude for learning if they are actively engaged in some part of the subject matter. Questions might include:

- **What do the different street signs mean?**
- **How do you know what the signs mean even if they don't have words?**
- **Why do you think we have street signs?**

Have children work in mixed-ability groups. Give each child a task that they can do well. For instance, in groups of learners with varying abilities, assign each child a specific task, such as leading the group discussion, recording or drawing the work, presenting (but not explaining) the solution, and explaining the models and methods used by the group to solve the problem.

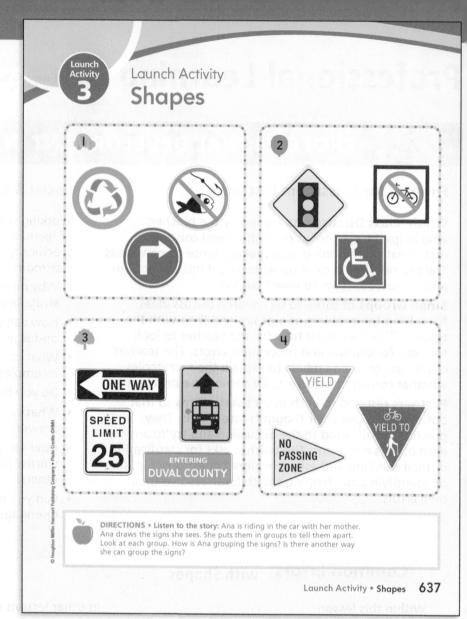

 DIRECTIONS • Listen to the story: Ana is riding in the car with her mother. Ana draws the signs she sees. She puts them in groups to tell them apart. Look at each group. How is Ana grouping the signs? Is there another way she can group the signs?

Launch Activity • Shapes **637**

ML ## Three Reads Language Routine

Read the problem stem three times and prompt the children with a different question each time.

- What is the problem about?
- What do each of the numbers describe?
- What math questions could you ask about the problem?

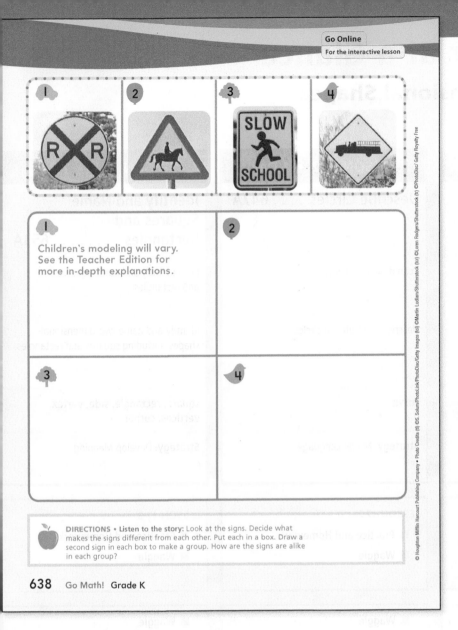

DIRECTIONS • **Listen to the story:** Look at the signs. Decide what makes the signs different from each other. Put each in a box. Draw a second sign in each box to make a group. How are the signs are alike in each group?

ANSWERS

Main problem: Answers will vary, but children should mention that all of the signs in group 1 are circles, all of the signs in group 2 are squares (4 equal sides), the signs in group 3 are rectangles, and the signs in group 4 are triangles. Children might also say that signs could be grouped by color, pictures, words, or other characteristics.

Children's answers will vary, but they should draw a circular sign for number 1, a triangular sign for number 2, a rectangular sign for 3, and a square sign for 4. Children should use words like *round, straight,* and the number of sides and corners to describe their signs.

Prompts for Productive Perseverance

For Launch Activity lessons, the exploration of math concepts is more critical than finding a solution. Children should be encouraged to think about new math ideas in an atmosphere that is conducive to learning, with minimal pressure. They learn to solve the problem in different ways and are able to choose the method that works well for them.

What if children can't start working or can't enter into the conversation for this lesson?
Use one or more of these opening prompts:

- *What information do you know about the problem?*
- *Can you draw a picture that represents what you know?*
- *What numbers are in the problem?*
- *What is given in the problem that might help you answer the question?*

How can I help children who are frustrated?
Ask these leading questions:

- *Think about a starting point. How can you enter into this problem?*
- *What information do you have?*
- *What are you working on? What have you done so far?*
- *What comes next? What are you solving for?*
- *What information do you need to get unstuck? Talk to your partner (or group).*

To increase children's understanding of their own thinking, ask:
- *How are all of shapes in this group alike?*
- *What is different about the shapes in this group compared to the other group?*
- *What is a way to describe the shapes in the group?*

Launch Activity • Shapes 638

Chapter at a Glance
Two-Dimensional Shapes

	LESSON 17.1 • 1 Day	LESSON 17.2 • 1 Day	LESSON 17.3 • 1 Day
Lesson at a Glance	Identify and Name Circles 641A	Describe Circles 647A	Identify and Name Squares and Rectangles 653A
I Can	I can identify and name circles.	I can describe circles.	I can identify and name squares and rectangles.
Learning Goal	Identify and name two-dimensional shapes, including circles.	Describe attributes of circles.	Identify and name two-dimensional shapes, including squares and rectangles.
Vocabulary	two-dimensional shape, circle	curve	square, rectangle, side, vertex, vertices, corner
Multilingual Support	**Strategy:** Develop Meanings	**Strategy:** Model Language	**Strategy:** Develop Meaning

Practice and Fluency	LESSON 17.1 ◆ ■ Practice and Homework ■ Waggle	LESSON 17.2 ◆ ■ Practice and Homework ■ Waggle	LESSON 17.3 ◆ ■ Practice and Homework ■ Waggle
MTSS RtI **Intervention and Enrichment**	■ Waggle ◆ ■ Reteach 17.1 ◆ ■ Tier 2 Intervention Skill S33 ◆ ■ Tier 3 Intervention Skill E33 ◆ Tabletop Flipchart ◆ Enrich 17.1	■ Waggle ◆ ■ Reteach 17.2 ◆ ■ Tier 2 Intervention Skill S33 ◆ ■ Tier 3 Intervention Skill E33 ◆ Tabletop Flipchart ◆ Enrich 17.2	■ Waggle ◆ ■ Reteach 17.3 ◆ ■ Tier 2 Intervention Skill S36 ◆ ■ Tier 3 Intervention Skill E36 ◆ Tabletop Flipchart ◆ Enrich 17.3

See the Grab-and-Go!™ Centers Kit **for more small-group activities.**

Version 2.0
Differentiated Centers Kit

The kit provides literature, games, and activities for small-group learning.

◆ Print/Printable Resource
■ Interactive Resource

	LESSON 17.4 • 1 Day	**LESSON 17.5 • 1 Day**	**LESSON 17.6 • 1 Day**
Lesson at a Glance	Describe Squares and Rectangles 659A	Identify and Name Triangles. 665A	Describe Triangles . . 671A
I Can	I can describe squares and rectangles.	I can identify and name triangles.	I can describe triangles.
Learning Goal	Describe attributes of squares and rectangles.	Identify and name two-dimensional shapes, including triangles.	Describe attributes of triangles.
Vocabulary	sides of equal length	triangle	
Multilingual Support	**Strategy:** Model Language	**Strategy:** Develop Meanings	**Strategy:** Rephrase

Practice and Fluency	LESSON 17.4 ◆ ■ Practice and Homework ■ Waggle	LESSON 17.5 ◆ ■ Practice and Homework ■ Waggle	LESSON 17.6 ◆ ■ Practice and Homework ■ Waggle
***MTSS* RtI** **Intervention and Enrichment**	■ Waggle ◆ ■ Reteach 17.4 ◆ ■ Tier 2 Intervention Skill S49 ◆ ■ Tier 3 Intervention Skill E49 ◆ Tabletop Flipchart ◆ Enrich 17.4	■ Waggle ◆ ■ Reteach 17.5 ◆ ■ Tier 2 Intervention Skill S48 ◆ ■ Tier 3 Intervention Skill E48 ◆ Tabletop Flipchart ◆ Enrich 17.5	■ Waggle ◆ ■ Reteach 17.6 ◆ ■ Tier 2 Intervention Skill S34 ◆ ■ Tier 3 Intervention Skill E34 ◆ Tabletop Flipchart ◆ Enrich 17.6

◆ Print/Printable Resource
■ Interactive Resource

	LESSON 17.7 • 1 Day	LESSON 17.8 • 1 Day	LESSON 17.9 • 1–2 Days
Lesson at a Glance	Identify and Name Hexagons 677A	Describe Hexagons 683A	Compare Two-Dimensional Shapes 689A
I Can	I can identify and name hexagons.	I can describe hexagons.	I can compare two-dimensional shapes based on their similarities and differences.
Learning Goal	Identify and name two-dimensional shapes, including hexagons.	Describe attributes of hexagons.	Use the words *alike* and *different* to compare two-dimensional shapes by attributes.
Vocabulary	hexagon		alike, different
Multilingual Support	**Strategy:** Develop Meanings	**Strategy:** Model Language	**Strategy:** Develop Meanings
Practice and Fluency	LESSON 17.7 ◆ ■ Practice and Homework ■ Waggle	LESSON 17.8 ◆ ■ Practice and Homework ■ Waggle	LESSON 17.9 ◆ ■ Practice and Homework ■ Waggle
MTSS (RtI) **Intervention and Enrichment**	■ Waggle ◆ ■ Reteach 17.7 ◆ ■ Tier 2 Intervention Skill S35 ◆ ■ Tier 3 Intervention Skill E35 ◆ Tabletop Flipchart ◆ Enrich 17.7	■ Waggle ◆ ■ Reteach 17.8 ◆ ■ Tier 2 Intervention Skill S35 ◆ ■ Tier 3 Intervention Skill E35 ◆ Tabletop Flipchart ◆ Enrich 17.8	■ Waggle ◆ ■ Reteach 17.9 ◆ ■ Tier 2 Intervention Skill S33-S35, S49 ◆ ■ Tier 3 Intervention Skill E33-E35, E49 ◆ Tabletop Flipchart ◆ Enrich 17.9

◆ Print/Printable Resource
■ Interactive Resource

LESSON 17.10 • 1 Day

Lesson at a Glance

Create Shapes...... 695A

I Can

I can combine shapes to make larger shapes.

Learning Goal

Combine shapes to make larger shapes.

Vocabulary

Multilingual Support

Strategy: Define

Practice and Fluency

LESSON 17.10

◆ ■ **Practice and Homework**

■ **Waggle**

MTSS (RtI)

Intervention and Enrichment

■ Waggle

◆ ■ Reteach 17.10

◆ ■ Tier 2 Intervention Skill S50

◆ ■ Tier 3 Intervention Skill E50

◆ Tabletop Flipchart

◆ Enrich 17.10

Consider the difference between personal bias and systemic bias and how that influences the mathematics experiences of culturally and linguistically diverse children.

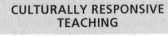

Image Credit: © HMH

CULTURALLY RESPONSIVE TEACHING

Cultural Competence

Engage in courageous conversations about bias, race, racism, and culture, and reflect on how they may unintentionally reproduce patterns of marginalization in mathematics.

◆ Print/Printable Resource
■ Interactive Resource

Spatial Sense

A primary aim of engaging learners in the study of two-dimensional shapes is to develop their spatial sense.

- Spatial sense is "an intuition about shapes and the relationships among shapes" (Van de Walle, 2007, p. 408).

- Such intuition can be supported by giving children experiences with naming, describing, and sorting shapes.

- Being able to talk about shapes and their characteristics is an indicator of spatial sense. An example is describing shapes by the number of vertices and sides.

Recognizing Attributes to Sort

It is important to provide opportunities to develop language to help children classify and describe objects.

From the Research
" ...[L]earning the characteristic properties of a geometrical shape is essential because they can form the basis of higher levels of thinking and help in gaining a practical and intuitive grasp of the mathematics of space. "
(Triadafillidis, 1995, p. 225)

Vocabulary

When children are exposed to shapes, they will use vocabulary that is accessible to them.

- When children describe a triangle as having "three points," introducing the formal vocabulary of *vertex* will help them transition to using the formal language of geometry.

- Modeling the use of the formal vocabulary informs children without discrediting the development that they have reached by using their own informal vocabulary.

Mathematical Practices and Processes

Model with mathematics.

Geometry is the perfect mathematical content to empower children to use mathematical modeling. For example, young children can select geometric shapes to represent objects they see in the classroom or their home environments (e.g., a rectangle may represent a picture frame or the bricks on the school walls). When they consider the characteristics of mathematical models they may ask questions such as, "Why are circles better models for bicycle tires than triangles?" This examination of characteristics enhances their understanding of the shape.

For more professional learning, go online to Teacher's Corner.

Instructional Journey

While every classroom may look a little different, this instructional model provides a framework to organize small-group and whole-group learning for meaningful student learning.

Whole Group
Engage

5 minutes

Readiness
- Problem of the Day
- Fluency Builder or Vocabulary Builder
- Access Prior Knowledge

Engagement
- I Can
- Making Connections
- Learning Activity

Small and Whole Group
Explore

15–20 minutes

Exploration
- Listen and Draw, Unlock the Problem
- Multilingual Support and Strategy
- Common Errors

Small Group
Explain

15–20 minutes

Quick Check
- ✓ Share and Show

Differentiated Instruction
Grab-and-Go!™
Version 2.0

Intervention
- Waggle
- Reteach
- Tier 2 and Tier 3 MTSS
- Tabletop Flipchart Mini Lessons

Language Support
- Vocabulary Activities
- Language Routines
- Multilingual Glossary

Enrichment
- Waggle Games
- Ready for More
- Enrich

Whole Group
Elaborate

5 minutes

- Math on the Spot Videos
- Higher-Order Thinking Problems

Evaluate

- I Can Reflection
- Exit Ticket
- Practice and Homework
- Fluency Practice
- Waggle

Assessment

Diagnostic	Formative	Summative
• Show What You Know	• Lesson Quick Check	• Chapter Review • Chapter Test • Performance Assessment Task

Grab-and-Go!™
Version 2.0
Differentiated Centers Kit
The kit provides literature, games, and activities for small-group learning.

Strategies for
Multilingual Learners

Understanding a child's language development is helpful in differentiating teaching and assessment. Assessing a child's understanding of mathematical concepts can be done by listening, speaking, reading, and writing. The level of support a child needs determines how best to assess that child's understanding of mathematical concepts.

Planning for Instruction			
Language Support	**Substantial** (WIDA Level 1)*	**Moderate** (WIDA Levels 2 & 3)*	**Light** (WIDA Levels 4 & 5)*
Child's Use of Language	• uses single words • uses common short phrases • heavily relies on visual supports and use of manipulatives	• uses simple sentences • uses some academic vocabulary • relies on visual supports and use of manipulatives	• uses a variety of sentences • uses academic vocabulary • benefits from visual supports and manipulatives
Ways to Assess Understanding	**Listening:** points to pictures, words, or phrases to answer questions **Speaking:** answers *yes/no* questions **Reading:** matches symbols to math terms and concepts **Writing:** draws a visual representation of a problem	**Listening:** matches, categorizes, or sequences information based on visuals **Speaking:** begins to explain reasoning, asks math questions, repeats explanations from peers **Reading:** identifies important information to solve a problem **Writing:** uses simple sentences and visual representations	**Listening:** draws conclusions and makes connections based on what they heard **Speaking:** explains and justifies concepts and solutions **Reading:** understands information in math contexts **Writing:** completes sentences using some academic vocabulary

* For more information on WIDA Standards, visit their website at:
https://wida.wisc.edu/.

- Look for strategies throughout the lesson to support multilingual learners.
- Log on to ED to find additional multilingual activities and Vocabulary Cards.

In This Chapter

Key Academic Vocabulary

Current Development • Vocabulary

two-dimensional shape, circle, curve, square, side, vertex, vertices, corner, sides of equal length, triangle, rectangle, hexagon, alike, different

Using Language Routines to Develop Understanding

 Language routines provide opportunities for children to develop an understanding of mathematical language and concepts by listening, speaking, reading, and writing. More information on these language routines can be found on the Language Support Cards.

Compare and Contrast

Children share their work with a partner to compare and contrast their strategies.

Language Support	Substantial (WIDA Level 1)*	Moderate (WIDA Levels 2 & 3)*	Light (WIDA Levels 4 & 5)*
Language Routine Differentiation	Children will physically point out similarities and differences on visual representations. They may use short phrases such as "the same" and "different" to verbally compare and contrast their strategies.	Children would rely on visual representations to inform their simple-sentence discussions as they compare and contrast their strategies.	Children would be able to use some academic vocabulary to compare and contrast their strategies with a partner or small group.
Possible Student Work	When shown a circle and then a group of shapes including circles, triangles, rectangles, and squares, children may point to the circles and say "the same." They may point to the triangles, rectangles, and squares, and say "different." Children may also point to the features of the shapes (such as the curve of the circle and the sides and vertices of the other shapes) to point out differences.	When shown a circle and then a group of shapes including circles, triangles, rectangles, and squares, children may point to the circles and say "These are circles. They are the same." They may point to the triangles, rectangles, and squares, and say "These are not circles. They are different." Children may also point to the features of the shapes (such as the curve of the circle and the sides and vertices of the other shapes) to point out differences.	When shown a circle and then a group of shapes including circles, triangles, rectangles, and squares, children may point to the circles and say "These are all circles. I know because they have a curve." They may point to the triangles, rectangles, and squares, and say "These are not circles. I know because they have sides and corners and do not have a curve."

* For more information on WIDA Standards, visit their website at:
https://wida.wisc.edu/.

Assessing Prior Knowledge

Have children complete **Show What You Know** on their own. Items tested are the prerequisite skills for this chapter.

Diagnostic Interview Task

The alternative interview tasks below evaluate children's understanding of each **Show What You Know** skill. The diagnostic chart may be used for intervention on prerequisite skills.

MATERIALS two-dimensional shapes, connecting cubes

- Give the child a variety of shapes. Show the child a circle. Have the child find a shape that is alike. Repeat the process with a triangle and then a square.
- Place five cubes on the table. Have the child count the cubes and write how many. Repeat the process using three cubes and then six cubes.

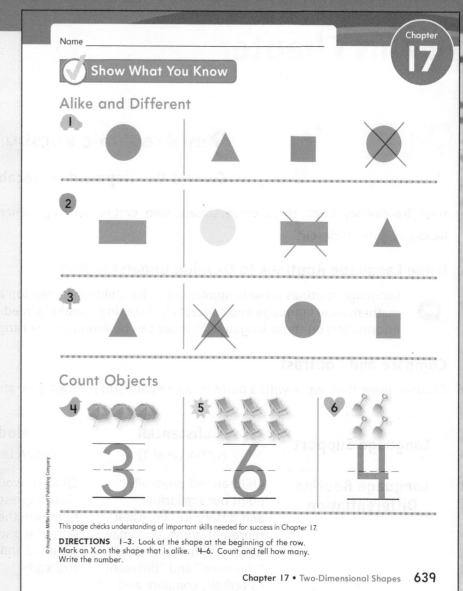

✓ **Show What You Know**

Alike and Different

This page checks understanding of important skills needed for success in Chapter 17.

DIRECTIONS 1–3. Look at the shape at the beginning of the row. Mark an X on the shape that is alike. 4–6. Count and tell how many. Write the number.

Chapter 17 • Two-Dimensional Shapes **639**

✓ Show What You Know • Diagnostic Assessment

Use to determine if children need intervention for the chapter's prerequisite skills.

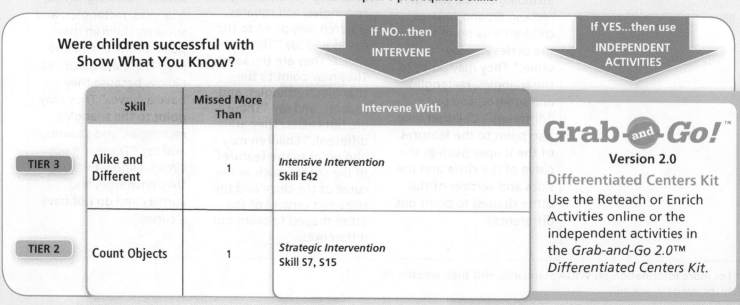

If NO...then
INTERVENE

If YES...then use
INDEPENDENT ACTIVITIES

Were children successful with Show What You Know?

	Skill	Missed More Than	Intervene With
TIER 3	Alike and Different	1	*Intensive Intervention* Skill E42
TIER 2	Count Objects	1	*Strategic Intervention* Skill S7, S15

Grab-and-Go!™
Version 2.0
Differentiated Centers Kit

Use the Reteach or Enrich Activities online or the independent activities in the *Grab-and-Go 2.0™ Differentiated Centers Kit.*

Vocabulary Builder

different

alike

DIRECTIONS Tell what you know about the ladybugs. Some of the ladybugs are different. Circle those ladybugs and tell why they are different. Tell what you know about the butterflies.

Check children's work.

© Houghton Mifflin Harcourt Publishing Company

Vocabulary Builder

Children use multiple strategies to develop grade-appropriate vocabulary.

Have children complete the activities on the page by working alone or with partners.

Look at the page with children. Talk about and name the various insects.

Tell what you know about the ladybugs.

- **How are some of the ladybugs different?** Some are playing an instrument.

Have children circle those ladybugs.

- **Tell what you know about the butterflies.**

- **How are the butterflies alike?** All of the butterflies have 2 wings. **How are they different?** The butterflies' wings have different designs on them.

School-Home Letter is available in English and Spanish online, and in multiple other languages.

Intervention Options MTSS Rtl Response to Intervention

Use Show What You Know, Lesson Quick Check, and Assessments to diagnose children's intervention levels.

TIER 1	TIER 2	TIER 3	ENRICHMENT
On-Level Intervention	**Strategic Intervention**	**Intensive Intervention**	**Independent Activities**
For children who are generally at grade level but need early intervention with the lesson concepts, use:	For children who need small-group instruction to review concepts and skills needed for the chapter, use:	For children who need one-on-one instruction to build foundational skills for the chapter, use:	For children who successfully complete lessons, use:
			• Waggle Practice and Games
• Reteach	▲ Prerequisite Skills Activities	▲ Prerequisite Skills Activities	
• Tabletop Flipchart Mini Lesson	▲ Tier 2 Activity	▲ Tier 3 Activity	Version 2.0
• Waggle			Differentiated Centers Kit
▲ Tier 1 Activity			• Ready for More Activity for every lesson
			• Enrich

Lesson at a Glance
Identify and Name Circles

SNAPSHOT

Mathematical Standards

- Describe objects in the environment using names of shapes, and describe the relative positions of these objects using terms such as *above, below, beside, in front of, behind,* and *next to.*

Mathematical Practices and Processes

- Use appropriate tools strategically.
- Construct arguments and critique reasoning of others.
- Look for and make use of structure.
- Attend to precision.

(I Can) **Objective**

I can identify and name circles.

Learning Goal

Identify and name two-dimensional shapes, including circles.

Language Objective

Small teams of children discuss how to identify and name circles.

MATERIALS

- MathBoard
- two-dimensional shapes

ACROSS THE GRADES

Grade K

Identify two- and three-dimensional figures regardless of their size or orientation. Figures are limited to circles, triangles, rectangles, squares, spheres, cubes, cones and cylinders.

After

Identify, compare and sort two- and three-dimensional figures based on their defining attributes. Figures are limited to circles, semi-circles, triangles, rectangles, squares, trapezoids, hexagons, spheres, cubes, rectangular prisms, cones and cylinders.

ABOUT THE MATH

Teaching for Depth

A circle is defined as a closed curve lying in a plane, all points of which are equidistant from the center.

To add even more meaning to the term *circle*, use activities like these.

- Have children trace circles in the air as you say the following. **Trace around and around. Circles are round. Circles do not have straight parts.**

- Draw a circle and an oval. Help children compare them.

- Provide a piece of string about two yards long with a piece of chalk tied to one end. On a paved surface outdoors, let a child hold one end of the string on the ground while another child stretches the string and traces a shape—a circle—on the paved surface. Let children walk or skip around it.

For more professional learning, go online to Teacher's Corner.

DAILY ROUTINES

🖥 Problem of the Day 17.1

Have children count aloud together to 17. Then ask them to draw to show 17.

Check children's work.

🖥 Vocabulary   circle, two-dimensional shape

• Interactive Student Edition
• Multilingual Glossary

Vocabulary Builder

Explain that two-dimensional shapes are flat. Show examples of two-dimensional shapes. Draw a circle and have children name and describe it. It is a circle; it is round or curved. It looks like a plate, wheel, or ring.

Have children find classroom objects that are shaped like circles. Possible answers: rim of wastebasket, outline of clock, plate, bottoms of cups

• **What are some foods that are round like circles?** Possible answers: whole pizzas, pancakes, bagels, rice cakes

FOCUSING ON THE WHOLE STUDENT

Access Prior Knowledge

Invite children to explore two-dimensional shapes.

• **How could you sort the shapes?** by color, shape, or size
• **Decide how you want to sort. Then sort a handful of shapes.**

Have children share their sets and explain how they sorted them. Check visually.

I Can Objective

I can identify and name circles.

Making Connections

Draw circles, squares, and triangles on chart paper or the board. Ask children to talk about the shapes and name any of the shapes they know. Point out and name the circles.

Learning Activity

Guide children to describe circles. Ask the following questions.

• **What does a circle look like?** Possible answers: It is round. It is the same shape as a wheel.

• **What classroom objects are shaped like a circle?** Possible answers: a round rug; the lid of a jar; the bottom of a cup

Explore

Listen and Draw Real World

Materials two-dimensional shapes

Read aloud this problem as children listen.

Jack has a sticker collection. He wants to sort the stickers into sets. One set will be circles. How will Jack know which stickers are circles?

Help children locate and read the word *circles*. Hold up a circle and trace around it with your finger, saying that it is a round and two-dimensional, or flat, shape.

Tell children that "figure" and "shape" can be used interchangeably in a mathematical context. For example, *two-dimensional shape* and *two-dimensional figure* mean the same thing.

 Use appropriate tools strategically.

Give children assorted two-dimensional shapes and have them sort out the circles, naming them as they do so.

- **Look at your shapes. Sort them into sets:** *circles* and *not circles*. **Trace and color them.**
- **How many shapes on the left of the sorting mat are circles?** all of the shapes
- **How many shapes on the right of the sorting mat are circles?** none of the shapes
- **What else can you say about a circle?** It is round and flat.

Reread the problem.

 Attend to precision.

- **How will Jack know which stickers are circles?** He can find stickers that are round and flat.

Name _____

Identify and Name Circles

(I Can) identify and name circles.

Listen and Draw Real World

circles	not circles

© Houghton Mifflin Harcourt Publishing Company

DIRECTIONS Place two-dimensional shapes on the page. Identify and name the circles. Sort the shapes by circles and not circles. Trace and color the shapes on the sorting mat.

Check children's work.

Chapter 17 • Lesson 1 **641**

 Multilingual Support

STRATEGY: Develop Meanings

Children can understand the meanings of geometrical terms by identifying shapes.

Draw several different sizes and colors of circles on the board. **What shapes are these?** circles **How do you know?** Make sure children include that the figures are two-dimensional (flat) and round. Have children define *circle*. Possible answer: A circle is round and flat.

Ask children to draw a picture using different-sized circles. Then have them describe their drawings.

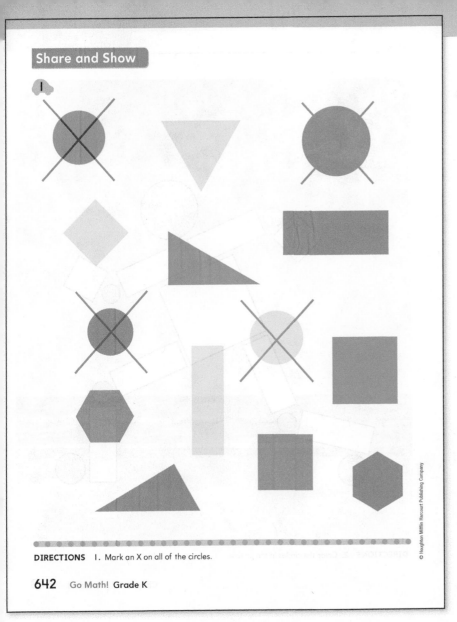

DIRECTIONS 1. Mark an X on all of the circles.

③ Explain

Share and Show

- **Look at the shapes on the page in Problem 1. Are all of the shapes the same?** no
- **Are any of the shapes circles?** yes

(MP) Look for and make use of structure.

- **How do you know that they are circles?** They are round and flat.

Have children find all of the circles and then mark them with an X.

- **How many circles are on the page?** 4
- **Describe the circles.** Possible answers: The circles are round and flat. They are small, medium, and large. They are blue, yellow, green, and red.

> ⚠ **Common Errors**
>
> **Error** Children may have difficulty identifying circles.
>
> **Example** Children name other shapes as circles.
>
> **Springboard to Learning** Have children trace a circle. Establish that the circle is round and flat. With children, name real-world things that are round like a circle such as a ring or hoop. Have them draw circles in the air or on a table using a finger.

Ready for More ⏲ Visual Individual/Partners

Materials crayons, paper

Distribute crayons and a piece of paper to each child.

Challenge children to draw a spider with eight legs using only circles. Remind them that they can use different-sized circles in their picture.

Have children trade their picture with a partner. Have each child count how many circles they find in the picture and write the number.

Repeat the activity with other pictures, such as a round table.

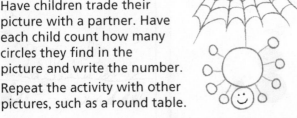

④ Elaborate

Share and Show

Guide a discussion about the circles in the picture. Children may notice a circle is used to represent the head, and circles are used to represent the feet, elbows, and knees on the person in the picture.

• **Color the circles.**
• **How many circles did you color?** 7

Use the checked problem for Quick Check.

✓ **Quick Check** **MTSS** (RtI)

If ➤ a child misses the checked problem

Then ➤ **Differentiate Instruction** with
  • Reteach 17.1
  • Waggle

Higher-Order Thinking

(MP) **Construct arguments and critique reasoning of others.**

Read this problem to children.

• **How are the circles different than the other shapes on the person in the picture?** Possible answer: The circles are round. The other shapes are not round.

• **Can two shapes be different sizes and both be circles?** Yes, something can be a circle as long as it is flat and has curved sides all around.

• **What are two objects you could use to show why this rule is true?** Children should name two circle-shaped objects of different sizes, such as a penny and a jar lid.

Math on the Spot Use this video to help children model and solve this type of problem.

Name _____

2 ✓

© Houghton Mifflin Harcourt Publishing Company

DIRECTIONS 2. Color the circles in the picture.

Chapter 17 • Lesson 1   643

Meeting Individual Needs

Reteach 17.1   **MTSS** (RtI1)

LESSON 17.1
Reteach

Name _____

Identify and Name Circles

🔎 Place a circle on each shaded circle. Color the other circles in the picture.

90

Enrich 17.1

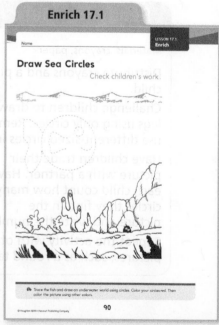

LESSON 17.1
Enrich

Name _____

Draw Sea Circles

Check children's work.

🔎 Trace the fish and draw an underwater world using circles. Color your circles red. Then color the picture using other colors.

90

3

4

Check children's work.

DIRECTIONS 3. Dante puts his shapes in a row. Which shape is a circle? Mark an X on that shape. 4. Draw an object you have seen in real life that is shaped like a circle.

HOME ACTIVITY • Have your child show you an object that is shaped like a circle.

Problem Solving Applications

Have children look at **Problem 3**. Read the problem. Ask children to explain how they will solve the problem.

(MP) Look for and make use of structure.

- **How many shapes do you see?** 5
- **Are they all circles?** no
- **How many circles do you see?** 1

Draw an oval and a circle. Explain that the oval looks like a "stretched out" or "squashed" circle. Tell children that it is not a circle; it is a shape called an oval.

- **Mark an X on the circle.** Check visually.

(MP) Attend to precision.

Before children draw, ask them to tell how they know that a circle is a circle. Guide them to explain that a circle is a round and flat shape.

Have children draw to show what they know about circles.

DIFFERENTIATED INSTRUCTION • Independent Activities

Grab-and-Go!

Version 2.0

Differentiated Centers Kit

Tabletop Flipchart

Mini-lessons for reteaching to targeted small groups

Readers

Supports key math skills and concepts in real-world situations.

Games

Reinforce math content and vocabulary

Activities

Meaningful and fun math practice

⑤ Evaluate | Formative Assessment

I Can

Have children work in teams of three or four to discuss and answer the I Can statement.

I can identify and name circles by . . . knowing that a circle is round and flat.

Exit Ticket

Have children tell a friend about their drawing.

Practice and Homework

Identify and Name Circles

Use the Practice and Homework pages to provide children with more practice of the concepts and skills presented in this lesson. Children master their understanding as they complete practice items.

Name ______________________

LESSON 17.1
Practice and Homework

Identify and Name Circles

1

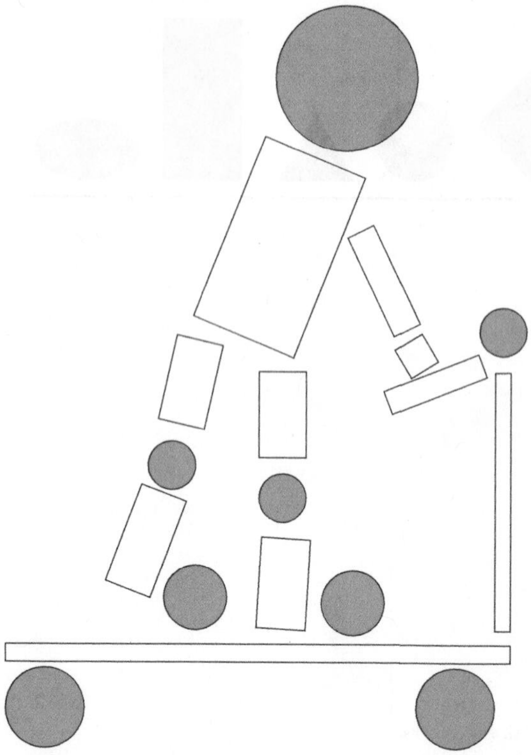

DIRECTIONS 1. Color the circles in the picture.

Lesson Check

Spiral Review

15 16 17 18 19

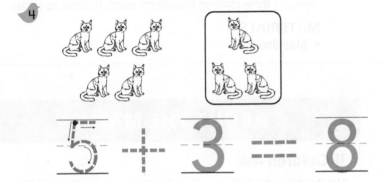

5 + 3 = 8

DIRECTIONS 2. Color the circle. 3. Count forward. Trace and write the numbers in order. 4. Trace and write to complete the addition sentence about the sets of cats.

© Houghton Mifflin Harcourt Publishing Company

Lesson at a Glance
Describe Circles

SNAPSHOT

Mathematical Standards
● Correctly name shapes regardless of their orientations or overall size.

Mathematical Practices and Processes
● Attend to precision.
● Model with mathematics.
● Construct arguments and critique reasoning of others.
● Look for and make use of structure.
● Use appropriate tools strategically.

(I Can) Objective
I can describe circles.

Learning Goal
Describe attributes of circles.

Language Objective
Teams of three children brainstorm words to describe circles.

MATERIALS
• MathBoard

ACROSS THE GRADES

Grade K

Identify two- and three-dimensional figures regardless of their size or orientation. Figures are limited to circles, triangles, rectangles, squares, spheres, cubes, cones and cylinders.

After

Identify, compare and sort two- and three-dimensional figures based on their defining attributes. Figures are limited to circles, semi-circles, triangles, rectangles, squares, trapezoids, hexagons, spheres, cubes, rectangular prisms, cones and cylinders.

ABOUT THE MATH

If Children Ask

While discussing classroom objects that are shaped like circles, a child might show a ball and ask, "This ball is round. Is it a circle?"

That is a good and very natural question! A circle is all points in a plane that are the same distance from a center point. A sphere is all points in space that are the same distance from a center point. A circle is a plane or two-dimensional shape while a sphere is a three-dimensional shape.

But how do you answer the child's question? You might explain that a circle is flat and does not take up space. A sphere is not flat and takes up space. Things shaped like balls—basketballs or baseballs—have a special math name. They are called spheres, and we will work with them in the next chapter.

For more professional learning, go online to Teacher's Corner.

Problem of the Day 17.2

Name some numbers on the calendar that have all straight parts.

Name numbers that have all curved parts.

Name some numbers that have both curved and straight parts. 1, 4, and 7 have straight parts; 3, 6, 8, 9, and 0 have curved parts; 2, 5, and sometimes 9 have both straight and curved parts.

Discuss the shapes of numerals on the calendar, pointing out the numerals as children talk about them.

Vocabulary curve

- Interactive Student Edition
- Multilingual Glossary

Vocabulary Builder

Have children trace a straight path in the air.

- **Now trace a curve—a path that is not straight.**

Choose various children to walk to the door in straight paths and in curved paths.

Write some letters such as *o, k, d, w,* and *s* on the board. Let children identify them as having straight or curved parts or both. *K* and *w* have straight parts; *s* and *o* are curved; *d* has both straight and curved parts.

Sketch a circle. Have children draw a circle on their MathBoards. Let volunteers describe their circles. Ask children to draw another circle. Then have volunteers tell how their circles are the same and different.

FOCUSING ON THE WHOLE STUDENT

Access Prior Knowledge

Use six circles to draw a caterpillar on the board.

- **What shape do you see repeated in my caterpillar?** a circle

- **How many circles do you see?** 6

Invite children to draw their own caterpillars using six or more circles.

① Engage

with the Interactive Student Edition

I Can Objective

I can describe circles.

Making Connections

Point out a classroom object, such as a clock, that is a circle.

- **What shape is the clock?** It is a circle.

- **What does a circle look like?** Possible answer: It is round.

Learning Activity

Have children draw circles to help them identify the features of a circle. Ask the following questions.

- **How do you draw a circle?** Possible answer: I draw a round shape with no straight lines.

- **How is a circle different from other shapes you know?** Possible answers: It goes around and around; it is not drawn with straight lines.

Explore

Listen and Draw

Read aloud this problem as children listen.

Julia drew a shape and wanted her friend Tara to guess what shape she drew. She gave Tara this hint: "My shape is round and curved. I traced around a cup to draw it." What shape did Julia draw?

 Model with mathematics.

Call attention to the circle on the page.

- **Find the worm sitting on the curve and read the word** *curve*. **Trace your finger around the curve of the circle.**

Have children use the circle shown to talk about the curve.

- **Is the curve straight?** no
- **Trace around the curve.**

Reread the problem.

- **What shape did Julia draw?** a circle
- **What rules about circles helped you know?**
  A circle is round and curved and Julia's hint was that her shape is round and curved.

Name _____

Describe Circles

(I Can) describe circles.

Listen and Draw

curve

© Houghton Mifflin Harcourt Publishing Company

DIRECTIONS Use your finger to trace around the circle. Talk about the curve. Trace around the curve.

Check children's work.

Chapter 17 • Lesson 2   **647**

Multilingual Support

STRATEGY: Model Language

Children can learn language structure by repeating shape words modeled by a proficient speaker.

Draw two lines on the board, one straight and one curved. Have children echo as you point to the lines: **This line is straight. This line is curved.**

Have each child draw a curve. Then have them trace the curve with their fingers while saying *curve*. Ask children to tell how the curve is different from a straight line. Possible answer: The curve is bent, and the line is not.

Have children draw a circle. Ask them to trace the circle and describe the shape.

1

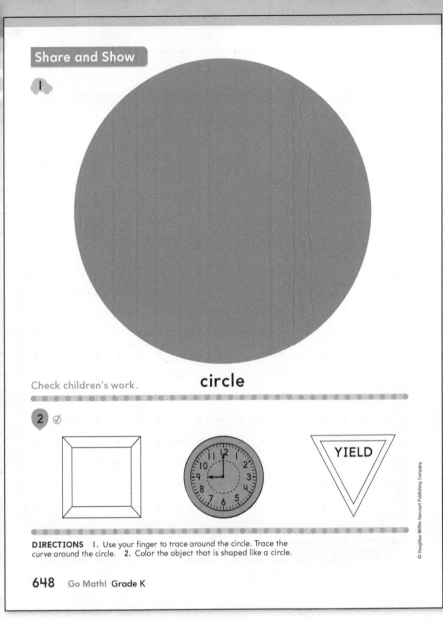

circle

Check children's work.

2

  YIELD

DIRECTIONS 1. Use your finger to trace around the circle. Trace the curve around the circle. 2. Color the object that is shaped like a circle.

© Houghton Mifflin Harcourt Publishing Company

Ready for More

 Visual
Individual/Partners

Materials two-dimensional shapes, paper bags, spinners (blank and 2-section)

Label the spinner **Circles** on one section and **Not Circles** on the other. Distribute bags filled with shapes. Have children spin the pointer and read what to look for. Have the child pull a shape from the bag that matches what is on the spinner.

Continue until all shapes are matched. Then have players sort the shapes into two sets: circles and not circles.

Ask children to discuss how the two sets are different.

③ Explain

Share and Show

Call attention to the circle on the page. Ask children to trace around the circle with a finger. Help children locate and read the word *circle*.

(MP) Attend to precision.

Look at Problem 2 with children and have them name the objects—frame, clock, sign.

- **Which object is shaped like a circle?** the clock **Color it.**

Have children brainstorm the names of objects in the classroom that are shaped like a circle.

(MP) Construct arguments and critique reasoning of others.

Have children explain how they know whether each object is shaped like a circle. If necessary, review that a circle is flat, round, and curved. Use the checked problem for Quick Check.

✓ Quick Check MTSS RtI

If a child misses the checked problem

Then **Differentiate Instruction** with
- Reteach 17.2
- Waggle

⚠ Common Errors

Error Children may not recognize everyday objects that are shaped like circles.

Example Children color the frame instead of the clock in Problem 2.

Springboard to Learning Draw some everyday objects on the board that are shaped like circles, such as a plate or a wheel. Explain that these objects may have other details, but they should just look at the outside of each object to see if it is a circle. Have children trace the outside of the objects.

④ Elaborate

Share and Show

 Use appropriate tools strategically.

Focus children's attention on the dotted grid on the page. Read the directions.

- **To draw a circle, what do you need to know?** A circle is round and curved.

Demonstrate how to draw a circle on the grid using a paper clip. Choose a dot in the middle of the grid on which to place the pencil that holds one end of the paper clip. Show children how to keep that pencil still. Place the drawing pencil in the other end of the paper clip and pull slightly as you draw to create a smooth, curved, and closed circle.

Higher-Order Thinking

 Model with mathematics.

Tape a piece of yarn to the board or place the yarn on a felt board in the shape of a circle. **What shape is this?** a circle **If you were inside the circle, is there an opening through which you could get out?** no **This is called a closed shape, because there are no open spaces on the yarn.**

Now tape a piece of yarn to the board or place the yarn on a felt board in the shape of an open curve. **If you were inside this shape, could you get out?** yes **This shape is called an open shape because there is an open space on the yarn.** Have children draw an open shape and then a closed shape.

Math on the Spot Use this video to help children model and solve this type of problem.

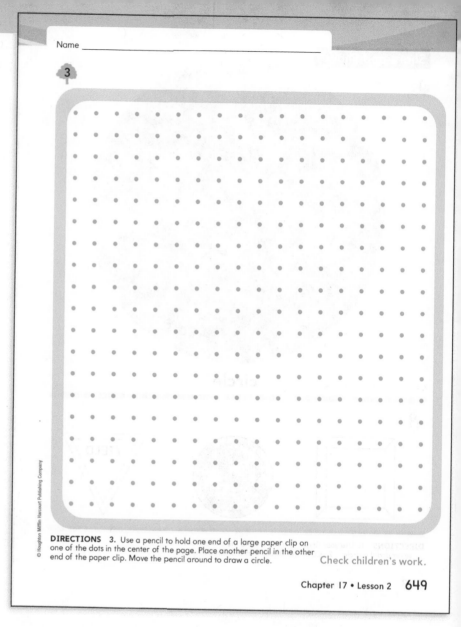

Name _____

DIRECTIONS 3. Use a pencil to hold one end of a large paper clip on one of the dots in the center of the page. Place another pencil in the other end of the paper clip. Move the pencil around to draw a circle.

Check children's work.

Chapter 17 • Lesson 2   649

Meeting Individual Needs

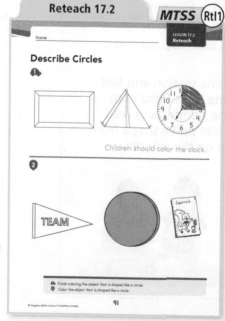

Reteach 17.2   **MTSS** (RtI1)

Describe Circles

Enrich 17.2

Complete the Circle

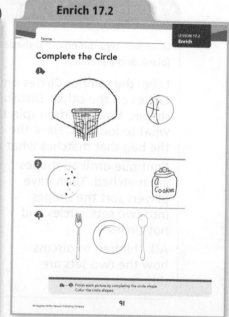

4

Check children's work.

© Houghton Mifflin Harcourt Publishing Company

Problem Solving Applications

MP **Look for and make use of structure.**

Problem 4 Read the riddle for children. Ask children to explain how they will solve the problem.

- **What shape do you know that has a curve?** a circle
- **What shape will you draw?** a circle

⑤ Evaluate | Formative Assessment

I Can

Have children work in teams of three to brainstorm words to answer the I Can statement.

I can describe circles by . . . saying that they are flat shapes that are round and curved.

Exit Ticket

Invite children to draw and compare their circles with a friend.

DIFFERENTIATED INSTRUCTION • Independent Activities

Grab-and-Go!™
Version 2.0
Differentiated Centers Kit

Tabletop Flipchart

Mini-lessons for reteaching to targeted small groups

Readers

Supports key math skills and concepts in real-world situations.

Games

Reinforce math content and vocabulary

Activities

Meaningful and fun math practice

Describe Circles

Use the Practice and Homework pages to provide children with more practice of the concepts and skills presented in this lesson. Children master their understanding as they complete practice items.

Describe Circles

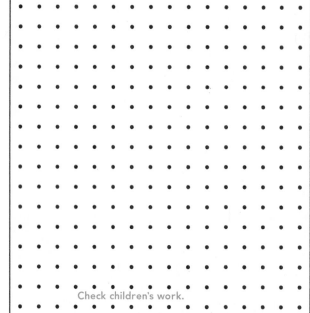

Check children's work.

© Houghton Mifflin Harcourt Publishing Company

DIRECTIONS 1. Use a pencil to hold one end of a large paper clip on one of the dots in the center. Place another pencil in the other end of the paper clip. Move the pencil around to draw a circle. **2.** Color the object that is shaped like a circle.

Chapter 17 • Lesson 2 **651**

CROSS-CURRICULAR

SCIENCE

Discuss the difference between natural and human-made objects.

- **What things found in nature have a curve, like a circle?**
  Possible answers: the sun, a grape, the center of a sunflower

Have children describe the object they name. Then have them draw a picture.

Use the children's pictures to create a bulletin board of natural objects that have a curve like a circle.

SOCIAL STUDIES

- Discuss how some stories have been passed down from long ago and are still told today.
- Explain that people long ago made an alphabet so they could write down stories and information they wanted to share and keep.
- Tell children that some letters and numbers are made with circles.
- Help children name the letters and numbers that are formed using circles: a, b, d, g, o, p, q and 0, 6, 9, 10.

Lesson Check

3

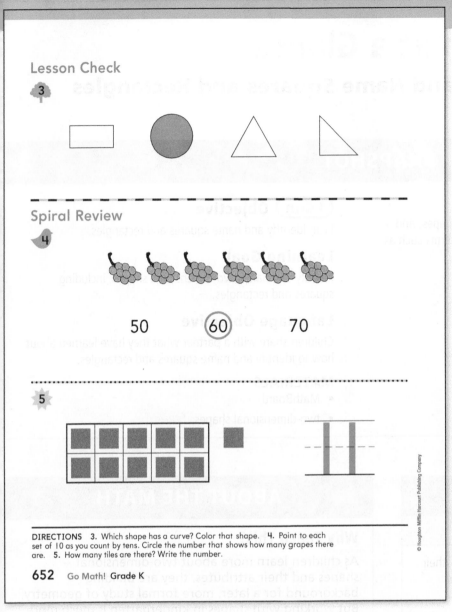

- -

Spiral Review

4

50   (60)   70

5

© Houghton Mifflin Harcourt Publishing Company

DIRECTIONS 3. Which shape has a curve? Color that shape. 4. Point to each set of 10 as you count by tens. Circle the number that shows how many grapes there are. 5. How many tiles are there? Write the number.

652 Go Math! **Grade K**

Lesson at a Glance
Identify and Name Squares and Rectangles

SNAPSHOT

Mathematical Standards

- Describe objects in the environment using names of shapes, and describe the relative positions of these objects using terms such as *above, below, beside, in front of, behind,* and *next to.*

Mathematical Practices and Processes

- Use appropriate tools strategically.
- Model with mathematics.
- Attend to precision.
- Construct arguments and critique reasoning of others.
- Express regularity in repeated reasoning.
- Reason abstractly and quantitatively.

(I Can) Objective

I can identify and name squares and rectangles.

Learning Goal

Identify and name two-dimensional shapes, including squares and rectangles.

Language Objective

Children share with a partner what they have learned about how to identify and name squares and rectangles.

MATERIALS

- MathBoard
- two-dimensional shapes

ACROSS THE GRADES

Grade K

Identify two- and three-dimensional figures regardless of their size or orientation. Figures are limited to circles, triangles, rectangles, squares, spheres, cubes, cones and cylinders.

After

Identify, compare and sort two- and three-dimensional figures based on their defining attributes. Figures are limited to circles, semi-circles, triangles, rectangles, squares, trapezoids, hexagons, spheres, cubes, rectangular prisms, cones and cylinders.

ABOUT THE MATH

Why Teach This?

As children learn more about two-dimensional shapes and their attributes, they are building background for a later, more formal study of geometry. But working with shapes in kindergarten is much more than this. Knowing about shapes lays a foundation for understanding the world. Working with shapes strengthens children's spatial sense.

Geometry, with its focus on shapes and positions, is a different aspect of mathematics than working with numbers. But geometry also connects to numbers as children tell, for example, how many sides or vertices a shape has. Geometry also connects to other subject areas such as art, science, and social studies.

Shapes can be two-dimensional (lying in a plane, or "flat") or three-dimensional (solid). It is important to introduce correct mathematical language when studying shapes.

For more professional learning, go online to Teacher's Corner.

DAILY ROUTINES

 Problem of the Day 17.3

Show how you can put together counters to make 8.

Check children's answers.

 Vocabulary corner, rectangle, side, square, vertex, vertices

• Interactive Student Edition
• Multilingual Glossary

Vocabulary Builder

rectangle, square, side, vertex, vertices, corner

Ask children to draw to show each term. Check children's drawings.

FOCUSING ON THE WHOLE STUDENT

Social & Emotional Learning

Self-Management During the lesson, help children identify and try new strategies to solve a problem. *When a strategy isn't working, try a different strategy. Did the way you found objects shaped like circles work for finding objects shaped like squares? What did you do differently? Once you have tried a few different ways, you will have a toolbox of strategies that you can use to solve problems that are alike.*

Access Prior Knowledge

Use iTools: Geometry to show a circle.

• **How would you describe this shape?** It is round and curved.

• **What is the name of this shape?** a circle

Show the name of the shape to children. Have them repeat the word *circle* with you.

• **Trace a circle in the air.**

I Can Objective

I can identify and name squares and rectangles.

Making Connections

Draw circles, squares, rectangles, and triangles on chart paper or the board. Ask children to talk about the shapes and name any of the shapes they know. As a group, point out and name the squares and rectangles.

Learning Activity

Guide children to describe squares. Ask the following questions.

• **What does a square look like?** Possible answers: It has four lines. It is the same shape as a window.

• **What classroom objects are shaped like a square?** Possible answers: some rugs, some windows, the tops of some tables

• **What does a rectangle look like?** Possible answer: It has four lines, but they are not all the same length.

• **What classroom objects are shaped like a rectangle?** Possible answers: the door, math books

Explore

Listen and Draw

Materials two-dimensional shapes

Read aloud this problem as children listen.

Cheng has a collection of shapes. He wants to sort out all of the squares. How will Cheng know which shapes are squares?

Help children locate and read the word *squares*. Hold up a square and identify a side.

- **Squares have four straight sides that match. Trace each side of the square with your finger and count 1, 2, 3, 4.**

Hold up a square. Point to a corner and explain that a corner is where two sides meet. Tell children that another word for *corner* is *vertex*, or *vertices* when you are talking about more than one.

 Use appropriate tools strategically.

Give children assorted plane shapes. Then have children sort the shapes.

- **Trace and color the shapes.**
- **How many shapes on the left of the sorting mat are squares?** all the shapes
- **How many shapes on the right of the sorting mat are squares?** none of the shapes
- **How can you describe a square?** It has four straight sides that match and four corners or vertices.

Reread the problem.

- **How will Cheng know which shapes are squares?** He can find the shapes that have four straight sides that match and four corners or vertices.

 Construct arguments and critique reasoning of others.

Encourage children to describe shapes they know in detail. Children may use mathematical terms, such as *vertices*, or informal language, such as *corners*. Either usage is acceptable as long as children accurately describe shapes.

Name _____

Identify and Name Squares and Rectangles

(I Can) identify and name squares and rectangles.

Listen and Draw

squares	not squares

DIRECTIONS Place two-dimensional shapes on the page. Identify and name the squares. Sort the shapes by squares and not squares. Trace and color the shapes on the sorting mat.

Check children's work.

Chapter 17 • Lesson 3   **653**

 Multilingual Support

STRATEGY: Develop Meaning

Children can define words by matching visuals to their definitions.

Show a variety of classroom objects. Have children identify the ones that are squares. **How do you know these objects are squares?** Have children trace each shape and echo, **There are four straight sides that match.**

Use the word *square* in context to help children understand the shape. Have each child point to one square object or drawing and use it to describe squares. Make sure they say that the shape has four straight sides that match.

rectangles	not rectangles

DIRECTIONS 1. Place two-dimensional shapes on the page. Identify and name the rectangles. Sort the shapes by rectangles and not rectangles. Trace and color the shapes on the sorting mat. Check children's work.

Ready for More

 Visual / Kinesthetic
Individual / Partners

Materials paper squares folded in fourths lengthwise and crosswise; scissors

Have children cut their paper squares along the fold lines, and then exchange them with another child.

Invite children to rearrange the squares to form the original square.

Have children write how many squares there are in all. 5

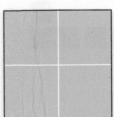

---

③ Explain

Share and Show Math Board

Materials two-dimensional shapes

Read aloud this problem as children listen.

Mrs. Lin has frames of all different shapes in her frame store. She wants to sort the frames. One set of frames will be rectangles. Can you help her sort?

Give children assorted flat shapes. Help children locate and read the word *rectangles*. Hold up a rectangle and define it as a shape with four straight sides and four vertices. Guide children to understand that a rectangle has two pairs of sides that match in length.

 Attend to precision.

- **Look at your shapes. Find the ones that are rectangles. On the mat, sort your shapes into two sets: rectangles and not rectangles.** Check visually.
- **Trace and color the shapes.**
- **How many shapes on the left of the sorting mat are rectangles?** all the shapes
- **How many shapes on the right of the sorting mat are rectangles?** none of the shapes
- **What is the same about all of the rectangles?** They have four straight sides and four corners, and two pairs of matching sides.

Reread the problem.

Reason abstractly and quantitatively.

- **How will Mrs. Lin's daughter know which frames are rectangles?** She will look for frames that have four straight sides, four vertices, and two pairs of matching sides.
- **What other shape do you know with four straight sides and four corners/vertices?** a square

Explain that a square is a actually special type of rectangle, since it is a shape with 4 sides and 4 corners. Elicit from children that what makes a square special is that it has four straight matching sides *(sides of equal length)*.

④ Elaborate

Share and Show

Discuss the shapes on page 655.

- **Are all the shapes the same?** no
- **Name some of the shapes you see.** Possible answers: triangles, circles, trapezoid, hexagons, squares, and rectangles

Have children find the rectangles and mark an X on each. Then, ask children find the squares and draw a loop around each one.

 Express regularity in repeated reasoning.

If children mark an X on the squares (in addition to looping them), ask them to explain why. If children are able to explain that they marked the squares in this manner because squares are a special type of rectangle, accept their X marks as correct.

Use the checked problem for Quick Check.

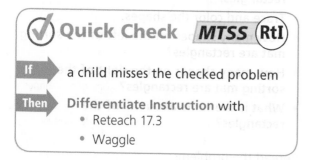

Supporting All Learners

Discuss the fact that all squares are rectangles, but not all rectangles are squares. This concept can be difficult for children to understand, but it is a good opportunity to discuss how two different answers to the same problem can be equally correct. Talk about the importance of respecting someone else who has a different answer. Even when someone has an answer that is incorrect, they deserve respect for being willing to talk about their understanding. Remind children that mistakes are valuable tools to help them learn and grow.

- **How many rectangles did you find?** 5 **How do you know which shapes are rectangles?** I know rectangles have four straight sides and four corners, with two pairs of matching sides.

- **How many squares did you find?** 2 **How do you know which shapes are squares?** I know squares have four straight matching sides and four vertices.

Math on the Spot Use this video to help children model and solve this type of problem.

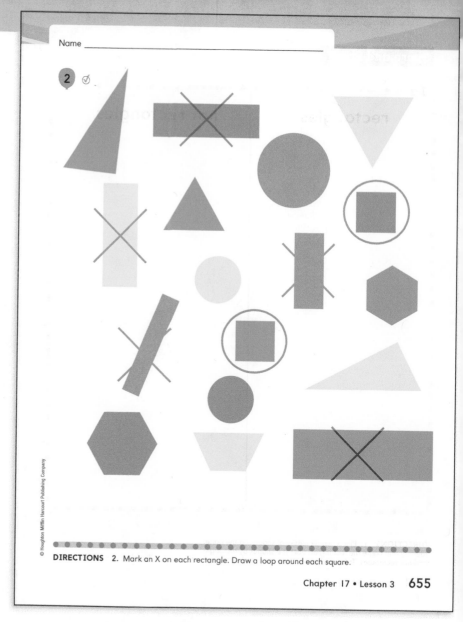

Name _____

© Houghton Mifflin Harcourt Publishing Company

DIRECTIONS 2. Mark an X on each rectangle. Draw a loop around each square.

Chapter 17 • Lesson 3 **655**

Meeting Individual Needs

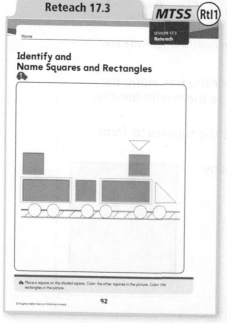

Reteach 17.3

Identify and Name Squares and Rectangles

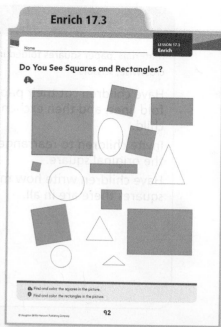

Enrich 17.3

Do You See Squares and Rectangles?

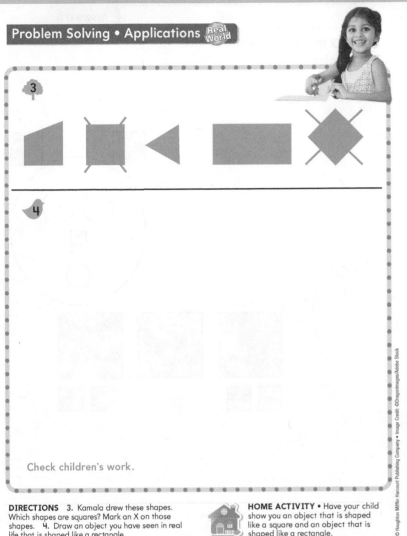

3

4

Check children's work.

DIRECTIONS 3. Kamala drew these shapes. Which shapes are squares? Mark an X on those shapes. 4. Draw an object you have seen in real life that is shaped like a rectangle.

 **HOME ACTIVITY** • Have your child show you an object that is shaped like a square and an object that is shaped like a rectangle.

656 Go Math! Grade K

Problem Solving Applications *Real World*

 Construct arguments and critique reasoning of others.

Have children look at **Problem 3.** Ask them to explain how they will solve the problem.

- **How many shapes do you see?** 5
- **Are they all squares?** no
- **How many squares are there?** 2 Mark an X on the squares.

 Model with mathematics.

Problem 4 Read the problem to children. Before children draw, ask them to describe a rectangle. After they have completed the problem, have children tell a classmate about their drawing.

⑤ Evaluate | Formative Assessment

I Can

Have children work with partners to answer the I Can statement.

I can identify and name squares and rectangles by . . . finding shapes with four straight sides and four vertices. Rectangles have two pairs of sides that match, and squares have four sides that match.

Exit Ticket

Have children explain the difference between a square and a rectangle.

DIFFERENTIATED INSTRUCTION • Independent Activities

Grab-and-Go!
Version 2.0
Differentiated Centers Kit

Tabletop Flipchart

Mini-lessons for reteaching to targeted small groups

Readers

Supports key math skills and concepts in real-world situations.

Games

Reinforce math content and vocabulary

Activities

Meaningful and fun math practice

Identify and Name Squares and Rectangles

Use the Practice and Homework pages to provide children with more practice of the concepts and skills presented in this lesson. Children master their understanding as they complete practice items.

Name _____

Identify and Name Squares and Rectangles

DIRECTIONS I. Color the squares in the picture.

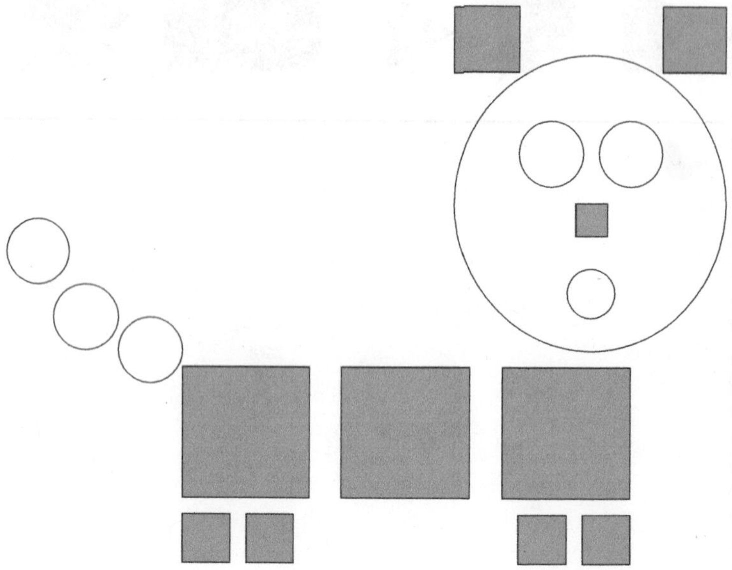

© Houghton Mifflin Harcourt Publishing Company

Chapter 17 • Lesson 3   657

PROFESSIONAL LEARNING   **MATH TALK IN ACTION**

Jin: I have another shape that has four sides.	**Amanda:** Oh, right. They can be different colors.
Teacher: Yes. That shape has four sides, too. But it is not a square.	**Teacher:** Yes. They can be different colors, but they can also be different sizes.
Jin: Why?	**Amanda:** I thought all squares had to have sides that match.
Teacher: Because the sides do not match. For a shape to be a square, it has to have four sides that match.	
Jin: What is the name of this shape?	**Teacher:** Yes. You are correct. A square has four sides that match, but each square can be different. There can be a square with all short sides or one with all long sides.
Teacher: That is a rectangle. It has four sides, but the four sides do not all match. Squares are also rectangles. But they are special rectangles.	
Amanda: Are all squares the same?	**Amanda:** I get it now.
Teacher: That is a good question. No, they are not.	

Lesson Check

2

Spiral Review

3

4

2 and 2 4

DIRECTIONS 2. Which shape is a rectangle? Color the rectangle. 3. How many tiles are there? Write the number. 4. Trace the number of puppies. Trace the number of puppies being added. Write the number that shows how many puppies there are now.

658 Go Math! Grade K

Lesson at a Glance
Describe Squares and Rectangles

SNAPSHOT

Mathematical Standards
- Correctly name shapes regardless of their orientations or overall size.

Mathematical Practices and Processes
- Use appropriate tools strategically.
- Model with mathematics.
- Construct arguments and critique reasoning of others.
- Attend to precision.
- Reason abstractly and quantitatively.

(I Can) **Objective**

I can describe squares and rectangles.

Learning Goal

Describe attributes of squares and rectangles.

Language Objective

Small teams of children discuss how to describe squares and rectangles.

MATERIALS
- MathBoard
- two-color counters
- modeling clay
- straws or coffee stirrers

ACROSS THE GRADES

Grade K

Identify two- and three-dimensional figures regardless of their size or orientation. Figures are limited to circles, triangles, rectangles, squares, spheres, cubes, cones and cylinders.

After

Identify, compare and sort two- and three-dimensional figures based on their defining attributes. Figures are limited to circles, semi-circles, triangles, rectangles, squares, trapezoids, hexagons, spheres, cubes, rectangular prisms, cones and cylinders.

ABOUT THE MATH

Teaching for Depth

In this lesson, children do activities with squares and rectangles. The activities engage children in using their hands and minds and help them internalize the content.

As children explore two-dimensional shapes, help them develop a strong understanding of the similarities and differences by pointing out attributes of straight sides, vertices, and curves. It is important to use correct mathematical language when describing attributes. In lessons about squares and rectangles, emphasize that the corners or vertices are *square* corners and *square* vertices. This will prevent misunderstanding when children learn about parallelograms in later grades.

For more professional learning, go online to Teacher's Corner.

DAILY ROUTINES

🖥 Problem of the Day 17.4

Tell about what you see.

Which lines are straight?

Which lines are not straight?
Check children's answers.

Discuss the questions. Choose a child to move in a straight path to different places in the classroom. Have others move to the same places on paths that are not straight. Guide children to see that the shortest path is a straight one.

🖥 Vocabulary sides of equal length

- Interactive Student Edition
- Multilingual Glossary

Vocabulary Builder

Have children draw shapes that have sides of equal length. Have them highlight all of the sides that are equal in length. Children should highlight all of the sides.

FOCUSING ON THE WHOLE STUDENT

Access Prior Knowledge

Have children make models of squares using clay and toothpicks.

- **Roll the clay into four small balls for the corners. Press the ends of four toothpicks into the clay to form a square. Make sure the shape lies flat and is closed.**
- **What shape do you have?** a square
- **How do you know it is a square?** It has four straight sides that match and 4 square vertices.

---

① Engage

with the Interactive Student Edition

I Can Objective
I can describe squares and rectangles.

Making Connections
Point out a classroom object, such as a window, that is a square.

- **What shape is the window?** It is a square.
- **What does a square look like?** Possible answer: It has four straight sides that match.

Point out another classroom object, such as a table, that is a rectangle.

- **What shape is the table?** It is a rectangle.
- **What does a rectangle look like?** Possible answer: It has four sides with two pairs of matching sides.

Learning Activity
Have children draw squares and rectangles to help them identify the features of the shapes. Ask the following questions.

- **How do you draw a square?** Possible answer: I draw four lines that meet.
- **How is a square different from other shapes you know, like a circle?** Possible answer: A square is drawn with four straight lines, but a circle curves.
- **How would you draw a rectangle?** Possible answer: I would draw one lines, then another line below it that is the same length. Then I would connect the two lines with two shorter lines.

② Explore

Listen and Draw

Materials **two-color counters**

Read aloud this problem as children listen.

Alanna needs a square frame for her soccer picture. How many sides should the frame have?

Call attention to the blue square on the page. Remind children that even though the square has been turned so that a corner is at the bottom instead of a straight side, it is still a square. Ask children to trace around the square with a finger. Have children use counters to complete the activity.

 Attend to precision.

• **Place a counter on each corner, or vertex. How many vertices do you see?** 4 **Write the number.**

Have children remove the counters.

• **Trace around each side. What number will you write?** 4 **Why?** because the square has four sides

• **What do you know about the four sides of a square?** They match; the four sides are all of equal length.

 Construct arguments and critique reasoning of others.

• **Think about what you wrote. How do you know that the picture shows a square?** Possible answer: I know this shape is a square because it has four equal sides and four square corners/vertices.

Name _____

Describe Squares and Rectangles

(I Can) describe squares and rectangles.

Listen and Draw

Check children's work.

square

4 vertices

4 sides

DIRECTIONS Place a counter on each corner, or vertex. Write how many corners, or vertices. Trace around the sides. Write how many sides. Check children's work.

 Multilingual Support

STRATEGY: Model Language

Children can learn correct pronunciation and sentence structure by repeating geometric words and sentences modeled by a proficient speaker.

Have children repeat the following sentences: **A square has four sides of equal length. A square has four vertices.** Then ask: **How are the number of sides and vertices of a square the same?** A square has four sides and four vertices.

Have children draw a square. Ask them to describe their drawings.

Repeat the activity, this time focusing on the attributes of a rectangle.

rectangle

Check children's work.

1

 vertices

2

 sides

DIRECTIONS 1. Place a counter on each corner, or vertex. Write how many corners, or vertices. 2. Trace around the sides. Write how many sides.

Ready for More

⏱ Kinesthetic
Individual/Partners

Materials pattern blocks, crayons, paper

Invite children to use blocks to build squares and rectangles of different sizes.

Have children trace the different shapes that they created to show their work.

Have children exchange their drawings with a partner and count and write the number of sides and vertices of the shape.

Ask children to discuss whether using different numbers of blocks to build a shape changes the number of sides and vertices the shape has.

③ Explain

Share and Show 📋 Math Board

Materials two-color counters

Call attention to the red rectangle. Ask children to trace around it with a finger.

(MP) Reason abstractly and quantitatively.

- **Place a counter on each vertex, or corner. How many vertices do you see?** 4 **Write the number.**

- **Trace around each side of the rectangle. What number will you write?** 4 **Why?**
  because a rectangle has four straight sides

Review that this rectangle has four vertices and four sides. Some children may note that two of the sides are long and two are short. Reiterate to children that a rectangle does not necessarily have 4 sides of equal length; it has two pairs of sides, and each pair of sides has an equal length.

Use the checked problems for Quick Check.

✓ Quick Check 🟥 MTSS RtI

If ▶ a child misses the checked problems

Then ▶ **Differentiate Instruction** with
- Reteach 17.4
- Waggle

⚠ Common Errors

Error Children may not be able to identify the vertices.

Example Children do not know the number of vertices that a square has.

Springboard to Learning Draw a square. Ask children to locate the corners. Remind them that *vertex* means "corner," or where the sides meet. Then ask children to draw a dot on each vertex (corner) and count the dots.

4 Elaborate

Share and Show

First, demonstrate how to draw a square on a grid using four dots as the four corners. Heavily trace a dot as your first vertex. Be sure to count aloud the number of spaces between the dots each time you draw a side. This demonstrates that all the sides are of *equal length*.

 Use appropriate tools strategically.

Have children draw a square in the top grid. Explain that it can be any size, but the sides must match; they must have be of equal length.

- **How can you tell if all four sides are of equal length?** I can count the spaces between the dots on each side.

- **How can you identify the vertices?** I can find and circle where two sides meet.

After children complete a square, help them count the spaces between the dots to make sure that the sides of the square are of equal length and the vertices are square. Then allow children to color their squares.

Next, demonstrate how to draw a rectangle by marking four dots and connecting them in such a way to show two parallel lines (two long sides of the rectangle). Then connect the ends of these lines to form two shorter parallel lines (the other two sides of the rectangle).

- **How many vertices, or corners, does a rectangle have?** 4 **How many sides does a rectangle have?** 4

Have children draw a rectangle in the bottom grid. If a child draws a square, reinforce that a square is a special kind of rectangle.

After children finish their drawings, have partners compare their work. Point out that rectangles can have two long and two short sides, or four sides of equal length. Since rectangles have two pairs of sides that match, this is still true even if all four sides match.

Higher-Order Thinking

Ask children to compare squares and rectangles.

- **How do the dots show how a square and rectangle are different?** Possible answer: For a square, I connect the same number of dots for each side. For a rectangle, the two long sides connect the same number of dots and the two short sides connect the same number of dots, but those numbers may not be the same.

Math on the Spot Use this video to help children model and solve this type of problem.

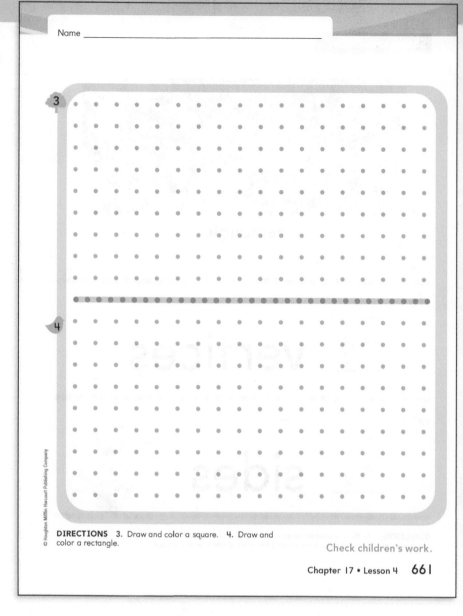

Name _____

DIRECTIONS 3. Draw and color a square. 4. Draw and color a rectangle.

Check children's work.

Chapter 17 • Lesson 4 **661**

Meeting Individual Needs

Reteach 17.4   **MTSS** (Rtl1)   **Enrich 17.4**

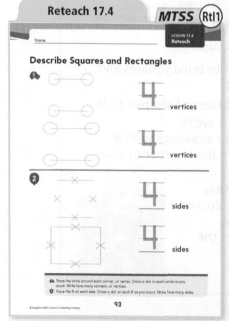

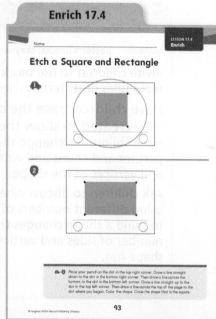

5

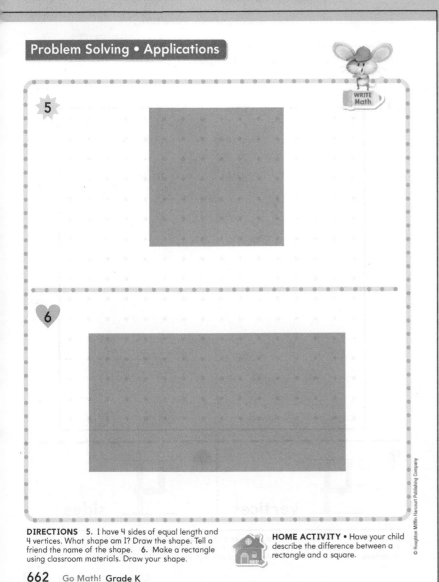

6

DIRECTIONS **5.** I have 4 sides of equal length and 4 vertices. What shape am I? Draw the shape. Tell a friend the name of the shape. **6.** Make a rectangle using classroom materials. Draw your shape.

 HOME ACTIVITY • Have your child describe the difference between a rectangle and a square.

662 Go Math! **Grade K**

© Houghton Mifflin Harcourt Publishing Company

Problem Solving Applications

 WRITE Math

(MP) Model with mathematics.

Read the riddle for the children. Ask children to explain how they will solve the riddle.

- **What shape has four sides of equal length?** a square

- **What shape has four square vertices?** a square; also accept rectangle

- **What shape has both four sides of equal length and four square vertices?** a square

- **What shape will you draw?** a square

Remind children to try to make the sides of equal length and the vertices square as they draw.

Materials modeling clay, straws or coffee stirrers

Problem 6 Have children make models of rectangles using classroom materials. Help children roll the clay into small balls for the corners.

⑤ Evaluate | Formative Assessment

I Can

Have children work in teams of three or four to answer the I Can statement.

I can describe squares and rectangles by . . . identifying that the shape has 4 straight sides and 4 corners; squares have 4 sides of equal length, and rectangles have two pairs of sides of equal length.

Exit Ticket

Invite children to complete the two sentence frames and draw pictures to match.

Every square has ____.

Every rectangle has ____.

DIFFERENTIATED INSTRUCTION • Independent Activities

Grab-and-Go!

Version 2.0

Differentiated Centers Kit

Tabletop Flipchart

Mini-lessons for reteaching to targeted small groups

Readers

Supports key math skills and concepts in real-world situations.

Games

Reinforce math content and vocabulary

Activities

Meaningful and fun math practice

Describe Squares and Rectangles

Use the Practice and Homework pages to provide children with more practice of the concepts and skills presented in this lesson. Children master their understanding as they complete practice items.

Describe Squares and Rectangles

1 Check children's work.

2 ____ vertices

3 ____ sides

DIRECTIONS 1. Draw and color a square or a rectangle. Write the name of the shape.
2. Place a counter on each corner, or vertex, of the shape that you drew. Write how many corners, or vertices. 3. Trace around the sides of the shape that you drew. Write how many sides.

Chapter 17 • Lesson 4   663

Lesson Check

 **4 vertices**

Spiral Review

 20

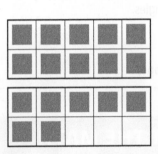 17

DIRECTIONS 4. How many vertices does the square have? Write the number.
5. Count and tell how many pieces of fruit. Write the number. 6. How many tiles are there? Write the number.

Continue to practice concepts and skills with Lesson Check. Use Spiral Review to engage children in previously taught concepts and to promote content retention.

Lesson at a Glance
Identify and Name Triangles

SNAPSHOT

Mathematical Standards
- Describe objects in the environment using names of shapes, and describe the relative positions of these objects using terms such as above, below, beside, in front of, behind, and next to.

Mathematical Practices and Processes
- Use appropriate tools strategically.
- Model with mathematics.
- Attend to precision.
- Construct arguments and critique reasoning of others.
- Look for and make use of structure.
- Reason abstractly and quantitatively.

(I Can) Objective
I can identify and name triangles.

Learning Goal
Identify and name two-dimensional shapes, including triangles.

Language Objective
Pairs of children list for another pair the ways you can identify and name triangles.

MATERIALS
- MathBoard
- two-dimensional shapes

ACROSS THE GRADES

Grade K
Identify two- and three-dimensional figures regardless of their size or orientation. Figures are limited to circles, triangles, rectangles, squares, spheres, cubes, cones and cylinders.

After
Identify, compare and sort two- and three-dimensional figures based on their defining attributes. Figures are limited to circles, semi-circles, triangles, rectangles, squares, trapezoids, hexagons, spheres, cubes, rectangular prisms, cones and cylinders.

ABOUT THE MATH

Using Two-Dimensional Shapes
Using two-dimensional manipulatives as children learn shape names and attributes helps children make visual discriminations. Working with the shapes keeps children's attention; handling and showing the two-dimensional shapes aids children's explanations as they refer to them.

The shapes are small, and as children move them to different orientations they begin to understand that shapes such as triangles can appear many different ways.

Children can feel the sides and vertices of the two-dimensional shapes, point to them, and trace along the sides with their fingers. Because they deal with shapes of different sizes and colors, children learn that shapes have constant attributes no matter what their sizes, colors, and orientations.

For more professional learning, go online to Teacher's Corner.

DAILY ROUTINES

🖥 Problem of the Day 17.5

Have children draw a circle and a square.
Check children's drawings.

🖥 Vocabulary triangle

- Interactive Student Edition
- Multilingual Glossary

Vocabulary Builder

triangle

Ask children to draw a triangle.
Check children's drawings.

FOCUSING ON THE WHOLE STUDENT

Access Prior Knowledge

Make a large square on the classroom floor using masking tape.

Invite children to take turns walking on the square. Have children count each side as they walk on it.

Then ask a volunteer to stand inside or outside of the square.

❶ Engage

with the Interactive Student Edition

I Can Objective

I can identify and name triangles.

Making Connections

Draw circles, squares, and triangles on chart paper or the board. Ask children to talk about the shapes and name any of the shapes they know. Point out and name the triangles.

Learning Activity

Guide children to describe triangles. Ask the following questions.

- **What does a triangle look like?** Possible answers: It has three lines. It is the same shape as a slice of pizza.

- **What classroom objects are shaped like a triangle?** Possible answers: part of an art project, floor tile

2 Explore

Listen and Draw

Materials two-dimensional shapes

Read aloud this problem as children listen.

Aidan has a button collection. He wants to sort all the buttons that are shaped like triangles. How will Aidan know which ones to sort?

Help children locate and read the word *triangles*. Hold up a triangle and trace the sides with your finger.

- **A triangle has three straight sides. The three sides do not have to be the same length. Not all triangles look the same.**

Show different types of triangles, pointing out that they all have three sides.

(MP) Use appropriate tools strategically.

- **Look at your two-dimensional shapes. Sort them on the mat in sets of *triangles* and *not triangles*. Then trace and color them.**
- **How many shapes on the left of the sorting mat are triangles?** all of the shapes
- **How many shapes on the right of the sorting mat are triangles?** none of the shapes
- **What is the same about all of the triangles?** They all have three straight sides.

Reread the problem.

- **How will Aidan know which buttons are shaped like triangles?** He can find the buttons that have three straight sides.

Name _____

Identify and Name Triangles

(I Can) identify and name triangles.

Listen and Draw

triangles	not triangles

DIRECTIONS Place two-dimensional shapes on the page. Identify and name the triangles. Sort the shapes by triangles and not triangles. Trace and color the shapes on the sorting mat.

Check children's work.

Chapter 17 • Lesson 5   **665**

(ML) Multilingual Support

STRATEGY: Develop Meanings

Children can define geometric terms by matching visuals to their definitions.

Show children several squares and triangles. Point to one of the squares. **What is this shape?** square **How do you know?** Possible answer: It has four straight sides. Repeat with one of the triangles. **What shape is this?** triangle **How do you know?** Possible answer: It has three straight sides.

Ask: **What is the difference between a square and a triangle?** Children should explain that squares have four straight sides and triangles have three straight sides.

I

DIRECTIONS 1. Mark an X on all of the triangles.

3 Explain

Share and Show

Call attention to the shapes in Problem 1.

- **Look at the shapes on the page. Are all of the shapes the same?** no
- **Can you name any of the shapes?** Children may name squares, circles, triangles, and rectangles

(MP) **Reason abstractly and quantitatively.**

- **Are any of the shapes triangles?** yes **How do you know?** A triangle has three straight sides.

Have children find all of the triangles on the page and then mark an X on each one.

- **How many triangles did you find?** 5
- **Do you see triangles that look the same but are turned different ways? If so, which ones?** yes, the green and red; also the yellow and the smaller blue

(MP) **Look for and make use of structure.**

- **How do you know they are still triangles?** They have three straight sides, and that's what makes a triangle a triangle.

Discuss that triangles can be different sizes and be in different positions, but they all have three straight sides.

Common Errors

Error Children may have difficulty identifying triangles.

Example Children name other shapes as triangles.

Springboard to Learning Have children trace a triangle, using a different color for each side. Then have them count the sides and establish that a triangle has three sides. Then have children differentiate a triangle from other shapes the same way.

Ready for More 🕐 Kinesthetic Individual/Partners

Materials triangle and square pattern blocks, paper bag

Place an assortment of triangle and square pattern blocks in a paper bag. Demonstrate how to reach in, pick a shape, and describe and name the shape before pulling it out.

Have children take a turn describing and guessing the name of the shape before they pull it out of the bag.

Continue until all of the shapes in the bag have been described and named.

Elaborate

Share and Show

 Model with mathematics.

Talk about the picture in Problem 2 and explain that the objects pictured are made up of triangles and other shapes. Ask the children to identify the triangles and then color them. If children can, have them identify the other shapes.

Use the checked problem for Quick Check.

✓ Quick Check **MTSS (RtI)**

If a child misses the checked problem

Then Differentiate Instruction with
- Reteach 17.5
- Waggle

Higher-Order Thinking

Construct arguments and critique reasoning of others.

Read the following problem to children.

- **What is the same and different about a square and a triangle?** Possible answer: They both have straight sides and vertices or corners. A triangle has three sides and three vertices or corners. The sides of a triangle do not have to be the same length. A square has four sides of equal length and four vertices or corners.

Children should compare the shapes and determine that they both have straight sides and vertices or corners but have a different number of each.

Math on the Spot Use this video to help children model and solve this type of problem.

Name _____

2

DIRECTIONS 2. Color the triangles in the picture.

Meeting Individual Needs

Reteach 17.5   **MTSS (RtI1)**

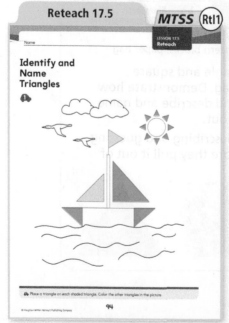

Identify and Name Triangles

Enrich 17.5

Identify and Name Triangles

3

4

Check children's work.

DIRECTIONS 3. Layla put her shapes in a row. Which shapes are triangles? Mark an X on those shapes. 4. Draw an object you have seen in real life that is shaped like a triangle.

HOME ACTIVITY • Have your child show you an object that is shaped like a triangle.

Problem Solving Applications

Have children look at **Problem 3**. Read the problem and ask children to explain how they will solve it.

(MP) **Attend to precision.**

- **How many shapes do you see?** 5
- **Are they all triangles?** no
- **How many circles do you see?** 1
- **How would you describe it?** It is round and curved.
- **How many squares do you see?** 1 **How many straight sides does it have?** 4
- **How many triangles do you see?** 2 **How many straight sides do they each have?** 3

Ask children to mark an X on the triangles.

(MP) **Reason abstractly and quantitatively.**

Problem 4 Have children draw to show what they know about triangles.

Before children draw, ask them to tell how they know that a triangle is a triangle. Guide them to explain that a triangle is a shape that has three straight sides.

DIFFERENTIATED INSTRUCTION • Independent Activities

Grab-and-Go!™
Version 2.0
Differentiated Centers Kit

Tabletop Flipchart

Mini-lessons for reteaching to targeted small groups

Readers

Supports key math skills and concepts in real-world situations.

Games

Reinforce math content and vocabulary

Activities

Meaningful and fun math practice

---

⑤ Evaluate | Formative Assessment

I Can

Have pairs of children exchange lists of ideas to answer the I Can statement.

I can identify and name triangles by . . .
knowing that a triangle is a shape with three straight sides.

Exit Ticket

After children draw, have them tell a friend about their drawing.

Practice and Homework

Identify and Name Triangles

Use the Practice and Homework pages to provide children with more practice of the concepts and skills presented in this lesson. Children master their understanding as they complete practice items.

Identify and Name Triangles

1

2

DIRECTIONS 1–2. Color the triangles in the picture.

Chapter 17 • Lesson 5 **669**

CROSS-CURRICULAR

SCIENCE

Materials two-dimensional shapes, empty box

- Ask children to watch as you let several shapes fall to the ground. Ask a volunteer to identify and name the shapes. Discuss how objects fall to the floor or the ground when nothing stops the fall.
- Hold several shapes above an empty box and ask children to watch as you drop several shapes into it. Have a volunteer identify and name the shapes.
- Ask children to tell what happened and why. Discuss the fact that the shapes did not fall to the floor or the ground because the box held them up.

SOCIAL STUDIES

Materials crayons, paper, scissors

- Take children on a neighborhood walk to look for different shapes. Look for shapes on trees, flowers, sidewalks, and buildings.
- Have children choose a shape or two that they saw on the walk and cut that shape out of construction paper. Children can use the shapes that they cut out to create a picture of what they saw.
- Remind children that they can use more than one shape to create their picture.

Lesson Check

Spiral Review

1	2	3	4	5	6	7	8	9	10
11	12	13	14	15	16	17	18	19	20
21	22	23	24	25	26	27	28	29	30

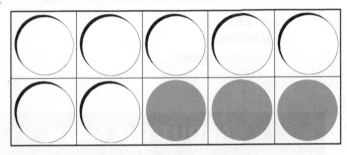

DIRECTIONS 3. Which shape is a triangle? Color the triangle. 4. Begin with 1 and count forward to 24. What is the next number? Draw a line under that number. 5. How many more counters would you place to model a way to make 10? Draw the counters.

670 Go Math! Grade K

SNAPSHOT

Mathematical Standards
● Correctly name shapes regardless of their orientations or overall size.

Mathematical Practices and Processes
● Express regularity in repeated reasoning.
● Model with mathematics.
● Attend to precision.
● Construct arguments and critique reasoning of others.
● Look for and make use of structure.
● Use appropriate tools strategically.

(I Can) Objective
I can describe triangles.

Learning Goal
Describe attributes of triangles.

Language Objective
Children name some familiar objects that are shaped like a triangle and describe what makes them similar.

MATERIALS
● MathBoard
● two-color counters

ACROSS THE GRADES

Grade K
Identify two- and three-dimensional figures regardless of their size or orientation. Figures are limited to circles, triangles, rectangles, squares, spheres, cubes, cones and cylinders.

After
Identify, compare and sort two- and three-dimensional figures based on their defining attributes. Figures are limited to circles, semi-circles, triangles, rectangles, squares, trapezoids, hexagons, spheres, cubes, rectangular prisms, cones and cylinders.

ABOUT THE MATH

If Children Ask
A child may hold up a paper triangle or two-dimensional shape manipulative and say, "My triangle has two sides—the front side and the back side. Is that right?" The child who asks a question like this clearly is confused about what we mean by sides of shapes. Since we refer to the front side and back side of pieces of paper, it is easy to see how such confusion arises.

Explain that sides of shapes form the outside borders of that shape. Have the child trace a finger along the side of a paper triangle and the sides of a two-dimensional shape manipulative.

You might also have the child glue three short pieces of yarn to paper to form a triangle. Saying, "Lay down the three pieces of yarn for the three sides" may help to clarify. Children may also use dough to make three long, thin "snakes," then mold these together as sides of a triangle.

For more professional learning, go online to Teacher's Corner.

DAILY ROUTINES

🖥 Problem of the Day 17.6

Write the following numbers on the board.

Count as I point to the numbers.

11   12   13   14   15   16   17   18   19

Tell what the number 14 means.

Tell what the number 18 means.

ten ones and four ones; ten ones and eight ones

Lead children in counting from 11 to 19. Point to numerals at random and have children read them. Lead a discussion of what 14 means. 10 ones and 4 ones

🖥 Vocabulary

- Interactive Student Edition
- Multilingual Glossary

Fluency Builder

Materials Fifty Chart

Show children a fifty chart. Lead them in counting from 1 to 50.

Ask a volunteer to point to the fifty chart as you ask the following questions.

- **What number is one greater than 43?** 44
- **What number is two less than 49?** 47

Have a different volunteer repeat with similar questions.

FOCUSING ON THE WHOLE STUDENT

Access Prior Knowledge

Have children make models of triangles using clay and toothpicks.

- **Roll the clay into three small balls for the corners. Press the ends of three toothpicks into the clay to form a triangle. Make sure the shape is closed.**
- **What shape do you have?** a triangle
- **How do you know it is a triangle?** It has three straight sides.

I Can Objective

I can describe triangles.

Making Connections

Point out a classroom object, such as the musical instrument, that is a triangle.

- **What shape is the instrument?** It is a triangle.
- **What does a triangle look like?** Possible answer: It has three straight sides.

Learning Activity

Have children draw triangles to help them identify the features of a triangle. Ask the following questions.

- **How do you draw a triangle?** Possible answer: I draw three lines that meet at three corners.
- **How is a triangle different from a square?** Possible answer: A square is drawn with four straight lines, but a triangle has three straight lines.

⚠ Common Errors

Error Children may not be able to identify vertices.

Example Children do not know the number of vertices that a triangle has.

Springboard to Learning Draw a triangle. Remind children that a vertex is where two sides meet. Have children trace each side with a different color crayon. Then have them find where two colors meet and draw a dot on it. Repeat for each vertex and count the dots.

Explore

Listen and Draw Real World

Read aloud this problem as children listen.

Sofia placed three straws on a table and made a shape. The end of each straw touched the end of another straw. What shape did Sofia make?

Call attention to the triangle on the page.

- **Trace a finger around the triangle. Find the worm on the side and the word *side*.**
- **How many sides does the triangle have?** 3
- **Trace around the sides.**
- **Find the worm sitting on the vertex and the word *vertex*. How many vertices does a triangle have?** 3

Remind children that the words *vertices* and *corners* mean the same thing, places where two sides meet.

- **Draw an arrow pointing to a different vertex.** Check visually.

Elicit from children that a triangle has three straight sides and three vertices, or corners.

Reread the problem.

(MP) **Look for and make use of structure.**

- **What shape did Sofia make with her three straws?** a triangle
- **How do you know?** Sofia used three straws for three sides and made three vertices.

Make sure children note the patterns they have observed in different triangles.

Name _____

Describe Triangles

(I Can) describe triangles.

Listen and Draw

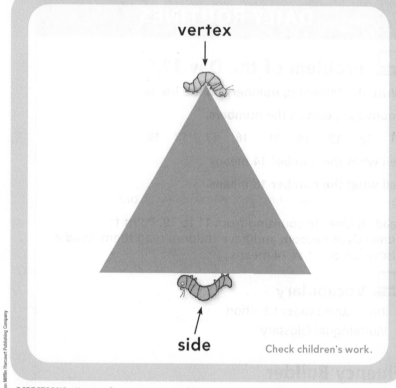

vertex

side

Check children's work.

DIRECTIONS Use your finger to trace around the triangle. Talk about the number of sides and the number of vertices. Draw an arrow pointing to another vertex. Trace around the sides.

Chapter 17 • Lesson 6   671

 **Multilingual Support**

STRATEGY: Rephrase

Children can demonstrate their understanding of triangles by rephrasing what they see and hear.

Show children a drawing of a large triangle. Say: **I can tell this shape is a triangle. A triangle has three straight sides. A triangle has three vertices.**

Have children rephrase your description of the triangle. Possible answers: The shape is a triangle because it has three sides and three corners.

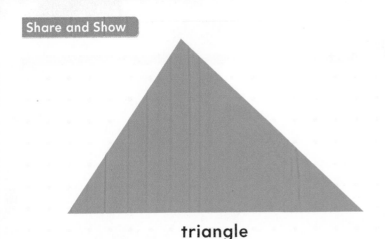

triangle

Check children's work.

1.

3 vertices

3 sides

DIRECTIONS 1. Place a counter on each corner, or vertex. Write how many corners, or vertices. 2. Trace around the sides. Write how many sides.

672 Go Math! Grade K

Ready for More

Kinesthetic / Individual / Partners

Materials craft sticks, crayons, paper

Place craft sticks of various lengths out for children to explore. Have children choose 3 sticks and create a triangle using them. Remind children about the attributes of a triangle and encourage children to work together. Once a triangle is created, children may trace their triangle onto a piece of paper.

Children may repeat this activity several times. Ask children to discuss what they notice about their triangles as well as how they are similar and different to their partner's.

3 Explain

Share and Show

Materials two-color counters

Ask children to trace around the triangle with a finger. Have children use counters to complete the activity.

 Use appropriate tools strategically.

- Place a counter on each vertex, or corner. How many vertices do you see? 3 Write the number.
- Trace around each side. What will you write for the number of sides? 3
- What shape has three vertices and three sides? a triangle
- What do you notice about the sides of this triangle? Possible answer: They are not sides of equal length.

 Construct arguments and critique reasoning of others.

Have children explain what is the same about this triangle and other triangles they have seen. All have three straight sides and three corners.

Review that the sides can all be the same length or different lengths, but if there are three sides it is a triangle.

Use the checked problems for Quick Check.

 Quick Check MTSS RtI

If → a child misses the checked problems

Then → Differentiate Instruction with
- Reteach 17.6
- Waggle

④ Elaborate

Share and Show

(MP) **Model with mathematics.**

Focus children's attention on the dotted grid. Read the instructions.

Explain to children that that they can begin on any dot as a vertex, or corner, of a triangle. Demonstrate how to draw a triangle by using three dots and connecting them. Ask children to draw and color a triangle. Remind them that the sides do not have to be the same length. Check visually.

Higher-Order Thinking

(MP) **Attend to precision.**

Read this problem to children. Talk about strategies they can use to solve it.

- **If you draw three dots that are not in a row, and you connect them, what shape will you make?** a triangle

Children need an understanding that they will be connecting the dots so that a triangle will be formed. Have them complete the problem and share their triangles.

Have children use words such as *sides* and *vertices* to explain to a partner why the shape they drew is a triangle.

Math on the Spot Use this video to help children model and solve this type of problem.

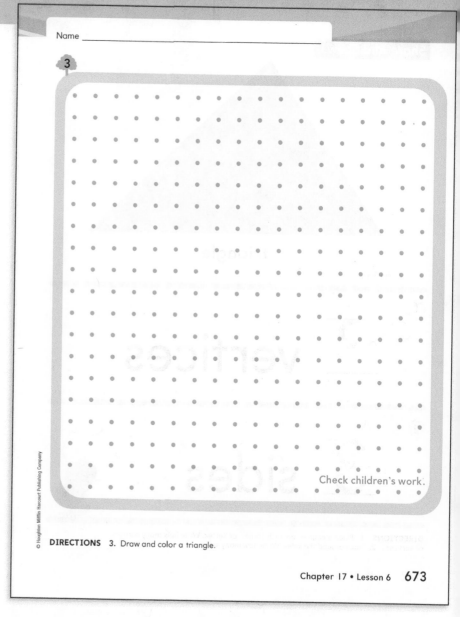

Name _____

Check children's work.

© Houghton Mifflin Harcourt Publishing Company

DIRECTIONS 3. Draw and color a triangle.

Chapter 17 • Lesson 6 **673**

Meeting Individual Needs

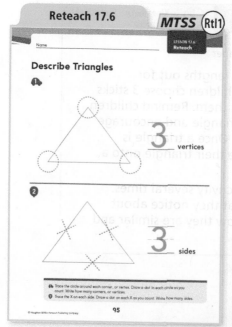

Reteach 17.6

MTSS (RtI1)

Name _____

Describe Triangles

3 vertices

3 sides

Enrich 17.6

Name _____

Triangle Repair

Check children's work.

673 Go Math! Grade K

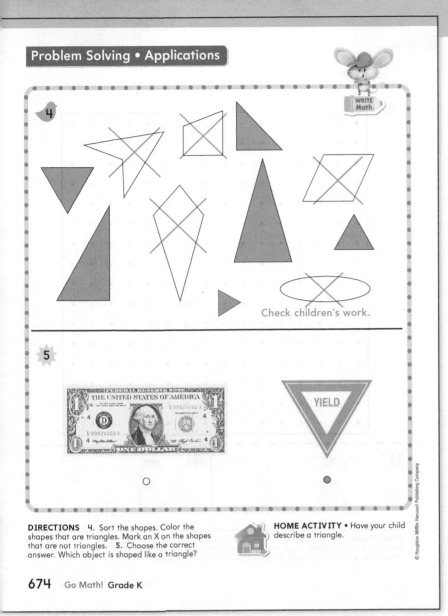

4

Check children's work.

5

YIELD

○   ●

DIRECTIONS 4. Sort the shapes. Color the shapes that are triangles. Mark an X on the shapes that are not triangles. 5. Choose the correct answer. Which object is shaped like a triangle?

HOME ACTIVITY • Have your child describe a triangle.

© Houghton Mifflin Harcourt Publishing Company

Problem Solving Applications

 WRITE) Math

(MP) **Express regularity in repeated reasoning.**

Problem 4 Children sort shapes into two categories: triangles and not triangles.
Problem 5 Children identify the object that is shaped like a triangle.

⑤ Evaluate | Formative Assessment

I Can

Have children name familiar objects that are shaped like triangles and describe their similarities to answer the I Can statement.

I can describe triangles by . . . saying they are shapes that have three sides and three vertices.

Exit Ticket

Invite children to draw and compare their triangles with a friend.

DIFFERENTIATED INSTRUCTION • Independent Activities

Grab-and-Go!™
Version 2.0
Differentiated Centers Kit

Tabletop Flipchart

Mini-lessons for reteaching to targeted small groups

Readers

Supports key math skills and concepts in real-world situations.

Games

Reinforce math content and vocabulary

Activities

Meaningful and fun math practice

Describe Triangles

Use the Practice and Homework pages to provide children with more practice of the concepts and skills presented in this lesson. Children master their understanding as they complete practice items.

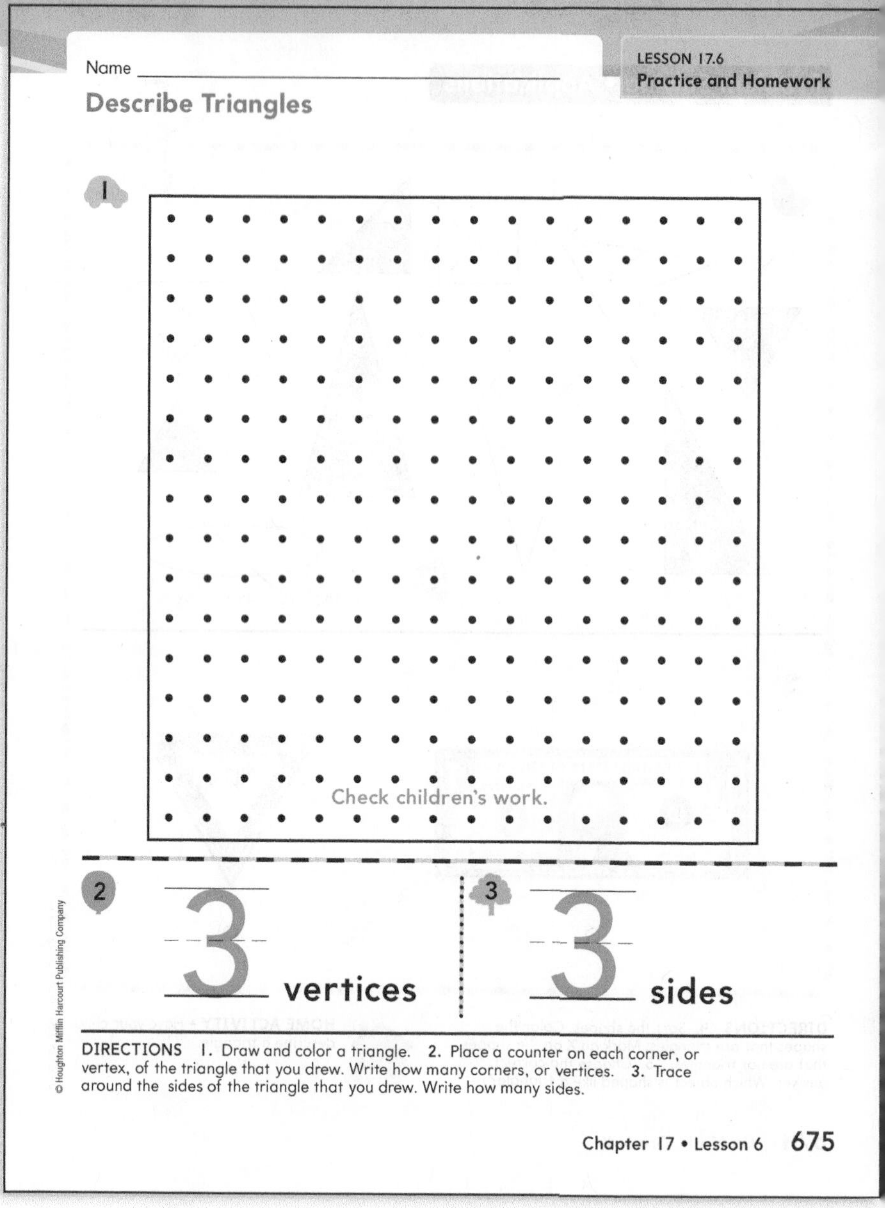

Describe Triangles

1

Check children's work.

2

3 vertices

3

3 sides

DIRECTIONS 1. Draw and color a triangle. 2. Place a counter on each corner, or vertex, of the triangle that you drew. Write how many corners, or vertices. 3. Trace around the sides of the triangle that you drew. Write how many sides.

Chapter 17 • Lesson 6 **675**

Lesson Check

___3___ sides

Spiral Review

$$5 - 2 = \underline{3}$$

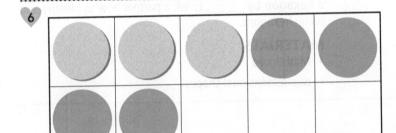

DIRECTIONS 4. How many sides does the triangle have? Write the number. 5. How many kittens are left? Write the number. 6. How many more counters would you place to model a way to make 7? Draw the counters.

676 Go Math! **Grade K**

© Houghton Mifflin Harcourt Publishing Company

LESSON **17.7**

Lesson at a Glance

Identify and Name Hexagons

SNAPSHOT

Mathematical Standards

- Describe objects in the environment using names of shapes, and describe the relative positions of these objects using terms such as *above, below, beside, in front of, behind,* and *next to.*

Mathematical Practices and Processes

- Model with mathematics.
- Attend to precision.
- Express regularity in repeated reasoning.
- Look for and make use of structure.
- Reason abstractly and quantitatively.
- Use appropriate tools strategically.

I Can Objective

I can identify and name hexagons.

Learning Goal

Identify and name two-dimensional shapes, including hexagons.

Language Objective

Children use the sentence frame, **You can tell if a shape is a hexagon by ______**, to tell a partner how to identify and name hexagons.

MATERIALS

- MathBoard
- two-dimensional shapes

ACROSS THE GRADES

Grade K

Identify two- and three-dimensional figures regardless of their size or orientation. Figures are limited to circles, triangles, rectangles, squares, spheres, cubes, cones and cylinders.

After

Identify, compare and sort two- and three-dimensional figures based on their defining attributes. Figures are limited to circles, semi-circles, triangles, rectangles, squares, trapezoids, hexagons, spheres, cubes, rectangular prisms, cones and cylinders.

ABOUT THE MATH

Teaching for Depth

The two-dimensional shapes that children have learned about in this chapter have been circles and regular polygons. You may want to help children see that the attributes they have learned for identifying polygons sometimes apply to irregular polygons as well.

Draw figures like these on the board.

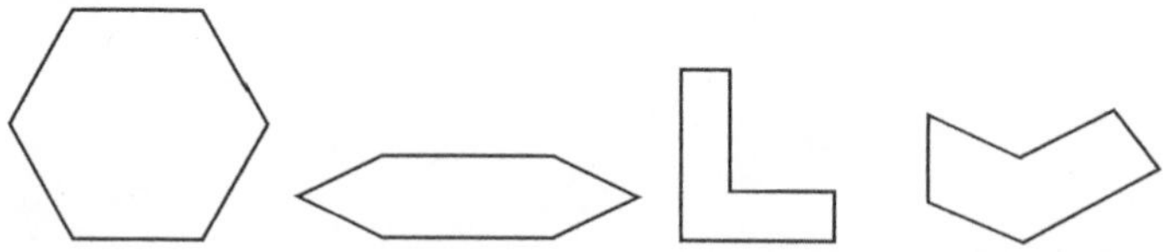

Ask children how many of these shapes are hexagons. Children may say that only the first shape is a hexagon. Have volunteers come to the board and count the sides. Explain that the sides of a hexagon do not need to be of equal length, so all of these six-sided shapes are hexagons.

For more professional learning, go online to Teacher's Corner.

DAILY ROUTINES

🖥 **Problem of the Day 17.7**

How many sides are on this blue shape? 4

How many sides are on this red shape? 3

Which shape has more sides? square

🖥 **Vocabulary** hexagon

• Interactive Student Edition
• Multilingual Glossary

Vocabulary Builder

hexagon

Ask children to draw hexagons they have seen in real life.
Check children's examples. Possible answer: stop sign

FOCUSING ON THE WHOLE STUDENT

Access Prior Knowledge

Use iTools: Geometry. Show each shape: square, rectangle,
triangle, circle, hexagon.

Have children identify and name each shape. Then have
children count the number of straight sides and vertices.

You can repeat the activity, putting the shapes in a
different order.

❶ Engage

with the Interactive Student Edition

I Can Objective

I can identify and name hexagons.

Making Connections

Draw hexagons on chart paper or the board. Some
of the hexagons should have sides that are all the
same length, and others should not.

• **How are these shapes alike?** All of the shapes
  have six sides.

• **How are these shapes different?** Some have sides
  that are all the same length and others do not.

• **Do you think these shapes are more like
  triangles and rectangles, or more like circles?
  Explain.** Possible answer: I think they are like
  triangles and rectangles because they have
  straight sides.

Learning Activity

Identify that the shapes you drew are all hexagons.
Ask the following questions.

• **How many straight sides does a hexagon have?** 6

• **What objects are shaped like a hexagon?**
  Possible answers: some tiles, snowflakes. Accept
  reasonable responses.

② Explore

Listen and Draw

Materials two-dimensional shapes

Read aloud this problem as children listen.

Nadine has a picture collection of different shapes. She wants to sort out all of the hexagons. How will Nadine know which shapes are hexagons?

Help children locate and read the word *hexagons*.

Hold up a hexagon and identify a side. Then point to and count each of the six sides.

- **Hexagons have six straight sides. Trace each side of the hexagon with a finger and count 1, 2, 3, 4, 5, 6.**

Give children assorted two-dimensional shapes. Read the labels on the sorting mat. Then have children sort out the hexagons, identifying and naming them as they are sorted.

 Use appropriate tools strategically.

- **Look at your shapes. Sort them on the mat into sets: *hexagons* and *not hexagons*. Trace and color the shapes.**
- **How many shapes on the left of the sorting mat are hexagons?** all of the shapes
- **How many shapes on the right of the sorting mat are hexagons?** none of the shapes
- **What is the same about the hexagons?** They all have six straight sides.
- **How will Nadine know which shapes are hexagons?** She can find the shapes that have six vertices.

 Look for and make use of structure.

- **How could you tell that a shape is a hexagon and not a rectangle?** Both shapes have straight sides, but a hexagon has six sides and a rectangle has only four sides.

Name _____

Identify and Name Hexagons

(I Can) identify and name hexagons.

Listen and Draw

hexagons	not hexagons

© Houghton Mifflin Harcourt Publishing Company

DIRECTIONS Place two-dimensional shapes on the page. Identify and name the hexagons. Sort the shapes by hexagons and not hexagons. Trace and color the shapes on the sorting mat.

Check children's work.

ML ## Multilingual Support

STRATEGY: Develop Meanings

Children can define geometric terms by matching visuals to their definitions. Show children a hexagon, a rectangle, a triangle, and a circle. Ask them to identify the hexagon and remove all shapes that are not hexagons from the group.

- **How do you know these shapes are not hexagons?** Possible answers: The triangle has three straight sides, not six. The circle has no straight sides.

Have children describe and then draw a hexagon.

1

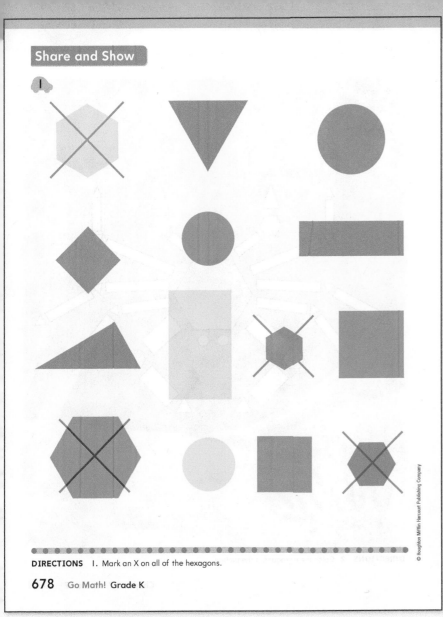

DIRECTIONS 1. Mark an X on all of the hexagons.

678 Go Math! **Grade K**

3 Explain

Share and Show

Call attention to the shapes on the page.

- **Look at the shapes on the page. Are all of the shapes the same?** no
- **Which shapes can you name?** Children may name circles, squares, rectangles, triangles, and hexagons.
- **Are any of the shapes hexagons?** yes

 Reason abstractly and quantitatively.

- **How do you know which shapes are hexagons?** The hexagons are the shapes with six straight sides.

Have children find all of the hexagons and mark them with an X.

- **How many hexagons did you find?** 4

⚠️ Common Errors

Error Children may not be able to keep track of the number of sides as they count.

Example Children count five sides instead of six for a hexagon.

Springboard to Learning Have children place a small pencil mark on each side of the hexagon as they count the sides.

Ready for More 🕐 Kinesthetic Individual/Partners

Materials magazines, catalogs, safety scissors, glue, construction paper

Ahead of time, label sheets of construction paper with headings such as: Circles, Rectangles, Hexagons, and so on. Give each set of partners a set of labeled sheets.

Each child searches the catalogs and magazines to find examples of objects that model the two-dimensional shape written on the top of their paper. They might find picture frames for the squares, doors for rectangles, and rings for circle shapes.

Have children make a poster for each shape by gluing the pictures on the construction paper.

④ Elaborate

Share and Show

Talk about the picture shown on the page. Have children find the hexagon shapes. Remind children that a hexagon is a two-dimensional (or flat) figure with six straight sides.

- **Color the hexagon shapes.**
- **How many hexagons did you color?** 5
- **How are the hexagons different from the other shapes in the picture?** Possible answer: The hexagons have six sides. The other shapes do not.

Use the checked problem for Quick Check.

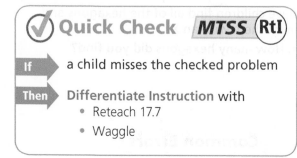

⊘ Quick Check   **MTSS** **RtI**

If → a child misses the checked problem

Then → **Differentiate Instruction** with
- Reteach 17.7
- Waggle

Higher-Order Thinking

Have children draw their own pictures using outlines of circles, hexagons, and other shapes. Have children work with a partner to name the shapes in the picture.

 **Attend to precision.**

- **Which other shape do you think a hexagon is most like? Why do you think so? Use math words in your answer.** Possible answer: I think a hexagon is most like a circle. It has straight sides, but it looks almost round.

Math on the Spot Use this video to help children model and solve this type of problem.

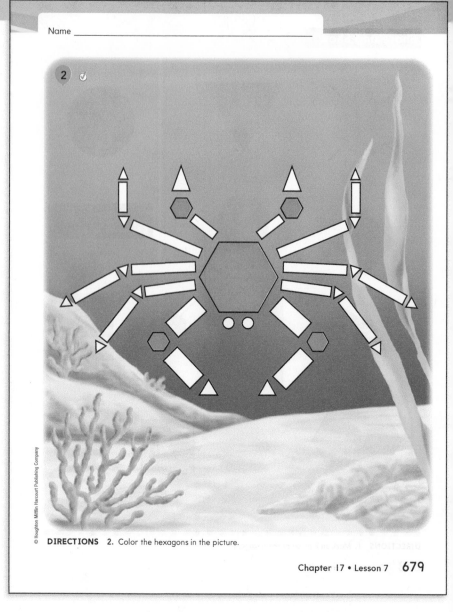

Name _____

2 ⊘

© Houghton Mifflin Harcourt Publishing Company

DIRECTIONS **2.** Color the hexagons in the picture.

Chapter 17 • Lesson 7   **679**

Meeting Individual Needs

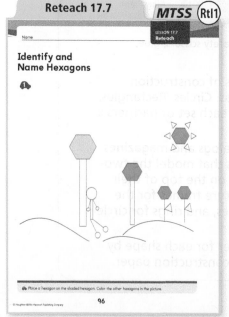

Reteach 17.7   **MTSS** **RtI1**

Name _____

Identify and Name Hexagons

🔍

Place a hexagon on the shaded hexagon. Color the other hexagons in the picture.

© Houghton Mifflin Harcourt Publishing Company

96

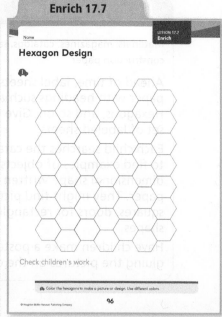

Enrich 17.7

Name _____

Hexagon Design

🔍

Check children's work.

Color the hexagons to make a picture or design. Use different colors.

© Houghton Mifflin Harcourt Publishing Company

96

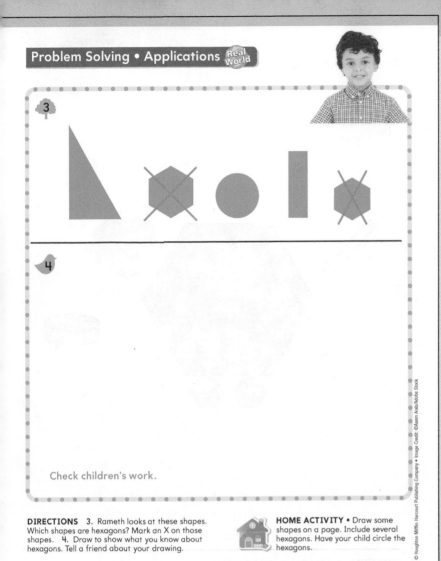

Check children's work.

DIRECTIONS 3. Rameth looks at these shapes. Which shapes are hexagons? Mark an X on those shapes. 4. Draw to show what you know about hexagons. Tell a friend about your drawing.

HOME ACTIVITY • Draw some shapes on a page. Include several hexagons. Have your child circle the hexagons.

Problem Solving Applications

(MP) **Model with mathematics.**

Read **Problem 3** and discuss how to complete it.

(MP) **Express regularity in repeated reasoning.**

- **How many shapes do you see?** 5
- **Are they all hexagons?** no
- **How many hexagons are there?** 2 **Mark an X on the hexagons.**

Problem 4 Before children draw, ask them to tell how they know that a hexagon is a hexagon.

⑤ Evaluate | Formative Assessment

I Can

Have children complete the sentence frame and use it to answer the I Can statement.

You can tell if a shape is a hexagon by ___.

I can identify and name hexagons by . . .
knowing that they are shapes with six straight sides.

Exit Ticket

After children draw, have them take turns sharing their completed drawings.

DIFFERENTIATED INSTRUCTION • Independent Activities

Grab and Go!™
Version 2.0
Differentiated Centers Kit

Tabletop Flipchart

Mini-lessons for reteaching to targeted small groups

Readers

Supports key math skills and concepts in real-world situations.

Games

Reinforce math content and vocabulary

Activities

Meaningful and fun math practice

Practice and Homework

Identify and Name Hexagons

Use the Practice and Homework pages to provide children with more practice of the concepts and skills presented in this lesson. Children master their understanding as they complete practice items.

Identify and Name Hexagons

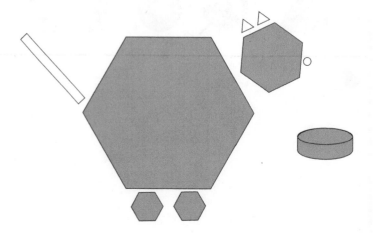

© Houghton Mifflin Harcourt Publishing Company

DIRECTIONS 1. Color the hexagons in the picture.

Chapter 17 • Lesson 7   **681**

Lesson Check

2

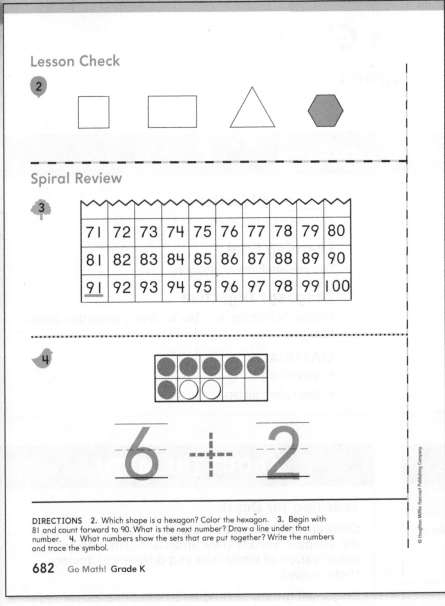

Spiral Review

3

71	72	73	74	75	76	77	78	79	80
81	82	83	84	85	86	87	88	89	90
9̲1̲	92	93	94	95	96	97	98	99	100

4

$$6 + 2$$

DIRECTIONS 2. Which shape is a hexagon? Color the hexagon. **3.** Begin with 81 and count forward to 90. What is the next number? Draw a line under that number. **4.** What numbers show the sets that are put together? Write the numbers and trace the symbol.

Continue to practice concepts and skills with Lesson Check. Use Spiral Review to engage children in previously taught concepts and to promote content retention.

Lesson at a Glance
Describe Hexagons

SNAPSHOT

Mathematical Standards
- Correctly name shapes regardless of their orientations or overall size.

Mathematical Practices and Processes
- Attend to precision.
- Construct arguments and critique reasoning of others.
- Look for and make use of structure.
- Reason abstractly and quantitatively.
- Model with mathematics.

(I Can) Objective
I can describe hexagons.

Learning Goal
Describe attributes of hexagons.

Language Objective
Children brainstorm as a class to identify words that describe hexagons.

MATERIALS
- MathBoard
- two-color counters

ACROSS THE GRADES

Grade K

Identify two- and three-dimensional figures regardless of their size or orientation. Figures are limited to circles, triangles, rectangles, squares, spheres, cubes, cones and cylinders.

After

Identify, compare and sort two- and three-dimensional figures based on their defining attributes. Figures are limited to circles, semi-circles, triangles, rectangles, squares, trapezoids, hexagons, spheres, cubes, rectangular prisms, cones and cylinders.

ABOUT THE MATH

Teaching for Depth

Children studied some simple geometric shapes in this chapter. Solidify their understanding with an investigation of similarities and differences among these shapes.

Give small groups of children straws of various lengths and small balls of clay. Demonstrate how to make a hexagon using six straws and six balls of clay.

Ask children to make concrete models of a triangle, a square, a rectangle, and a hexagon by using the straws as sides and balls of clay as vertices. Have groups present and discuss their shapes.

Bring out points like the following during the discussions: **Is a square a rectangle? How are these shapes different from circles? Are all these shapes flat shapes? How is a hexagon different from a triangle?**

For more professional learning, go online to Teacher's Corner.

DAILY ROUTINES

 **Problem of the Day 17.8**

How many rectangles are shown? What is special about the last rectangle?

4; It is a square.

As children count the rectangles, remind them that the orientation of the shape does not change the name of the shape.

Vocabulary

- Interactive Student Edition
- Multilingual Glossary

Build Number Sense

- **What number is 10 ones and 5 more?** 15
- **What number is 10 ones and 7 more?** 17
- **Describe the number 18.** 10 ones and 8 more ones

Continue with other numbers from 11 to 19.

FOCUSING ON THE WHOLE STUDENT

Access Prior Knowledge

Materials two-dimensional shapes

Hold up a circle for the class. Ask a series of yes-or-no questions to help children identify and describe it.

- **Does it have curved sides?** yes
- **Does it have any corners?** no
- **Is it a circle?** yes

Have children chorally say the name of the shape. Then have a volunteer name an object that is shaped like a circle. Repeat the activity with a square, a rectangle, and a triangle.

1 Engage

with the Interactive Student Edition

I Can Objective

I can describe hexagons.

Making Connections

Draw a five-sided shape.

- **Is this shape a hexagon? How do you know?** No. It does not have six sides.
- **How many more sides would it need to be a hexagon? Explain.** One more; It has five sides, but a shape needs six sides to be a hexagon.

Learning Activity

Have children draw hexagons to help them identify the features of a hexagon. Ask the following questions.

- **How do you draw a hexagon?** Possible answer: I draw a flat, closed shape with six straight sides.
- **How is a hexagon different from a square?** Possible answer: A hexagon has six sides, not four. The sides do not have to be the same length.

② Explore

Listen and Draw

Read aloud this problem as children listen.

Carol is missing a shape for her puzzle. She wants her brother to guess what shape she is missing. She gives him a clue: "My shape has six sides and six vertices." What shape is Carol missing from her puzzle?

 Model with mathematics.

Have children look at the hexagon on the page.

- **Trace around the hexagon with your finger. Find the worm sitting on the side and the word** *side*.
- **How many sides does the hexagon have?** 6

Point to a corner and review that a corner is where two sides meet. Remind children that the word vertex is another name for corner, and the word vertices is used to name more than one vertex.

- **Find the worm sitting on the vertex and the word** *vertex*.
- **How many vertices, or corners, does the hexagon have?** 6
- **Trace around the sides of the hexagon.**
- **Draw an arrow pointing to another vertex.**

Reread the problem.

- **What shape is Carol missing?** a hexagon
- **• How do you know?** Carol's clue was that the shape has six sides and six vertices. A hexagon has six sides and six vertices.

Name _____

Describe Hexagons

(I Can) describe hexagons.

Listen and Draw

vertex

side

DIRECTIONS Use your finger to trace around the hexagon. Talk about the number of sides and the number of vertices. Draw an arrow pointing to another vertex. Trace around the sides.

Check children's work.

Chapter 17 • Lesson 8 **683**

© Houghton Mifflin Harcourt Publishing Company

ⓂⓁ Multilingual Support

STRATEGY: Model Language

Children can learn correct pronunciation and sentence structure by repeating geometry words and sentences that are modeled by a fluent English speaker.

Describe a *hexagon* and have children repeat each of these sentences:

Hexagons have six sides.

Hexagons have six vertices.

Have children draw a hexagon and describe what they drew. Make sure they include that the hexagon has six sides and six vertices.

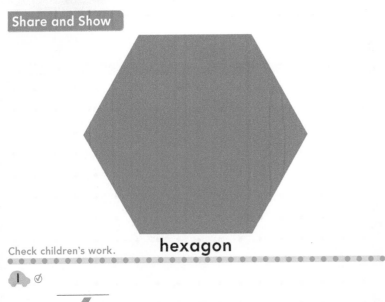

hexagon

Check children's work.

1

6 vertices

2

6 sides

© Houghton Mifflin Harcourt Publishing Company

DIRECTIONS 1. Place a counter on each corner, or vertex. Write how many corners, or vertices. 2. Trace around the sides. Write how many sides.

684 Go Math! Grade K

Ready for More

Kinesthetic
Individual/Partners

Materials crayons

Have children trace all of these shapes onto paper to make a picture: circle, square, triangle, rectangle, and hexagon.

Have children color all the circles red, all of the triangles green, all of the squares yellow, all of the rectangles purple, and all of the hexagons blue.

Have children exchange their drawings with a partner and identify the shapes in their partner's drawing.

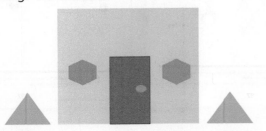

3 Explain

Share and Show

Materials two-color counters

Call attention to the hexagon at the top of the page. Have children trace around the hexagon. Then have children use counters to complete the page.

(MP) **Look for and make use of structure.**

- **Place a counter on each corner, or vertex. How many vertices do you see?** 6 **Write the number.**
- **How do you know that the hexagon has six vertices?** Possible answer: I laid out one counter for each corner. I counted six counters.

Have children remove the counters.

- **Trace around each side. What number will you write?** 6

Read the completed lines with children: **six vertices, six sides.** Explain that those words describe a hexagon.

- **This hexagon has the same number of sides and vertices. What is that number?** 6

✓ Quick Check MTSS RtI

If a child misses the checked problems

Then **Differentiate Instruction** with
- Reteach 17.8
- Waggle

! Common Errors

Error Children may not be able to tell the difference between sides and vertices.

Example Children count sides and vertices together when asked to count sides.

Springboard to Learning Have children draw a circle on each vertex, or corner, and draw an × on each side. They can count each × to find the number of sides.

④ Elaborate

Share and Show

(MP) **Reason abstractly and quantitatively.**

Call attention to the dotted grid on the page. Read the directions.

- **What do you need to know to draw a hexagon?** I need to know that a hexagon has six sides and six vertices.

Demonstrate for children how to draw a hexagon on a grid using six dots as the six vertices. Circle any six dots, but be sure that no set of three dots is in a row. Then draw six lines to connect the six vertices.

Have children draw a hexagon. Explain that it can be any size they choose. Because this grid is a square grid, hexagons drawn on it will may be regular. Assure children that as long as their shapes have six connected sides, the shapes are hexagons. When children complete a hexagon, have them count the vertices to make sure that there are six. Then have children color the hexagon.

Higher-Order Thinking

(MP) **Construct arguments and critique reasoning of others.**

Have children make a smaller hexagon than the one they already drew. Discuss how children chose the vertices to make a smaller hexagon.

Have children explain to a partner how they would draw a hexagon on the grid that is larger than any of the ones they have drawn.

Possible answer: I would connect six dots on the grid. I would be sure that the sides that connect the dots are longer than any others I have drawn before.

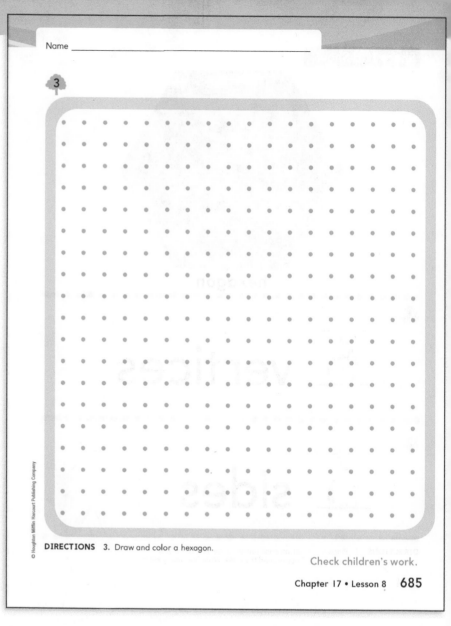

Name _____

3

DIRECTIONS 3. Draw and color a hexagon.

Check children's work.

Chapter 17 • Lesson 8 **685**

Meeting Individual Needs

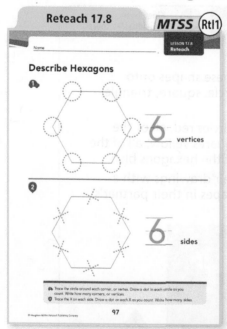

Reteach 17.8 **MTSS** (Rtl1)

Name _____

Describe Hexagons

6 vertices

6 sides

❶ Trace the circle around each corner, or vertex. Draw a dot in each circle as you count. Write how many corners, or vertices.
❷ Trace the X on each side. Draw a dot on each X as you count. Write how many sides.

97

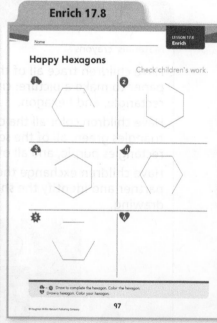

Enrich 17.8

Name _____

Happy Hexagons

Check children's work.

❶ – ❹ Draw to complete the hexagon. Color the hexagon.
❺ – ❻ Draw a hexagon. Color your hexagon.

97

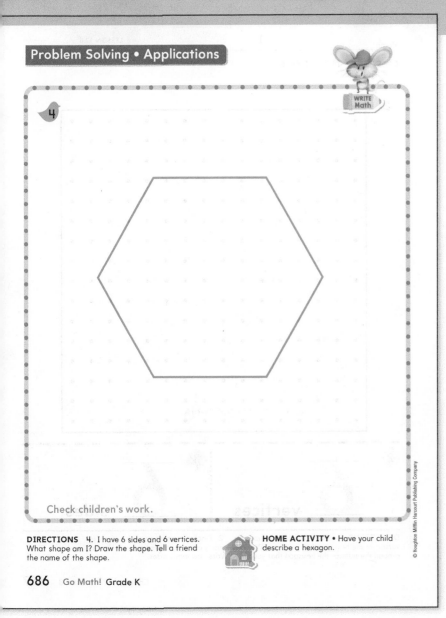

4

Check children's work.

DIRECTIONS 4. I have 6 sides and 6 vertices. What shape am I? Draw the shape. Tell a friend the name of the shape.

HOME ACTIVITY • Have your child describe a hexagon.

© Houghton Mifflin Harcourt Publishing Company

Problem Solving Applications

 WRITE Math

(MP) **Attend to precision.**

Problem 4 Read the riddle aloud. Ask children to explain how they will solve the riddle.

- **What shape has six sides?** a hexagon
- **What shape has six vertices?** a hexagon
- **How would you describe a hexagon?** A hexagon has six straight sides and six vertices. It is a flat, closed shape.

Invite children to draw a hexagon and share and compare the number of sides in their hexagon. Then have children compare the number of vertices in their hexagons.

⑤ Evaluate | Formative Assessment

I Can

Have children brainstorm as a class to answer the I Can statement.

I can describe hexagons by . . . saying that they are closed shapes that have six sides and vertices.

Exit Ticket

Have children compare their hexagons with a friend and discuss similarities and differences.

DIFFERENTIATED INSTRUCTION • Independent Activities

Grab-and-Go!™
Version 2.0
Differentiated Centers Kit

Tabletop Flipchart

Mini-lessons for reteaching to targeted small groups

Readers

Supports key math skills and concepts in real-world situations.

Games

Reinforce math content and vocabulary

Activities

Meaningful and fun math practice

Describe Hexagons

Use the Practice and Homework pages to provide children with more practice of the concepts and skills presented in this lesson. Children master their understanding as they complete practice items.

Describe Hexagons

1

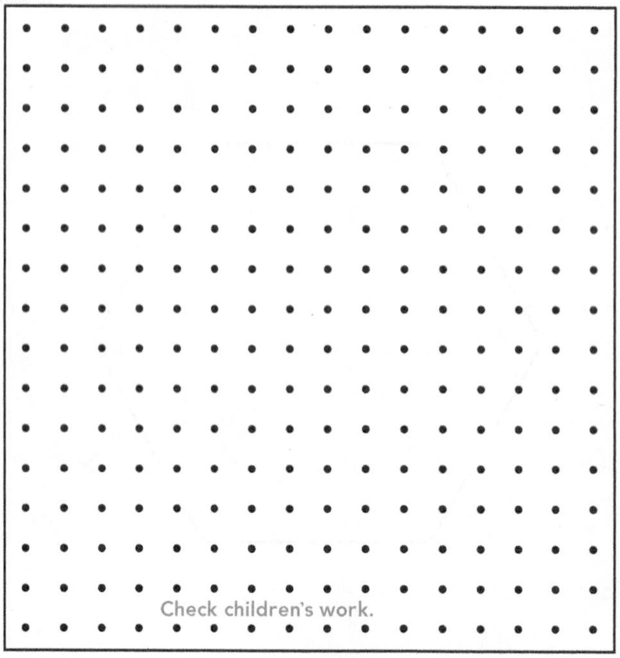

Check children's work.

2

6 vertices

3

6 sides

DIRECTIONS 1. Draw and color a hexagon. 2. Place a counter on each corner, or vertex, of the hexagon that you drew. Write how many corners, or vertices. 3. Trace around the sides of the hexagon that you drew. Write how many sides.

© Houghton Mifflin Harcourt Publishing Company

Lesson Check

 6 sides

Spiral Review

$6 + 3 = 9$

 20

Check children's work.

DIRECTIONS 4. How many sides does the hexagon have? Write the number.
5. Complete the addition sentence to show the numbers that match the cube train.
6. Draw a set that has 20 connecting cubes. Write the number.

© Houghton Mifflin Harcourt Publishing Company

Continue to practice concepts and skills with Lesson Check. Use Spiral Review to engage children in previously taught concepts and to promote content retention.

Lesson at a Glance
Compare Two-Dimensional Shapes

SNAPSHOT

Mathematical Standards

- Analyze and compare two- and three-dimensional shapes, in different sizes and orientations, using informal language to describe their similarities, differences, parts (e.g., number of sides and vertices/"corners") and other attributes (e.g., having sides of equal length).

Mathematical Practices and Processes

- Use appropriate tools strategically.
- Construct arguments and critique reasoning of others.
- Look for and make use of structure.
- Reason abstractly and quantitatively.
- Attend to precision.

(I Can) Objective

I can compare two-dimensional shapes based on their similarities and differences.

Learning Goal

Use the words *alike* and *different* to compare two-dimensional shapes by attributes.

Language Objective

Children sort pictures of two-dimensional shapes and use a sentence frame, _____ **and** _____ **are alike (different) because** _____, to compare two-dimensional shapes.

MATERIALS
- MathBoard
- two-dimensional shapes

ACROSS THE GRADES

Grade K

Compare two-dimensional figures on the basis of their similarities, differences and positions. Sort two-dimensional figures on the basis of their similarities and differences. Figures are limited to circles, triangles, rectangles and squares.

After

Identify, compare, and sort two- and three-dimensional figures on the basis of their defining attributes. Figures are limited to circles, semicircles, triangles, rectangles, squares, trapezoids, hexagons, spheres, cubes, rectangular prisms, cones and cylinders.

ABOUT THE MATH

 Look for and make use of structure.

When comparing shapes, children should be able to see structure. Children learn that a shape may be round and curved or may have a certain number of sides and vertices.

As children become familiar with more shapes, they learn that the attributes of a shape's structure can be used to identify the shape. In later grades, children will learn to look for more than the number of sides and vertices (e.g., the presence of parallel sides).

It is important for children to understand that shapes have a certain structure and that the structure defines the shape. Children can then use their knowledge of structure to solve problems; for example, children should see two sides that meet and know that a triangle can be made by adding one more side.

For more professional learning, go online to Teacher's Corner.

DAILY ROUTINES

 Problem of the Day 17.9

Write the following numbers on the board.

Read each number.

7   14   19

Tell the number that comes before each number when you count. 6, 13, 18

Tell the number that comes after each number when you count. 8, 15, 20

 Vocabulary

- Interactive Student Edition
- Multilingual Glossary

Vocabulary Builder alike, different

Alike, Different

Draw a triangle, rectangle, square, hexagon, and circle. Have children name each one. Point to the triangle and the rectangle.

- **How are these shapes alike?** Possible answer: They have straight sides. **How are these shapes different?** Possible answer: The triangle has three sides and the rectangle has four sides.

Point to the circle and the hexagon.

- **How are these shapes alike?** Possible answer: They are both flat shapes. **How are these shapes different?** Possible answer: The hexagon has straight sides and the circle is curved.

Have volunteers take turns selecting two different shapes and tell about them using *alike* or *different*.

FOCUSING ON THE WHOLE STUDENT

Access Prior Knowledge

Hold up a paper bag filled with assorted two-dimensional shapes. Ask children to guess what is inside the bag.

Have volunteers take turns reaching inside and pulling out one shape at a time, naming the shape, and telling something about the shape.

❶ Engage

with the Interactive Student Edition

I Can Objective

I can compare two-dimensional shapes based on their similarities and differences.

Making Connections

Guide children in using the words *alike* and *different*. Display pairs of same-colored objects that differ in type or size, such as a small red ball and a large red ball, a white sneaker and a white sandal, or a yellow crayon and a yellow hat. Ask children to tell how the pairs of objects are alike, or the same. Then ask children to identify how the pairs of objects are different. Repeat with other pairs of objects that vary by type or size.

Learning Activity

Have children compare pairs of two-dimensional shapes. Ask the following questions.

- **How are the two shapes alike?** Check children's answers.

- **How are the two shapes different?** Check children's answers.

Explore

Listen and Draw Real World

Read aloud this problem as children listen.

Erica colors some shapes. She uses blue to color shapes with curves. She uses red to color shapes with three sides and three vertices. She uses green to color shapes with four vertices and four sides. And she uses yellow to color shapes with six sides and six vertices. What shapes does Erica color blue? red? green? yellow?

Have children locate the worms at the top of the page and review the words *vertex*, *curve*, and *side*.

As you ask the questions below, encourage children to use the words from the top of the page for their answers.

(MP) Construct arguments and critique reasoning of others.

• **How are rectangles and squares alike?**
Possible answers: They are alike because both have four sides and four corners or vertices. They are both rectangles.

• **Why is a square a special type of rectangle?**
A square has four sides of equal length.

Have children compare the triangle and circle.

• **How are the triangle and circle alike?**
Possible answer: They are alike because they are both closed shapes.

• **How are they different?** Possible answer: They are different because the triangle has straight sides and the circle has curves.

Have children compare the triangle and hexagon.

• **How are the triangle and hexagon alike?**
Possible answer: They are alike because they both have straight sides and corners.

Read the directions explaining how to color the shapes. Pause as children complete each step. Reread the problem.

• **What shapes will Erica color green?** rectangles
blue? circles **red?** triangles **yellow?** hexagons

Have children summarize how the shapes are alike and different.

Compare Two-Dimensional Shapes

I Can compare two-dimensional shapes based on their similarities and differences.

Listen and Draw

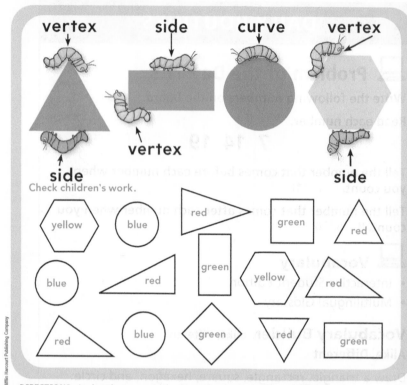

Check children's work.

DIRECTIONS Look at the worms and the shapes. Use the words *alike* and *different* to compare the shapes. Use blue to color the shapes with curves. Use red to color the shapes with three vertices and three sides. Use green to color the shapes with four vertices and four sides. Use yellow to color the shapes with six sides and six vertices.

Chapter 17 • Lesson 9   **689**

(ML) Multilingual Support

STRATEGY: Develop Meanings

Children can define geometric terms by matching each visual to the relevant definition.

Place various shapes on a table. Have children sort the shapes by the number of sides. Then ask children to describe each group. **Which group includes shapes with three sides?** Check visually. **What are the shapes in this group called?** triangles

Repeat with each group. Have children describe the qualities of each group, such as the number of sides or vertices the group has in common, or its curved or straight sides.

1.

alike	different

Check children's work.

DIRECTIONS I. Place two-dimensional shapes on the page. Sort the shapes by the number of vertices. Draw the shapes on the sorting mat. Use the words *alike* and *different* to tell how you sorted the shapes.

© Houghton Mifflin Harcourt Publishing Company

③ Explain

Share and Show

Materials two-dimensional shapes

Direct attention to the page and read the labels. Explain that children will sort shapes using the words *alike* and *different*.

Have each child choose a number of vertices for the set of shapes that are alike.

 Use appropriate tools strategically.

- Put all the shapes that have the number of vertices you picked in the *alike* side.
- Put all the shapes that do not have that number of vertices in the *different* side.

After children sort the shapes, have them draw (or trace) the shapes on the sorting mat. Hold a discussion of how children sorted, using the words *alike* and *different*.

⚠ Common Errors

Error Children may have difficulty deciding which shapes are alike.

Example Children may have a sorting rule of three vertices but sort both triangles and squares as alike.

Springboard to Learning Have children count the vertices for each shape and compare those numbers using the sorting rule. The numbers must be the same for the shapes to be alike.

Ready for More 🕐 Visual Individuals

Materials paper, paint

Provide each child with two pieces of paper and some paint. Invite children to paint two pictures, one using two alike shapes and one using two different shapes. Ideas might include painting a tree, a house, a hat, or a robot.

Have children label each painting *Alike* or *Different*.

Different   Alike

④ Elaborate

Share and Show

 Reason abstractly and quantitatively.

Children will sort two-dimensional shapes.

- **Choose a way to sort for the number of sides. Shapes with that number of sides will be alike. Shapes with a different number of sides will be different.**

- **Sort the shapes by the way you picked. Check your work by comparing the number of sides.**

- **Compare the shapes. How are they alike?** Possible answer: They have the same number of sides. **How are they different?** Possible answer: They have different numbers of sides and vertices.

Use the checked problem for Quick Check.

 Quick Check **MTSS** **RtI**

If ➤ a child misses the checked problem

Then ➤ **Differentiate Instruction** with
  - Reteach 17.9
  - Waggle

Higher-Order Thinking

 Look for and make use of structure.

Present children with a set of shapes that includes squares, rectangles that are not squares, and triangles. Ask children to tell which shapes do not belong, and why. triangles Draw a square that sits on one of its vertices. Ask if it belongs, and why. Yes, it has four sides. Repeat with other four-sided shapes that are not rectangles.

Math on the Spot Use this video to help children model and solve this type of problem.

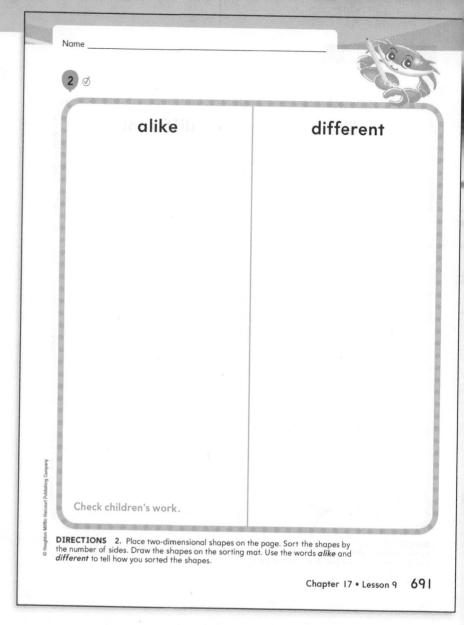

Name _____

2 ✓

alike	different

Check children's work.

DIRECTIONS 2. Place two-dimensional shapes on the page. Sort the shapes by the number of sides. Draw the shapes on the sorting mat. Use the words *alike* and *different* to tell how you sorted the shapes.

Chapter 17 • Lesson 9   691

Meeting Individual Needs

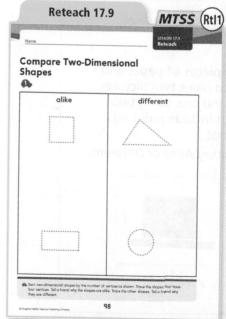

Reteach 17.9   **MTSS** **RtI1**

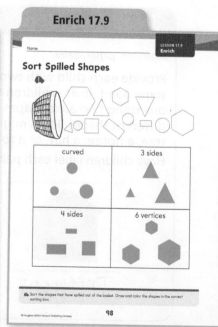

Enrich 17.9

3

Check children's work.

 4

curve	no curve

Check children's work.

DIRECTIONS 3. I have a curve. What shape am I? Draw the shape. 4. Draw to show shapes sorted by curves and no curves.

 **HOME ACTIVITY** • Describe a shape and ask your child to name the shape that you are describing.

© Houghton Mifflin Harcourt Publishing Company

DIFFERENTIATED INSTRUCTION • Independent Activities

 # Grab and Go!

Version 2.0
Differentiated Centers Kit

Tabletop Flipchart
Mini-lessons for reteaching to targeted small groups

Readers
Supports key math skills and concepts in real-world situations

Games
Reinforce math content and vocabulary

Activities
Meaningful and fun math practice

Problem Solving Applications

Read aloud the riddle for **Problem 3**. Ask children to explain how they will answer the riddle.
- **What shape that is curved can you name?** a circle

(MP) **Construct arguments and critique reasoning of others.**

Invite children to tell a friend about their drawing and to explain why it is a solution to the riddle.

Read the directions for **Problem 4**.
- **What shape is curved?** a circle **Draw a circle on the left side of the mat.**

(MP) **Attend to precision.**

- **What shapes have no curves?** a triangle, a square, a hexagon, and a rectangle **What shapes will you draw on the right side of the sorting mat?** triangle, square, hexagon, rectangle

⑤ Evaluate | Formative Assessment

I Can
Have children sort pictures of two-dimensional shapes and use the sentence frame to answer the I Can statement.

____ and ____ are alike (different) because ____.
I can compare two-dimensional shapes based on their similarities and differences by . . .
choosing a number of sides or vertices and making a set of shapes with that number and labeling it *alike*. I can put all the other shapes in another set and label it *different*.

Exit Ticket
Have each child share their drawing with a partner. Have children name the shapes in each set.

Practice and Homework

Compare Two-Dimensional Shapes

Use the Practice and Homework pages to provide children with more practice of the concepts and skills presented in this lesson. Children master their understanding as they complete practice items.

Compare Two-Dimensional Shapes

alike	different

Check children's work.

DIRECTIONS 1. Place two-dimensional shapes on the page. Sort the shapes by the number of sides. Draw the shapes on the sorting mat. Use the words *alike* and *different* to tell how you sorted the shapes.

© Houghton Mifflin Harcourt Publishing Company

Chapter 17 • Lesson 9   **693**

CROSS-CURRICULAR

SCIENCE

Materials drawing paper, crayons

- Ask children to name their favorite animals and to tell what they know about them. Compare two of the animals, noting how they are alike or different.
- Have children suggest how they might use shapes to draw their favorite animal, and draw it for them on the whiteboard.
- After the drawing is completed, have children identify the shapes that were used.
- Then give children crayons and drawing paper, and invite
  them to use shapes to draw any animal, real or imaginary.

SOCIAL STUDIES

Materials American flag

- Display an American flag. Discuss how it is a symbol for the United States. Tell children that some people like to wave American flags, especially on days like July 4, Memorial Day, and Flag Day.
- Ask children to identify the flag's matching sides that are long and the matching sides that are short.
- **What shape is an American flag if it has two long sides and two short sides?** a rectangle
- Then call attention to other parts of the flag, such as the stripes, the stars, and the blue box surrounding the stars.
- **What parts of this flag are alike?** the stars
- **How are the stripes different?** Possible answers: color, length

Lesson Check

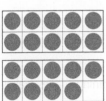

Check children's work.

Spiral Review

3

4

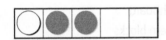

DIRECTIONS **2.** Look at the shape. Draw a shape that is alike in some way. Tell how the two shapes are alike. **3.** Count and tell how many. Write the number. **4.** How many of each color counter? Write the numbers.

694 Go Math! Grade K

© Houghton Mifflin Harcourt Publishing Company

Continue to practice concepts and skills with Lesson Check. Use Spiral Review to engage children in previously taught concepts and to promote content retention.

Lesson at a Glance
Create Shapes

SNAPSHOT

Mathematical Standards
- Compose simple shapes to form larger shapes.

Mathematical Practices and Processes
- Use appropriate tools strategically.
- Reason abstractly and quantitatively.
- Attend to precision.
- Construct arguments and critique reasoning of others.
- Look for and make use of structure.
- Model with mathematics.

(I Can) Objective
I can combine shapes to make larger shapes.

Learning Goal
Combine shapes to compose larger shapes.

Language Objective
Children will describe how combining shapes makes a new shape.

MATERIALS
- MathBoard
- pattern blocks

ACROSS THE GRADES

Grade K
Combine two-dimensional figures to form a given composite figure. Figures used to form a composite shape are limited to triangles, rectangles and squares.

After
Compose and decompose two- and three-dimensional figures. Figures are limited to semi-circles, triangles, rectangles, squares, trapezoids, hexagons, cubes, rectangular prisms, cones and cylinders.

ABOUT THE MATH
Children have composed and decomposed numbers and now will apply the same idea to composing and decomposing shapes. Using the two-dimensional shapes that they know (squares, circles, triangles, rectangles, and hexagons), children will combine them to make a new shape. In this lesson, children identify the shapes that have been joined or they show how to join given shapes to make a new one. Sometimes, the shape that is being made is defined. Other times, children will simply use the shapes with which they are familiar to create their own new shape.

For more professional learning, go online to Teacher's Corner.

DAILY ROUTINES

Problem of the Day 17.10

Write the following numbers on the board. Read each number.

8; 12; 17

Tell the next number when you count backward. 7; 11; 16

Tell the next number when you count forward. 9; 13; 18

Vocabulary

- Interactive Student Edition
- Multilingual Glossary

Vocabulary Builder

Subtract Within 5

Materials subtraction fact cards (within 5), connecting cubes

- Show children the subtraction fact $5 - 4 = \boxed{}$.
- **You can use connecting cubes to model this subtraction equation. How many cubes will you start with?** 5 **Why?** That is the number in all.
- **Now you take apart the number that is shown after the minus symbol. What is that number?** 4
- **Count to find how many are left.**
- **What number goes in the box?** 1

FOCUSING ON THE WHOLE STUDENT

Access Prior Knowledge

Choose one or more of the following activities.

- Have a group discussion about combining things to make other things (ingredients, colors, building materials, etc.).
- Draw a tic-tac-toe grid on the board and show children how the game is played.

Culturally Responsive Education

While learning the names and attributes of shapes is important, it is equally important (if not more so) for students to apply that knowledge in problem-solving situations. We want to challenge all students to both create new shapes and determine which shapes can be used to form a given larger shape in order to help build those higher-order thinking skills students need to succeed.

1 Engage

with the Interactive Student Edition

I Can Objective

I can combine shapes to make larger shapes.

Making Connections

On the board, draw a rectangle with a diagonal line from corner to corner.

- **How many rectangles do you see?** 1 **How many triangles do you see?** 2
- **How do the triangles relate to the rectangle?** Possible answers: The triangles are inside the rectangle. The triangles combine to make the rectangle.

Learning Activity

Guide children in cutting apart and putting shapes together. Give children three paper rectangles and safety scissors.

- **Cut the first rectangle apart along the diagonal. What shapes did you get?** two triangles

Have children put the shapes together to reform the rectangle and discuss what they did.

Repeat the activity with a second rectangle, having children cut across the middle along the short side. Then challenge children to find a third way to cut the third rectangle and repeat again.

2 Explore

Unlock the Problem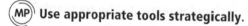

Materials pattern blocks

Read aloud this problem as children listen.

Lauren only has triangles. She wants to make other shapes. How can she make other shapes by joining triangles?

Help children use their triangle pattern blocks to fill in the outlines on the page and then draw and color the pattern blocks that they use.

(MP) **Use appropriate tools strategically.**

- **Fill in the red shape with green triangles. How many triangles did you use?** 2 **Trace and color the triangles.**

- **Fill in the blue shape with green triangles. How many triangles did you use?** 3 **Draw and color the triangles.**

- **Fill in the hexagon at the bottom of the page with green triangles. How many triangles did you use?** 6 **Draw and color the triangles.**

(MP) **Reason abstractly and quantitatively.**

- **How can Lauren make a shape like the red shape?** She can join two triangles.

- **How can she make a shape like the blue shape?** She can join three triangles.

- **How can she make a hexagon?** She can join six triangles.

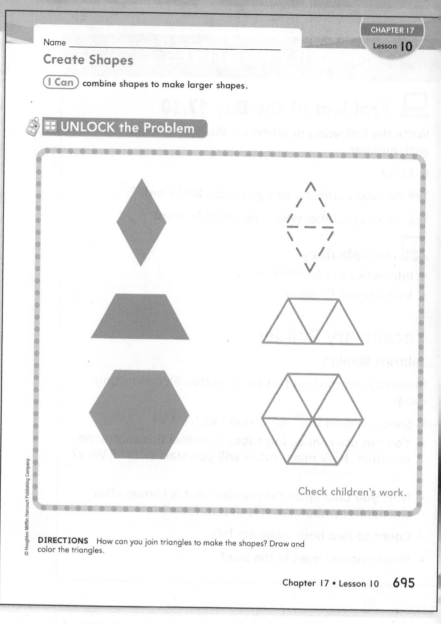

Name _____

Create Shapes

(I Can) combine shapes to make larger shapes.

⊞ UNLOCK the Problem

Check children's work.

DIRECTIONS How can you join triangles to make the shapes? Draw and color the triangles.

Chapter 17 • Lesson 10 **695**

(ML) Multilingual Support

STRATEGY: Define

- Have children stand in a circle. Review the names of the shapes *triangle*, *square*, and *rectangle*. Have children repeat the names of each shape.

- Call out a shape and have children arrange themselves in the form of the shape.

- Ask children which shape they like best and encourage them to explain their reasoning.

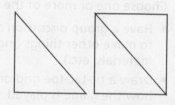

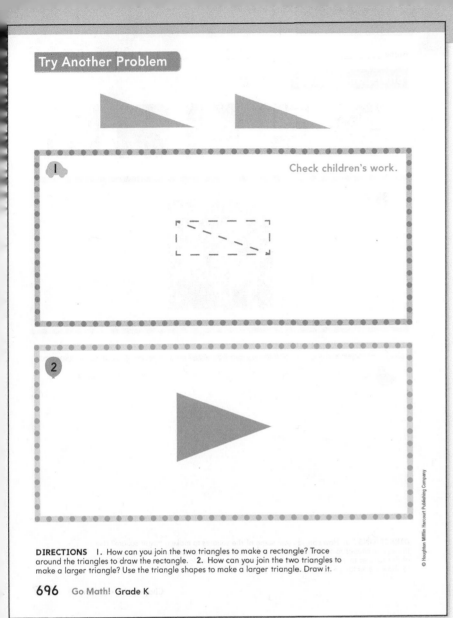

Check children's work.

1

2

DIRECTIONS 1. How can you join the two triangles to make a rectangle? Trace around the triangles to draw the rectangle. 2. How can you join the two triangles to make a larger triangle? Use the triangle shapes to make a larger triangle. Draw it.

© Houghton Mifflin Harcourt Publishing Company

③ Explain

Try Another Problem

Discuss how larger shapes can be made by joining smaller shapes.

- **What shapes are at the top of the page?**
  triangles

- **Look at the triangles. Place the triangles to make the gray rectangle. Trace around the triangles you placed.**

(MP) **Look for and make use of structure.**

Explain and demonstrate how a triangle can be flipped or turned to make a shape.

- **Now you will join the two triangles to make a larger triangle. Trace around the triangles.**

Remind children they may need to flip or turn the triangles to compose the larger one. Allow time for children to discuss and explain how they joined smaller shapes to compose larger ones.

⚠ Common Errors

Error Children do not understand how to use smaller shapes to make a bigger shape.

Example Children cannot make a larger triangle.

Springboard to Learning Tell children to join two triangles together in different ways until the shape they form is another triangle. Demonstrate how to flip and turn the shapes to see all possible ways to join them.

Ready for More
Visual
Individual / Partners

Materials pattern blocks

Hand children a sheet of paper with three hexagons outlined on it. Have children trace the pattern block(s) under each hexagon that could fill the outline.

Children should switch papers with a partner and use the pattern block(s) shown to fill the outline. They can outline the blocks they drew and color in the traced shapes.

④ Elaborate

Share and Show

Make sure children each have five squares as seen at the top of the page.

- **Think how you can join some or all of the small squares to make a larger square.**

Discuss whether it is possible to make a square using all five squares. Help children conclude that it is not possible.

Call attention to Problem 4. Tell children to use some or all of the square shapes to make a rectangle. Have children trace around the outside of the squares to show the rectangle they composed. Discuss how there are many possible ways to make the shape. Call on a volunteer to show their work.

Use the checked problems for Quick Check.

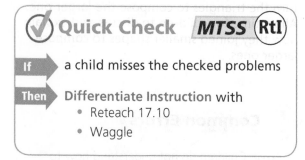

Quick Check **MTSS** **(RtI)**

If ▶ a child misses the checked problems

Then ▶ Differentiate Instruction with
- Reteach 17.10
- Waggle

(MP) **Construct viable arguments and critique the reasoning of others.**

- **Who can show us a different way to make a rectangle? How do you know this new shape is a rectangle?** Possible answer: The larger shape has 4 corners and 4 straight sides. There are two pair of sides of equal length.

Higher-Order Thinking

(MP) Attend to precision.

Have children choose a rectangle, a triangle, and a square and place them next to each other with at least one side touching. Have children trace the outline of the three pattern blocks. Have them identify how many sides and how many vertices there are in the shape they made.

Math on the Spot Use this video to help children model and solve this type of problem.

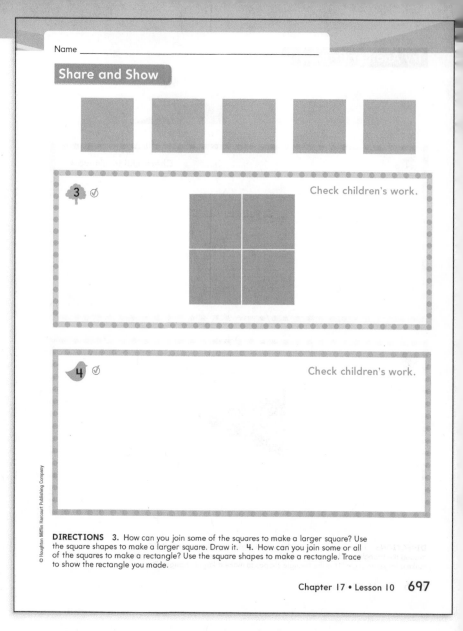

Name _____

Share and Show

3. ✓   Check children's work.

4. ✓   Check children's work.

DIRECTIONS **3.** How can you join some of the squares to make a larger square? Use the square shapes to make a larger square. Draw it. **4.** How can you join some or all of the squares to make a rectangle? Use the square shapes to make a rectangle. Trace to show the rectangle you made.

© Houghton Mifflin Harcourt Publishing Company

Chapter 17 • Lesson 10   **697**

Meeting Individual Needs

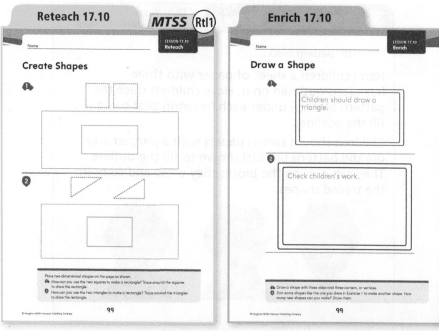

Reteach 17.10   **MTSS (RtI1)**

Name _____

Create Shapes

1.

2.

Place two-dimensional shapes on the page as shown.
1a. How can you use the two squares to make a rectangle? Trace around the squares to draw the rectangle.
1b. How can you use the two triangles to make a rectangle? Trace around the triangles to draw the rectangle.

© Houghton Mifflin Harcourt Publishing Company   **99**

Enrich 17.10

Name _____

Draw a Shape

1.   Children should draw a triangle.

2.   Check children's work.

1. Draw a shape with three sides and three corners, or vertices.
2. Join some shapes like the one you drew in Exercise 1 to make another shape. How many new shapes can you make? Draw them.

© Houghton Mifflin Harcourt Publishing Company   **99**

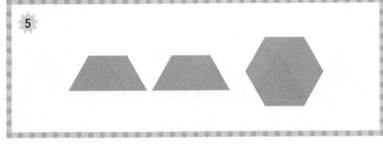

Check children's work.

DIRECTIONS 5. How can you join these shapes to make a hexagon? Use the shapes to make a hexagon. Draw it. 6. Which shapes could you join to make a larger shape that looks like a flower? Draw and color to show the shapes you used.

HOME ACTIVITY • Have your child join shapes to form a larger shape and then tell you about the shape.

698 Go Math! **Grade K**

On Your Own

Read **Problem 5** aloud. Ask children to explain how they will solve the problem.

Explain that children may need to rotate one of these shapes a different way to compose the hexagon (turning one to join the other on a different side to make the hexagon). Remind children that they can use two-dimensional shapes to represent the problem.

Read the directions for **Problem 6** to children.

(MP) **Model with mathematics.**

- **Which shapes could you join to make a larger shape that looks like a flower?** Possible answer: a hexagon and triangles

- **Use whichever pattern blocks you like. You should feel free to turn and move the shapes as you need to compose the flower you want to create. Then trace or draw to show how you joined the shapes.**

Allow volunteers to share their drawings with the class. Have children identify and discuss the many different ways there are to make a shape that looks like a flower.

5 Evaluate | Formative Assessment

I Can

Have children explain to a partner in their own words how to demonstrate the skill for the I Can statement.

I can combine shapes to make larger shapes by . . . joining different shapes to form a new shape and then drawing the new shape.

Exit Ticket

Give an example of a shape you created.

DIFFERENTIATED INSTRUCTION • Independent Activities

Grab-and-Go!

Version 2.0
Differentiated Centers Kit

Tabletop Flipchart

Mini-lessons for reteaching to targeted small groups

Readers

Supports key math skills and concepts in real-world situations.

Games

Reinforce math content and vocabulary

Activities

Meaningful and fun math practice

Create Shapes

Use the Practice and Homework pages to provide children with more practice of the concepts and skills presented in this lesson. Children master their understanding as they complete practice items.

Create Shapes

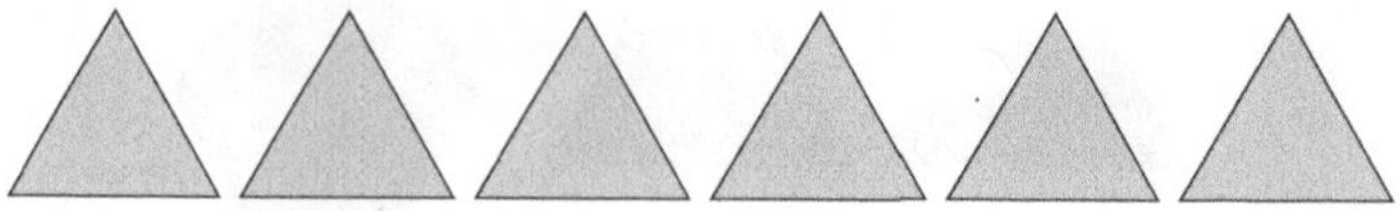

1

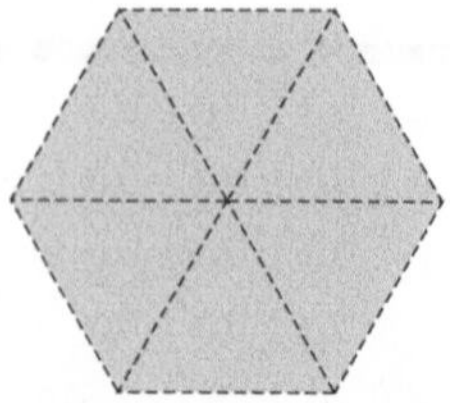

2

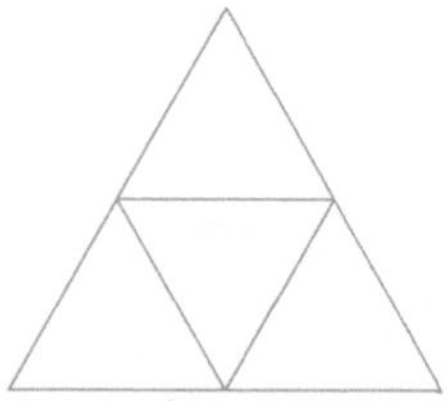

DIRECTIONS Place triangles on the page as shown. **1.** How can you join all of the triangles to make a hexagon? Trace around the triangles to draw the hexagon. **2.** How can you join some of the triangles to make a larger triangle? Trace around the triangles to draw the larger triangle.

Chapter 17 • Lesson 10   **699**

Lesson Check

3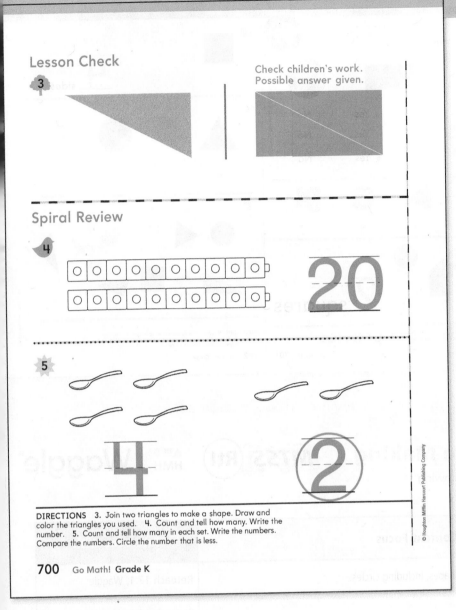

Check children's work.
Possible answer given.

Spiral Review

4

20

5

4   ②

DIRECTIONS 3. Join two triangles to make a shape. Draw and color the triangles you used. 4. Count and tell how many. Write the number. 5. Count and tell how many in each set. Write the numbers. Compare the numbers. Circle the number that is less.

© Houghton Mifflin Harcourt Publishing Company

Continue to practice concepts and skills with Lesson Check. Use Spiral Review to engage children in previously taught concepts and to promote content retention.

Chapter Review

Summative Assessment

Use the **Chapter Review** to assess children's progress in Chapter 17.

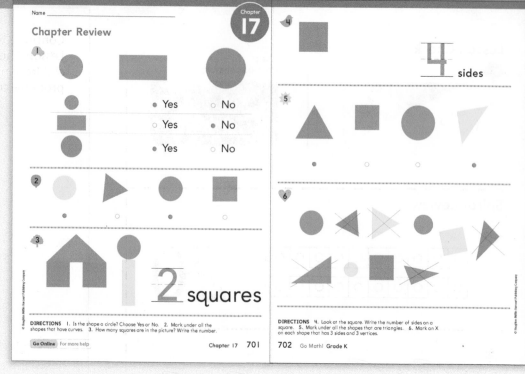

Online, Data-Driven Decision Making

MTSS **RtI** **HMH** **Waggle**

Based on the results of the Chapter Review, use the following resources to review skills.

Item	Lesson	Content Focus	Intervene With
1	17.1	Identify and name two-dimensional shapes, including circles.	Reteach 17.1, Waggle
2	17.2	Describe attributes of circles.	Reteach 17.2, Waggle
3	17.3	Identify and name two-dimensional shapes, including squares.	Reteach 17.3, Waggle
4	17.4	Describe attributes of squares.	Reteach 17.4, Waggle
5	17.5	Identify and name two-dimensional shapes, including triangles.	Reteach 17.5, Waggle
6	17.6	Describe attributes of triangles.	Reteach 17.6, Waggle
7	17.7	Identify and name two-dimensional shapes, including hexagons.	Reteach 17.7, Waggle
8	17.4	Describe attributes of rectangles.	Reteach 17.4, Waggle
9	17.10	Combine shapes to make larger shapes.	Reteach 17.10, Waggle
10, 11	17.9	Use the words alike and *different* to compare two-dimensional shapes by attributes.	Reteach 17.9, Waggle
12	17.8	Describe attributes of hexagons.	Reteach 17.8, Waggle

Name _____

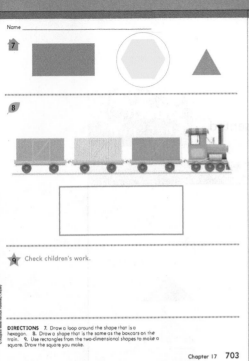

8

9 Check children's work.

© Houghton Mifflin Harcourt Publishing Company

DIRECTIONS 7. Draw a loop around the shape that is a hexagon. 8. Draw a shape that is the same as the boxcars on the train. 9. Use rectangles from the two-dimensional shapes to make a square. Draw the square you make.

Chapter 17   **703**

10

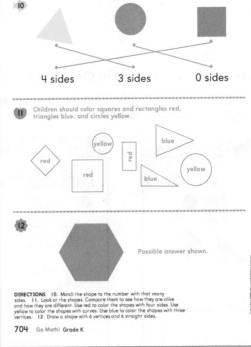

4 sides   3 sides   0 sides

11 Children should color squares and rectangles red, triangles blue, and circles yellow.

12 Possible answer shown.

DIRECTIONS 10. Match the shape to the number with that many sides. 11. Look at the shapes. Compare them to see how they are alike and how they are different. Use red to color the shapes with four sides. Use yellow to color the shapes with curves. Use blue to color the shapes with three vertices. 12. Draw a shape with 6 vertices and 6 straight sides.

704   Go Math! Grade K

© Houghton Mifflin Harcourt Publishing Company

Performance Assessment Task

See the Performance Tasks to assess children's understanding of the content. For each task, you will find sample student work for each of the response levels in the task scoring rubric.

Portfolio   Performance Assessment Tasks may be used for portfolios.

Summative Assessment

Use the **Chapter Test** to assess children's progress in Chapter 17.

Chapter Tests are found in the *Assessment Guide*. Test items are presented in formats consistent with high-stakes assessments.

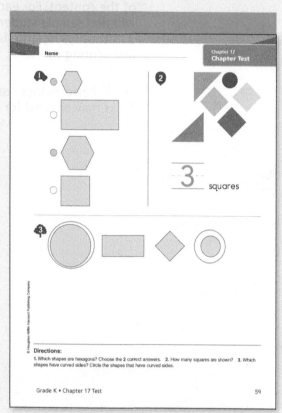

Name _____

Chapter 17
Chapter Test

1.

2.

3

squares

3.

Directions:
1. Which shapes are hexagons? Choose the 2 correct answers. 2. How many squares are shown? 3. Which shapes have curved sides? Circle the shapes that have curved sides.

Grade K • Chapter 17 Test   59

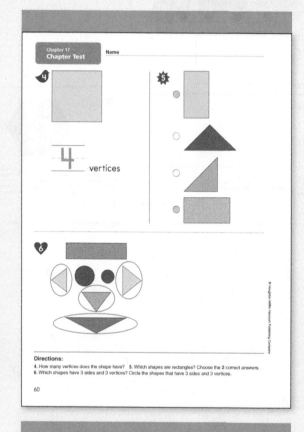

Chapter 17
Chapter Test   Name _____

4.

4

vertices

5.

6.

Directions:
4. How many vertices does the shape have? 5. Which shapes are rectangles? Choose the 2 correct answers.
6. Which shapes have 3 sides and 3 vertices? Circle the shapes that have 3 sides and 3 vertices.

60

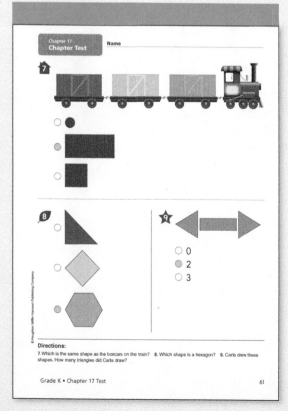

Chapter 17
Chapter Test   Name _____

7.

8.

9.
- ○ 0
- ● 2
- ○ 3

Directions:
7. Which is the same shape as the boxcars on the train? 8. Which shape is a hexagon? 9. Carla drew these shapes. How many triangles did Carla draw?

Grade K • Chapter 17 Test   61

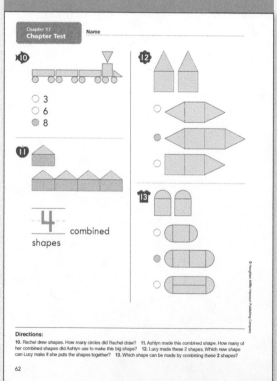

Chapter 17
Chapter Test   Name _____

10.
- ○ 3
- ○ 6
- ● 8

11.

4

combined shapes

12.

13.

Directions:
10. Rachel drew shapes. How many circles did Rachel draw? 11. Ashlyn made this combined shape. How many of her combined shapes did Ashlyn use to make this big shape? 12. Lucy made these 2 shapes. Which new shape can Lucy make if she puts the shapes together? 13. Which shape can be made by combining these 2 shapes?

62

Teacher Notes

	LESSON 18.1 • 1 Day	LESSON 18.2 • 1 Day	LESSON 18.3 • 1 Day
Lesson at a Glance	Identify, Name, and Describe Spheres . . . 707A	Identify, Name, and Describe Cubes. 713A	Identify, Name, and Describe Cylinders . . 719A
I Can	I can identify, name, and describe spheres.	I can identify, name, and describe cubes.	I can identify, name, and describe cylinders.
Learning Goal	Identify, name, and describe three-dimensional shapes, including spheres.	Identify, name, and describe three-dimensional shapes, including cubes.	Identify, name, and describe three-dimensional shapes, including cylinders.
Vocabulary	**three-dimensional shape, sphere, curved surface**	**cube, flat surface, edge**	**cylinder**
Multilingual Support	**Strategy:** Rephrase	**Strategy:** Model Language	**Strategy:** Model Concepts

Practice and Fluency	LESSON 18.1 ◆ ■ Practice and Homework ■ Waggle	LESSON 18.2 ◆ ■ Practice and Homework ■ Waggle	LESSON 18.3 ◆ ■ Practice and Homework ■ Waggle
MTSS RtI **Intervention and Enrichment**	■ Waggle ◆ ■ Reteach 18.1 ◆ ■ Tier 2 Intervention Skill S39 ◆ ■ Tier 3 Intervention Skill E39 ◆ Tabletop Flipchart ◆ Enrich 18.1	■ Waggle ◆ ■ Reteach 18.2 ◆ ■ Tier 2 Intervention Skill S40 ◆ ■ Tier 3 Intervention Skill E40 ◆ Tabletop Flipchart ◆ Enrich 18.2	■ Waggle ◆ ■ Reteach 18.3 ◆ ■ Tier 2 Intervention Skill S37 ◆ ■ Tier 3 Intervention Skill E37 ◆ Tabletop Flipchart ◆ Enrich 18.3

See the Grab-and-Go!™ Centers Kit for more small-group activities.

Grab-●and●-Go!™
Version 2.0
Differentiated Centers Kit

The kit provides literature, games, and activities for small-group learning.

◆ Print/Printable Resource
■ Interactive Resource

	LESSON 18.4 • 1 Day	**LESSON 18.5 • 1 Day**	**LESSON 18.6 • 1 Day**
Lesson at a Glance	Identify, Name, and Describe Cones..... 725A	Compare Three-Dimensional Objects 731A	Two- and Three-Dimensional Shapes 737A
I Can	I can identify, name, and describe cones.	I can compare three-dimensional shapes based on their similarities and differences.	I can identify and sort two- and three-dimensional shapes.
Learning Goal	Identify, name, and describe three-dimensional shapes, including cones.	Compare three-dimensional shapes.	Look at the surfaces of an object to tell what kind of flat or solid shape it is.
Vocabulary	cone		flat, solid
Multilingual Support	**Strategy:** Model Concepts	**Strategy:** Model Concepts	**Strategy:** Restate

Practice and Fluency	LESSON 18.4 ◆ ■ Practice and Homework ■ Waggle	LESSON 18.5 ◆ ■ Practice and Homework ■ Waggle	LESSON 18.6 ◆ ■ Practice and Homework ■ Waggle
***MTSS* (RtI)** **Intervention and Enrichment**	■ Waggle ◆ ■ Reteach 18.4 ◆ ■ Tier 2 Intervention Skill S38 ◆ ■ Tier 3 Intervention Skill E38 ◆ Tabletop Flipchart ◆ Enrich 18.4	■ Waggle ◆ ■ Reteach 18.5 ◆ ■ Tier 2 Intervention Skill S37–40 ◆ ■ Tier 3 Intervention Skill E37–40 ◆ Tabletop Flipchart ◆ Enrich 18.5	■ Waggle ◆ ■ Reteach 18.6 ◆ ■ Tier 2 Intervention Skill S54/S55 ◆ ■ Tier 3 Intervention Skill E54/E55 ◆ Tabletop Flipchart ◆ Enrich 18.6

Chapter at a Glance
Three-Dimensional Solids

	LESSON 18.7 • 1 Day	**LESSON 18.8 • 1 Day**	**LESSON 18.9 • 1 Day**
Lesson at a Glance	Above and Below . . . 743A	Beside and Next To 749A	In Front Of and Behind 755A
I Can	I can use the words *above* and *below* to compare the positions of two- and three-dimensional shapes.	I can use the words *beside* and *next to* to compare the positions of two- and three-dimensional shapes.	I can use the words *in front of* and *behind* to compare the positions of two- and three-dimensional shapes.
Learning Goal	Use the terms *above* and *below* to describe shapes in the environment.	Use the terms *beside* and *next to* to describe shapes in the environment.	Use the terms *in front of* and *behind* to describe shapes in the environment.
Vocabulary	above, below	beside, next to	in front of, behind
Multilingual Support	**Strategy:** Illustrate Understanding	**Strategy:** Rephrase	**Strategy:** Rephrase

Practice and Fluency	LESSON 18.7 ◆ ■ **Practice and Homework** ■ **Waggle**	LESSON 18.8 ◆ ■ **Practice and Homework** ■ **Waggle**	LESSON 18.9 ◆ ■ **Practice and Homework** ■ **Waggle**
MTSS (RtI) **Intervention and Enrichment**	■ Waggle ◆ ■ Reteach 18.7 ◆ ■ Tier 2 Intervention Skill S51 ◆ ■ Tier 3 Intervention Skill E51 ◆ Tabletop Flipchart ◆ Enrich 18.7	■ Waggle ◆ ■ Reteach 18.8 ◆ ■ Tier 2 Intervention Skill S52 ◆ ■ Tier 3 Intervention Skill E52 ◆ Tabletop Flipchart ◆ Enrich 18.8	■ Waggle ◆ ■ Reteach 18.9 ◆ ■ Tier 2 Intervention Skill S53 ◆ ■ Tier 3 Intervention Skill E53 ◆ Tabletop Flipchart ◆ Enrich 18.9

◆ Print/Printable Resource
■ Interactive Resource

Identify Three-Dimensional Solids

Children should have opportunities to identify three-dimensional solids.

- Identification experiences can happen with geometric solids (e.g., wooden or plastic models of geometric three-dimensional solids) or with everyday objects (e.g., gift boxes, soup cans, basketballs, etc.).

- When children use their observation skills to determine what is or what is not a particular three-dimensional solid, they are building their knowledge of these solids and their characteristics.

Sort Three-Dimensional Solids

Sorting three-dimensional solids is a way to see if children understand and can distinguish attributes of the shapes.

From the Research

❝Learning geometry involves the formation of both fuzzy and formal categories. Before geometry instruction, and even in primary-grade teaching, as children encounter shapes in the physical world, and those shapes are named by adults, children treat shapes as fuzzy categories—shapes are identified but not defined.❞ (Battista, 2007, p. 863)

Describe Three-Dimensional Solids

A good starting place for children to describe three-dimensional solids is to use characteristics of the shapes that are inherent in their physical structure.

- Children can describe three-dimensional solids by indicating whether or not the solids have curved or flat surfaces.

- Another way to describe solids is to tell whether or not they can roll or stack.

Mathematical Practices and Processes

Look for and make use of structure.

Through children's language and mathematical actions, teachers can make inferences about whether or not children are able to **see structure**. This is particularly true with geometry. Consider a child examining a cube with six flat sides and a cylinder with two flat sides and a curved surface. The child might make several observations that form a foundation for classifying geometric solids. Examples of such observations include that: both objects have flat sides (bases); both objects can sit flat on any of its sides; one of the objects has squares for all the sides and one has circles for its flat sides. Soon, children will use these ideas as a structure on which to build more mathematical ideas and complete their understanding of geometry.

📱 For more professional learning, go online to Teacher's Corner.

nstructional Journey

While every classroom may look a little different, this instructional model provides a amework to organize small-group and whole-group learning for meaningful student learning.

Whole Group
Engage

5 minutes

Readiness
- Problem of the Day
- Fluency Builder or Vocabulary Builder
- Access Prior Knowledge

Engagement
- I Can
- Making Connections
- Learning Activity

Small and Whole Group
Explore

15–20 minutes

Exploration
- Listen and Draw, Unlock the Problem
- Multilingual Support and Strategy
- Common Errors

Small Group
Explain

15–20 minutes

Quick Check
☑ Share and Show

Differentiated Instruction

Grab and Go!™
Version 2.0

Intervention
- Waggle
- Reteach
- Tier 2 and Tier 3 MTSS
- Tabletop Flipchart Mini Lessons

Language Support
- Vocabulary Activities
- Language Routines
- Multilingual Glossary

Enrichment
- Waggle Games
- Ready for More
- Enrich

Whole Group
Elaborate

5 minutes
- Math on the Spot Videos
- Higher-Order Thinking Problems

Evaluate

- I Can Reflection
- Exit Ticket
- Practice and Homework
- Fluency Practice
- Waggle

Assessment

Diagnostic	Formative	Summative
• Show What You Know	• Lesson Quick Check	• Chapter Review • Chapter Test • Performance Assessment Task

Grab and Go!™
Version 2.0
Differentiated Centers Kit
The kit provides literature, games, and activities for small-group learning.

Strategies for
Multilingual Learners

Understanding a child's language development is helpful in differentiating teaching and assessment. Assessing a child's understanding of mathematical concepts can be done by listening, speaking, reading, and writing. The level of support a child needs determines how best to assess that child's understanding of mathematical concepts.

Planning for Instruction			
Language Support	**Substantial** (WIDA Level 1)*	**Moderate** (WIDA Levels 2 & 3)*	**Light** (WIDA Levels 4 & 5)*
Child's Use of Language	• uses single words • uses common short phrases • heavily relies on visual supports and use of manipulatives	• uses simple sentences • uses some academic vocabulary • relies on visual supports and use of manipulatives	• uses a variety of sentences • uses academic vocabulary • benefits from visual supports and manipulatives
Ways to Assess Understanding	**Listening:** points to pictures, words, or phrases to answer questions **Speaking:** answers *yes/no* questions **Reading:** matches symbols to math terms and concepts **Writing:** draws a visual representation of a problem	**Listening:** matches, categorizes, or sequences information based on visuals **Speaking:** begins to explain reasoning, asks math questions, repeats explanations from peers **Reading:** identifies important information to solve a problem **Writing:** uses simple sentences and visual representations	**Listening:** draws conclusions and makes connections based on what they heard **Speaking:** explains and justifies concepts and solutions **Reading:** understands information in math contexts **Writing:** completes sentences using some academic vocabulary

* For more information on WIDA Standards, visit their website at:
https://wida.wisc.edu/.

• Look for strategies throughout the lesson to support multilingual learners.

• Log on to ED to find additional multilingual activities and Vocabulary Cards.

In This Chapter

Key Academic Vocabulary

Current Development • Vocabulary

three-dimensional shape, sphere, curved surface, cube, flat surface, edge, cylinder, cone, flat, solid, above, below, beside, next to, in front of, behind

Using Language Routines to Develop Understanding

 Language routines provide opportunities for children to develop an understanding of mathematical language and concepts by listening, speaking, reading, and writing. More information on these language routines can be found on the Language Support Cards.

Stronger and Clearer Each Time

1 Children show their thinking with math tools and visuals.
2 Children share their thinking and receive feedback with a partner or a group.
3 Children revoice feedback and revise their work.

Language Support	Substantial (WIDA Level 1)*	Moderate (WIDA Levels 2 & 3)*	Light (WIDA Levels 4 & 5)*
Language Routine Differentiation	1 Children can show their thinking using visuals and/or manipulatives. 2 Children can answer yes/no or single-word-answer questions about their reasoning. Allow children to rely heavily on their visual representations. 3 Children revise their work based on feedback.	1 Children can show their thinking using words and/or visuals. 2 Children can verbally communicate with their partner or group using visual representations to support their reasoning. 3 Children repeat feedback and revise their work.	1 Children can show their thinking using words and visuals. 2 Children can use academic vocabulary to verbally communicate with their partner or group. 3 Children revoice feedback and revise their work.
Possible Student Work	**Example:** **Teacher:** Is this block the same shape as a sphere? **Child:** No. **Teacher:** Is this block the same shape as a cube? **Child:** Yes.	**Example:** **Teacher:** What three-dimensional shape does this block look like? **Child:** The block looks like a cube.	**Example:** **Teacher:** What three-dimensional shape does this block look like? **Child:** The block looks like a cube because it has six flat surfaces shaped like squares.

* For more information on WIDA Standards, visit their website at:
https://wida.wisc.edu/.

Assessing Prior Knowledge

Have children complete **Show What You Know** on their own. Items tested are the prerequisite skills for this chapter.

Diagnostic Interview Task

The alternative interview tasks below evaluate children's understanding of each **Show What You Know** skill. The diagnostic chart may be used for intervention on prerequisite skills.

Materials two-dimensional shapes

- Give the child a variety of two-dimensional shapes. Have the child place all of the squares in one set and all of the triangles in another set.
- Give the child a large triangle. **How many sides does this triangle have?** 3 **How many vertices does this triangle have?** 3 If necessary, explain that vertices are corners. Have the child point to a vertex and then count how many vertices there are. Repeat the process with a rectangle.
- Give the child a variety of two-dimensional shapes. Have the child place all of the squares in one set, all of the circles in another set, and all of the triangles in a third set.

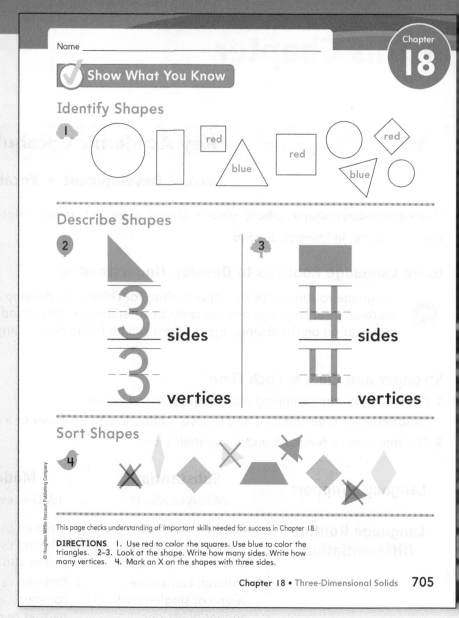

Name _____

✓ Show What You Know

Identify Shapes

Describe Shapes

2. 3 sides
    3 vertices

3. 4 sides
    4 vertices

Sort Shapes

4.

This page checks understanding of important skills needed for success in Chapter 18.

DIRECTIONS 1. Use red to color the squares. Use blue to color the triangles. 2–3. Look at the shape. Write how many sides. Write how many vertices. 4. Mark an X on the shapes with three sides.

Chapter 18 • Three-Dimensional Solids **705**

✓ Show What You Know • Diagnostic Assessment

Use to determine if children need intervention for the chapter's prerequisite skills.

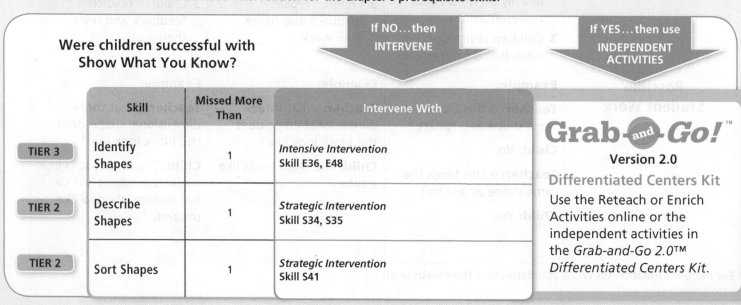

	Skill	Missed More Than	Intervene With
TIER 3	Identify Shapes	1	*Intensive Intervention* Skill E36, E48
TIER 2	Describe Shapes	1	*Strategic Intervention* Skill S34, S35
TIER 2	Sort Shapes	1	*Strategic Intervention* Skill S41

Were children successful with Show What You Know?

If NO...then **INTERVENE**

If YES...then use **INDEPENDENT ACTIVITIES**

Grab-and-Go!™ Version 2.0 Differentiated Centers Kit Use the Reteach or Enrich Activities online or the independent activities in the *Grab-and-Go 2.0*™ *Differentiated Centers Kit.*

Vocabulary Builder

rectangle

circle

square

triangle

DIRECTIONS Mark an X on the food shaped like a circle. Draw a line under the food shaped like a square. Circle the food shaped like a triangle.

706 Go Math! Grade K

© Houghton Mifflin Harcourt Publishing Company

Vocabulary Builder

Children use multiple strategies to develop grade-appropriate vocabulary.

Have children complete the activities on the page by working alone or with partners.

Look at the page with children. Talk about the different shapes.

Trace your finger around the following objects.

- **What shape is the clock?** circle
- **What shape is the bookcase?** rectangle
- **What shape is the window?** square

Have children mark an X on the food shaped like a circle. Have children draw a line under the food shaped like a square. Have children draw a loop around the food shaped like a triangle.

School-Home Letter is available in English and Spanish online, and in multiple other languages.

Intervention Options *MTSS* (RtI) Response to Intervention

Use Show What You Know, Lesson Quick Check, and Assessments to diagnose children's intervention levels.

TIER 1	TIER 2	TIER 3	ENRICHMENT
On-Level Intervention	**Strategic Intervention**	**Intensive Intervention**	**Independent Activities**
For children who are generally at grade level but need early intervention with the lesson concepts, use:	For children who need small-group instruction to review concepts and skills needed for the chapter, use:	For children who need one-on-one instruction to build foundational skills for the chapter, use:	For children who successfully complete lessons, use:
• Reteach	▲ Prerequisite Skills Activities	▲ Prerequisite Skills Activities	• Waggle Practice and Games
• Tabletop Flipchart Mini Lesson	▲ Tier 2 Activity	▲ Tier 3 Activity	**Grab and Go!**
• Waggle			Version 2.0
▲ Tier 1 Activity			Differentiated Centers Kit
			• Ready for More Activity for every lesson
			• Enrich

Lesson at a Glance
Identify, Name, and Describe Spheres

SNAPSHOT

Mathematical Standards

- Describe objects in the environment using names of shapes, and describe the relative positions of these objects using terms such as *above*, *below*, *beside*, *in front of*, *behind*, and *next to*.

Mathematical Practices and Processes

- Attend to precision.
- Express regularity in repeated reasoning.
- Look for and make use of structure.
- Model with mathematics.

(I Can) Objective

I can identify, name, and describe spheres.

Learning Goal

Identify, name, and describe three-dimensional shapes, including spheres.

Language Objective

Children use their student book as a resource to help them explain how to identify, name, and describe spheres.

MATERIALS

- MathBoard
- three-dimensional shapes

ACROSS THE GRADES

Grade K

Identify two- and three-dimensional figures, regardless of their size or orientation. Figures are limited to circles, triangles, rectangles, squares, spheres, cubes, cones, and cylinders.

After

Identify, compare, and sort two- and three-dimensional figures on the basis of their defining attributes. Figures are limited to circles, semicircles, triangles, rectangles, squares, trapezoids, hexagons, spheres, cubes, rectangular prisms, cones and cylinders.

ABOUT THE MATH

Why Teach This?

Since birth, children have lived in a three-dimensional world. As part of their vocabulary building and extension of mathematical knowledge, kindergarten children are ready to describe and identify three-dimensional shapes or solid shapes such as spheres, cylinders, cubes, and cones.

In this chapter, children will expand and deepen their knowledge as they learn the names of the shapes, sort them according to their properties, and compare them to two-dimensional, or flat, shapes. They will find and identify the many examples of these geometric shapes in their school environment. This helps them become more aware of mathematics in real life. It also lays the foundation for later work with volume and surface area of three-dimensional shapes.

For more professional learning go online to Teacher's Corner.

💻 **Problem of the Day 18.1**

How many Mondays are there this month?

Help children count the number of Mondays.

💻 **Vocabulary** curved surface, sphere, three-dimensional shape

- Interactive Student Edition
- Multilingual Glossary

Vocabulary Builder

Materials three-dimensional shapes; spherical classroom objects such as balls, globes, snow globes

Explain that three-dimensional shapes are not flat. Remind children of the two-dimensional shapes that they know. Emphasize how they are flat.

Tell children that you will now show them a three-dimensional shape.

Show a sphere and have children describe its shape. round all over or curved Stress the word *curved*: **The sphere has a *curved* surface.** Pass the sphere around so that children can feel it and look at it from all angles. Have a child demonstrate that the sphere can roll.

Have children identify other classroom objects as sphere

FOCUSING ON THE WHOLE STUDENT

Access Prior Knowledge

Use iTools: Geometry to show a sphere, a cube, and a cylinder. Invite children to play "Guess How I Sorted" with you. Place the sphere and cylinder in one set and the cube in another. Point to the sphere-and-cylinder set.

- **These shapes are alike. How are they alike?** Possible answers: One is a sphere and has all curved surfaces. It can roll. The other is a cylinder. It has some curved sufaces and some flat surfaces. It can roll.

- **How are these shapes sorted?** Possible answers: by finding shapes with (or without) curved surfaces, or shapes that can (or cannot) roll

① Engage

with the Interactive Student Edition

I Can Objective

I can identify, name, and describe spheres.

Making Connections

Draw a square, a circle, a triangle, and a rectangle.

- **Which shapes have parts that are flat?** square, triangle, rectangle
- **Which shapes have parts that are curved?** circle

Learning Activity

Show a football and a basketball. Explain that these are the two balls that Scout and Rafferty find. Ask, **Which is shaped like a sphere?** Guide children toward recognizing and identifying a sphere.

- **What do Scout and Rafferty find?** two kinds of balls
- **What does Scout want to know?** which ball is shaped like a sphere
- **Do the balls have curved surfaces or flat surfaces?** curved surfaces

❷ **Explore**

Listen and Draw

Materials three-dimensional shapes

Read aloud this problem as children listen.

Ray has four shapes. One shape is a sphere. How can Ray describe the sphere?

 Attend to precision.

Have children use a cube, a cylinder, a cone, and a sphere. Hold up a sphere and ask children to hold up a shape that is like it. Introduce the name of the shape—sphere.

- **How can you describe a sphere?** Accept reasonable answers.

- **What can you tell about the surface of a sphere?** Possible answers: It is round. It has a curved surface. It does not have any flat surfaces.

Remind children that "figure" and "shape" can be used interchangeably in a mathematical context. For example, *three-dimensional shape* and *three-dimensional figure* mean the same thing.

Read the labels on the sorting mat. Have children place the three-dimensional shapes onto the page and sort them. Have children describe the sphere. Then have children match a picture of each shape to the shapes on the mat and glue the pictures onto the page.

- **I am holding a shape that has no flat surfaces. What shape am I holding?** a sphere

Reread the problem about Ray.

- **How can Ray describe his sphere?** Ray can say a sphere is round and has curves. It has no flat surfaces.

 Look for and make use of structure.

- **Name some things that are shaped like a sphere. How are they alike?** The shapes have curved surfaces and no flat surfaces.

Name _____

Identify, Name, and Describe Spheres

(**I Can**) identify, name, and describe spheres.

Listen and Draw

sphere	not a sphere

Check children's work.

DIRECTIONS Place three-dimensional shapes on the page. Identify and name the sphere. Sort the shapes on the sorting mat. Describe the sphere. Match a picture of each shape to the shapes on the sorting mat. Glue the shape pictures on the sorting mat.

Chapter 18 • Lesson 1 **707**

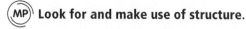 **Multilingual Support**

STRATEGY: Rephrase

Children can demonstrate their understanding by rephrasing ideas about shapes.

- Point to the circle. **This is a circle. It is a flat shape.** Hold up the sphere. **This is a sphere. It is a solid shape.**

Let each child hold the sphere and touch the circle. Then ask children to tell in their own words how the sphere is different from the circle. Make sure they mention that the circle is flat and the sphere has a curved surface.

Ask children to find in the room other objects that are spheres.

1

sphere

flat surface

curved surface

2 ✓

© Houghton Mifflin Harcourt Publishing Company

DIRECTIONS 1. Look at the sphere. Circle the words that describe a sphere. 2. Color the spheres.

708 Go Math! Grade K

Ready for More

Visual Small Group

Materials magazines, scissors, large paper, glue

Provide small groups with materials and two-column charts labeled *spheres* and *not spheres*.

Have children find and cut out pictures of three-dimensional objects that are spheres and objects that are not spheres.

Have children glue the pictures onto the charts in the correct column. Invite them to share their posters about solid shapes.

sphere

3 Explain

Share and Show

Ask children to name the red shape at the top of the page. Read the label *sphere* with children. Explain that the surface of an object is all of the outside, or the surfaces are all of the outer parts. Rub your hands around the surface of the sphere to demonstrate the meaning of the word. Talk about the sphere's curved surface.

- **How many flat surfaces does a sphere have?** none **How do you know?** Possible answer: The whole surface feels rounded.

- **What word could you use to describe the surface of a sphere?** curved

Read the descriptions next to the sphere. Instruct children to circle the correct description. curved surface

- **Now look at Problem 2. How many spheres do you see?** 2

- **Why are the other shapes not called spheres?** They have some flat surfaces.

Have children color the two spheres.

Use the checked problem for Quick Check.

✓ Quick Check   MTSS RtI

If	a child misses the checked problem
Then	Differentiate Instruction with • Reteach 18.1 • Waggle

! Common Errors

Error Children may confuse circles with spheres.

Example Children call a sphere a circle.

Springboard to Learning Have children trace a circle. Then have them hold a sphere. Guide children to see that both are round but that only the circle is flat. The sphere is not flat; it is curved like a ball.

④ Elaborate

Share and Show

(MP) **Model with mathematics.**

Look at Problem 3 together.

• **What do you see?** a bookcase filled with objects

Have children take turns naming the objects shown on the shelves, starting with the top shelf—balloon, cylinder, block, can, horn, globe, wrapped present, baseball, book.

• **Which objects are shaped like a sphere?** the balloon, the globe, and the baseball

Have children cross out each object shaped like a sphere. Encourage children to name other objects that they know are shaped like a sphere.

Ask children to look at the middle shelf on the page. Have children take turns naming each object and identifying the matching three-dimensional shape. can, cylinder; horn, cone; globe, sphere

Higher-Order Thinking

(MP) **Express regularity in repeated reasoning.**

Have children talk about these shapes found in the problem: a sphere, a cylinder, and a cone. Display the three solid shapes.

• **How are the surfaces of a cylinder, a cone, and a sphere the same?** They all have curved surfaces.

• **How are the surfaces of a cylinder and a cone the same?** Both have curved and flat surfaces.

Math on the Spot Use this video to help children model and solve this type of problem.

Name _____

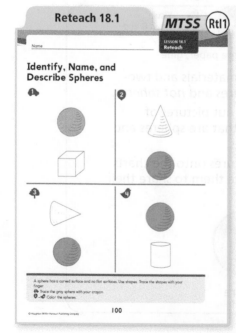

© Houghton Mifflin Harcourt Publishing Company

DIRECTIONS 3. Identify the objects that are shaped like a sphere. Mark an X on those objects.

Meeting Individual Needs

Reteach 18.1   MTSS (Rtl1)   **Enrich 18.1**

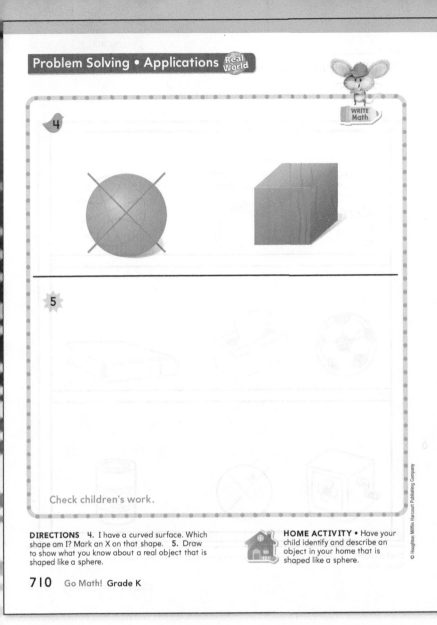

4

5

Check children's work.

DIRECTIONS 4. I have a curved surface. Which shape am I? Mark an X on that shape. 5. Draw to show what you know about a real object that is shaped like a sphere.

HOME ACTIVITY • Have your child identify and describe an object in your home that is shaped like a sphere.

DIFFERENTIATED INSTRUCTION • Independent Activities

Grab and Go!
Version 2.0
Differentiated Centers Kit

Tabletop Flipchart

Mini-lessons for reteaching to targeted small groups

Readers

Supports key math skills and concepts in real-world situations

Games

Reinforce math content and vocabulary

Activities

Meaningful and fun math practice

Problem Solving Real World
Applications

(MP) **Look for and make use of structure.**

Read the riddle for **Problem 4**. Ask children to explain how they will solve the riddle.

- **Look at Problem 4. Which shape has a curved surface?** Possible answers: the sphere; the red shape; the one that is shaped like a ball
- **Cross out that shape.**

Problem 5 Before children begin drawing to show what they know about objects shaped like spheres, discuss what children have already learned about the features of a sphere. Include in the discussion the fact that a sphere has a curved surface.

⑤ Evaluate | Formative Assessment

I Can

Have children use their student book as a resource to help them answer the I Can statement.

I can identify, name, and describe spheres by . . . knowing that a sphere has only a curved surface and no flat surfaces. I know that a ball is a sphere.

Exit Ticket

Have children share their completed drawings and tell what they know about what all spheres have in common.

Identify, Name, and Describe Spheres

Use the Practice and Homework pages to provide children with more practice of the concepts and skills presented in this lesson. Children master their understanding as they complete practice items.

Identify, Name, and Describe Spheres

© Houghton Mifflin Harcourt Publishing Company

DIRECTIONS 1. Identify the objects that are shaped like a sphere. Mark an X on those objects.

Chapter 18 • Lesson 1 **711**

CROSS-CURRICULAR

SCIENCE

Materials paper bag, three-dimensional shapes

• Talk about how people use their senses to see, hear, taste, smell, and touch. As you point to your eyes, ears, mouth, nose, and hands, discuss how each is used.

• Explain that children are going to focus on their sense of touch by using their hands.

• Have children watch as you place different shapes into a paper bag. Only one shape should be a sphere.

• Have children take turns reaching into the bag to find the sphere. Ask that they use only their sense of touch.

SOCIAL STUDIES

Materials globe

• Display a globe and identify it for children.

• **What is this globe a model of?** planet Earth

• **What shape is the globe and planet Earth?** a sphere

• Help children locate the oceans. **Which color on the globe is used to show water?** blue

• Talk about the globe. Determine the colors used to show land.

Lesson Check

2

Spiral Review

3

4

DIRECTIONS   2. Which shape is a sphere? Mark an X on the shape.   3. Which shape is a square? Color the square.   4. How many school buses are there? Write the number.

© Houghton Mifflin Harcourt Publishing Company

Continue to practice concepts and skills with Lesson Check. Use Spiral Review to engage children in previously taught concepts and to promote content retention.

Lesson at a Glance
Identify, Name, and Describe Cubes

SNAPSHOT

Mathematical Standards
- Describe objects in the environment using names of shapes, and describe the relative positions of these objects using terms such as *above*, *below*, *beside*, *in front of*, *behind*, and *next to*.

Mathematical Practices and Processes
- Express regularity in repeated reasoning.
- Attend to precision.
- Construct arguments and critique reasoning of others.
- Look for and make use of structure.
- Reason abstractly and quantitatively.

(I Can) Objective
I can identify, name, and describe cubes.

Learning Goal
Identify, name, and describe three-dimensional shapes, including cubes.

Language Objective
Teams of three children take turns whispering how to identify, name, and describe cubes.

MATERIALS
- MathBoard
- three-dimensional shapes

ACROSS THE GRADES

Grade K
Identify two- and three-dimensional figures, regardless of their size or orientation. Figures are limited to circles, triangles, rectangles, squares, spheres, cubes, cones, and cylinders.

After
Identify, compare and sort two- and three-dimensional figures on the basis of their defining attributes. Figures are limited to circles, semicircles, triangles, rectangles, squares, trapezoids, hexagons, spheres, cubes, rectangular prisms, cones, and cylinders.

ABOUT THE MATH

Use Three-Dimensional Models

In this chapter, children will use sets of three-dimensional models. The models are safe with no sharp points or edges. As children hold and arrange the models, they have opportunities to feel and see their surfaces. Working with models complements working with pictures and helps children understand differences between three-dimensional and two-dimensional objects.

As they hold and examine the cube models in this lesson, children will explore a cube's six flat surfaces, or faces. They will recognize that the flat surfaces meet together to form an edge. Children will stack and slide cubes and see that they do not roll. They will also recognize that the flat surfaces are all the same size. They are shaped like squares.

sphere   cylinder   cube

 For more professional learning go online to Teacher's Corner.

🖥 Problem of the Day 18.2

Read each number. Put the numbers in counting order.

11, 15, 12, 14, 10, 13

Which number is greater than 14? less than 11? 10, 11, 12, 13, 14, 15; 15; 10

Have a child point to the numbers in counting order and lead the class in saying them. Have children tell the number that is greater than 14 and the number that is less than 11.

🖥 Vocabulary cube, flat surface, edge

• Interactive Student Edition
• Multilingual Glossary

Vocabulary Builder

Materials three-dimensional shapes

• Show a cube. Have children describe its shape.
• Stress the word *flat*. Have children count the flat surfaces of the cube. 6 flat surfaces
• Discuss how a cube cannot roll because all its faces are flat.
• Have children identify classroom objects that are cubes.

FOCUSING ON THE WHOLE STUDENT

Access Prior Knowledge

Brainstorm with children a list of balls that people use for sports. Display sports balls such as a soccer ball, basketball, tennis ball, football, baseball, softball, and golf ball.

• **What is alike about all the sports balls?** They have curved surfaces.
• **Are all the sports ball spheres?** No—the football is not a sphere, but the rest are.
• **Why is a sphere a good shape for a ball?** A sphere-shaped ball can roll, spin, and bounce.

① Engage

with the Interactive Student Edition

I Can Objective

I can identify, name, and describe cubes.

Making Connections

Lead children in analyzing what they have learned about spheres. Show children a cylinder, a cone, and a sphere. Ask about the properties of each. Now draw part of a shape, such as a curved line or a right angle. **Which shapes could this be part of?**

Point out an item in the room that is shaped like a circle. **How is a circle like a sphere?**

Learning Activity

Help children understand how to identify objects shaped like a cube.

• **What shape has six flat surfaces?** a cube

⚠ Common Errors

Error Children may miscount the number of flat surfaces that a cube has.

Example Children write " 4 flat surfaces" in Problem 2.

Springboard to Learning Provide children with dot stickers. Have children stick a dot on each flat surface that they count so they can keep track of each surface counted. Help them see that a cube has six flat surfaces.

---

② Explore

Listen and Draw

Materials three-dimensional shapes

Read aloud this problem as children listen.

Maya has four shapes. One shape is a cube.
How can Maya describe the cube?

MP **Attend to precision.**

Have children use a cube, a cylinder, a cone, and a sphere. Hold up a cube and ask children to hold up a shape that is like it. Say the name of the shape—*cube*. Allow children to examine the flat surfaces of the cube. Explain that these flat surfaces come together to form the edges of the cube.

• **How can you describe a cube?** Accept reasonable answers.

• **What can you tell about the surfaces of a cube?** They are flat. There are six flat surfaces.

Read the labels on the page. Have children place the solid shapes on the page. Point to a cube. **What is this solid shape's name?** cube

• **Sort all the shapes on the page.**

Have children match a picture of each shape to the solids on the page. Have them glue the pictures onto the page, in the correct column.

MP **Construct arguments and critique reasoning of others.**

• **I have a shape that has curves. Is it a cube? Explain.** No, a cube has no curves.

Reread the problem about Maya.

• **How can Maya describe her cube?** Maya can say that a cube is a shape that has six flat surfaces.

To further support children's understanding of a cube's shape, have children build cubes by using clay balls and either toothpicks or equal-sized pieces of straw.

Name _____

Identify, Name, and Describe Cubes

I Can identify, name, and describe cubes.

Listen and Draw

cube	not a cube

Check children's work.

DIRECTIONS Place three-dimensional shapes on the page. Identify and name the cube. Sort the shapes on the sorting mat. Describe the cube. Match a picture of each shape to one of the shapes on the sorting mat. Glue the shape pictures on the sorting mat.

Chapter 18 • Lesson 2 **713**

ML ## Multilingual Support

STRATEGY: Model Language

Children can learn correct pronunciation and sentence structure by repeating geometry words and sentences that are modeled by a proficient speaker.

Show children a cube. Describe it, and have children repeat this sentence: **A cube has six flat surfaces.**

Have children find in the room objects that are shaped like cubes. For each object, have them tell how they know it is a cube. Then have them count the sides aloud and repeat again: **A cube has six flat surfaces.**

1

cube

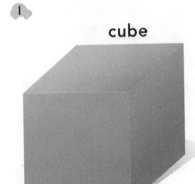

(flat surface)

curved surface

2 ✓

6 flat surfaces

DIRECTIONS 1. Look at the cube. Circle the words that describe a cube. 2. Use a cube to count how many flat surfaces there are. Write the number.

3 Explain

Share and Show

Ask children to name the blue shape at the top of the page. Read the word *cube* with children. Read the words next to the cube. Instruct children to circle the words that describe the cube. flat surface

- **Name the shape of the flat surface.** square
- **How many curved surfaces does a cube have?** none **How do you know?**
  Possible answer: None of the surfaces look rounded.

(MP) **Reason abstractly and quantitatively.**

Show children a real-world cube, such as a cube-shaped gift box, and a geometric solid cube. Help children count the flat surfaces by counting the top and bottom and then going around the middle. Tell children that they need to keep track of which flat surface they start counting with so that they do not count any flat surface twice.

- **Look at Problem 2. How many flat surfaces does a cube have?** 6 **Write 6 on the line.**

Read the completed line with children:
6 flat surfaces. Explain that those words describe a cube.

Use the checked problem for Quick Check.

✓ Quick Check MTSS RtI

If → a child misses the checked problem

Then → **Differentiate Instruction** with
- Reteach 18.2
- Waggle

Ready for More

Visual / Kinesthetic
Individual / Partner

Materials non-pointed toothpicks or straws, craft sticks, clay

Display a model of a cube made from 12 toothpicks (to represent the edges) and 8 small balls of clay (at the corners).

Distribute 12 toothpicks or 12 $1\frac{1}{2}$-inch pieces of straws, 12 craft sticks, and clay to partners.

Have children use your model as a guide to create two cubes. Have one partner make a cube out of clay and toothpicks (or straws). Have the other partner make a cube out of clay and craft sticks.

Have partners discuss how the cubes are alike and different. Possible answers: The shapes are both cubes. The cubes are different sizes.

④ Elaborate

Share and Show

Look at Problem 3 together.

Have children take turns naming the objects shown on the shelves of the bookshelf, starting with the top shelf—soccer ball, shape sorter, drum, pillow, waffle cone, baseball box, alphabet block, toy tent, watermelon.

- **Which objects are shaped like a cube?**
  the shape sorter, the baseball box, the alphabet block
- **How do you know that they are cubes?**
  Possible answer: They each have six flat surfaces.

Have children cross out each object shaped like a cube.

 Look for and make use of structure.

Call attention to the shelves on the page.

- **Look at all of the cubes that you marked.**
- **How are they alike?** All have six flat surfaces.
- **How are they different?** size, color, how you use them
- **How are cubes different from spheres?**
  Possible answers: Cubes do not roll and spheres do; cubes have flat surfaces and spheres have curved surfaces.
- **Name another cube-shaped object that could take the place of the soccer ball on the shelf.** Possible answers: tissue box, gift box

Higher-Order Thinking

 Attend to precision.

Ask children to think about the flat surfaces of cubes as well as the size of the surfaces. Ask children how they can use what they know about the sides and vertices of two-dimensional shapes to find the sides and vertices of three-dimensional shapes.

Math on the Spot Use this video to help children model and solve this type of problem.

Name _____

3

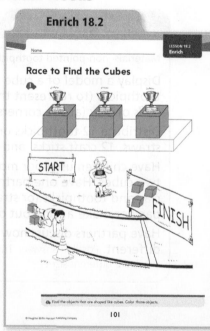

DIRECTIONS 3. Identify the objects that are shaped like a cube. Mark an X on those objects.

Meeting Individual Needs

Reteach 18.2   MTSS (RtI1)

LESSON 18.2
Reteach

Name _____

Identify, Name, and Describe Cubes

❶

❷

___ flat surfaces

❶ Look at the pictures that show all the flat surfaces on one cube. Count how many flat surfaces. Touch each number as you count. **❷** Write the number that shows how many flat surfaces.

101

Enrich 18.2

LESSON 18.2
Enrich

Name _____

Race to Find the Cubes

❶

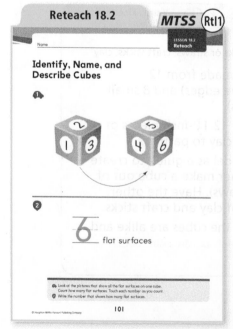

START

FINISH

❶ Find the objects that are shaped like cubes. Color those objects.

101

4

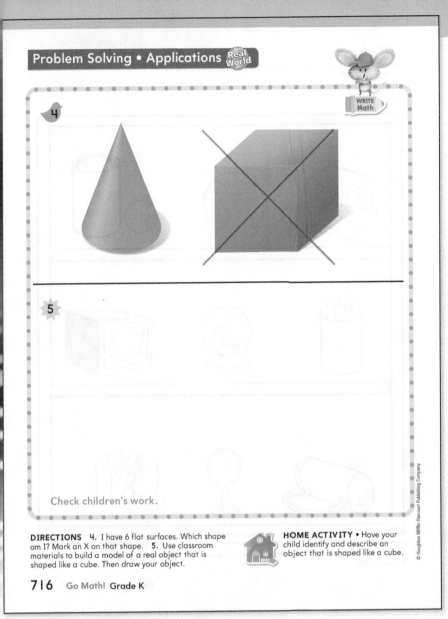

WRITE Math

5

Check children's work.

DIRECTIONS **4.** I have 6 flat surfaces. Which shape am I? Mark an X on that shape. **5.** Use classroom materials to build a model of a real object that is shaped like a cube. Then draw your object.

HOME ACTIVITY • Have your child identify and describe an object that is shaped like a cube.

716 Go Math! Grade K

© Houghton Mifflin Harcourt Publishing Company

Problem Solving Real World Applications

 Express regularity in repeated reasoning

Read the riddle for **Problem 4**. Ask children to use what they know about cubes to explain how they will solve the riddle.

- **Look at Problem 4. Which shapes have flat surfaces?** both shapes
- **Which shape has six flat surfaces?** the blue cube

Read the directions for **Problem 5**. Before children build and draw to show what they know about a real object shaped like a cube, discuss the features of a cube, including that a cube has six flat surfaces.

⑤ Evaluate | Formative Assessment

I Can

Have teams of three children take turns whispering the answer to the I Can statement.

I can identify, name, and describe cubes by . . . knowing that a cube has 6 flat surfaces that are the same size.

Exit Ticket

Invite children to share their drawings and tell what they know about cubes.

DIFFERENTIATED INSTRUCTION • Independent Activities

Grab and Go!™

Version 2.0

Differentiated Centers Kit

Tabletop Flipchart
Mini-lessons for reteaching to targeted small groups

Readers
Supports key math skills and concepts in real-world situations

Games
Reinforce math content and vocabulary

Activities
Meaningful and fun math practice

Identify, Name, and Describe Cubes

Use the Practice and Homework pages to provide children with more practice of the concepts and skills presented in this lesson. Children master their understanding as they complete practice items.

Identify, Name, and Describe Cubes

© Houghton Mifflin Harcourt Publishing Company

DIRECTIONS 1. Identify the objects that are shaped like a cube. Mark an X on those objects.

Chapter 18 • Lesson 2   **717**

PROFESSIONAL DEVELOPMENT   MATH TALK IN ACTION

As children work on this page, they discuss what they are learning about cubes.

Teacher: Do you see any objects in our classroom that are shaped like cubes?

Beth: I think that our cubbies are shaped like cubes but with one flat surface missing. That is where we put our things.

Efrain: My crayon box is shaped like a cube.

Aba: I think that the crayon box is not really a cube because all the flat surfaces are not squares.

Teacher: What do you mean, Aba?

Aba: Look at the cube. All the flat surfaces are the same size. They are all squares.

Efrain: I see what you mean. The flat surfaces on the crayon box are different-sized rectangles. So I guess that box is not a cube.

Teacher: So what else do you notice about cubes?

Karl: The corners are square, too. They are not pointy like a cone.

Beth: You can turn a cube over, but you cannot roll one.

Karl: Yes, the thing that rolls best is a sphere. I can roll a sphere in all directions.

Teacher: You are all thinking like mathematicians about these shapes. Good work, class!

Lesson Check

Spiral Review

  sides

71	72	73	74	75	76	77	78	79	80
81	82	83	84	85	86	87	88	89	90
91	92	93	94	95	96	97	98	99	100

DIRECTIONS 2. Which shape is a cube? Mark an X on that shape. 3. How many sides does the square have? Write that number. 4. Begin with 81 and count forward to 90. What is the next number? Draw a line under that number.

Lesson at a Glance
Identify, Name, and Describe Cylinders

SNAPSHOT

Mathematical Standards

- Describe objects in the environment using names of shapes, and describe the relative positions of these objects using terms such as *above*, *below*, *beside*, *in front of*, *behind*, and *next to*.

Mathematical Practices and Processes

- Attend to precision.
- Model with mathematics.
- Construct arguments and critique reasoning of others.
- Look for and make use of structure.
- Reason abstractly and quantitatively.

(I Can) Objective

I can identify, name, and describe cylinders.

Learning Goal

Identify, name, and describe three-dimensional shapes, including cylinders.

Language Objective

Children use hand gestures and words to identify, name, and describe cylinders.

MATERIALS

- MathBoard
- three-dimensional shapes

ACROSS THE GRADES

Grade K

Identify two- and three-dimensional figures regardless of their size or orientation. Figures are limited to circles, triangles, rectangles, squares, spheres, cubes, cones and cylinders.

After

Identify, compare and sort two- and three-dimensional figures based on their defining attributes. Figures are limited to circles, semi-circles, triangles, rectangles, squares, trapezoids, hexagons, spheres, cubes, rectangular prisms, cones and cylinders.

ABOUT THE MATH

Teaching for Depth

In this lesson, children will handle, sort, and identify cylinders.

Show a variety of real-world cylinders of different sizes. Draw children's attention to the idea that although the cylinders appear quite different, each has the same attributes—two circular flat surfaces that are the same size and a curved surface.

Provide modeling clay or dough for children to mold cylinders, as well as cubes and spheres. Encourage children to compare their models with others and with the three-dimensional shapes.

For more professional learning go online to Teacher's Corner.

DAILY ROUTINES

 Problem of the Day 18.3

What are the names of these shapes? How can you describe them?

Show children solids of a cylinder, cube, and sphere and have them identify and describe each shape.
cylinder, cube, sphere; Accept reasonable answers.

 Vocabulary cylinder
- Interactive Student Edition
- Multilingual Glossary

Vocabulary Builder

Materials three-dimensional shapes

- Show a cylinder and have children describe its shape. curved with two flat surfaces
- Review the word *curved*. Pass around the cylinder so children can feel the curved surface of the cylinder. Stress the word *flat* and have children feel the flat top and bottom surfaces of the cylinder.
- Have children compare how a cylinder can roll along the curved surface, but not on the flat ones.
- Have children identify other classroom objects as cylinders.

FOCUSING ON THE WHOLE STUDENT

Access Prior Knowledge

Use iTools: Geometry to show a sphere and a cube side by side. Have children name each shape.

- **How are these shapes alike?** They are both three-dimensional shapes. They are solids.
- **How are they different?** The sphere has a curved surface. The cube has six flat surfaces.

① Engage

with the Interactive Student Edition

I Can Objective
I can identify, name, and describe cylinders.

Making Connections
Have children tell what they know about two-dimensional shapes.

- **What are some of the shapes we have learned about?** circles, triangles, rectangles, squares
- **What circles do you see around the classroom?** Accept reasonable answers.
- **What things in the classroom are round?** Accept reasonable answers.

Learning Activity
Show a picture of a trash can and a can of food. **What is the shape of these objects?** Lead children toward understanding attributes of cylinders.

- **What do you wonder?** What the shape of the trash can and a can of food is called.
- **What words can you use to describe the shape of the object?** round, flat
- **What two-dimensional shape does the object remind you of?** circle, rectangle

❷ Explore

Listen and Draw

Materials three-dimensional shapes

Read aloud this problem as children listen.

Michael has four shapes. One is a cylinder.
How can Michael describe the cylinder?

Have children use a cylinder, a cube, a cone, and a sphere. Hold up a cylinder and ask children to hold up a shape that is like it. Introduce the name of the shape—*cylinder*. Read the labels on the sorting mat.

 Attend to precision.

• **Place the three-dimensional shapes on the page. Hold up the cylinder.**

• **Sort the shapes on the sorting mat.**

• **How can you describe a cylinder?** Accept reasonable answers.

• **What can you tell about the surfaces of a cylinder?** It has two flat surfaces and a curved surface.

Have children match a picture of each shape to the shapes on the mat. Have children glue the shape pictures on the mat.

• **My shape has a curved surface and two flat surfaces. What shape is it? Explain.** a cylinder; because a cylinder has both curved and flat surfaces

Reread the problem about Michael.

• **How can Michael describe his cylinder?** Michael can say a cylinder is a shape that has a curved surface and two flat surfaces that are the same size.

Name _____

Identify, Name, and Describe Cylinders

(I Can) identify, name, and describe cylinders.

Listen and Draw Real World

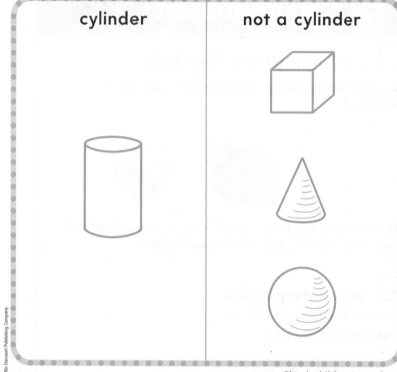

Check children's work.

DIRECTIONS Place three-dimensional shapes on the page. Identify and name the cylinder. Sort the shapes on the sorting mat. Describe the cylinder. Match a picture of each shape to the shapes on the sorting mat. Glue the shape pictures on the sorting mat.

© Houghton Mifflin Harcourt Publishing Company

Chapter 18 • Lesson 3   **719**

ML **Multilingual Support**

STRATEGY: Model Concepts

Children can identify three-dimensional shapes when they are modeled.

Place three-dimensional shapes on the table. Point to and identify the object shaped like a cylinder. Then have children name and describe the cylinder. Next, ask them to identify the other three-dimensional shapes.

Ask children to name other everyday objects that are shaped like cylinders. If time permits, children can look through magazines or books to find objects that are shaped like cylinders.

1

cylinder

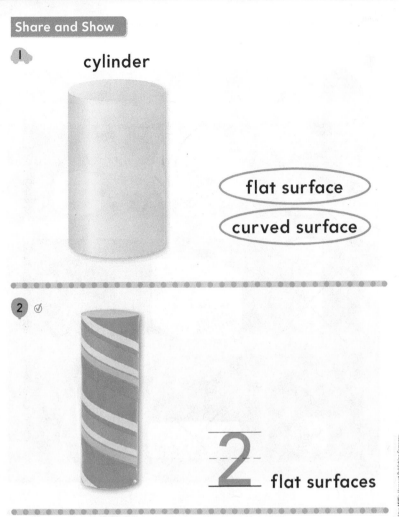

flat surface

curved surface

2 ✓

2 flat surfaces

DIRECTIONS 1. Look at the cylinder. Circle the words that describe a cylinder.
2. Use a cylinder to count how many flat surfaces. Write the number.

Ready for More 🕐 Visual Partners

Materials magazines, scissors, posterboard, glue

Have a child draw pictures or cut out pictures from magazines of objects that are shaped like cylinders.

Have partners work together to make a poster titled *Cylinders All Around Us*.

③ Explain

Share and Show

Ask children to name the yellow shape on the page. Read the word *cylinder*.

Read the words next to the cylinder. Instruct children to circle the words that describe a cylinder and explain how they know which words to circle. I know that a cylinder has flat surfaces and a curved surface. So I circle both sets of words.

(MP) **Model with mathematics.**

- **Look at Problem 2.**

Show children a real-world cylinder, such as a can, and a geometric solid cylinder. Point out the surfaces on the top and bottom of the shape.

- **How can you describe the flat surfaces of the cylinder?** Possible answer: round, same size
- **What word can you use to describe the surface of a cylinder that is not flat?** curved

Demonstrate how to count the flat surfaces.

- **How many flat surfaces does a cylinder have?** 2 Write the number.

Use the checked problem for Quick Check.

✓ Quick Check MTSS RtI

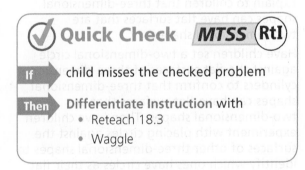

If → child misses the checked problem

Then → **Differentiate Instruction with**
- Reteach 18.3
- Waggle

⚠ Common Errors

Error Children may not be able to describe a cylinder.

Example Children identify the two flat surfaces but not the curved surface.

Springboard to Learning Have children hold a cylinder and identify the two flat surfaces. Then call attention to the curved surface. Show children that the cylinder can roll because it has a curved surface.

© Houghton Mifflin Harcourt Publishing Company

④ Elaborate

Share and Show

Have children look at Problem 3.

- **Which objects in the bookshelf are shaped like a cylinder?** the can of tuna, the can of tennis balls, the mailing tube
- **How do you know they are cylinders?** They have two flat surfaces and a curved surface.

Have children mark an X on each object shaped like a cylinder.

Encourage children to name other objects they know that are shaped like a cylinder.

 **Construct arguments and critique reasoning of others.**

Show children a circle and a cylinder.

- **How are a cylinder and a circle alike?** Possible answers: A circle has a curved edge and a cylinder has curved surfaces; a circle and a cylinder have curved parts.
- **How is a cylinder different from a circle?** Possible answer: A cylinder can be tall, but a circle is flat.

Higher-Order Thinking

 Look for and make use of structure.

Explain to children that three-dimensional shapes can have flat surfaces that are two-dimensional shapes.

Have children set a two-dimensional circle against the flat surfaces of three-dimensional cylinders to confirm that three-dimensional shapes can have flat surfaces that are two-dimensional shapes. Then have children experiment with placing circles against the surfaces of other three-dimensional shapes to identify which ones have circles as their flat surfaces.

Math on the Spot Use this video to help children model and solve this type of problem.

Name _____

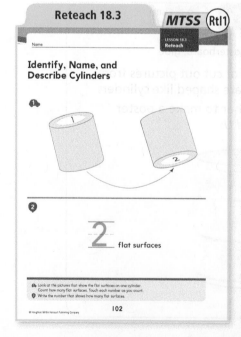

DIRECTIONS 3. Identify the objects that are shaped like a cylinder. Mark an X on those objects.

Meeting Individual Needs

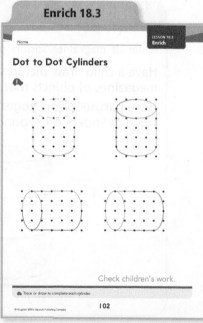

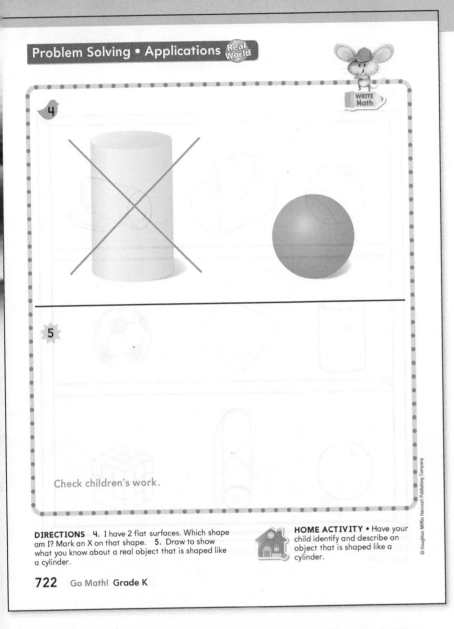

4

5

Check children's work.

DIRECTIONS 4. I have 2 flat surfaces. Which shape am I? Mark an X on that shape. 5. Draw to show what you know about a real object that is shaped like a cylinder.

HOME ACTIVITY • Have your child identify and describe an object that is shaped like a cylinder.

© Houghton Mifflin Harcourt Publishing Company

722 Go Math! Grade K

Problem Solving **Real World** Applications

(MP) **Reason abstractly and quantitatively.**

Read the riddle for **Problem 4**.

• **Which shape is the answer to the riddle?**
  cylinder

• **Mark an X on that shape.**

Have children use what they have learned about cylinders to explain why their answers are correct.

(MP) **Model with mathematics.**

Problem 5 Invite children to make suggestions about what they might draw to show what they know about a real object that is shaped like a cylinder.

5 Evaluate | Formative Assessment

I Can

Have children use hand gestures and words to answer the I Can statement.

I can identify, name, and describe cylinders by . . . knowing that a cylinder has a curved surface and two flat surfaces. Some cylinders are cans and tubes.

Exit Ticket

After children complete their drawings, ask volunteers to share their drawings and describe how they know that their objects are shaped like a cylinder.

DIFFERENTIATED INSTRUCTION • Independent Activities

Grab-and-Go!™
Version 2.0
Differentiated Centers Kit

Tabletop Flipchart

Mini-lessons for reteaching to targeted small groups

Readers

Supports key math skills and concepts in real-world situations.

Games

Reinforce math content and vocabulary

Activities

Meaningful and fun math practice

Practice and Homework

Identify, Name, and Describe Cylinders

Use the Practice and Homework pages to provide children with more practice of the concepts and skills presented in this lesson. Children master their understanding as they complete practice items.

Identify, Name, and Describe Cylinders

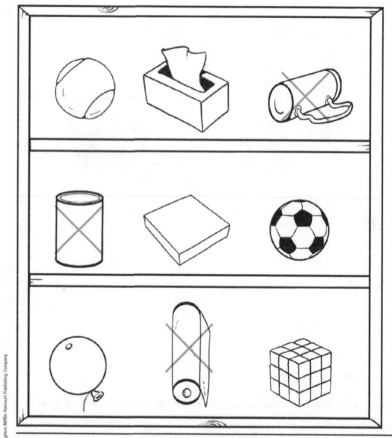

© Houghton Mifflin Harcourt Publishing Company

DIRECTIONS 1. Identify the objects that are shaped like a cylinder. Mark an X on those objects.

Chapter 18 • Lesson 3 **723**

Lesson Check

2

- -

Spiral Review

3

 **vertices**

· ·

4

  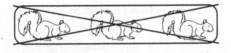

$$5 - 3 = 2$$

DIRECTIONS 2. Which shape is a cylinder? Mark an X on the shape. 3. How many vertices does the triangle have? Write the number. 4. Write the number to show how many squirrels are being taken from the set.

724 Go Math! **Grade K**

Continue to practice concepts and skills with Lesson Check. Use Spiral Review to engage children in previously taught concepts and to promote content retention.

Lesson at a Glance
Identify, Name, and Describe Cones

SNAPSHOT

Mathematical Standards
- Describe objects in the environment using names of shapes, and describe the relative positions of these objects using terms such as *above*, *below*, *beside*, *in front of*, *behind*, and *next to*.

Mathematical Practices and Processes
- Model with mathematics.
- Attend to precision.
- Reason abstractly and quantitatively.
- Look for and make use of structure.

(I Can) Objective
I can identify, name, and describe cones.

Learning Goal
Identify, name, and describe three-dimensional shapes, including cones.

Language Objective
Children find pictures of objects that can help them identify, name, and describe cones.

MATERIALS
- MathBoard
- three-dimensional shapes

ACROSS THE GRADES

Grade K
Identify two- and three-dimensional figures regardless of their size or orientation. Figures are limited to circles, triangles, rectangles, squares, spheres, cubes, cones and cylinders.

After
Identify, compare and sort two- and three-dimensional figures based on their defining attributes. Figures are limited to circles, semi-circles, triangles, rectangles, squares, trapezoids, hexagons, spheres, cubes, rectangular prisms, cones and cylinders.

ABOUT THE MATH

Teaching for Depth
A cone is a solid shape with one face and one vertex. The face does not have to be a circle, it can be any shape. The vertex does not have to be centered above the face. In this chapter, however, children use a circular cone with a circular face.

Help children see that the orientation of a shape does not define the shape. Hold a cone with the vertex up and ask children what shape it is. Repeat with the vertex down and to the side, and guide children to observe that the shape is still a cone.

For more professional learning, go online to Teacher's Corner.

DAILY ROUTINES

💻 Problem of the Day 18.4

What is the shape of a bubble? What is the shape of a can of peas? sphere; cylinder

💻 Vocabulary cone

- Interactive Student Edition
- Multilingual Glossary

Vocabulary Builder

Materials three-dimensional shapes

- Show a cone and have children describe its shape. curved with one flat surface and a point

- Review the word *curved*. Pass around the cone so children can feel the curved surface of the cone. Stress the word *flat* and have children feel the flat surface of the cone.

- Have children compare how a cone can roll along the curved surface but not on the flat one.

- Have children identify classroom objects as cones.

FOCUSING ON THE WHOLE STUDENT

Access Prior Knowledge

Hold up a sphere.

- **What is this shape?** a sphere

- **What are some objects shaped like a sphere in the classroom?**

Repeat with a cube and a cylinder.

① Engage

with the Interactive Student Edition

I Can Objective

I can identify, name, and describe cones.

Making Connections

Lead children to recall what they have learned about cylinders. Draw a circle, a triangle, a rectangle, and a square on the board. Ask children to point out straight and curved lines.

- **What are some words we can use to describe the parts of shapes?** Possible answers: sides, lines, vertices, points, curves, round

Choose or draw an item with a flat surface and one with a curved surface and ask children to tell which type of surface each has.

Learning Activity

Show a picture of an orange traffic cone. Help children to understand the properties of cones.

- **What do you know about the name of the object?** the name is the same as the shape

- **Where have you seen the object before?** in a parking lot

Explore

Listen and Draw

Materials three-dimensional shapes

 Model with mathematics.

Read the problem aloud as children listen.

Dennis has four shapes to sort. He wants to sort them into two sets: cone and not a cone. What will his sets look like?

Put out a cone, cube, cylinder, and sphere. Hold up and name the cone. Read the labels on the sorting mat.

- **Place the three-dimensional shapes on the page. Which shape is the cone?** Children should identify the cone and name it.

- **Sort the shapes on the sorting mat.**

(MP) **Look for and make use of structure.**

- **How can you describe a cone?** Accept reasonable answers.

- **What can you tell about the surfaces of a cone?** It has a flat surface, a curved surface, and a point.

- **Notice that the cone has a point and a cylinder does not.**

Have children match a picture of each shape to the shapes on the mat. Have children glue the shape pictures on the mat. Reread the problem about Dennis. Discuss what Dennis's two sets will look like.

Name _____

Identify, Name, and Describe Cones

(I Can) identify, name, and describe cones.

Listen and Draw

cone	not a cone

Check children's work.

DIRECTIONS Place three-dimensional shapes on the page. Identify and name the cone. Sort the shapes on the sorting mat. Describe the cone. Match a picture of each shape to the shapes on the sorting mat. Glue the shape pictures on the sorting mat.

Chapter 18 • Lesson 4   **725**

(ML) ## Multilingual Support

STRATEGY: Model Concepts

Children can understand the properties of three-dimensional shapes if they are modeled.

Have children watch as you roll the cone.

- **I can roll the cone, so it has a curved surface.** Have children watch as you stand the cone on its base and slide it gently across the table. **I can slide the cone, so it has a flat surface.**

- Invite children to roll and slide the cone. **Do curved surfaces roll or slide?** roll **Do flat surfaces roll or slide?** slide

Have children describe other three-dimensional shapes. Possible answers: I can roll a sphere. I cannot slide a sphere.

I

cone

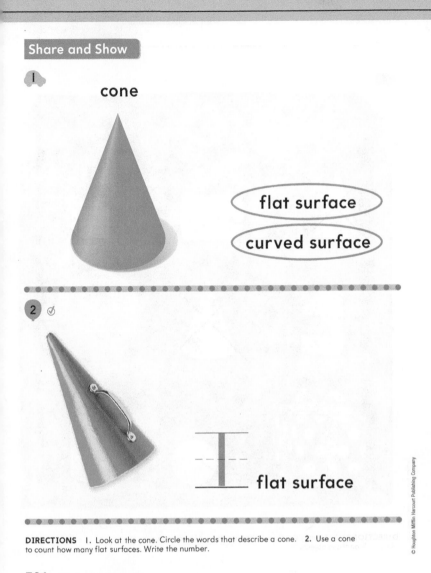

flat surface

curved surface

2 ✓

flat surface

© Houghton Mifflin Harcourt Publishing Company

DIRECTIONS 1. Look at the cone. Circle the words that describe a cone. 2. Use a cone to count how many flat surfaces. Write the number.

Ready for More
Visual Partners / Individual

Materials three-dimensional shapes, paper bags, spinners

Prepare paper bags by filling them with three-dimensional shapes. Each partner group will receive one bag, as well as one spinner. Label the spinner *Cones* on one side and *Not Cones* on the other. Children will spin the pointer and pull a shape from the bag that matches what is on the spinner.

Children will continue the activity until all the shapes are matched. Encourage children to discuss how they knew which shapes were cones.

---

3 Explain

Share and Show

(MP) **Attend to precision.**

- **Look at the red shape. What is it?** cone **How do you know?** It has a curved surface, a flat surface, and a point.
- **Which words can you use to describe the surfaces of a cone?** *flat* and *curved*

Read the words next to the cone. Instruct children to circle the words that describe a cone. *flat surface; curved surface*

- **Look at Problem 2.**

Show children a real-world cone, such as a party hat, and a geometric solid cone. Point out the surface on the bottom of the solid.

- **How can you describe the shape of the flat surface on a cone?** Possible answers: round, circle
- **What word can you use to describe the surface of a cone that is not flat?** *curved*
- **How many flat surfaces does a cone have?** 1 **Write the number.**

Use the checked problem for Quick Check.

✓ Quick Check   MTSS (RtI)

If ➤ a child misses the checked problem

Then ➤ **Differentiate Instruction** with
- Reteach 18.4
- Waggle

! Common Errors

Error Children may not be able to describe a cone.

Example In Problem 1, children choose only "curved surface."

Springboard to Learning Hold up a solid cone. Run your hand over the curved surface and the flat surface as you name them. Show children that the cone will slide on its flat surface. Have children slide a cone.

Chapter 18 • Lesson 4   726

4 Elaborate

Share and Show

Call on volunteers to name the objects going across each shelf of the bookshelf in order.

- **Which objects are shaped like a cone?** the solid cone shape, the party hat
- **How do you know?** They have a flat surface, a curved surface, and a point.
- **Mark each cone-shaped object with an X.**

Higher-Order Thinking

(MP) **Reason abstractly and quantitatively.**

Read aloud the following problem to children. Discuss strategies they can use to solve it.

- **Eric has a shape that has flat and curved surfaces. Do you know whether his shape is a cone or a cylinder? What other information do you need?** Possible answer: No, I would need to know whether it had one or two flat surfaces, or if it had a point.

Children should understand that the clues can lead to more than one shape. The shape may be a cylinder or a cone. They would need to know how many flat surfaces it has, or whether it has a point. Have children give clues about a shape while other children guess.

Math on the Spot Use this video to help children model and solve this type of problem.

Name _____

3

DIRECTIONS 3. Identify the objects that are shaped like a cone. Mark an X on those objects.

Chapter 18 • Lesson 4   **727**

Meeting Individual Needs

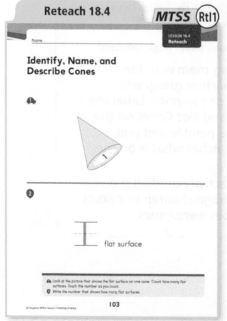

Reteach 18.4

Identify, Name, and Describe Cones

MTSS Rtl1

Enrich 18.4

Where Are the Cones?

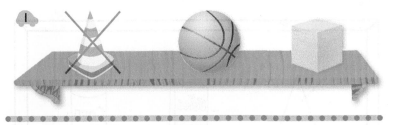

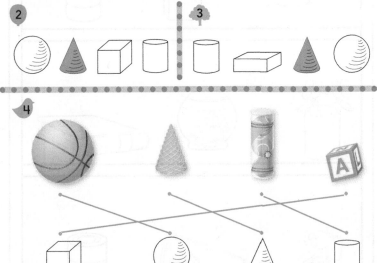

DIRECTIONS 1. Mark an X on the object that is shaped like a cone. 2. Color the cone. 3. Color the shape that has 1 flat surface and a curved surface. 4. Draw lines to match the objects to their shapes.

HOME ACTIVITY • Have your child identify and describe an object in your home that is shaped like a cone.

728 Go Math! Grade K

DIFFERENTIATED INSTRUCTION • Independent Activities

Problem Solving Applications

(MP) **Look for and make use of structure.**

Problem 1 Children identify a real-world object in the shape of a cone.

Problem 2 Children identify the cone from a group of three-dimensional figures.

Problem 3 Children identify a cone from its description.

(MP) **Model with mathematics.**

Problem 4 Children match real-world objects to three-dimensional shapes.

⑤ Evaluate | Formative Assessment

I Can

Have children find pictures of cones to answer the I Can statement.

I can identify, name, and describe cones by . . .

finding the shape that has a curved surface, a flat surface, and a point. Some examples of cones are party hats or ice cream cones.

Exit Ticket

Have students draw pictures of real-life objects that are shaped like cones. Students can share their drawings and explain how they know the object they drew is a cone.

Practice and Homework

Identify, Name, and Describe Cones

Use the Practice and Homework pages to provide children with more practice of the concepts and skills presented in this lesson. Children master their understanding as they complete practice items.

Identify, Name, and Describe Cones

© Houghton Mifflin Harcourt Publishing Company

DIRECTIONS 1. Identify the objects that are shaped like a cone. Mark an X on those objects.

Chapter 18 • Lesson 4   **729**

Lesson Check

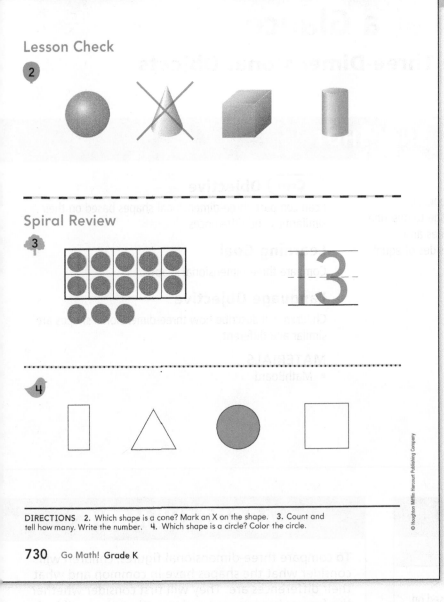

Spiral Review

DIRECTIONS 2. Which shape is a cone? Mark an X on the shape. 3. Count and tell how many. Write the number. 4. Which shape is a circle? Color the circle.

Lesson at a Glance
Compare Three-Dimensional Objects

SNAPSHOT

Mathematical Standards

● Analyze and compare two- and three-dimensional shapes, in different sizes and orientations, using informal language to describe their similarities, differences, parts (e.g., number of sides and vertices/"corners") and other attributes (e.g., having sides of equal length).

Mathematical Practices and Processes.

● Attend to precision.
● Look for and make use of structure.
● Express regularity in repeated reasoning.
● Model with mathematics.

(I Can) Objective

I can compare three-dimensional shapes based on their similarities and differences.

Learning Goal

Compare three-dimensional shapes.

Language Objective

Children will describe how three-dimensional shapes are similar and different.

MATERIALS

• MathBoard

ACROSS THE GRADES

Grade K

Compare three-dimensional figures based on their similarities, differences and positions. Sort three-dimensional figures based on their similarities and differences. Figures are limited to spheres, cubes, cones and cylinders.

After

Identify, compare and sort two- and three-dimensional figures based on their defining attributes. Figures are limited to circles, semi-circles, triangles, rectangles, squares, trapezoids, hexagons, spheres, cubes, rectangular prisms, cones and cylinders.

ABOUT THE MATH

To compare three-dimensional figures, children will consider what the shapes have in common and what their differences are. They will first consider whether the figures have curved surfaces. Then they will look at the number and kind of the flat surfaces that the shapes have. Another attribute to take into account would be whether a figure has a point. In this lesson, children will base their comparisons on the surfaces of the three-dimensional figures. If children struggle to see the shapes of the surfaces, provide a model and have them trace it onto paper. The resulting two-dimensional figure is the shape of the face.

For more professional learning go online to Teacher's Corner.

Problem of the Day 18.5

Name an object that has the following shape.

cone   cube

cylinder   sphere

Check children's answers.

 Vocabulary

• Interactive Student Edition
• Multilingual Glossary

Fluency Builder

Add Within 5

Materials addition fact cards (within 5), connecting cubes

Show the addition fact card for $4 + 1 = \square$.

• **You can use two colors of cubes to model this addition equation. Make a cube train with four blue cubes and one red cube.**

• **How many cubes do you have in all?** 5 **What number goes in the box?** 5

Distribute a fact card to each pair. Have them make two-color models to show the addition equation. Then have them tell how many in all. Notice which children are able to count forward to find the number in all.

FOCUSING ON THE WHOLE STUDENT

Access Prior Knowledge

• Have a group conversation about what hay bales are used for. Have children describe where they have seen hay bales used before.

• Working as a class, make a list of 10 things you might see around a barn or a zoo.

 Social & Emotional Learning

Self-Management Discuss with children what it means to stay on task. *When I am focused on a task, I am thinking about it and not about anything else. If my phone rings and I look at it, I am no longer on task because I am paying attention to my phone. How do you know when you are staying on task? What do you do when you are distracted to get back on task? And when you are on task, how do you know when your work is complete?*

---

① Engage

with the Interactive Student Edition

I Can Objective

I can compare three-dimensional shapes based on their similarities and differences.

Making Connections

Ask children to tell you what they know about squares and cubes.

Show children a number cube.

• **What is the name of this shape?** cube

• **What are some other things that come in the shape of a cube?** Answers will vary.

• **What shape is a globe?** sphere

Learning Activity

Show children a picture of a cubical hay bale. Direct children toward identifying the faces of a cube as squares.

• **Is the face of the hay bale round?** no

• **How many lines does the face of the hay bale have?** 4

• **How many corners does the face of the hay bale have?** 4

> **! Common Errors**
>
> **Error** In Problem 2, children color the cube rather than the cone.
>
> **Springboard to Learning** Have children roll a cone on the desk. Have them point to the curved surface and feel the curve with their fingers. Remind children that a cone rolls because it has a curved surface. Ask children to point to the flat surface. Have them trace the flat surface with the tip of their fingers and tell you what shape it is. circle Have children hold a cube. Can you roll the cube? no Have children place the cube on one of its flat surfaces on the desk. Remind children that a cube has no curved surfaces and its flat surfaces are square.

② Explore

Unlock the Problem

Materials three-dimensional shapes

Read aloud this problem as children listen.

Kelly has a cone, a cube and a cylinder. Each three-dimensional shape has a flat surface shaped like a circle or a square. Which of Kelly's shapes has a face that is a circle? Which of Kelly's shapes has a flat surface that is shaped like a square?

Have children point to and name each three-dimensional shape on the page.

(MP) **Look for and make use of structure.**

- **Use your three-dimensional solids. Look at the cone. Can a cone roll?** yes **How do you know?** The outside is a curved surface.

- **Can you roll a cone when its point is up?** no **Why not?** Because it sits on a flat surface.

Have children point to the flat surface on the cone on the page. Point out the dashed line around the flat surface.

- **Trace the dashed line of the cone. What shape is the flat surface on a cone?** a circle **Draw a line from the cone and connect it to a circle on the other side of the page.**

Discuss with children the shape of the flat surfaces of the cube and the cylinder. If necessary, help children locate the dashed lines on the cube and cylinder. Have them trace the dashed lines on the shapes and draw a line matching the three-dimensional shape to the two-dimensional shape.

- **Which of Kelly's shapes have a flat surface that is a circle?** the cone and the cylinder **Which of Kelly's shapes has a flat surface that is a square?** the cube

---

Name _____

Compare Three-Dimensional Objects

(I Can) compare three-dimensional shapes based on their similarities and differences.

 UNLOCK the Problem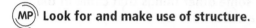

DIRECTIONS Trace the dashed part of each three-dimensional shape. Draw lines to match the flat surfaces of the three-dimensional shapes to the two-dimensional shapes.

Chapter 18 • Lesson 5 **731**

(ML) ## Multilingual Support

STRATEGY: Model Concepts

Materials objects that are cubes, cylinders, and cones; paper bags

- Gather objects such as pencils, number cubes, board game pieces, or blocks. Distribute them among the paper bags.

- Give each group a paper bag with objects. Have children feel an object in the bag without looking and name a three-dimensional shape. Accept all reasonable answers.

- Have children in the group name the shape of the flat surface of the object. Accept all reasonable answers.

I

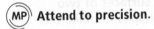

2 ☑

3 ☑

DIRECTIONS 1. Which three-dimensional shape has a flat surface shaped like a circle? Color the shape. 2. Which three-dimensional shape does not have a flat surface shaped like a square? Color the shape. 3. Which three-dimensional shape has a flat surface shaped like a square? Color the shape.

732 Go Math! Grade K

③ Explain

Try Another Problem

Guide children to Problem 1. Have them analyze the given information.

- **What shapes do you see?** a cube and a cylinder
- **Which one of these shapes has a flat surface that is shaped like a circle?** the cylinder **Trace along the edge of the flat surface with your finger.**
- **Color the cylinder.**

Explain that on a cylinder there are two flat surfaces, one at the top and one on the bottom.

Repeat in a similar way for Problem 2.

- **Look at Problem 3. What shapes do you see?** a cone and a cube
- **Which one of these shapes has a flat surface that is shaped like a square?** the cube

(MP) **Attend to precision.**

Have children justify their solution.

- **How do you know your answer is correct?** Possible answer: When I trace along the edge of a flat surface of the cube, it makes a square.
- **Color the cube.**

Use the checked problems for Quick Check.

☑ **Quick Check** **MTSS** (RtI)

If → a child misses the checked problems

Then → **Differentiate Instruction** with
- Reteach 18.5
- Waggle

Ready for More 🕐 Bodily / Kinesthetic Whole Class

Materials objects that are cubes, cylinders, and cones; paper bags

- Have children walk around the classroom or outside.
- Point out some three-dimensional objects, and ask children to describe them.
- Tell children to imagine tracing the objects onto paper. What shapes would they see?

Share and Show

 Look for and make use of structure.

Focus children's attention on Problem 4.

- **What object is first in Problem 4?** a block
  What three-dimensional shape is the block shaped like? a cube
- **What shape is the flat surface on a cube?** a square **Mark an X in the box under the square.**

Continue in this same way for Problems 5 through 8. Once finished, children can look around the classroom and find objects that are three-dimensional. Have children tell a partner what a flat surface of the three-dimensional object is shaped like.

Higher-Order Thinking

 Model with mathematics.

- Matt traced the flat surfaces of two three-dimensional shapes to make this picture.

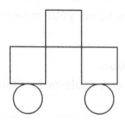

- **Which shapes could Matt have traced?** cube, cylinder, cone

Help children understand that Matt must have traced a cube to make the square shapes, but that he could have used either a cone or a cylinder to make the circle shape.

Math on the Spot Use this video to help children model and solve this type of problem.

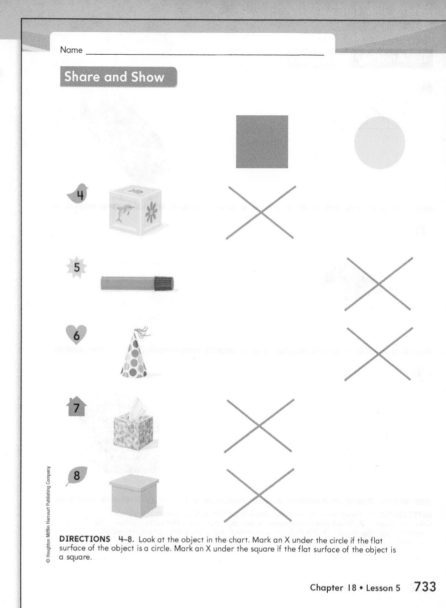

Name _____

Share and Show

DIRECTIONS 4–8. Look at the object in the chart. Mark an X under the circle if the flat surface of the object is a circle. Mark an X under the square if the flat surface of the object is a square.

Meeting Individual Needs

Reteach 18.5

MTSS (RtI1)

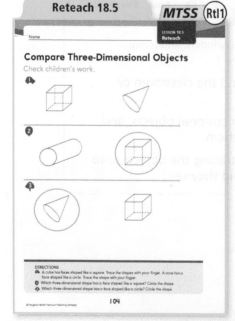

Name _____

LESSON 18.5
Reteach

Compare Three-Dimensional Objects

Check children's work.

DIRECTIONS A cube has faces shaped like a square. Trace the shapes with your finger. A cone has a face shaped like a circle. Trace the shape with your finger. ① Which three-dimensional shape has a face shaped like a square? Circle the shape. ② Which three-dimensional shape has a face shaped like a circle? Circle the shape.

104

Enrich 18.5

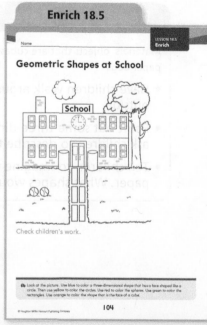

Name _____

LESSON 18.5
Enrich

Geometric Shapes at School

Check children's work.

① Look at the picture. Use blue to color a three-dimensional shape that has a face shaped like a circle. Then use yellow to color the circles. Use red to color the spheres. Use green to color the rectangles. Use orange to color the shape that is the face of a cube.

104

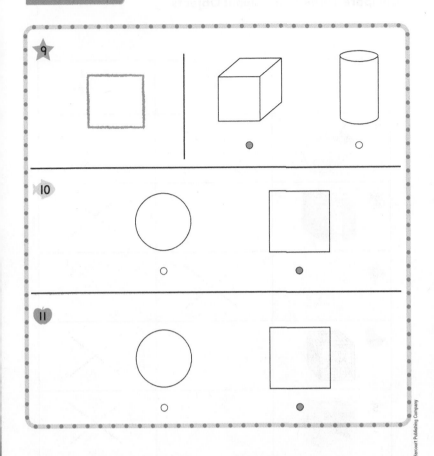

DIRECTIONS Choose the correct answer.
9. Saya traced a block to make a square. Which shape did she use? 10. Which shape is not the flat surface on a cone? 11. Which shape is the flat surface on a cube?

HOME ACTIVITY • Have your child identify a household object that is shaped like a three-dimensional shape. Have your child tell you what shape the flat surface of the object is.

734 Go Math! Grade K

DIFFERENTIATED INSTRUCTION • Independent Activities

Grab and Go!™
Version 2.0
Differentiated Centers Kit

Tabletop Flipchart

Mini-lessons for reteaching to targeted small groups

Readers

Supports key math skills and concepts in real-world situations.

Games

Reinforce math content and vocabulary

Activities

Meaningful and fun math practice

---

④ Elaborate

On Your Own

(MP) **Express regularity in repeated reasoning.**

Problem 9 Children must visualize the two-dimensional shape that results from tracing a three-dimensional figure.

Problems 10 and 11 Read the problems aloud to children. Remind them to fill in the bubble of the correct answer.

⑤ Evaluate | Formative Assessment

I Can

Have children work with a partner to describe how shapes are alike and different to demonstrate the skill for the I Can statement.

I can compare three-dimensional shapes based on their similarities and differences by . . . seeing which ones have curved or flat surfaces. The flat surfaces are shaped like two-dimensional shapes. A cylinder and cone have flat surfaces that are shaped like circles. A cube has flat surfaces that are shaped like squares.

Exit Ticket

Draw to show the difference between flat and curve surfaces.

Compare Three-Dimensional Objects

Use the Practice and Homework pages to provide children with more practice of the concepts and skills presented in this lesson. Children master their understanding as they complete practice items.

Compare Three-Dimensional Objects

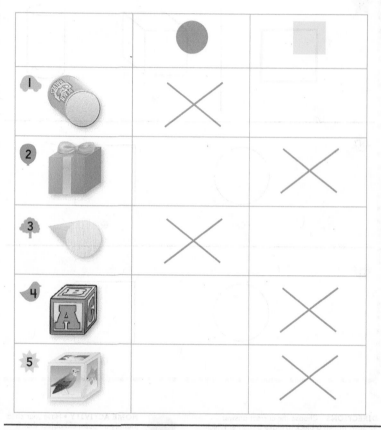

© Houghton Mifflin Harcourt Publishing Company

DIRECTIONS 1–5. Look at the object in the chart. Mark an X under the circle if the flat surface of the object is a circle. Mark an X under the square if the flat surface of the object is a square.

Chapter 18 • Lesson 5   **735**

Lesson Check

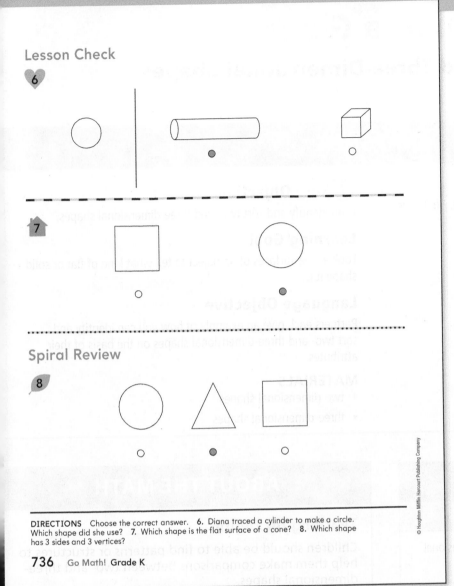

6

7

Spiral Review

8

© Houghton Mifflin Harcourt Publishing Company

DIRECTIONS Choose the correct answer. **6.** Diana traced a cylinder to make a circle. Which shape did she use? **7.** Which shape is the flat surface of a cone? **8.** Which shape has 3 sides and 3 vertices?

Continue to practice concepts and skills with Lesson Check. Use Spiral Review to engage children in previously taught concepts and to promote content retention.

Lesson at a Glance
Two- and Three-Dimensional Shapes

SNAPSHOT

Mathematical Standards
- Identify shapes as two-dimensional (lying in a plane, "flat") or three-dimensional ("solid").

Mathematical Processes and Practices
- Model with mathematics.
- Look for and make use of structure.
- Express regularity in repeated reasoning.
- Construct arguments and critique reasoning of others.
- Attend to precision.

(I Can) Objective
I can identify and sort two- and three-dimensional shapes.

Learning Goal
Look at the surfaces of an object to tell what kind of flat or solid shape it is.

Language Objective
Partners each give an example of how you can identify and sort two- and three-dimensional shapes on the basis of their attributes.

MATERIALS
- two-dimensional shapes
- three-dimensional shapes

ACROSS THE GRADES

Grade K
Identify shapes as two-dimensional ("flat") or three-dimensional ("solid").

After
Distinguish between defining attributes versus non-defining attributes.

ABOUT THE MATH

Teaching for Depth
Children should be able to find patterns or structures to help them make comparisons between two- and three-dimensional shapes.

In this chapter, children learn that three-dimensional, or solid, shapes have flat surfaces or curved surfaces, or both. A cube, for example, has six flat surfaces. Children learn that some solids, such as a sphere, have no flat surfaces at all.

As they analyze and compare two- and three-dimensional objects, children will start to see the relationship between flat and solid shapes, and will recognize that the faces of solid shapes look like the flat shapes.

For more professional learning, go online to Teacher's Corner.

DAILY ROUTINES

🖥 Problem of the Day 18.6

Tell the number that comes before when you count. Then tell the number that comes after.

15   21   35

14, 16; 20, 22; 34, 36

🖥 Vocabulary flat, solid

- Interactive Student Edition
- Multilingual Glossary

Fluency Builder

Three-Dimensional Shapes

Materials three-dimensional shapes

Explain to children that you will say the name of a three-dimensional shape, such as *cube*. Then you will show a three-dimensional shape. Children should give a thumbs-up if the shape is a cube, or a thumbs-down if the shape is any other three-dimensional shape. Repeat for other shapes.

FOCUSING ON THE WHOLE STUDENT

Access Prior Knowledge

Choose one or more of the following activities.

- Put on a cone-shaped party hat and say: **I am a cone.** Then ask: **Can I slide? Can I roll? Do I have a flat side? Do I have a point?**
- Give sets of partners a command such as stack, slide, or roll. Have them experiment to find out if they can complete the command with cones.

I Can Objective

I can identify and sort two- and three-dimensional shapes.

Making Connections

Ask children to tell what they know about the attributes of cones.

- **Hold up a cylinder and a cone. What is the same about these two shapes?** They can both roll. Both have one or more flat surfaces. **What is different about these two shapes?** Possible answer: The cone has a point.

- **Can the cone stack on top of the cylinder? Explain.** Yes. The cone has a flat side, so it can stack on the cylinder's flat side. **Can the cylinder stack on top of the cone? Explain.** No. The cone has a point, so nothing can stack on top of it.

Learning Activity

Guide children to focus more closely on sorting two-dimensional and three-dimensional shapes.

- Hold up a cone, with its flat side facing out. **What shape does the flat side of the cone look like?** a circle

- Hold up the cone and a circle. **What is different about the cone and the circle?** Possible answer: The cone is a three-dimensional shape, and the circle is a two-dimensional shape; The cone can roll, but the circle can't.

② Explore

Unlock the Problem

Materials two-dimensional shapes, three-dimensional shapes

Read aloud this problem as children listen.

Olivia has some shapes to sort. She wants to sort them into two sets: two-dimensional shapes and three-dimensional shapes. What shapes should Olivia put in each set?

 Model with mathematics.

Put out flat shapes: circle, triangle, rectangle, hexagon, square. Also put out solid figures: sphere, cone, cube, cylinder. Read the labels on the sorting mat. Introduce the terms *flat* and *solid*. Explain that two-dimensional shapes are *flat* and three-dimensional shapes are *solid*. Hold up a circle.

- **What shape is this?** a circle **How do you know?** It is round and curved.
- **Is a circle flat or solid?** flat
- **Point to the part of your mat where you would put this shape. Why would you put it there?** A circle is a flat shape.

Repeat the questioning with a cylinder.

Name _____

Two- and Three-Dimensional Shapes

(I Can) identify and sort two- and three-dimensional shapes.

▦ UNLOCK the Problem

two-dimensional shapes	three-dimensional shapes

Check children's work.

DIRECTIONS Place shapes on the page. Sort the shapes on the sorting mat into sets of two-dimensional and three-dimensional shapes. Match a picture of each shape to a shape on the sorting mat. Glue the pictures onto the sorting mat.

Chapter 18 • Lesson 6 **737**

 ## Multilingual Support

STRATEGY: Restate

Children can understand geometric concepts by using familiar terms to describe them.

- Show children the two-dimensional shapes. **These are two-dimensional shapes. How are the shapes the same?** Each shape is one flat surface. Explain that these shapes are also called flat shapes.
- Show children the three-dimensional shapes. **These are three-dimensional shapes. How are the shapes the same?** The shapes are not flat and they have flat or curved surfaces. Explain that these shapes are also called solid shapes.

I.

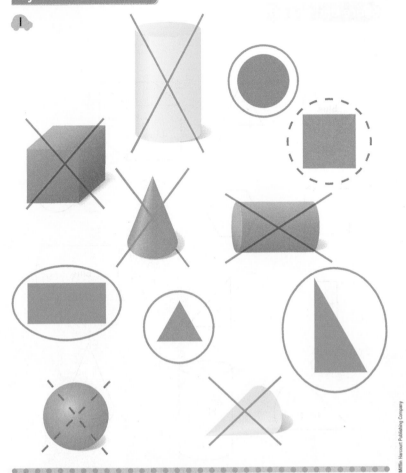

DIRECTIONS 1. Identify the two-dimensional, or flat, shapes. Trace a loop around the square. Loop the other flat shapes. Identify the three-dimensional, or solid, shapes. Trace an X on the sphere. Mark an X on the other solid shapes.

Ready for More

 Kinesthetic
Individual / Partner

Materials three-dimensional shapes

Show children a cylinder. **What two-dimensional shapes do you see on this three-dimensional shape?** circles

Have children work in pairs to make a chart showing the two-dimensional shape(s) found on each three-dimensional shape. Label the columns "three-dimensional shapes" and "two-dimensional shapes." Have children paste in the first column a picture of a three-dimensional shape. In the second column, have them draw or trace all two-dimensional shapes that can be found on the three-dimensional shape.

---

③ Explain

Try Another Problem

Draw attention to the pictures of two-dimensional and three-dimensional shapes.

- **Find the shape with the gray circle around it. Describe it.** Possible answers: It is a square. It is flat. It is two-dimensional.

Trace the circle around the square.

- **What other two-dimensional or flat shapes are on the page?** circle, triangle, rectangle
- **Circle the two-dimensional or flat shapes.**
- **Find the shape with the gray X on it. Describe it.** Possible answers: It is a sphere. It is solid. It is three-dimensional. **Trace the X on the sphere.**
- **What other three-dimensional, or solid, shapes are on the page?** cube, cylinder, cone
- **Cross out the three-dimensional, or solid, shapes.**

(MP) **Look for and make use of structure.**

Discuss with children how they decided whether each shape was a two-dimensional (flat) figure or a three-dimensional (solid) figure.

⚠ Common Errors

Error Children may confuse flat shapes with solid shapes.

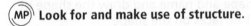

Example In Problem 1, children confuse the sphere with a circle.

Springboard to Learning Remind children that a sphere has curved surfaces; it is not flat. Explain that although a circle is round like a sphere, it is flat. Provide a sphere and a circle for children to explore.

Share and Show

Have children identify the two-dimensional, or flat, shapes and the three-dimensional, or solid, shapes. Ask children to color the flat shapes red and the solid shapes blue.

Use the checked problem for Quick Check.

 Quick Check *MTSS* (RtI)

If ➤ a child misses the checked problem

Then ➤ Differentiate Instruction with
- Reteach 18.6
- Waggle

Higher-Order Thinking

Have children pick up a solid shape that has only flat surfaces. Have children name the solid shape and name and draw the shape of the flat surfaces on the shape. cube, squares

(MP) **Express regularity in repeated reasoning.**

Display flat and solid shapes. Have children describe their surfaces and tell whether each shape is two-dimensional or three-dimensional.

Math on the Spot Use this video to help children model and solve this type of problem.

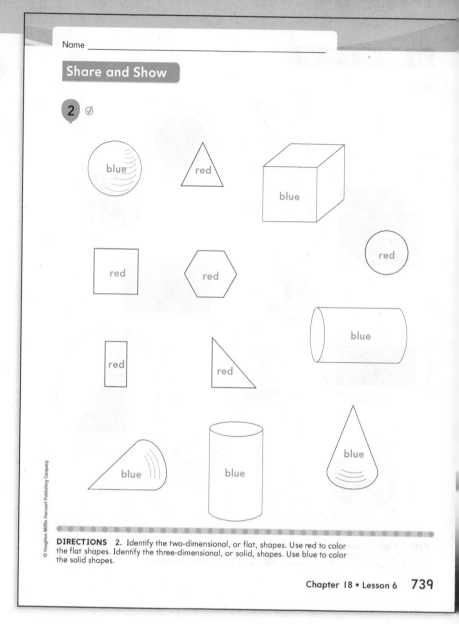

Name _____

Share and Show

2 ✓

DIRECTIONS 2. Identify the two-dimensional, or flat, shapes. Use red to color the flat shapes. Identify the three-dimensional, or solid, shapes. Use blue to color the solid shapes.

Chapter 18 • Lesson 6   **739**

Meeting Individual Needs

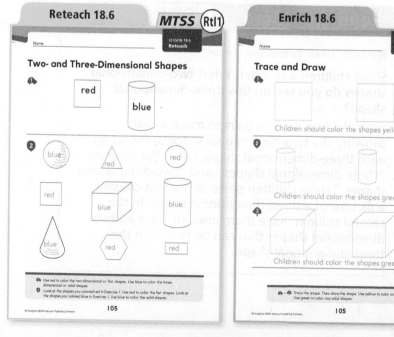

3

Check children's work.

4

Check children's work.

DIRECTIONS 3. Use classroom materials to model a real object that has a flat shape. Draw the object and name the shape. **4.** Draw a real object that has a solid shape. Name the shape.

HOME ACTIVITY • Have your child identify a household object that is shaped like a three-dimensional shape. Have your child name the three-dimensional shape.

740 Go Math! Grade K

DIFFERENTIATED INSTRUCTION • Independent Activities

Grab-and-Go!™
Version 2.0
Differentiated Centers Kit

Tabletop Flipchart
Mini-lessons for reteaching to targeted small groups

Readers
Supports key math skills and concepts in real-world situations

Games
Reinforce math content and vocabulary

Activities
Meaningful and fun math practice

---

④ Elaborate

On Your Own

Read the directions for **Problem 3**. Before children work with classroom materials to model two-dimensional figures, review that a flat shape has one flat surface.

MP Attend to precision.

Have children explain what their drawings show about flat shapes. Encourage children to use math words, such as the names of two-dimensional shapes, in their explanations.

MP Construct arguments and critique reasoning of others.

For **Problem 4**, review that a solid shape may have one curved surface, several flat surfaces, or both flat and curved surfaces.

Have children draw a real object that shows a solid shape. Ask them to explain how they know the drawing shows a solid shape.

⑤ Evaluate | Formative Assessment

I Can

Have children work in pairs. Ask partners to give examples of how to demonstrate the skill for the I Can statement.

I can identify and sort two- and three-dimensional shapes by . . . looking at the shapes to find whether they are flat or solid shapes. I can look at the surfaces to tell what kinds of flat or solid shapes they are.

Exit Ticket

Invite partners to show and share their drawings and to tell what they know about flat and solid shapes. Remind them to use math words, such as the names of three-dimensional shapes, when they talk about their drawings.

Practice and Homework

Two- and Three-Dimensional Shapes

Use the Practice and Homework pages to provide children with more practice of the concepts and skills presented in this lesson. Children master their understanding as they complete practice items.

Name ______________________

LESSON 18.6
Practice and Homework

Two- and Three-Dimensional Shapes

1

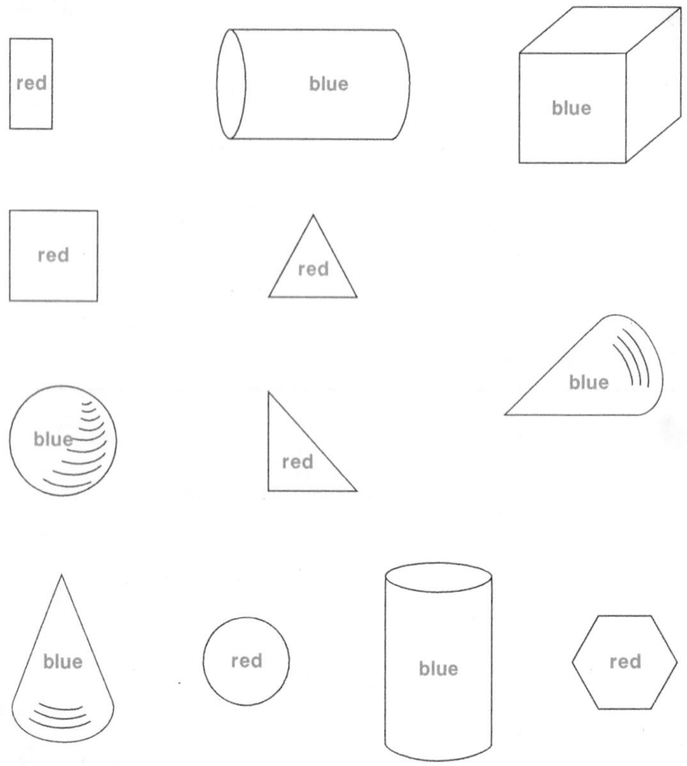

red
blue
blue
red
red
blue
blue
red
blue
red
blue
red

DIRECTIONS 1. Identify the two-dimensional, or flat, shapes. Use red to color the flat shapes. Identify the three-dimensional, or solid, shapes. Use blue to color the solid shapes.

Lesson Check

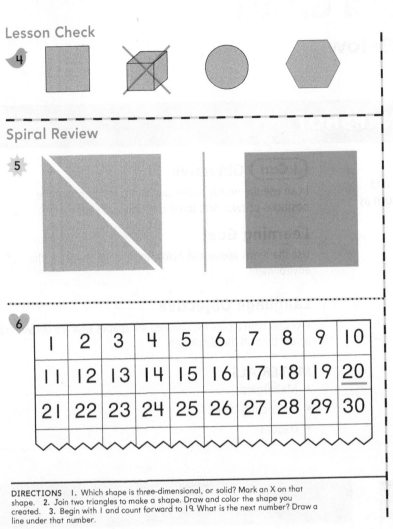

Spiral Review

1	2	3	4	5	6	7	8	9	10
11	12	13	14	15	16	17	18	19	20
21	22	23	24	25	26	27	28	29	30

DIRECTIONS 1. Which shape is three-dimensional, or solid? Mark an X on that shape. 2. Join two triangles to make a shape. Draw and color the shape you created. 3. Begin with 1 and count forward to 19. What is the next number? Draw a line under that number.

© Houghton Mifflin Harcourt Publishing Company

742 Go Math! Grade K

Lesson at a Glance
Above and Below

Mathematical Standards

- Describe objects in the environment using names of shapes, and describe the relative positions of these objects using terms such as *above*, *below*, *beside*, *in front of*, *behind*, and *next to*.

Mathematical Practices and Processes

- Model with mathematics.
- Attend to precision.
- Construct arguments and critique reasoning of others.

(I Can) Objective

I can use the words *above* and *below* to compare the positions of two- and three-dimensional shapes.

Learning Goal

Use the terms *above* and *below* to describe shapes in the environment.

Language Objective

Working with a partner, children list shapes that are above and below them in the classroom.

MATERIALS

- MathBoard
- connecting cubes
- crayons

ACROSS THE GRADES

Grade K

Compare three-dimensional figures based on their similarities, differences and positions. Sort three-dimensional figures based on their similarities and differences. Figures are limited to spheres, cubes, cones and cylinders.

After

Identify, compare and sort two- and three-dimensional figures based on their defining attributes. Figures are limited to circles, semi-circles, triangles, rectangles, squares, trapezoids, hexagons, spheres, cubes, rectangular prisms, cones and cylinders.

ABOUT THE MATH

Why Teach This?

In the next few lessons, children will use positional words to describe the placement of real-world shapes. Understanding and using positional words is an important part of developing children's spatial sense. Knowledge of positional words is needed for clear, precise communication with others.

People use positional or location words to tell where they are as they navigate the world. Following and giving directions require the use of positional words.

Besides the everyday usefulness of knowing positional words, children will later use them in mathematics as they study data, work with distance and direction, and learn about coordinate graphing.

For more professional learning go online to Teacher's Corner.

🖥 Problem of the Day 18.7

Count to 20. Name some numbers that are less than 20. Name some numbers that are greater than 20. Check children's answers.

Have children tell what they know about 20. Possible answers: 20 counters fill two ten frames. 20 is 2 tens. 20 is 18 and 2 more. 20 is less than 100.

🖥 Vocabulary above, below

- Interactive Student Edition
- Multilingual Glossary

Vocabulary Builder

Materials connecting cubes, vocabulary cards for *above*, *below*

Make a cube tower with red and blue cubes. Hold it vertically, with the red cubes on top.

- **Words such as *above* and *below* tell us where things are. You can say that the red cubes are above or over the blue cubes. How can you tell where the blue cubes are?** They are below, beneath, or under the red cubes.

Help children read the vocabulary cards and post them on the word wall.

FOCUSING ON THE WHOLE STUDENT

Access Prior Knowledge

Construct a box with an opening at one end to allow children to reach inside and identify a two- or three-dimensional shape by touch. Place several objects of different shapes into the box and see if children can identify the shapes.

Culturally Responsive Education

The relationships you build with the children in your class are instrumental to their success. It is important to show children that you have genuine care for their academic and overall well-being, particularly in the case of neurodiverse, culturally or linguistically diverse, and differently-abled children. When children are in a safe, affirming learning enviroment, they are better able to thrive socially, emotionally, and academically.

① Engage

with the Interactive Student Edition

I Can Objective

I can use the words *above* and *below* to compare the positions of two- and three-dimensional shapes.

Making Connections

Ask children to tell what they know about modeling two- and three-dimensional shapes. Display clay and four straw pieces.

- **How can you build a square using these materials?** You can stick straws together with clay to make a square.

- **How do I know where the corners are?** The corners are where the clay and straws meet.

- **Is my square two-dimensional or three-dimensional? Explain.** It is two-dimensional; it is flat.

- **Now, I want to build a cube. Can I use my square as one of the sides? Tell why.** Yes. A cube has squares for sides.

Learning Activity

Guide children to begin describing shapes by their position in relation to other things. Hold the shape model above your head.

- **Is this shape above my head?** yes

- **How do you know?** Possible answer: It is over your head. It is higher than your head.

② Explore

Listen and Draw

Materials connecting cubes, three-dimensional shapes

Read aloud this problem as children listen.

Monique sits in a chair. She holds a cube above her shoulders. Then she holds a cube below her knees. How can you show how Monique holds the cube?

(MP) **Model with mathematics.**

Give each child a connecting cube and reread the problem as children act it out. Ask them to describe the meaning of *above* and *below* as it relates to the problem. Possible answers: Above is when I put the cube higher. Below is when I put the cube lower.

Discuss the real-world three-dimensional shapes found in the picture.

- **Look at the objects below the shelf. Name the objects.** pencil holder, funnel, ball, pink box
- **What object below the shelf is shaped like a cylinder?** pencil holder **Trace the circle around the object.**
- **Look at the objects above the cabinet. Name them.** can with brushes, ball of yarn, green box
- **What object above the cabinet is shaped like a sphere?** ball of yarn **Trace the X on the object.**

(MP) **Construct arguments and critique reasoning of others.**

Distribute three-dimensional shapes to children. Give them directions such as "stack the cone above the cube" or "stack the cylinder below the cube."

Have children explain how they know they followed each direction correctly. Possible answer: I know I stacked the cylinder below the cube because the cylinder is lower than the cube.

Name _____

Above and Below

(I Can) use the words *above* and *below* to compare the positions of two- and three-dimensional shapes.

Listen and Draw

Check children's work.

DIRECTIONS Trace the circle around the object shaped like a cylinder that is below the shelf. Trace the X on the object shaped like a sphere that is above the cabinet.

© Houghton Mifflin Harcourt Publishing Company

 Multilingual Support

STRATEGY: Illustrate Understanding

Children can demonstrate their understanding of the terms *above* and *below* by drawing rather than by using language.

Have children fold a piece of paper in half and then open it. Give children the following instructions:

- **Draw a square above the fold.**
- **Draw a circle below the fold.**
- **Draw a triangle below the circle.**
- **Draw a star above the square.**

Then have children describe where all the shapes are.

I

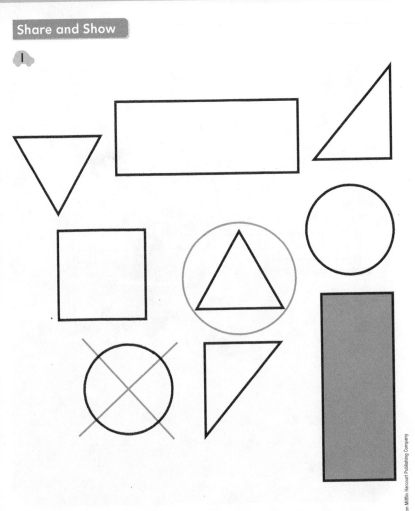

DIRECTIONS I. Mark an X on the circle that is below a square. Circle the triangle that is above another triangle. Color the rectangle that is below a circle.

744 Go Math! Grade K

3 Explain

Share and Show

Materials crayons

Discuss the page with children and invite them to identify each shape that they see.

As you read each sentence of the directions, pause to allow time for children to find the shape.

- **Mark an X on the circle that is below a square.**

(MP) **Attend to precision.**

- **Circle the triangle that is above another triangle. How do you know that the triangle is above another triangle?** It is higher than the other triangle.

- **Color the rectangle that is below a circle. What do you know about the location of the circle?** It is above the rectangle.

⚠️ **Common Errors**

Error Children may incorrectly identify an object as being above or below.

Example In Problem 1, children circle the triangle that is below, rather than above, the other triangle.

Springboard to Learning Hold a classroom object, such as a book, below a chair. Say *below*. Have children repeat the word. Hold the book above the chair. Say *above*. Have children repeat.

Ready for More 🕐 Auditory Small Group

Have children play a version of "Simon Says" using two-step directions.

- **Simon says hold your hands above your waist and below your head.**
- **Simon says hold your hands below your knees and above your ankles.**

Have children continue to play "Simon Says" using directions that include the words *above* and *below*.

A variation of this activity is to have children move objects as directed by Simon.

- **Simon says hold the ball below your neck and above your knees.**
- **Simon says hold the ball above your head and below the ceiling.**

④ Elaborate

Share and Show

Discuss the picture in Problem 2. Have children identify the objects in the picture.

Read each direction and pause to allow time for children to locate the objects.

- **Circle the ball that is above the net.** Children circle the volleyball above the net.

- **Mark an X on the box that is directly below the net.** Children mark an X on the box below the volleyball net.

Use the checked problem for Quick Check.

✓ **Quick Check** **MTSS** **RtI**

If →	a child misses the checked problem
Then →	Differentiate Instruction with • Reteach 18.7 • Waggle

MP **Attend to precision.**

Have children look at the picture in Problem 2. Have them find the cube-shaped objects and describe where the shapes are using the words *above* and *below*. Possible answer: One is on a post above the net; one is below the net.

- **Draw an object shaped like a sphere above an object shaped like a cube.** Check children's work.

Have children describe the positions of other objects in the picture using the terms *above* and *below*.

Math on the Spot Use this video to help children model and solve this type of problem.

Name _____

② ✓

© Houghton Mifflin Harcourt Publishing Company

DIRECTIONS 2. Circle the object shaped like a sphere above the net. Mark an X on the object shaped like a cube directly below the net.

Chapter 18 • Lesson 7 **745**

Meeting Individual Needs

Reteach 18.7 **MTSS** **RtI**

Name _____

LESSON 18.7
Reteach

Above and Below

Trace the circle around the object that is shaped like a sphere above the bench. Trace the X on the object that is shaped like a cube below the bench.

© Houghton Mifflin Harcourt Publishing Company   106

Enrich 18.7

Name _____

LESSON 18.7
Enrich

Above and Below Shapes

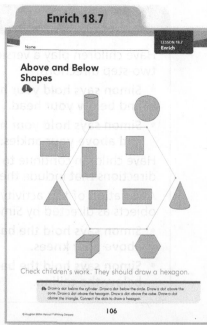

Check children's work. They should draw a hexagon.

Draw a dot below the cylinder. Draw a dot below the circle. Draw a dot above the hexagon. Draw a dot above the cube. Draw a dot above the triangle. Connect the dots to draw a hexagon.

© Houghton Mifflin Harcourt Publishing Company   106

3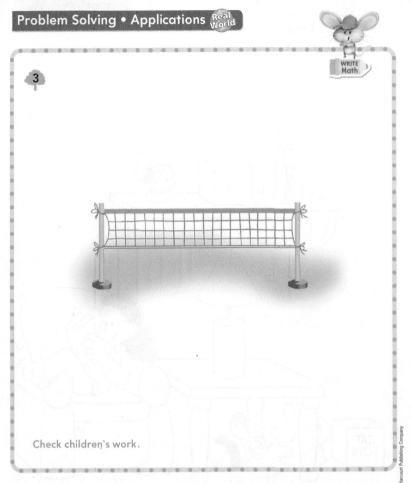

Check children's work.

DIRECTIONS 3. Draw a circle below the net. Draw a rectangle above the circle.

 **HOME ACTIVITY** • Tell your child you are thinking of something in the room that is above or below another object. Have your child tell you what the object might be.

© Houghton Mifflin Harcourt Publishing Company

DIFFERENTIATED INSTRUCTION • Independent Activities

 Grab and Go!™
Version 2.0
Differentiated Centers Kit

Tabletop Flipchart
Mini-lessons for reteaching to targeted small groups

Readers
Supports key math skills and concepts in real-world situations.

Games
Reinforce math content and vocabulary

Activities
Meaningful and fun math practice

Problem Solving Applications

Read the problem. Ask children to explain how they will solve the problem.
Talk about the picture of the net.

(MP) Construct arguments and critique reasoning of others.

Encourage children to share ideas about what real-world objects they might draw.

- **What is something that could be above the net?** Accept reasonable responses. .
- **What is something that could be below the net?** Accept reasonable responses.

⑤ Evaluate | Formative Assessment

I Can

Have children work with a partner to make a list of ideas to answer the I Can statement.

I can use the words *above* and *below* to compare the positions of two- and three-dimensional shapes by . . . saying that a shape is above, or higher than, another object. I can also say that a shape is below, or lower than, another object.

Exit Ticket

After they complete their drawings, have children show and describe the objects that they drew and tell where each is located.

Above and Below

Use the Practice and Homework pages to provide children with more practice of the concepts and skills presented in this lesson. Children master their understanding as they complete practice items.

DIRECTIONS   1. Mark an X on the object that is shaped like a sphere below the table. Circle the object that is shaped like a cube above the table.

Chapter 18 • Lesson 7   **747**

 PROFESSIONAL LEARNING | **MATHEMATICAL PRACTICES AND PROCESSES**

MP **Attend to precision.**

Mathematically proficient children use what they already know to build a logical progression of statements to explain their reasoning.

- A child might reason, "This box is below the table. I know that because *below* means 'lower.' It is lower than the table."

- Another child might support a statement of "The shelf is above the lamp" by saying, "I know that *above* means 'higher.' It is higher than something. So I know that the shelf is higher than the lamp."

Provide opportunities such as the following for children to use the terms *above* and *below* to describe locations.

Mr. Taylor's bookshelf has three shelves. He says to Bobby, "My book is above the bottom shelf. It is below the top shelf." On what shelf will Bobby find Mr. Taylor's book?

- **What do you already know that can help you solve this problem?** I know that *above* means "a higher place" and *below* means "a lower place."

- **How can you solve this problem?** Possible answer: I can draw a bookshelf with three shelves. Then I can find the shelf that is above the bottom shelf and below the top shelf. The book is on shelf number two.

Lesson Check

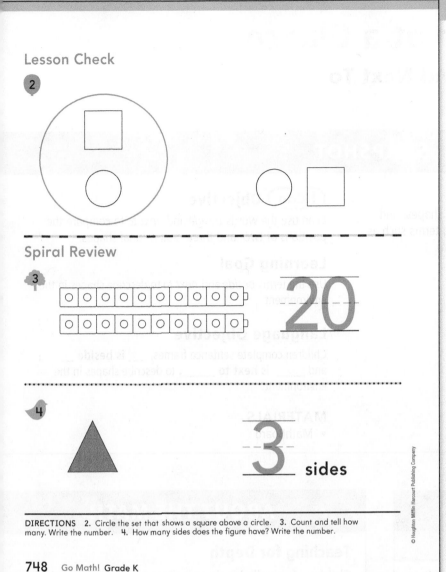

②

Spiral Review

③

20

④

_____ sides

DIRECTIONS 2. Circle the set that shows a square above a circle. 3. Count and tell how many. Write the number. 4. How many sides does the figure have? Write the number.

Continue to practice concepts and skills with Lesson Check. Use Spiral Review to engage children in previously taught concepts and to promote content retention.

© Houghton Mifflin Harcourt Publishing Company

Lesson at a Glance

Beside and Next To

SNAPSHOT

Mathematical Standards

- Describe objects in the environment using names of shapes, and describe the relative positions of these objects using terms such as *above*, *below*, *beside*, *in front of*, *behind*, and *next to*.

Mathematical Practices and Processes

- Attend to precision.
- Model with mathematics.
- Construct arguments and critique reasoning of others.
- Reason abstractly and quantitatively.
- Look for and make use of structure.

(I Can) Objective

I can use the words *beside* and *next to* to compare the positions of two- and three-dimensional shapes.

Learning Goal

Use the terms *beside* and *next to* to describe shapes in the environment.

Language Objective

Children complete sentence frames, ___ **is beside** _____; and _____ **is next to** _____, to describe shapes in the environment.

MATERIALS

- MathBoard

ACROSS THE GRADES

Grade K

Compare three-dimensional figures based on their similarities, differences and positions. Sort three-dimensional figures based on their similarities and differences. Figures are limited to spheres, cubes, cones and cylinders.

After

Identify, compare and sort two- and three-dimensional figures based on their defining attributes. Figures are limited to circles, semi-circles, triangles, rectangles, squares, trapezoids, hexagons, spheres, cubes, rectangular prisms, cones and cylinders.

ABOUT THE MATH

Teaching for Depth

Children typically begin using terms for spatial relations before coming to kindergarten. They use positional terms to tell about the location of people and things. For example, "I am inside the room." "The clock is above the door." Through ordinary daily activities, children learn many positional terms, such as *above*, *below*, *beside*, *next to*, *in front of*, and *behind*.

In this lesson, children use the terms *beside* and *next to* to describe location. They learn that they can use the words interchangeably to tell when something is at the side of something else. As children work through the lesson and go about their day, find opportunities to reinforce this language.

For more professional learning, go online to Teacher's Corner.

Problem of the Day 18.8

Describe a sphere, a cylinder, and a cube.

Display a sphere, a cylinder, and a cube. Have children describe them by telling about the surfaces of each solid.

Possible answers: A sphere has a curved surface; a cylinder has two flat surfaces and a curved surface. A cube has six flat surfaces.

 Vocabulary beside, next to

- Interactive Student Edition
- Multilingual Glossary

Vocabulary Builder

Materials three-dimensional shapes

Ask a child to choose a shape. Have the child face left. Have two more children choose shapes and line up shoulder to shoulder.

- **What shape is next to the [cone]?**
- **What shape is beside the [cone]?**
- **What shape is beside the [cone] and the [cube]?**

Repeat with other volunteers and other shapes.

FOCUSING ON THE WHOLE STUDENT

Access Prior Knowledge

Use iTools: Geometry to show the following shapes in a row: cylinder, sphere, cube. Left aligned and directly below this row, show a sphere, cube, and cylinder. Have children name each solid shape.

- **What is the shape that is above the cylinder?** cube
- **What is the shape that is below the cylinder?** sphere

Continue questioning children about the position of the shapes, using the terms *above* and *below*.

① Engage

with the Interactive Student Edition

I Can Objective

I can use the words *beside* and *next to* to compare the positions of two- and three-dimensional shapes.

Making Connections

Ask children to tell what they know about the terms *above* and *below*.

- **Is the ceiling above our heads? Explain.** Yes. It is over, or higher than, our heads.
- **What is below our feet? Explain.** The floor; it is lower than, or beneath, our feet.
- Place a cube below a child's desk and hold a cone above it. **Which shape is below the desk?** cube
- **Which shape is above the desk?** cone

Learning Activity

Using three-dimensional shapes, guide children to access what they may already know about the terms *beside* and *next to*.

- Move the cube next to the cone on the desk. **Is the cube next to the cone?** yes
- **Is it beside the cone?** yes

② Explore

Listen and Draw

(MP) **Model with mathematics.**

Read the problem aloud as children listen.

Jessie is in the gym. She sees a tennis ball, a soccer ball, and a football in a row. Coach says to get the one next to the football. Which one does she get?

Have children look at the picture on the page.

- **What three-dimensional objects do you see in this picture?** Possible answers: soccer balls, orange cones, a box

Introduce the terms *beside* and *next to*. Model standing beside your desk or chair. Have children stand beside their tables. Then have children stand next to their tables. Point out that *beside* and *next to* mean the same thing.

- **If you stand next to your table and a classmate stands beside his or her table, where are each of you standing?** Possible answers: by our table; at the side of our table

- **Look at the picture and find all the objects shaped like cones. What object is shaped like a cone beside the object shaped like a sphere? Trace the X.**

- **What object is shaped like a sphere next to the object shaped like a cube? Trace the circle.**

Reread the problem about Jessie.

- **Which ball should Jessie get?** the soccer ball **Why?** It is the one next to or to the side of the football.

Name _____

CHAPTER 18
Lesson **8**

Beside and Next To

(I Can) use the words *beside* and *next to* to compare the positions of two- and three-dimensional shapes.

Listen and Draw Real World

DIRECTIONS Trace the X on the object shaped like a cone that is beside the object shaped like a sphere. Trace the circle around the object shaped like a sphere that is next to the object shaped like a cube. Check children's work.

Chapter 18 • Lesson 8   **749**

(ML) ## Multilingual Support

STRATEGY: Rephrase

Children can demonstrate an understanding of *beside* and *next to* by rephrasing.

Draw four circles on a piece of paper: one blue and one red, side by side on the left half of the page; one yellow and one green, side by side on the right half of the page.

- **Which circle is beside the red circle?** the blue circle Have children use sentence frames to rephrase the answer. **The _____ circle is _____ the _____ circle.**

Repeat with the other colors of circles.

I

Check children's work.

DIRECTIONS I. Mark an X on the bead shaped like a cube that is beside the bead shaped like a cone. Draw a circle around the bead shaped like a cone that is next to the bead shaped like a cylinder. Use the words next to and beside to name the position of other bead shapes.

750 Go Math! Grade K

© Houghton Mifflin Harcourt Publishing Company

③ Explain

Share and Show

Discuss the picture of the person making a necklace. Invite children to identify the various three-dimensional shaped beads they see in the picture.

Have children listen and follow directions.

- **Find a bead shaped like a cube that is beside the bead shaped like a cone. Mark an X on that bead.**

- **Find a bead shaped like a cone that is next to a bead shaped like a cylinder. Circle that bead.**

(MP) Reason abstractly and quantitatively.

Have children explain how they know their answers are correct.

> ⚠️ **Common Errors**
>
> **Error** Children may have difficulty recognizing *beside*.
>
> **Example** In Problem 1, children mark a bead shaped like a cube, but it is not beside the bead shaped like a cone.
>
> **Springboard to Learning** Help children identify the objects on the page. Review the meaning of *beside*. Relate *beside* to *next to*.

Ready for More 🕐 Kinesthetic Individual / Partners

Materials classroom objects shaped like cones, cubes, spheres, and cylinders

Have partners play a game of "I Spy" using the position words *beside*, *next to*, *above*, and *below*.

Set up a bookshelf or table with classroom objects shaped like cones, cubes, spheres, and cylinders.

One child gives a clue about an object on the bookshelf using position words to describe where the object is. The other child guesses the object.

Children repeat, taking turns giving clues.

④ Elaborate

Share and Show

Demonstrate the meaning of *beside* and *next to* with classroom objects. Direct attention to the page and have children identify the two-dimensional objects in the picture.

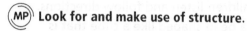 **Look for and make use of structure.**

- **How do you know which circle to color?**
- **How do you know which rectangle to circle?**
- **How do you know which triangle to put an X on?**

Use the checked problem for Quick Check.

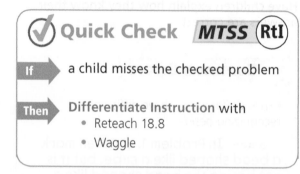

✓ Quick Check *MTSS* (RtI)

If ➤ a child misses the checked problem

Then ➤ Differentiate Instruction with
- Reteach 18.8
- Waggle

(MP) **Construct arguments and critique reasoning of others.**

Have children look at the picture.

- **How could you describe where the other circle is? Is there another way to describe one of the shapes that you marked?**
  Children's descriptions may include words other than *beside* or *next to*.

Higher-Order Thinking

(MP) **Model with mathematics.**

Have small groups gather several objects from the classroom and arrange them. Have one child describe an object based on its location. Then have the others identify which object is being described.

Math on the Spot Use this video to help children model and solve this type of problem.

Name _____

② ✓

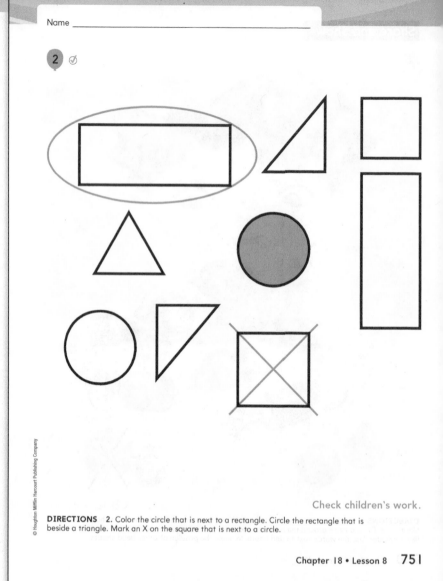

Check children's work.

DIRECTIONS 2. Color the circle that is next to a rectangle. Circle the rectangle that is beside a triangle. Mark an X on the square that is next to a circle.

Meeting Individual Needs

Reteach 18.8 *MTSS* (RtI1)

LESSON 18.8
Reteach

Name _____

Beside and Next To

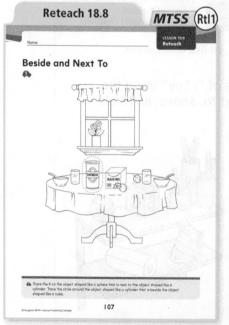

Trace the X on the object shaped like a sphere that is next to the object shaped like a cylinder. Trace the circle around the object shaped like a cylinder that is beside the object shaped like a cube.

107

Enrich 18.8

LESSON 18.8
Enrich

Name _____

Where Is the Cone?

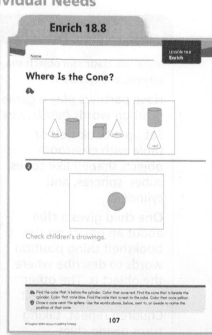

Check children's drawings.

Find the cone that is below the cylinder. Color that cone red. Find the cone that is beside the cylinder. Color that cone blue. Find the cone that is next to the cube. Color that cone yellow. Draw a cone near the sphere. Use the words above, below, next to, or beside to name the position of that cone.

107

3

Check children's work.

DIRECTIONS 3. Draw a square next to a rectangle. Draw a triangle beside a circle.

HOME ACTIVITY • Tell your child you are thinking of something in the room that is beside or next to another object. Have your child tell you the shape of the object.

Problem Solving Applications *Real World*

(MP) **Attend to precision.**

Problem 3 Read the directions. Call on volunteers to restate the directions in their own words.

Have children discuss what they will draw in the picture and explain why.

⑤ Evaluate | Formative Assessment

I Can

Have children complete one of the sentence frames to answer the I Can statement.

_____ is beside _____.

_____ is next to _____.

I can use the words *beside* and *next to* to compare the positions of two- and three-dimensional shapes by . . . telling about the locations of shapes such as boxes, balls, cones, and cans. When something is beside or next to me, it is at my side.

Exit Ticket

Draw or use pictures to show what you know about real world three-dimensional objects beside and next to other objects.

DIFFERENTIATED INSTRUCTION • Independent Activities

Grab-and-Go! ™
Version 2.0
Differentiated Centers Kit

Tabletop Flipchart

Mini-lessons for reteaching to targeted small groups

Readers

Supports key math skills and concepts in real-world situations.

Games

Reinforce math content and vocabulary

Activities

Meaningful and fun math practice

Beside and Next To

Use the Practice and Homework pages to provide children with more practice of the concepts and skills presented in this lesson. Children master their understanding as they complete practice items.

1

DIRECTIONS 1. Mark an X on the object shaped like a cylinder that is next to the object shaped like a sphere. Circle the object shaped like a cone that is beside the object shaped like a cube. Use the words next to and beside to name the position of other shapes.

Chapter 18 • Lesson 8 **753**

PROFESSIONAL LEARNING	MATH TALK IN ACTION

Teacher:	How can you describe the location of a cube that is to the side of a cone?
Tanya:	The cube is beside the cone.
Teacher:	Yes. Is there another way to describe the location of the cube?
Finn:	Is it above the cone?
Shira:	No, *above* the cube means higher than the cube. It is next to the cube when it is to the side.
Teacher:	How can a chair be beside and next to at the same time?
Matt:	*Beside* and *next to* mean almost the same thing.

Teacher:	Nice job. Look around the classroom. Name something that is beside and next to at the same time.
LaShawn:	The picture is beside the window and also next to the window.
Teacher:	Well done.
Cheng:	You say *next to* when someone's turn is coming up in line, right?
Teacher:	Close. You say that person is next. *Next to* are position words that show where something is.
Cheng:	So I can be next in line, but I am standing next to my friend?
Teacher:	Exactly!

Lesson Check

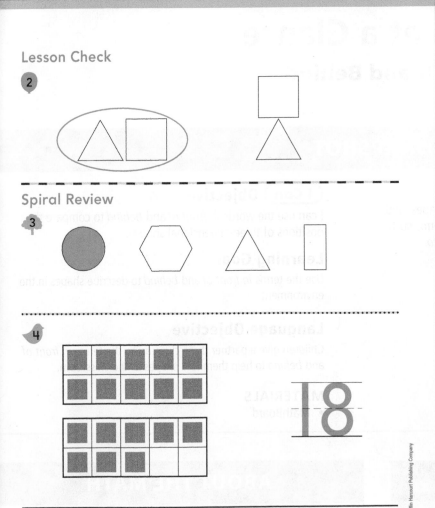

Spiral Review

© Houghton Mifflin Harcourt Publishing Company

DIRECTIONS 2. Circle the set that shows a square next to a triangle. 3. Which shape is a circle? Color the circle. 4. How many tiles are there? Write the number.

Continue to practice concepts and skills with Lesson Check. Use Spiral Review to engage children in previously taught concepts and to promote content retention.

Lesson at a Glance

In Front Of and Behind

SNAPSHOT

Mathematical Standards

● Describe objects in the environment using names of shapes, and describe the relative positions of these objects using terms such as *above, below, beside, in front of, behind,* and *next to.*

Mathematical Practices and Processes

● Model with mathematics.
● Attend to precision.
● Look for and make use of structure.
● Express regularity in repeated reasoning.

(I Can) Objective

I can use the words *in front of* and *behind* to compare the positions of three-dimensional shapes.

Learning Goal

Use the terms *in front of* and *behind* to describe shapes in the environment.

Language Objective

Children give a partner three clues using the terms *in front of* and *behind* to help them find shapes in the classroom.

MATERIALS

● MathBoard

ACROSS THE GRADES

Grade K

Compare three-dimensional figures based on their similarities, differences and positions. Sort three-dimensional figures based on their similarities and differences. Figures are limited to spheres, cubes, cones and cylinders.

After

Identify, compare and sort two- and three-dimensional figures based on their defining attributes. Figures are limited to circles, semi-circles, triangles, rectangles, squares, trapezoids, hexagons, spheres, cubes, rectangular prisms, cones and cylinders.

ABOUT THE MATH

Teaching for Depth

Spatial sense, according to Van de Walle, is "an intuition about shapes and the relationship among shapes." (*Elementary and Middle School Mathematics,* page 347) Some people think that spatial sense is inherent—you are born with it or not. But actually, children develop spatial sense over time by having multiple and valuable experiences with shape, location, and spatial relationships. Having strong spatial sense helps children understand number and measurement ideas.

In this chapter, children explore the concept of location with the positional words *before, after, beside, next to, in front of,* and *behind.* Understanding these concepts helps prepare children to learn numbers and measurement, as well as preparing them for work in later grades using grids to locate objects.

For more professional learning go online to Teacher's Corner.

Problem of the Day 18.9

What is the name of this solid shape? How can you describe this shape? Show children a cylinder shape. **Have them name the shape and describe it.**
cylinder; It has a curved surface and two flat surfaces, and it can stack and slide.

 Vocabulary behind, in front of

• Interactive Student Edition
• Multilingual Glossary

Vocabulary Builder

Materials three-dimensional shapes

Ask a child to choose a shape. Have him or her face left. Have two more children choose shapes and stand behind the first child.

• **What shape is *in front of* the [cone]?**

• **What shape is *behind* the [cone]?**

Repeat with other volunteers and other shapes.

FOCUSING ON THE WHOLE STUDENT

Access Prior Knowledge

Have children use objects to demonstrate positions of things in the classroom. Have a child stand beside a chair. Have another child stand next to the first child.

Repeat the activity with several children using different objects in the classroom.

① Engage

with the Interactive Student Edition

I Can Objective

I can use the words *in front of* and *behind* to compare the positions of three-dimensional shapes.

Making Connections

Ask children to tell what they know about the terms *next to* and *beside*.

• Place three objects, such as a stapler, a box of crayons, and a tissue box, on a desk. **Are the crayons next to the stapler?** yes

• **Are the crayons beside the stapler?** yes

• **Say a sentence about where the tissues and the crayons are. Use the words *beside* or *next to*.**
Possible answers: The crayons are beside (next to) the tissues. The tissues are beside (next to) the crayons.

Learning Activity

Guide children to access what they may already know about the terms *in front of* and *behind*.

• Invite volunteers to stand in front of and behind different objects in the classroom.
Check children's positioning.

② Explore

Listen and Draw

Read the problem aloud as children listen.

John, Beth, and Callie are in line to put their toys in the toy drive box. John is holding a sphere. Beth is holding a cube. Callie is holding a cylinder. Which shape is in front of the cube? Which shape is behind the cube?

(MP) Model with mathematics.

Discuss the picture with children. Call attention to the object on the floor.

- **What is the shape of the toy drive box?** a cube

Point out the boy holding the ball.

- **What is the shape of the ball the boy is holding?** a sphere
- **Trace the X on the object shaped like a sphere that is in front of the object shaped like a cube.** Children trace the X on the ball.

Point out the girl behind the boy.

- **Is the girl in front of or behind the boy holding the ball?** behind **What is the shape of the object she is holding?** a cube
- **Is the last girl in line behind or in front of the girl holding the cube?** behind **What is the shape of the object she is holding?** a cylinder
- **Trace the circle around the object shaped like a cylinder that is behind the object shaped like a cube.** Children circle the cylinder that the last girl in line is holding.

(MP) Attend to precision.

Reread the problem. Have three volunteers act out the problem. Have them each stand in a line and face left to show the order of the children in the problem.

- **Which shape is in front of the cube?** a sphere
- **Which shape is behind the cube?** a cylinder

Ask children to explain how they know when an object is in front of or behind another one. Possible answer: An object is in front if it comes before another object in a line. An object is behind if it comes after in a line.

Encourage children to restate the position of the shapes in complete sentences.

Name _____

In Front Of and Behind

(I Can) use the words *in front of* and *behind* to compare the positions of three-dimensional shapes.

Listen and Draw Real World

DIRECTIONS Trace the X on the object shaped like a sphere that is in front of the object shaped like a cube. Trace the circle around the object shaped like a cylinder that is behind the object shaped like a cube. Check children's work.

Chapter 18 • Lesson 9   **755**

(ML) Multilingual Support

STRATEGY: Rephrase

Children can demonstrate understanding of the position of objects by rephrasing.

Have two children form a line with you in the middle. Explain that *in front of* means someone is ahead of you and *behind* means someone is in back of you.

Have a group of children line up facing the classroom door. Select a child from the line.

- **[Alma] comes after [George].** Have children rephrase the statement using the sentence frame, **[Alma] is behind [George].**

Repeat the questions with other children in the line, using *comes before* and *in front of*.

1

DIRECTIONS 1. Mark an X on the object shaped like a cylinder that is behind the object shaped like a cube. Draw a circle around the object shaped like a sphere that is directly in front of the object shaped like a cone. Use the words *in front of* and *behind* to name the position of other shapes.

Check children's work.

© Houghton Mifflin Harcourt Publishing Company

③ Explain

Share and Show

Have children locate the train on the page and name the objects shown on the flatbed train cars. Read the directions.

- **Find the objects shaped like cylinders. Mark an X on the object shaped like a cylinder that is behind the object shaped like a cube.**
  Children place an X on the vertical blue cylinder.

- **Circle the object shaped like a sphere that is in front of the object shaped like a cone.**
  Children circle the blue sphere.

> ⚠ **Common Errors**
>
> **Error** Children may confuse *in front of* and *behind*.
>
> **Example** Children mark an X on the wrong cylinder.
>
> **Springboard to Learning** Explain that the way people or objects are facing tells who or what is in front of and who or what is behind. Point to each object in the picture and describe which object is in front of and which object is behind.

Culturally Responsive Education

As mentioned in previous chapters, movement is a traditional form of learning and showing knowledge in cultures around the world. Play movement games with children in small groups using position words—children can take turns calling for others to stand *in front of*, *behind*, *next to*, or *beside* one another. They can ask other children to hold something *above* their heads or to sit or stand *below* something in the classroom, too. Young children often internalize concepts more readily when learning is integrated with play.

Ready for More 🕐 Kinesthetic Individual / Partners

Materials stuffed animal, large paper bags, three-dimensional real-world objects shaped like spheres, cones, cubes, and cylinders

Give partners a bag filled with three-dimensional real-world objects. Have one partner place a stuffed animal on a desk.

One child takes two objects from the bag, identifies the three-dimensional shapes, and places them on the table, one in front of and one behind the stuffed animal.

The other child describes the position of the objects. For example, "The marble is in front of the animal."

Partners reverse roles and continue the activity.

Chapter 18 • Lesson 9   756

④ Elaborate

Share and Show

Have children look at the page and describe the shapes of the objects shown. Read the directions.

- **Mark an X on the object shaped like a cube that is in front of the object shaped like a cylinder.** Children should mark an X on the sewing box.

- **Circle the object shaped like a cylinder that is behind the object shaped like a sphere.** Children should circle the tall green cylinder.

Use the checked problem for Quick Check.

✓ Quick Check   *MTSS* (RtI)

If → a child misses the checked problem

Then → Differentiate Instruction with
- Reteach 18.9
- Waggle

(MP) **Look for and make use of structure.**

Have three children come to the front of the room and line up facing a classroom door. Ask questions such as, "Which child is in front of [David]? Which child is behind [Susan]?"

- **If the children turn to face away from the door, which child is now behind [Susan]? Draw and name that child.**

Higher-Order Thinking

(MP) **Express regularity in repeated reasoning.**

Using stuffed animals, have one child place an animal on the table. Other children take turns placing two other animals on the table and describing the positions of the three animals.

Math on the Spot Use this video to help children model and solve this type of problem.

Name _____

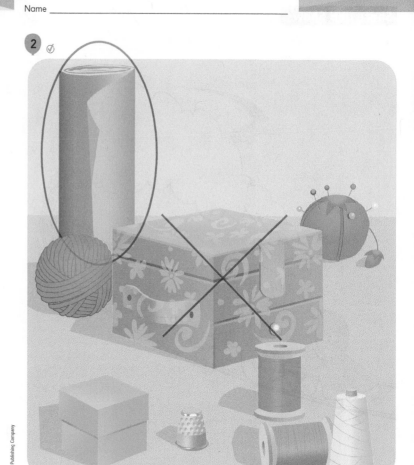

DIRECTIONS 2. Mark an X on the object shaped like a cube that is in front of the object shaped like a cylinder. Draw a circle around the object shaped like a cylinder that is behind the object shaped like a sphere. Use the words in front of and behind to name the position of other shapes.   Check children's work.

Meeting Individual Needs

Reteach 18.9   *MTSS* (RtI)

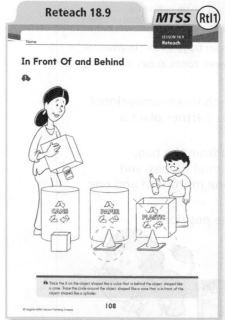

In Front Of and Behind

Trace the X on the object shaped like a cube that is behind the object shaped like a cone. Trace the circle around the object shaped like a cone that is in front of the object shaped like a cylinder.

108

Enrich 18.9

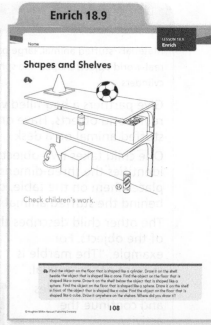

Shapes and Shelves

Check children's work.

Find the object on the floor that is shaped like a cylinder. Draw it on the shelf beside the object that is shaped like a cone. Find the object on the floor that is shaped like a cone. Draw it on the shelf below the object that is shaped like a sphere. Find the object on the floor that is shaped like a sphere. Draw it on the shelf in front of the object that is shaped like a cube. Find the object on the floor that is shaped like a cube. Draw it anywhere on the shelves. Where did you draw it?

108

3

Check children's work.

DIRECTIONS 3. Draw or use pictures to show what you know about real-world three-dimensional objects in front of and behind other objects.

HOME ACTIVITY • Tell your child you are thinking of something in the room that is in front of or behind another object. Have your child tell you the shape of the object.

© Houghton Mifflin Harcourt Publishing Company

758 Go Math! Grade K

Problem Solving Real World Applications

 Attend to precision.

Problem 3 Read the problem. Ask children to explain how they plan to draw real-world three-dimensional objects *in front of* and *behind* other objects.

⑤ Evaluate | Formative Assessment

I Can

Have children give a partner three clues to find shapes in the classroom to answer the I Can statement.

I can use the words *in front of* and *behind* to compare the positions of three-dimensional shapes by . . . telling the locations of shapes such as boxes, balls, cones, and cans. When something is in front of an object, it comes before the object in a line. When it is behind, it comes after the object.

Exit Ticket

When the drawings are completed, have children discuss and share their drawings to show what they know about real-world three-dimensional objects and the positional terms *in front of* and *behind*.

DIFFERENTIATED INSTRUCTION • Independent Activities

Version 2.0
Differentiated Centers Kit

Tabletop Flipchart
Mini-lessons for reteaching to targeted small groups

Readers
Supports key math skills and concepts in real-world situations.

Games
Reinforce math content and vocabulary

Activities
Meaningful and fun math practice

Practice and Homework

In Front Of and Behind

Use the Practice and Homework pages to provide children with more practice of the concepts and skills presented in this lesson. Children master their understanding as they complete practice items.

In Front Of and Behind

DIRECTIONS 1. Mark an X on the object shaped like a cylinder that is behind the object shaped like a cone. Draw a circle around the object shaped like a cylinder that is in front of the object shaped like a cube. Use the words in front of and behind to name the position of other shapes.

Chapter 18 • Lesson 9   **759**

PATH TO FLUENCY • Activity

Materials three-tiered bookshelf, real-world and solid shapes for a cone, cube, cylinder, sphere

Investigate Have children place objects on the bookshelf to show *above*, *below*, *beside* or *next to*, *in front of*, and *behind*.

Math Talk

- **Describe how you placed objects to show *above*, *below*, *beside* or *next to*, *in front of*, and *behind*.** Children should be able to accurately describe their actions.

- **How can you show an object that is above one object and beside another?** Possible answer: I can place a ball and a box on the top row. On the next shelf, I can put a cone below the ball. The ball is above the cone and beside the box.

- **How can you show an object that is below one object and in front of another?** Possible answer: I can place a ball on the top shelf and a box on the next shelf below the ball. I can put a pencil in front of the box. The pencil is below the ball and in front of the box.

Summarize See if children can verbalize the placement of objects using the position words *above*, *below*, *beside* or *next to*, *in front of*, and *behind*.

Watch for children who can use the correct shape names to identify the objects they are placing.

Children should be able to demonstrate and communicate an understanding of the spatial relationship of one object to another.

Lesson Check

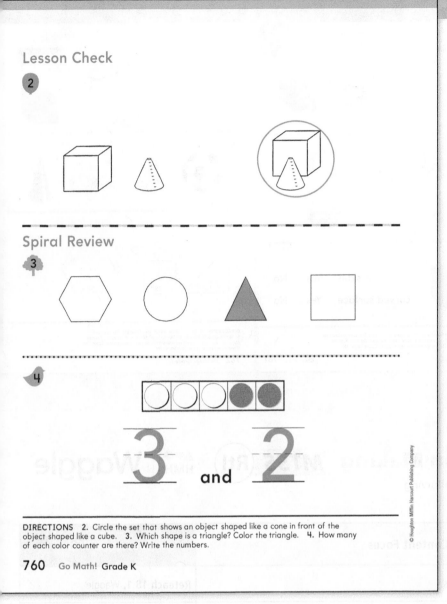

Spiral Review

DIRECTIONS 2. Circle the set that shows an object shaped like a cone in front of the object shaped like a cube. 3. Which shape is a triangle? Color the triangle. 4. How many of each color counter are there? Write the numbers.

760 Go Math! Grade K

Continue to practice concepts and skills with Lesson Check. Use Spiral Review to engage children in previously taught concepts and to promote content retention.

© Houghton Mifflin Harcourt Publishing Company

Summative Assessment

Use the **Chapter Review** to assess children's progress in Chapter 18.

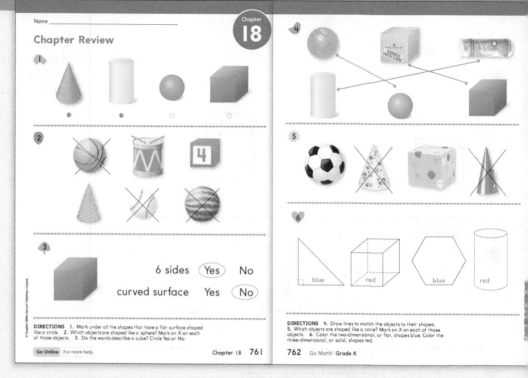

Online, Data-Driven Decision Making *MTSS* (Rtl) ▲◼● HMH | **Waggle**®

Based on the results of the Chapter Review, use the following resources to review skills.

Item	Lesson	Content Focus	Intervene With
2	18.1	Identify, name, and describe spheres.	**Reteach 18.1,** Waggle
3	18.2	Identify, name, and describe cubes.	**Reteach 18.2,** Waggle
7	18.3	Identify, name, and describe cylinders.	**Reteach 18.3,** Waggle
5	18.4	Identify, name, and describe cones.	**Reteach 18.4,** Waggle
1, 4	18.5	Compare three-dimensional shapes.	**Reteach 18.5,** Waggle
6	18.6	Identify and sort two- and three-dimensional shapes.	**Reteach 18.6,** Waggle
8, 12	18.7	Use the terms *above* and *below* to describe shapes in the environment.	**Reteach 18.7,** Waggle
9, 11	18.8	Use the terms *beside* and *next* to to describe shapes in the environment.	**Reteach 18.8,** Waggle
10	18.9	Use the terms *in front of* and *behind* to describe shapes in the environment.	**Reteach 18.9,** Waggle

Name _____

7 Check children's drawings.

8

9

10
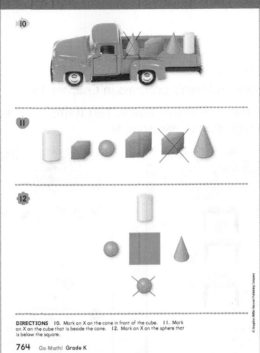

11

12

DIRECTIONS 7. Draw an object that has the shape of a cylinder. 8. Circle the shapes that show the cylinder above the cube. 9. Mark an X on the object shaped like a cylinder next to the object shaped like a cone.

Chapter 18 **763**

DIRECTIONS 10. Mark an X on the cone in front of the cube. 11. Mark an X on the cube that is beside the cone. 12. Mark an X on the sphere that is below the square.

764 Go Math! Grade K

Performance Assessment Task

See the Performance Tasks to assess children's understanding of the content. For each task, you will find sample student work for each of the response levels in the task scoring rubric.

📁 Performance Assessment Tasks may be used for portfolios.

Chapter Test

Summative Assessment

Use the **Chapter Test** to assess children's progress in Chapter 18.

Chapter Tests are found in the *Assessment Guide*. Test items are presented in formats consistent with high-stakes assessments.

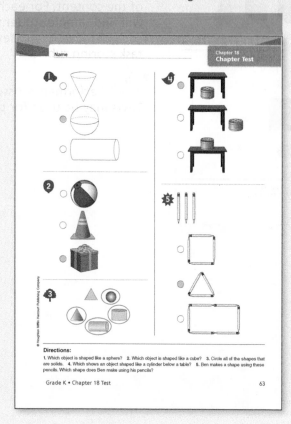

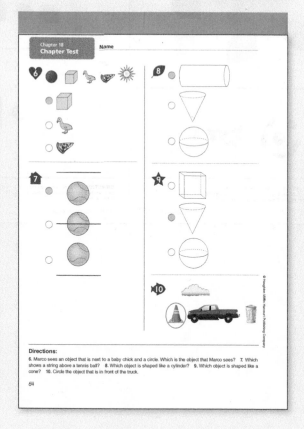

Teacher Notes

	LESSON 19.1 • 1 Day	LESSON 19.2 • 1 Day	LESSON 19.3 • 1 Day
Lesson at a Glance	Compare Lengths . . . 767A	Compare Weights . . . 773A	Length, Height, and Weight 779A
I Can	I can measure and compare length.	I can compare the weights of two objects.	I can describe several measurable attributes of a single object.
Learning Goal	Directly compare the lengths of two objects.	Directly compare the weights of two objects.	Describe several ways to measure one object.
Vocabulary	longer, shorter, taller, length, measure	heavier, lighter, weight	height
Multilingual Support	**Strategy:** Identify Relationships	**Strategy:** Identify Relationships	**Strategy:** Scaffold Language

	LESSON 19.1	LESSON 19.2	LESSON 19.3
Practice and Fluency	◆ ■ Practice and Homework ■ Waggle	◆ ■ Practice and Homework ■ Waggle	◆ ■ Practice and Homework ■ Waggle
MTSS (RtI) Intervention and Enrichment	■ Waggle ◆ ■ Reteach 19.1 ◆ ■ Tier 2 Intervention Skill S44 ◆ ■ Tier 3 Intervention Skill E44 ◆ Tabletop Flipchart ◆ Enrich 19.1	■ Waggle ◆ ■ Reteach 19.2 ◆ ■ Tier 2 Intervention Skill S45 ◆ ■ Tier 3 Intervention Skill E45 ◆ Tabletop Flipchart ◆ Enrich 19.2	■ Waggle ◆ ■ Reteach 19.3 ◆ ■ Tier 2 Intervention Skill S44/S45 ◆ ■ Tier 3 Intervention Skill E44/E45 ◆ Enrich 19.3

See the Grab-and-Go!™ Centers Kit for more small-group activities.

Grab-and-Go!™
Version 2.0
Differentiated Centers Kit

The kit provides literature, games, and activities for small-group learning.

◆ Print/Printable Resource
■ Interactive Resource

LESSON 19.4 • 1 Day

Lesson at a Glance

Compare Volume . . . 785A

I Can

I can compare volume and identify other measurable attributes of objects.

Learning Goal

Compare the volumes of objects.

Vocabulary

volume, more, less

Multilingual Support

Strategy: Define

Practice and Fluency

LESSON 19.4

◆ ■ Practice and Homework

■ Waggle

MTSS (RtI)

Intervention and Enrichment

■ Waggle
◆ ■ Reteach 19.4
◆ ■ Tier 2 Intervention Skill S43
◆ ■ Tier 3 Intervention Skill E43
◆ ■ Enrich 19.4

Reflect on the multiple representations children use and how assigning competence to those solution methods develops confidence.

CULTURALLY RESPONSIVE TEACHING

Cultural Competence

Leverage children's cultural funds of knowledge and ways of knowing, including multiple mathematical representations, to bridge new learning and position children as mathematically competent.

Image Credit: © HMH

◆ Print/Printable Resource
■ Interactive Resource

Length and Height

In the context of learning about length, children should be guided to make comparisons between objects that explicitly display the attribute of length and use terms such as *same as, shorter than,* and *longer than*.

- Aligning objects one below the other and comparing their lengths using language as described above is an example of direct measurement of length.

The red pencil is shorter.

The blue pencil is longer.

- Like length, height is the measurement of distance between two points.

- Comparisons of height are described by using words such as *taller, shorter, higher,* and *lower*.

Some children may discover that objects can have more than one measurable attribute.

Nonstandard Units

Children's first experience in measuring the length of objects should be with nonstandard units, particularly units that can be snapped together (e.g., connecting cubes) or easily placed side by side (e.g., square tiles).

From the Research

"Classroom research points to the importance of helping children go beyond procedural competence to learn about the mathematical underpinnings of measure so that procedures and concepts are mutually bootstrapped."
(Lehrer, 2003, p. 190)

Weight

Weight is the measurement of the pull of gravity on an object.

- A starting place for teaching children about weight is to give them an opportunity to hold objects in their hands to compare them.

- When comparing weights, use terms such as *heavier, lighter,* or *the same*.

- Ordering objects according to weight helps build understanding of the concept.

Mathematical Practices and Processes

Reason abstractly and quantitatively.

For young children to use abstract and quantitative reasoning in the context of measurement, they need many experiences physically comparing objects, discussing their comparisons of objects, and measuring objects with nonstandard units. When children measure a pair of scissors as 19 cubes long and measure an envelope as 15 cubes long, they use reasoning to make a conclusion based on this quantitative information. How they make sense of these quantities provides a foundation for how children will interpret measurements when they are using standard units.

For more professional learning, go online to Teacher's Corner.

Instructional Journey

While every classroom may look a little different, this instructional model provides a framework to organize small-group and whole-group learning for meaningful student learning.

Whole Group
Engage

5 minutes

Readiness
- Problem of the Day
- Fluency Builder or Vocabulary Builder
- Access Prior Knowledge

Engagement
- I Can
- Making Connections
- Learning Activity

Small and Whole Group
Explore

15–20 minutes

Exploration
- Listen and Draw, Unlock the Problem
- Multilingual Support and Strategy
- Common Errors

Small Group
Explain

15–20 minutes

Quick Check
☑ Share and Show

Differentiated Instruction

Version 2.0

Intervention
- Waggle
- Reteach
- Tier 2 and Tier 3 MTSS
- Tabletop Flipchart Mini Lessons

Language Support
- Vocabulary Activities
- Language Routines
- Multilingual Glossary

Enrichment
- Waggle Games
- Ready for More
- Enrich

Whole Group
Elaborate

5 minutes

- Math on the Spot Videos
- Higher-Order Thinking Problems

Evaluate

- I Can Reflection
- Exit Ticket
- Practice and Homework
- Fluency Practice
- Waggle

Assessment

Diagnostic	Formative	Summative
• Show What You Know	• Lesson Quick Check	• Chapter Review • Chapter Test • Performance Assessment Task

Version 2.0
Differentiated Centers Kit
The kit provides literature, games, and activities for small-group learning.

Strategies for
Multilingual Learners

Understanding a child's language development is helpful in differentiating teaching and assessment. Assessing a child's understanding of mathematical concepts can be done by listening, speaking, reading, and writing. The level of support a child needs determines how best to assess that child's understanding of mathematical concepts.

Planning for Instruction			
Language Support	**Substantial** (WIDA Level 1)*	**Moderate** (WIDA Levels 2 & 3)*	**Light** (WIDA Levels 4 & 5)*
Child's Use of Language	• uses single words • uses common short phrases • heavily relies on visual supports and use of manipulatives	• uses simple sentences • uses some academic vocabulary • relies on visual supports and use of manipulatives	• uses a variety of sentences • uses academic vocabulary • benefits from visual supports and manipulatives
Ways to Assess Understanding	**Listening:** points to pictures, words, or phrases to answer questions **Speaking:** answers *yes/no* questions **Reading:** matches symbols to math terms and concepts **Writing:** draws a visual representation of a problem	**Listening:** matches, categorizes, or sequences information based on visuals **Speaking:** begins to explain reasoning, asks math questions, repeats explanations from peers **Reading:** identifies important information to solve a problem **Writing:** uses simple sentences and visual representations	**Listening:** draws conclusions and makes connections based on what they heard **Speaking:** explains and justifies concepts and solutions **Reading:** understands information in math contexts **Writing:** completes sentences using some academic vocabulary

* For more information on WIDA Standards, visit their website at:
https://wida.wisc.edu/.

• Look for strategies throughout the lesson to support multilingual learners.
• Log on to ED to find additional multilingual activities and Vocabulary Cards.

In This Chapter

Key Academic Vocabulary

Current Development • Vocabulary

longer, shorter, taller, length, heavier, lighter, weight, height, volume, more, less, measure

Using Language Routines to Develop Understanding

 Language routines provide opportunities for children to develop an understanding of mathematical language and concepts by listening, speaking, reading, and writing. More information on these language routines can be found on the Language Support Cards.

Compare and Contrast

Children share their work with a partner to compare and contrast their strategies.

Language Support	Substantial (WIDA Level 1)*	Moderate (WIDA Levels 2 & 3)*	Light (WIDA Levels 4 & 5)*
Language Routine Differentiation	Children will physically point out similarities and differences on visual representations. They may use short phrases such as "the same" and "different" to verbally compare and contrast their strategies.	Children will rely on visual representations to inform their simple-sentence discussions as they compare and contrast their strategies.	Children will be able to use some academic vocabulary to compare and contrast their strategies with a partner or small group.
Possible Student Work	GREEN	GREEN 4	GREEN 4

Assessing Prior Knowledge

Have children complete **Show What You Know** on their own. Items tested are the prerequisite skills for this chapter.

Diagnostic Interview Task

The alternative interview tasks below evaluate children's understanding of each **Show What You Know** skill. The diagnostic chart may be used for intervention on prerequisite skills.

MATERIALS erasers, connecting cubes, numeral cards (8–15), two-color counters

Display a set of four erasers and a set of six erasers. Have the child count the erasers in each set.

- **Which set has fewer erasers?** the set of four erasers

Display 14 counters arranged in a circle and 9 counters in a rectangular array. Have the child count the counters in each set.

- **Which set has more counters?** the set with 14 counters

Display a 10-cube train and an 8-cube train. Have the child place the matching numeral card next to each set.

- **Which number is greater?** 10

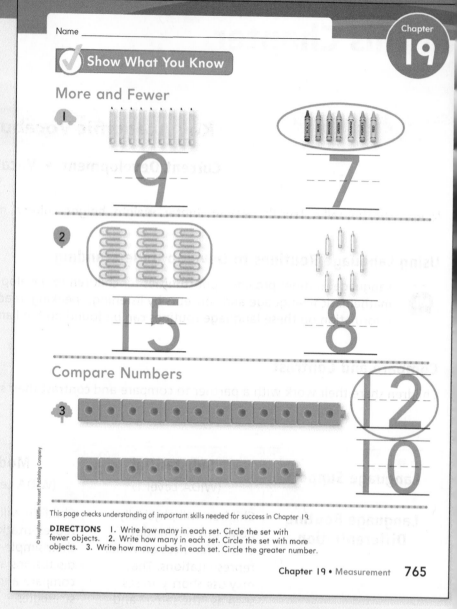

Name _____

✓ Show What You Know

More and Fewer

1.

9

7

2.

15

8

Compare Numbers

3.

This page checks understanding of important skills needed for success in Chapter 19.

DIRECTIONS 1. Write how many in each set. Circle the set with fewer objects. 2. Write how many in each set. Circle the set with more objects. 3. Write how many cubes in each set. Circle the greater number.

Chapter 19 • Measurement   **765**

✓ **Show What You Know • Diagnostic Assessment**

Use to determine if children need intervention for the chapter's prerequisite skills.

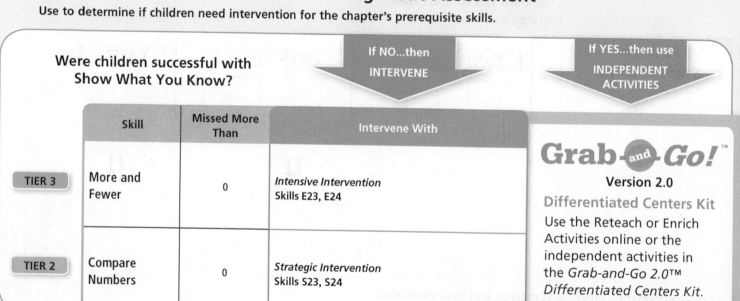

Were children successful with Show What You Know?

If NO...then **INTERVENE**

If YES...then use **INDEPENDENT ACTIVITIES**

	Skill	Missed More Than	Intervene With
TIER 3	More and Fewer	0	*Intensive Intervention* Skills E23, E24
TIER 2	Compare Numbers	0	*Strategic Intervention* Skills S23, S24

Grab and Go!

Version 2.0

Differentiated Centers Kit

Use the Reteach or Enrich Activities online or the independent activities in the *Grab-and-Go 2.0™ Differentiated Centers Kit.*

Vocabulary Builder

bigger

smaller

DIRECTIONS Are there more flowers in the bigger pot or the smaller pot? Circle to show the pot with more flowers.

766   Go Math! Grade K

© Houghton Mifflin Harcourt Publishing Company

Vocabulary Builder

Children use multiple strategies to develop grade-appropriate vocabulary. Have children complete the activities on the page by working alone or with partners.

Look at the page with children.

- **Are there more flowers in the bigger pot or the smaller pot?** smaller pot

Discuss with children that size is not necessarily an indication of weight or quantity. For example, the smaller pot contains more flowers than the bigger pot; the spade is smaller than a flower outside the window, but the spade is heavier.

Have children draw a bigger piece of art on the wall.

 **School-Home Letter** is available in English and Spanish online, and in multiple other languages.

Intervention Options   *MTSS* (RtI)   Response to Intervention

Use Show What You Know, Lesson Quick Check, and Assessments to diagnose children's intervention levels.

TIER 1	TIER 2	TIER 3	ENRICHMENT
On-Level Intervention	**Strategic Intervention**	**Intensive Intervention**	**Independent Activities**
For children who are generally at grade level but need early intervention with the lesson concepts, use:	For children who need small-group instruction to review concepts and skills needed for the chapter, use:	For children who need one-on-one instruction to build foundational skills for the chapter, use:	For children who successfully complete lessons, use:
			• Waggle Practice and Games
• Reteach	▲ Prerequisite Skills Activities	▲ Prerequisite Skills Activities	**Grab and Go!**
• Tabletop Flipchart Mini Lesson	▲ Tier 2 Activity	▲ Tier 3 Activity	Version 2.0
• Waggle			Differentiated Centers Kit
▲ Tier 1 Activity			• Ready for More Activity for every lesson
			• Enrich

Lesson at a Glance
Compare Lengths

SNAPSHOT

Mathematical Standards
- Describe measurable attributes of objects, such as length or weight. Describe several measurable attributes of a single object.
- Directly compare two objects with a measurable attribute in common, to see which object has "more of"/"less of" the attribute, and describe the difference.

Mathematical Practices and Processes
- Use appropriate tools strategically.
- Model with mathematics.
- Construct arguments and critique reasoning of others.
- Look for and make use of structure.
- Reason abstractly and quantitatively.

(I Can) Objective
I can measure and compare length.

Learning Goal
Directly compare the lengths of two objects.

Language Objective
Pairs of children describe and compare the lengths of two objects.

MATERIALS
- MathBoard
- connecting cubes

ACROSS THE GRADES

Grade K
Directly compare two objects that have an attribute which can be measured in common. Express the comparison using language to describe the difference.

After
Compare and order the length of up to three objects using direct and indirect comparison.

ABOUT THE MATH

Why Teach This?
Measurement is widely used in everyday life. Children and their families often refer to measurement ideas, such as how much children have grown, the lengths of walks they take, how heavy bags of groceries are, and how high buildings are. Measurement ideas are used in the classroom, too. Children decide whether items will fit in their backpacks, they put large blocks on certain shelves and smaller blocks on others, and they see that one train of cubes is longer than another.

Measurement bridges two other important areas of mathematics—geometry and number sense. Children have compared numbers, shapes, and lengths of sides. In this chapter, they will compare different measures.

For more professional learning go online to Teacher's Corner.

Problem of the Day 19.1

What number is one greater than 12? one greater than 8?
13; 9

What number is two greater than 10? two greater than 7?
12; 9

Vocabulary longer, measure, length, shorter, taller

- Interactive Student Edition
- Multilingual Glossary

Vocabulary Builder

Materials vocabulary cards for *longer* and *shorter*

Longer, Shorter

Show a 5-cube train. Trace along its length with your finger. Invite a child to build a cube train that is *longer* than yours. Invite another child to build a cube train that is *shorter* than yours. Have them use the vocabulary cards to label the longer and shorter cube trains.

Explain to children that when comparing lengths, both objects need to start at the same point. Show what happens when the cube trains do not start at the same point.

FOCUSING ON THE WHOLE STUDENT

Supporting All Learners

This chapter provides many opportunities for hands-on learning, which often allows children to better internalize understanding of concepts. In this lesson, children will be using cubes to measure. Allow children to measure items physically in the classroom as well, not just the images on the paper. Children can compare the length of objects in the classroom, too. In Lesson 19.2, children learn to compare weights. Again, this understanding is greatly benefited by holding objects and comparing as opposed to simply comparing visually. Provide a more complex comparison opportunity by giving children items of the same size, but clearly different weights. In Lesson 19.4, children learn about comparing volume, and comparing volume by measuring capacity can be both enjoyable and clarifying in terms of understanding.

① Engage

with the Interactive Student Edition

I Can Objective

I can measure and compare length.

Making Connections

Invite children to tell you what they remember about measuring.

- **What does it mean to measure something?** Possible answer: to find out how long or full something is
- **Why might you measure something?** Possible answer: to make sure you have the right amount of something

Learning Activity

Tell a story about Scout and Sher finding pine cones. Show children an image of actual pine cones.

Direct children to think about how to compare objects.

- **What did Scout and Sher find?** pine cones
- **How are the pine cones different?** Answers may vary; one looks bigger, one looks shorter, etc.
- **What do you want to know?** which pine cone is longer

② Explore

Listen and Draw

Discuss the meaning of the word *length* (the measure of how long something is). Read aloud this problem as children listen.

Ling has two pencils. How can she find which is longer and which is shorter?

- **To compare lengths, or find which object is longer or shorter, the objects must start at the same place.**

- **Compare the lengths of the two pencils in the picture. What do you need to check before you can compare the lengths of two objects?** that both objects start at the same place

- **Look at where each pencil ends. Which one is longer?** the one that sticks out farther

- **Which pencil is shorter?** the one that does not stick out as far

(MP) **Look for and make use of structure.**

- **How did you use the line to tell you which pencil is shorter?** Possible answer: Since both pencil points start at the line, I knew the one that ended sooner is shorter.

Have children compare the pencils using the terms *longer* and *shorter*. Have children trace around the longer pencil. Have them trace the X on the shorter pencil.

Reread the problem about Ling.

(MP) **Construct arguments and critique reasoning of others.**

- **How could Ling find out which pencil is longer and which is shorter?** She could place the two pencils at the same starting place and compare where each one ends.

Name _____

Compare Lengths

(I Can) measure and compare length.

Listen and Draw

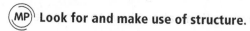

Check children's work.

DIRECTIONS Look at the pencils. Compare the lengths of the two pencils. Use the words *longer* or *shorter* to describe the lengths. Trace the circle around the longer pencil. Trace the X on the shorter pencil.

Chapter 19 • Lesson 1   **767**

(ML) ## Multilingual Support

STRATEGY: Identify Relationships

Draw on the board two pencils that are different lengths. Point to the shorter one and say, **This pencil is shorter than that pencil.** Point to the longer one and explain that it is longer.

Repeat with two same-size pencils, saying, **These are about the same length.**

Direct children's attention to the two pencils on the page. Review their relationship and ask children to point to the pair of pencils on the board that shows the same relationship as the pencils on the page.

1

Check children's work.

2   **3** ⊘

Check children's work.

Check children's work.

DIRECTIONS 1. Use connecting cubes to measure the length of the pencil. Trace and color the cube train. 2. Make a cube train that is shorter than the cube train shown. Draw and color the cube train. 3. Make a cube train that is taller than the cube train shown. Draw and color the cube train.

③ Explain

Share and Show

Materials connecting cubes

(MP) Use appropriate tools strategically.

For Problems 1–3, have children use connecting cubes to make cube trains.

- **Look at Problem 1. Use cubes to measure the pencil.**
- **Where will your cube train begin?** at the same line as the pencil **How many cubes will you use?** 6
- **Look at Problem 2. How many cubes are in the train?** 5 **How many cubes will you use to make a shorter train?** Possible answers: one to four cubes
- **Look at the yellow cube train in Problem 3. Make a cube train that is taller. How many cubes did you use?** Possible answers: four to eight cubes

(MP) Attend to precision.

Have children compare the cube trains in each problem, using the terms *longer* or *taller* or *the same length as* and tell why it is important that each cube train begins at the same point on the page.

Use the checked problem for Quick Check.

✓ **Quick Check** **MTSS** **RtI**

If ➤ a child misses the checked problem

Then ➤ **Differentiate Instruction** with
  - Reteach 19.1
  - Waggle

⚠ **Common Errors**

Error Children may not understand the term *taller*.

Example For Problem 3, children make a two-cube train.

Springboard to Learning Align two cube trains of different heights. Have children follow the height of each cube train with a finger and tell which cube train goes up farther. Explain that the cube train that goes up farther is the *taller* cube train.

Ready for More ⏰ Kinesthetic / Visual Partners

Materials small classroom objects

Have each child choose a small, easily measured item (such as a pencil). Ask partners to trade objects with each other.

Challenge each partner to find a classroom object that is the same length as his or her object. Tell children that the object they find must be a different kind of object (for example, a paintbrush, not a pencil).

Once children find the objects, have them draw both objects, one under the other to check size.

Children can share their work with each other and then with the class.

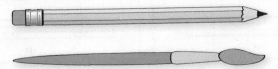

Share and Show

For Problems 4 through 6, have children use cubes to make, draw, and color cube trains.

- **Look at Problem 4. Make a cube train longer than the orange cube train. Where will the cube train begin?** on the same line as the orange cube train **How many cubes will you use?** Possible answers: five to ten cubes

Continue with similar questioning for Problems 5 and 6. Have children share their answers. Discuss why there is more than one possible answer for Problems 4 and 5, but not Problem 6.

 Reason abstractly and quantitatively.

Read the following problem.

- **Look at the cube train that you made in Problem 4. How could you make the cube train shorter?** Take away some cubes.

Read the following problems.

- **Compare the cube trains you made in Problems 5 and 6. Which one is shorter? Explain.** Children's responses should include that the shorter cube train is the one with fewer cubes.

- **Describe two ways you can make a cube train shorter than the glue stick in Problem 6.** I can count the cubes that measure the glue stick and make a train with fewer cubes. I can make a cube train that doesn't stick out as far when the ends of both trains are lined up.

Review with children words they could use to compare the lengths of two cube trains.

Math on the Spot Use this video to help children model and solve this type of problem.

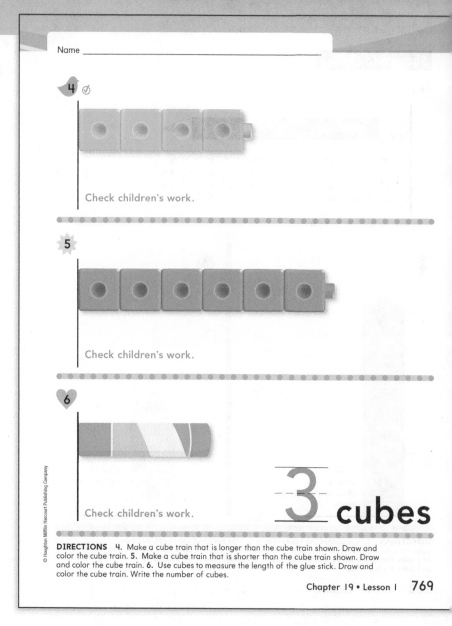

Name _____

4 ✓

Check children's work.

5

Check children's work.

6

Check children's work.

3 cubes

DIRECTIONS 4. Make a cube train that is longer than the cube train shown. Draw and color the cube train. 5. Make a cube train that is shorter than the cube train shown. Draw and color the cube train. 6. Use cubes to measure the length of the glue stick. Draw and color the cube train. Write the number of cubes.

Chapter 19 • Lesson 1   769

Meeting Individual Needs

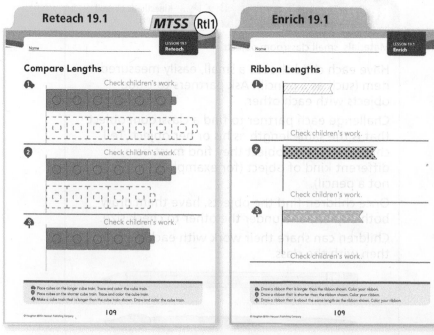

Reteach 19.1   MTSS (Rtl1)   **Enrich 19.1**

Compare Lengths

Check children's work.

Ribbon Lengths

Check children's work.

7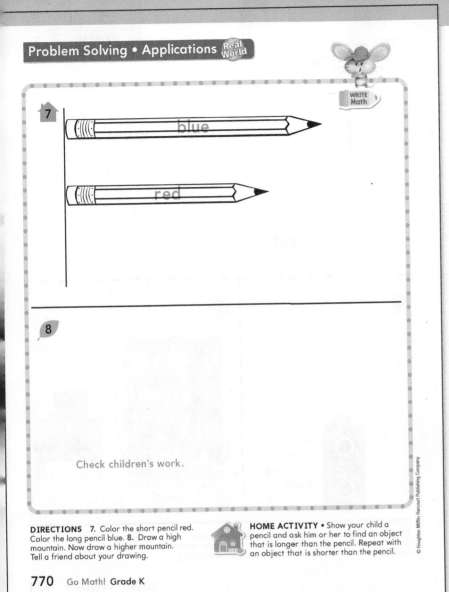

blue

red

8

Check children's work.

DIRECTIONS 7. Color the short pencil red. Color the long pencil blue. **8.** Draw a high mountain. Now draw a higher mountain. Tell a friend about your drawing.

HOME ACTIVITY • Show your child a pencil and ask him or her to find an object that is longer than the pencil. Repeat with an object that is shorter than the pencil.

770 Go Math! **Grade K**

Problem Solving Applications

Read the problem for **Problem 7**. Discuss the meaning of the term *about the same length*. Explain that when objects start at the same place and end at about the same place, they are about the same length. Ask children to explain how they will solve the problem.

- **Are the pencils the same length?** no

(MP) **Look for and make use of structure.**

- **Which pencil is shorter? Explain.** The bottom pencil is shorter because it does not stick out as far.

(MP) **Model with mathematics.**

Problem 8 Ask children what the problem is asking them to show in their drawings. Establish that they must show two mountains, one higher than the other.

5 Evaluate | Formative Assessment

I Can

Have pairs of children describe and compare two objects to answer the I Can statement.

I can measure and compare length by . . . putting two objects, one under the other, starting at the same place. I can see if one object is shorter than, longer than, or about the same length as the other object.

Exit Ticket

After children complete their drawings for **Problem 8,** invite them to tell a friend about their drawings and use the words *taller* and *shorter* to compare the items.

DIFFERENTIATED INSTRUCTION • Independent Activities

Version 2.0
Differentiated Centers Kit

Tabletop Flipchart

Mini-lessons for reteaching to targeted small groups

Readers

Supports key math skills and concepts in real-world situations.

Games

Reinforce math content and vocabulary

Activities

Meaningful and fun math practice

Compare Lengths

Use the Practice and Homework pages to provide children with more practice of the concepts and skills presented in this lesson. Children master their understanding as they complete practice items.

Name _____

LESSON 19.1
Practice and Homework

Compare Lengths

1.

_____ cubes

2.

3.

Check children's work.

© Houghton Mifflin Harcourt Publishing Company

DIRECTIONS I. Use cubes to measure the length of the crayon. Write how many cubes long it is. 2. Make a cube train that is taller than the cube train shown. Draw and color the cube train. 3. Circle the tall object.

Chapter 19 • Lesson I **771**

PATH TO FLUENCY • Activity

Make a Longer and a Shorter Cube Train

Materials connecting cubes

Investigate Have children make a longer and a shorter cube train than a given cube train and order the cube trains from longest to shortest.

Math Talk Show a three-cube train.

- **If you wanted to build a longer cube train, what would you have to do?** Possible answer: Start with a three-cube train and add some more cubes.

- **If you wanted to build a shorter cube train, what would you have to do?** Possible answer: Start with a three-cube train and take away some cubes.

- **How can you place the cube trains in order from longest to shortest ?** Possible answer: I can put all the cube trains on the same starting line. I can put the cube train that goes out the farthest on top. Then I can put the cube train that goes out the next farthest in the middle and the shortest cube train last.

Summarize Children should be able to make a longer and shorter cube train than the given cube train and then order the cube trains from longest to shortest.

- See if children can make a longer cube train.

- Watch if children are able to make a shorter cube train.

- Children should demonstrate an understanding of longer and shorter by ordering the cube trains.

- Children should be able to use appropriate vocabulary such as *longer than* and *shorter than* to compare the cube trains.

Lesson Check

 4

Check children's work.

Continue to practice concepts and skills with Lesson Check. Use Spiral Review to engage children in previously taught concepts and to promote content retention.

Spiral Review

 5

 6

Check children's work.

DIRECTIONS **4.** Make a cube train that is shorter than the cube train shown. Draw and color the cube train. **5.** Which shape is a sphere? Mark an X on the shape. **6.** Look at the shape. Draw a shape that is alike in some way. Tell how the two shapes are alike.

© Houghton Mifflin Harcourt Publishing Company

Lesson at a Glance
Compare Weights

SNAPSHOT

Mathematical Standards
- Describe measurable attributes of objects, such as length or weight. Describe several measurable attributes of a single object.
- Directly compare two objects with a measurable attribute in common, to see which object has "more of"/"less of" the attribute, and describe the difference.

Mathematical Practices and Processes
- Model with mathematics.
- Attend to precision.
- Construct arguments and critique reasoning of others.
- Reason abstractly and quantitatively.

(I Can) **Objective**

I can compare the weights of two objects.

Learning Goal
Directly compare the weights of two objects.

Language Objective
Children explain and demonstrate to a partner how to compare the weights of two objects.

MATERIALS
- MathBoard
- classroom objects

ACROSS THE GRADES

Grade K
Directly compare two objects that have an attribute which can be measured in common. Express the comparison using language to describe the difference.

After
Compare and order the length of up to three objects using direct and indirect comparison.

ABOUT THE MATH

Why Teach This?
In this lesson, children hold classroom objects in their hands to compare the weights. They use the words *heavier* and *lighter* as they make decisions comparing the weights of the objects.

Why use real objects? To clarify the weight concept, children must experience it. They must hold objects—ones with discernable differences in weight—in their hands to judge the relative weights. Later, children will develop enough background knowledge to be able to look at pictures of familiar objects and compare their weights.

For more professional learning go online to Teacher's Corner.

DAILY ROUTINES

🖥 Problem of the Day 19.2

Show children a table with nothing on it.

How many pencils are on the table? 0

How many pens are on the table? 0

How many books are on the table? 0

How many cubes are on the table? 0

🖥 Vocabulary   heavier, lighter, weight

- Interactive Student Edition
- Multilingual Glossary

Vocabulary Builder

Have children draw pictures to demonstrate understanding of the vocabulary terms. For each term, there should be two pictures. Have them circle the **heavier** object in the first set and the **lighter** object in the second set. Make sure that the third set is two objects that are about the same **weight**.

Check children's drawings.

FOCUSING ON THE WHOLE STUDENT

Access Prior Knowledge

Ask children to draw a row of 15 evenly-spaced dots.

- **Count the 15 dots together.**
- **Do you think a row of 20 evenly-spaced dots of the same size would be shorter or longer?** longer
- **Do you think a row of 10 evenly-spaced dots of the same size would be shorter or longer?** shorter

💬 Social & Emotional Learning

Social Awareness Discuss with children how they know when people are upset or having a hard time with their learning. *Sometimes other children say how they are feeling. What words do they use to let you know that they are upset? Remember how they talk about their feelings, and you will have words to describe your feelings the next time you are upset about your learning.*

❶ Engage

with the Interactive Student Edition

I Can Objective

I can compare the weights of two objects.

Making Connections

Invite children to tell you what they know about comparing things.

- **How can you tell which of two objects is longer or taller than another?** You can compare them.
- **What are some ways you can compare things?** Answers may vary. You can put them next to each other, you can measure them, etc.

Learning Activity

Tell a story about Rafferty and Scout finding a leaf and a rock in a bucket. Display a leaf and a rock for children. Tell them that Rafferty wants to take the lighter object back to a burrow, and Scout wants to help him by carrying the lighter object.

Guide children toward thinking about comparing weights.

- **What did Rafferty and Scout find in the bucket?** a leaf and a rock
- **What does Rafferty want to do?** take the lighter object back to his burrow
- **What does Scout want to know?** how to find out which object is lighter

② Explore

Listen and Draw 🌎

Discuss the meaning of the word *weight* (the measure of how heavy something is). Read aloud this problem as children listen.

Kareem holds a block in one hand and a book in the other. Which object do you think is heavier, the block or the book?

(MP) **Model with mathematics.**

Have a volunteer act out the problem with props. Have other children use the words *lighter* and *heavier* to compare the weights.

• **Which object is *lighter*, the block or the book?** the block **Trace the circle.**

• **Which object is *heavier*, the block or the book?** the book **Trace the X.**

• **Which object is bigger?** the book

• **Can you think of an object that is bigger than the book, but lighter?** Possible answer: a balloon

(MP) **Construct arguments and critique reasoning of others.**

• **What can you tell about the size of objects and their weights?** Sometimes a big object can feel light and a small object can feel heavy.

Help children conclude that a small object can be heavy and a big object can be light. Have children give examples, such as a large leaf and a small marble, a sheet of paper and a rock, a poster and a picture frame.

• **What are some ways to describe something that is big?** Answers may vary.

Name _____

Compare Weights

(I Can) compare the weights of two objects.

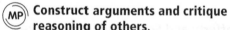 **Listen and Draw** 🌎

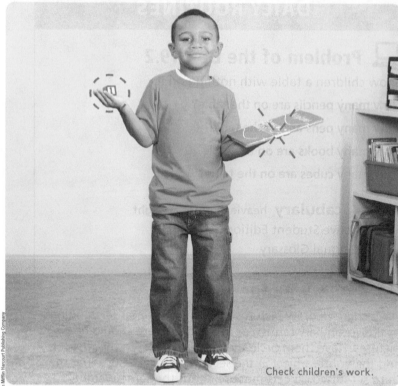

Check children's work.

DIRECTIONS Look at the picture. Compare the weights of the two objects. Use the words *heavier* or *lighter* to describe the weights. Trace the circle around the lighter object. Trace the X on the heavier object.

© Houghton Mifflin Harcourt Publishing Company

Chapter 19 • Lesson 2 **773**

(ML) **Multilingual Support**

STRATEGY: Identify Relationships

Collect a group of classroom objects.

Have children take turns selecting two objects from the group, holding one in each hand, and using the words *lighter*, *heavier*, or *about the same weight* to compare the weights.

For each pair of objects, ask children which one is bigger and encourage them to describe the relationship between the sizes and the weights of the objects.

left   right

DIRECTIONS Find the first object in the row and hold it in your left hand. Find the rest of the objects in the row and take turns holding each of the objects in your right hand. **1.** Trace to show the object that is heavier than the object in your left hand. **2.** Circle the object that weighs more than the object in your left hand. **3–4.** Circle the object that weighs less than the object in your left hand.

Ready for More   Kinesthetic Partners

Materials classroom objects

Display an assortment of objects of similar and different sizes and different weights.

Have one partner point to two objects and guess which is heavier and which is lighter without holding them.

Have partners take turns holding both objects and talk about whether the guess was correct.

Ask partners to take turns repeating the activity with different objects. Have partners make at least one conclusion based on their findings. Possible answer: A small object can be heavier than a large object.

---

③ Explain

Share and Show   Math Board

Children will need the items on this page. Point to the hands on the page to help children distinguish their own left and right hands. Tell children to think about how heavy the objects are as they hold them.

(MP) Attend to precision.

- **Look at Problem 1. Hold a pair of scissors in your left hand. Then hold a paper clip in your right hand. Put the paper clip down and pick up a book. Put the book down and pick up a rubber band.**
- **Which of the objects that you held in your right hand is heavier than the scissors?** the book **Trace around the book.**

Help children work through Problems 2–4 in a similar way.

- **How do you know when an object is heavier?** Possible answer: My hand feels like it is being pulled down more.

Use the checked problems for Quick Check.

✓ Quick Check   **MTSS** (RtI)

If ➤ a child misses the checked problems

Then ➤ **Differentiate Instruction** with
- Reteach 19.2
- Waggle

⚠ Common Errors

Error Children may confuse the terms *heavier* and *lighter*.

Example In Problem 2, children identify the pencil as being heavier.

Springboard to Learning Have children hold each of the items again. As they hold each pair of items, name the relationship. For example, say, **The backpack is *heavier* than the notebook. The notebook is *lighter* than the backpack.**

Share and Show

Children will need to find items in the classroom to complete the page. Work through the problems together. Begin by having children find a book and hold it in one of their hands.

Problem 5 Children find an object in the classroom that is lighter than the book and draw it in the workspace.

Problem 6 Children find an object in the classroom that is heavier than the book and draw it in the workspace.

Math on the Spot Use this video to help children model and solve this type of problem.

Higher-Order Thinking

Read the following problem.

Kelly bought two different-sized watermelons. She wants to serve the heavier one. Draw the two watermelons and circle the one she served.

Children could discuss that in this case, the larger watermelon weighs more than the smaller one. However, size is not always an indicator of a heavier weight. Ask if anyone can think of something smaller in size being heavier. Possible answer: An acorn is smaller than a feather, but it is heavier than the feather.

 Construct arguments and critique reasoning of others.

Challenge children to explain why a bigger watermelon would most likely be heavier than a smaller watermelon, even though bigger objects can be lighter than smaller objects. The two watermelons are the same kind of object.

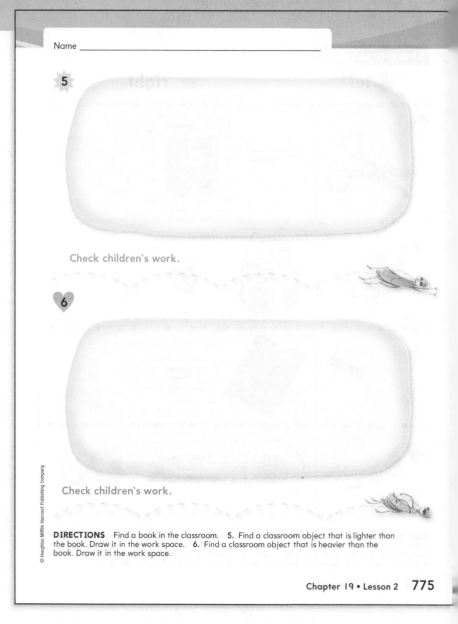

Name _____

5

Check children's work.

6

Check children's work.

DIRECTIONS Find a book in the classroom. **5.** Find a classroom object that is lighter than the book. Draw it in the work space. **6.** Find a classroom object that is heavier than the book. Draw it in the work space.

© Houghton Mifflin Harcourt Publishing Company

Meeting Individual Needs

Reteach 19.2   **MTSS** (Rtl1)   **Enrich 19.2**

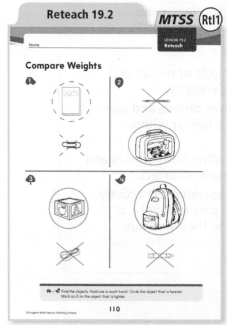

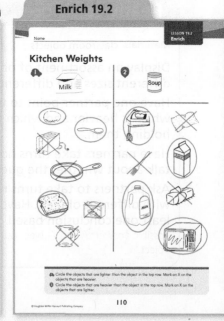

7

Check children's work.

DIRECTIONS 7. Draw to show something that is heavy and something that is light. Tell a friend about your drawing.

HOME ACTIVITY • Have your child compare the weights of two objects in a house. Then have your child use the terms *heavier* and *lighter* to describe the weights.

© Houghton Mifflin Harcourt Publishing Company

776 Go Math! **Grade K**

---

④ Elaborate

Problem Solving Applications **Real World**

 Express regularity in repeated reasoning.

Read the problem. Ask children to explain how they will solve it.

Before children draw to show what they know about comparing weights, establish that their drawing has to show two objects that they can compare by weight. One object should be heavier and one should be lighter. Have children suggest objects to draw.

⑤ Evaluate | Formative Assessment

I Can

Have children explain and demonstrate to a partner how to answer the I Can statement.

I can compare the weights of two objects by . . . holding two objects, one in each hand. I can see which one feels heavier and which one feels lighter.

Exit Ticket

Invite children to share their drawings and use the terms *heavier* and *lighter* to describe the weights of the objects they drew.

DIFFERENTIATED INSTRUCTION • Independent Activities

Grab and Go!™
Version 2.0
Differentiated Centers Kit

Tabletop Flipchart

Mini-lessons for reteaching to targeted small groups

Readers

Supports key math skills and concepts in real-world situations.

Games

Reinforce math content and vocabulary

Activities

Meaningful and fun math practice

Compare Weights

Use the Practice and Homework pages to provide children with more practice of the concepts and skills presented in this lesson. Children master their understanding as they complete practice items.

Compare Weights

DIRECTIONS Find the first object in the row and hold it in your left hand. Find the rest of the objects in the row and hold each object in your right hand. **1–2.** Circle the object that is lighter than the object in your left hand. **3–4.** Circle the object that is heavier than the object in your left hand.

Chapter 19 • Lesson 2   **777**

CROSS-CURRICULAR

SCIENCE

Materials identical empty paper cups, water, marbles, cotton balls, sand, and other materials, each labeled with the name of the material

- Explain that scientists measure different attributes of materials to see how they are related.
- Children will compare the other materials to water. Have them take turns holding a cup of a material and a cup of water to compare their weights.
- On the board, make two lists: **Heavier than Water** and **Lighter than Water**. As each child makes a comparison, write the results in the correct list.

Heavier than Water	Lighter than Water
marbles	cotton balls
sand	

SOCIAL STUDIES

- Discuss how trucks travel all over our country, bringing food to stores and restaurants. Tell children that two trucks of the same size are carrying different kinds of food. They will need to decide which truck has the heavier load.

Truck 1	Truck 2	Heavier Load
bags of raw rice	bags of rice cakes	Truck 1
boxes of fresh spinach	boxes of oranges	Truck 2
sacks of fresh corn	sacks of corn flakes	Truck 1

- Have children explain how they decided which load was heavier. Let children suggest loads for the trucks so the class can decide which load is heavier.

Lesson Check

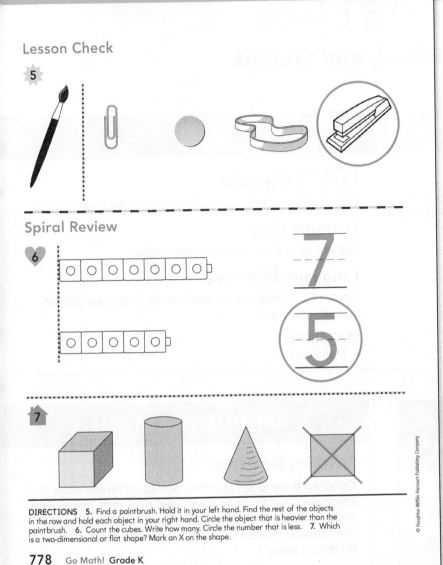

Spiral Review

© Houghton Mifflin Harcourt Publishing Company

DIRECTIONS 5. Find a paintbrush. Hold it in your left hand. Find the rest of the objects in the row and hold each object in your right hand. Circle the object that is heavier than the paintbrush. 6. Count the cubes. Write how many. Circle the number that is less. 7. Which is a two-dimensional or flat shape? Mark an X on the shape.

Continue to practice concepts and skills with Lesson Check. Use Spiral Review to engage children in previously taught concepts and to promote content retention.

Lesson at a Glance
Length, Height, and Weight

SNAPSHOT

Mathematical Standards
- Describe measurable attributes of objects, such as length or weight. Describe several measurable attributes of a single object.

Mathematical Processes and Practices
- Look for and make use of structure.
- Construct arguments and critique reasoning of others.
- Attend to precision.
- Express regularity in repeated reasoning.

(I Can) **Objective**

I can describe several measurable attributes of a single object.

Learning Goal
Describe several ways to measure one object.

Language Objective
Teams of 3–4 children draw and describe three ways you can measure one object.

MATERIALS
- MathBoard

ACROSS THE GRADES

Grade K
Describe measurable attributes of objects, such as length or weight. Describe several measurable attributes of a single object.

After
Order three objects by length; compare the lengths of two objects indirectly by using a third object.

ABOUT THE MATH

Teaching for Depth

Children have been learning about different ways to compare objects. They have used different measuring techniques to measure different attributes. By now they should realize that objects can be measured in different ways.

Children should understand that a single object can have measurements of length and weight. In this lesson, children will gain exposure to height and will also discuss measuring objects by weight.

These skills build the foundation for using units of measure in later grades and in real life to measure objects by inches, centimeters, ounces, or pounds.

For more professional learning go online to Teacher's Corner.

Problem of the Day 19.3

Look at the two cube towers.

- **Which one is taller?** the yellow tower
- **Which one is shorter?** the orange tower

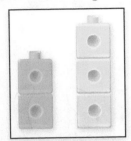

Have children use the words *taller* and *shorter* to compare the heights of two other objects.

Vocabulary height

- Interactive Student Edition
- Multilingual Glossary

Fluency Builder

Add Within 5

Materials addition fact cards (within 5)

Provide each child with an addition fact card. Allow a moment for children to solve the cards they have.

- **If you have a card with an answer of 4, raise your card so that everyone can see.** 2 + 2, 1 + 3, 3 + 1, 4 + 0, 0 + 4

Check children's fact cards. Look for any fact cards children may have raised with a different sum. Repeat the activity with other sums within 5.

FOCUSING ON THE WHOLE STUDENT

Access Prior Knowledge

Choose one or more of the following activities:

- Have children choose a classroom object and tell about its length, height, or weight.
- Have partners exchange a short dialogue about a trip to the supermarket or to another store in which they use the words *length*, *height*, and *weight*.

① Engage

with the Interactive Student Edition

I Can Objective

I can describe several measurable attributes of a single object.

Making Connections

Ask children to tell what they know about measuring objects.

- **When you decide which of two objects is shorter or longer, what are you comparing?** length
- **Keenan says his block tower is taller than Ellen's. What is he comparing?** height
- **What are you comparing when you find out if an object is lighter or heavier?** weight

Learning Activity

Guide children to think about the properties of objects. Ask the following questions.

- **What is length?** how long something is from side to side
- **What is height?** how tall or short something is
- **What is weight?** how light or heavy something is

Explore

Listen and Draw Real World

Read the problem aloud as children listen.

Tom and Kim want to measure their books in different ways. What are the ways they can measure their books?

Have children look at the book and the lines on the page. Explain that the lines show how to measure *length* and *height*.

Point to the horizontal line and read the word *length*. Discuss its meaning (the measure of how long something is).

(MP) **Attend to precision.**

- **Trace your finger over the line that shows how to measure the length of the book. How would you describe this line?** Possible answer: It goes from side to side.

Point to the vertical line and read the word *height*. Discuss its meaning (the measure of how tall something is).

- **Trace your finger over the line that shows how to measure the height of the book. How would you describe this line?** Possible answer: It goes from bottom to top.

- **Can you think of another way to measure the book?** by weight

Discuss the meaning of the word *weight* (the measure of how heavy something is). Demonstrate picking up a book and describing it as *heavy* or *light*. Reread the problem about Tom and Kim.

- **How can Tom and Kim measure their books?** They can measure their books by length, by height, and by weight.

Name _____

Length, Height, and Weight

(I Can) describe several measurable attributes of a single object.

Listen and Draw Real World

height

length

© Houghton Mifflin Harcourt Publishing Company

DIRECTIONS Look at the book. Trace your finger over the line that shows how to measure the height of the book. Trace your finger over the line that shows how to measure the length of the book. Talk about another way to measure the book. Check children's work.

Chapter 19 • Lesson 3 **779**

(ML) ## Multilingual Support

STRATEGY: Scaffold Language

Help children practice their comprehension by describing the *length*, *height*, and *weight* of books.

Give each group of children a book from the classroom. Review that the book can be measured in different ways: length, height, and weight.

Have a member of the group demonstrate how to measure the book by length, and have them describe the length.

Repeat with height and weight.

Share and Show

1

Check children's work.

2

Check children's work.

DIRECTIONS 1–2. Use red to trace the line that shows how to measure the length. Use blue to trace the line that shows how to measure the height. Talk about another way to measure the object.

780 Go Math! Grade K

© Houghton Mifflin Harcourt Publishing Company

Ready for More

⏱ Visual / Spatial
Individual / Partners

Materials glue, construction paper, pictures of objects that can easily show length and height

Give partners pictures of different objects. One partner glues a picture to construction paper and draws a line to show how to measure the object by height.

The other partner checks the picture to see if the line that shows height has been drawn correctly. Partners repeat the activity but this time draw a line to show how to measure an object by length.

Have partners discuss other ways that the object could be measured in real life.

 **Explain**

Share and Show Math Board

Materials red and blue crayons

Have children locate the tape dispenser in Problem 1. Point out the dashed lines at the bottom and side of the tape dispenser.

- **Which line shows how to measure the length of the tape dispenser?** Possible answer: the line that goes from side to side

Use red to trace this line.

- **Which line shows how to measure the height of the tape dispenser?** Possible answer: the line that goes from bottom to top

Use blue to trace this line.

- **Is there another way to measure the tape dispenser?** by weight

 Look for and make use of structure.

Guide children through Problem 2. Remind children that the lines on the page are there to show them how to measure. As children complete the problem, have them explain why they colored each line as they did.

 Common Errors

Error Children may confuse length and height.

Example Children color the wrong line red.

Springboard to Learning Remind children that lines showing length run side to side. Have them finger trace that line. Then tell them that lines going from bottom to top show height. Have them finger trace that line.

Share and Show

For **Problem 3**, call attention to the dashed lines around the backpack.

- **Which line shows how to measure the length of the backpack?** the line that goes from side to side

Use red to trace that line.

- **Which line shows how to measure the height of the backpack?** the line that goes from bottom to top

Use blue to trace that line.

Ask similar questions for **Problems 4–6**.

Children should discuss how they can measure by weight.

Use the checked problem for Quick Check.

✓ Quick Check   *MTSS* (RtI)

If →	a child misses the checked problem
Then →	Differentiate Instruction with • Reteach 19.3 • Waggle

Higher-Order Thinking

- Draw a book.
- Use red to draw the line that shows how to measure the length.
- Use blue to draw the line that shows how to measure the height.

(MP) **Construct arguments and critique reasoning of others.**

Children should discuss attributes that are measurable, such as distance around the book. Encourage them to think about attributes that cannot be measured, such as color or number of pages. Discuss the differences between attributes that can and cannot be measured.

Name _____

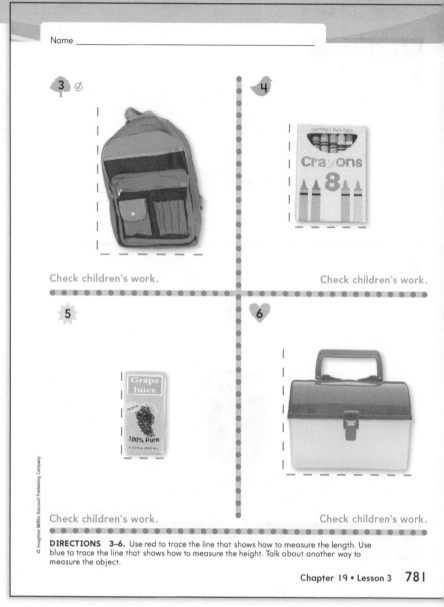

3 ✓

Check children's work.

4

Check children's work.

5

Check children's work.

6

Check children's work.

DIRECTIONS 3–6. Use red to trace the line that shows how to measure the length. Use blue to trace the line that shows how to measure the height. Talk about another way to measure the object.

Chapter 19 • Lesson 3   **781**

Meeting Individual Needs

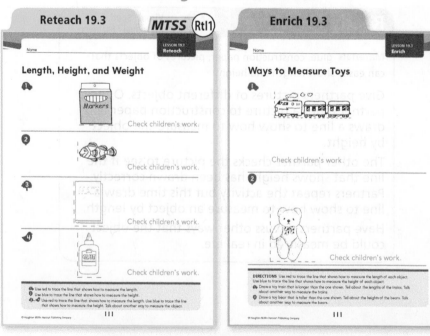

Reteach 19.3   *MTSS* (RtI)

Name _____

Length, Height, and Weight

Check children's work.

Enrich 19.3

Name _____

Ways to Measure Toys

Check children's work.

7

WRITE
Math

Check children's work.

DIRECTIONS 7. Draw to show what you know about measuring an object in more than one way.

HOME ACTIVITY • Show your child a household object that can be easily measured by length, height, and weight. Ask your child to describe the different ways to measure the object.

© Houghton Mifflin Harcourt Publishing Company

782   Go Math! Grade K

---

④ Elaborate

Problem Solving Applications

(MP) **Express regularity in repeated reasoning.**

After you read **Problem 7**, ask children to summarize what they are expected to do. Have them draw objects to show what they know about measuring by length and by height. Remind children to draw a horizontal line to show length and a vertical line to show height.

Have children explain why their drawings show how to measure an object in more than one way.

⑤ Evaluate | Formative Assessment

I Can

Have teams of children describe in their own words how to demonstrate the skill for the I Can statement.

I can describe several measurable attributes of a single object by ... measuring the height of an object by going from bottom to top. I can measure the weight of an object by holding it to see if it is heavy or light.

Exit Ticket

Invite children to share their drawings, describing how they measured by length and height, and then discuss with a friend that objects can also be measured by weight.

DIFFERENTIATED INSTRUCTION • Independent Activities

Grab and Go!™

Version 2.0

Differentiated Centers Kit

Tabletop Flipchart

Mini-lessons for reteaching to targeted small groups

Readers

Supports key math skills and concepts in real-world situations

Games

Reinforce math content and vocabulary

Activities

Meaningful and fun math practice

Length, Height, and Weight

Use the Practice and Homework pages to provide children with more practice of the concepts and skills presented in this lesson. Children master their understanding as they complete practice items.

Name _____

Length, Height, and Weight

1

Check children's work.

2

Markers

Check children's work.

3

Check children's work.

4

GLUE

Check children's work.

DIRECTIONS 1–4. Use red to trace the line that shows how to measure the length. Use blue to trace the line that shows how to measure the height. Talk about another way to measure the object.

© Houghton Mifflin Harcourt Publishing Company

Chapter 19 • Lesson 3   **783**

Lesson Check

1

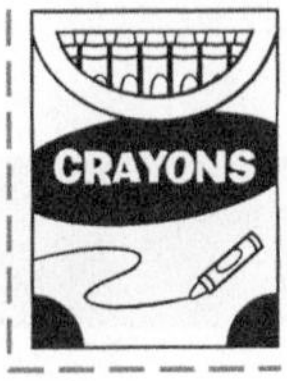

Check children's work.

Spiral Review

2

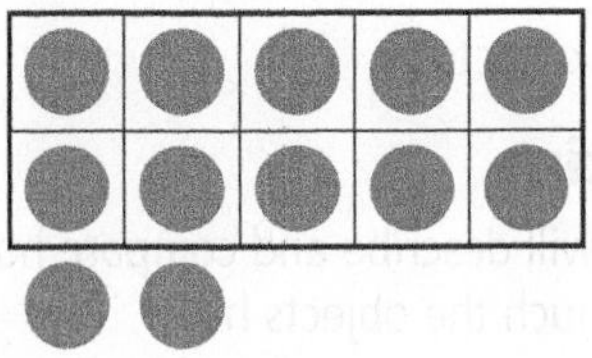

3

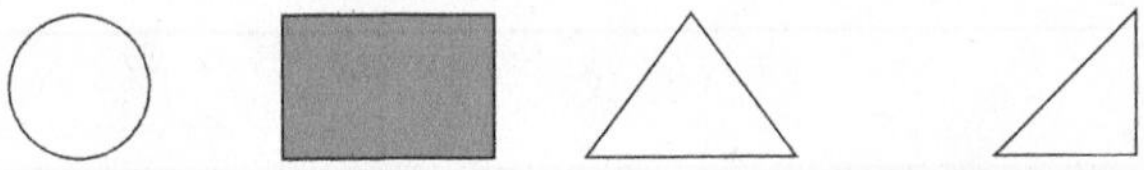

DIRECTIONS 1. Use red to trace the line that shows how to measure the length. Use blue to trace the line that shows how to measure the height. 2. Count and tell how many. Write the number. 3. Which shape is a rectangle? Color the rectangle.

Continue to practice concepts and skills with Lesson Check. Use Spiral Review to engage children in previously taught concepts and to promote content retention.

Lesson at a Glance
Compare Volume

SNAPSHOT

Mathematical Standards
● Describe measurable attributes of objects, such as length or weight. Describe several measurable attributes of a single object.

Mathematical Practices and Processes
● Express regularity in repeated reasoning.
● Model with mathematics.
● Attend to precision.
● Construct arguments and critique reasoning of others.
● Reason abstractly and quantitatively.
● Look for and make use of structure.

(I Can) Objective
I can compare volume and identify other measurable attributes of objects.

Learning Goal
Compare the volumes of objects.

Language Objective
With a partner, children will describe and compare how much space objects take up or how much the objects hold.

MATERIALS
• MathBoard

ACROSS THE GRADES

Grade K
Directly compare two objects that have an attribute which can be measured in common. Express the comparison using language to describe the difference.

After
Compare and order the length of up to three objects using direct and indirect comparison.

ABOUT THE MATH

Why Teach This?
In this lesson, children discuss an object's volume in several ways. They begin by describing how much space an object takes up. When comparing two objects, the object that takes up more space has the greater volume.

Another way to think about volume is to consider how much an object holds. Mathematically, this is called capacity, but it is sometimes used as a way to describe volume. *Full, more full*, and *less full* or *has less* and *has more* are terms that children use to describe this attribute. Another way children approach capacity is to fill objects with handfuls of sand, gravel, or beads to determine which object holds more and which object holds less. While not all objects have capacity, that is, not all objects can be filled, all objects have volume. By their very existence, they take up space.

For more professional learning go online to Teacher's Corner.

 **Problem of the Day 19.4**

How many faces does a cube have? Draw to show the number.

6; Check children's drawings.

 **Vocabulary** volume, more, less

- Interactive Student Edition
- Multilingual Glossary

Vocabulary Builder

Have children draw pictures to demonstrate understanding of the vocabulary terms. Then have children discuss with a partner other ways to describe their pictures.

Check children's drawings.

FOCUSING ON THE WHOLE STUDENT

Access Prior Knowledge

Read the following problem aloud to the class.

Marv and Luisa collect shells. Marv has 23 shells. Luisa has 19 shells. Who has more shells? Marv

Invite volunteers to share their answers and problem solving strategies. Then present similar problems to review comparing two quantities to determine which is more and which is less.

① Engage

with the Interactive Student Edition

I Can Objective

I can compare volume and identify other measurable attributes of objects.

Making Connections

Show children three cups of water—one full, one empty, and one about half full. Discuss with children how to describe them.

- **Which cup is full?** Children should identify the full cup.

- **Which cup is empty?** Children should identify the empty cup.

- **How would you describe the other cup?** Sample answer: half full

Learning Activity

Materials containers, cups, rice

- Give children two containers. Have them fill each with cups of beads or gravel, counting the number of cups as they fill the container.

- Have them use the measurement of the number of cups it takes to fill each container to decide which container holds more.

- **Which container holds more? Explain.** Possible answer: The container that holds the greater number of cups of beads (or gravel).

- If time allows, repeat with other containers.

 Common Errors

Error Children may lose track of the number of handfuls used to fill a container.

Example Children record too few handfuls and incorrectly identify the container that holds more.

Springboard to Learning Have children draw a circle for each handful as it is placed in a container. Then count the circles.

Explore

Listen and Draw

Have children think about how big cars are in real life.

 Model with mathematics.

- **Would a car fit in this classroom? Why or why not?** Possible answer: Yes, but we could not get it through the door.

Explain to children that they are going to be comparing *volume*.

 Construct arguments and critique reasoning of others.

- **Volume is the amount of space an object takes up. Can you think of an object that does not take up any space?** Possible answer: No, all objects take up space.

Have children draw two objects: one that takes up less space than a car and one that takes up more space than a car.

- **How do you know your object takes up more space than a car?** Possible answer: It is bigger than a car.

- **How do you know your object takes up less space than a car?** Possible answer: It would fit inside a car.

Have children share their drawings and reasoning. For each object, have them complete the sentence frame: ___ has more/less volume than a car.

 Attend to precision.

- **Would a rock work best for measuring length, weight, or volume?** Possible answer: weight

---

Name _____

Compare Volume

(I Can) compare volume and identify other measurable attributes of objects.

Listen and Draw

Check children's work.

takes up less space | takes up more space

DIRECTIONS Think about how big cars are in real life. Use red to draw something that takes up less space than a car. Use blue to draw something that takes up more space than a car.

Chapter 19 • Lesson 4   **785**

 **Multilingual Support**

STRATEGY: Define

Materials containers

- Children can define words by using them in context and by matching visuals to the words.

- Show children a large container such as a bucket and a small container such as a coffee mug.

- Have children identify which container would hold *more* and which would hold *less*.

- Then have children name containers that would hold more or less than either container.

1.

2.

Check children's work.

3.

DIRECTIONS 1. Circle the jar that is more full. Mark an X on the jar that is less full. 2. Use containers like the ones shown. Count how many handfuls of rice, sand, or beans you need to fill each container. Draw a line under the container that holds more. Draw a box around the container that holds less. 3. Circle the objects that have volume. Tell a friend how else you could measure each object.

786 Go Math! Grade K

© Houghton Mifflin Harcourt Publishing Company

---

③ Explain

Share and Show

Children will consider different aspects of volume as they compare objects on this page.

In Problem 1, children are shown two jars and asked to identify which is more full and which is less full.

(MP) Reason abstractly and quantitatively.

- **What does *more full* mean?** Sample answer: More full means that the jar has more in it.

- **How can you tell which jar is *less full*?** Sample answer: Since the jars are the same size, the one that is less full has a lower level inside.

Have children circle the jar that is more full and cross out the jar that is less full.

For Problem 2, provide a cup and a bowl for children to fill. Allow them to use handfuls of sand, gravel, or beads to fill each.

- **How will you know which holds more?** Sample answer: The one that holds more will take more handfuls to fill.

- **How will you know how many handfuls it takes to fill each object?** Sample answer: I will count 1 more every time I put a handful in the container.

For Problem 3, remind children that all objects have volume, even if they cannot hold something.

Use the checked problem for Quick Check.

Ready for More   Kinesthetic Individual / Partners

Materials containers

- Challenge children to find two containers, of different heights and widths, that hold about the same amount of gravel.

- Have partners check that the containers do hold about the same amount.

✓ Quick Check MTSS RtI

If ➤ a child misses the checked problem

Then ➤ **Differentiate Instruction with**
- Reteach 19.4
- Waggle

Share and Show

 Look for and make use of structure.

In Problem 4, children compare how much the jars have in them.

- **What does it mean to have less?** Possible answer: It means that there is a smaller amount in it.
- **How do you know if an object has more?** Possible answer: The amount in it is greater.

In Problem 5, children compare how much an object holds.

- **How is how much an object holds like how much an object has?** Sample answer: They both refer to how much is inside the object.

 Express regularity in repeated reasoning..

Problem 6 Children can draw any object. Have them tell a partner other ways they can measure their object.

Math on the Spot Use this video to help children model and solve this type of problem.

Supporting All Learners

Children may ask what is in the shakers in **Problem 4**. Tell students these are spices that are used in many cultures. The red spice is called paprika, and the orange spice is called turmeric. Paprika is used often in Mexican and Spanish dishes as well as Hungarian dishes. Turmeric originates from India, and it has been used as a spice and even as a medicine in some cultures.

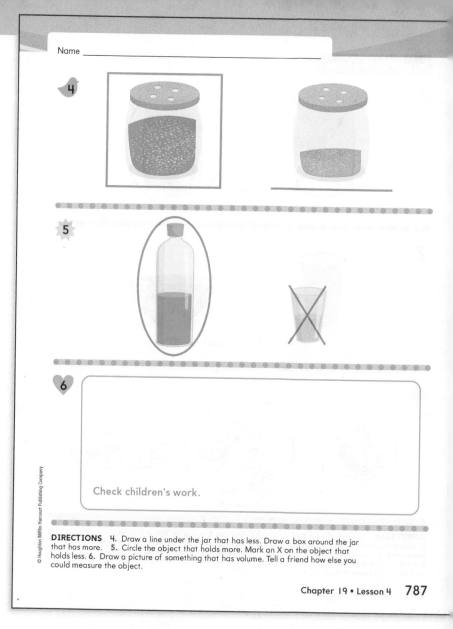

Name _____

4

5

6

Check children's work.

DIRECTIONS 4. Draw a line under the jar that has less. Draw a box around the jar that has more. 5. Circle the object that holds more. Mark an X on the object that holds less. 6. Draw a picture of something that has volume. Tell a friend how else you could measure the object.

Chapter 19 • Lesson 4 **787**

Meeting Individual Needs

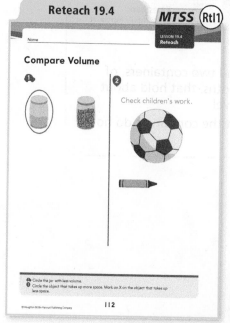

Reteach 19.4

MTSS Rtl1

Name _____

LESSON 19.4
Reteach

Compare Volume

1

2

Check children's work.

1. Circle the jar with less volume.
2. Circle the object that takes up more space. Mark an X on the object that takes up less space.

112

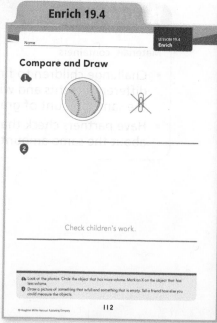

Enrich 19.4

Name _____

LESSON 19.4
Enrich

Compare and Draw

1

2

Check children's work.

1. Look at the photos. Circle the object that has more volume. Mark an X on the object that has less volume.
2. Draw a picture of something that is full and something that is empty. Tell a friend how else you could measure the objects.

112

7

Check children's work.

8

Check children's work.

DIRECTIONS 7. Color the jars so that the red jar has less and the blue jar has more. **8.** Draw a picture of something that is full and something that is empty. Describe each object to a friend. Tell if each object is heavy or light. Tell if each object is tall or short.

 HOME ACTIVITY • Since volume is the amount of space something takes up, challenge your child to think of something that does not have volume. Talk about how thoughts, feelings, and ideas do not have volume because we cannot see them.

788 Go Math! Grade K

④ Elaborate

Problem Solving Applications

(MP) **Model with mathematics.**

Problem 7 Children draw to compare how much an object has in it. The jars are the same size, so children should fill the blue jar more than the red jar.

Problem 8 Children draw to show understanding of the terms *full* and *empty*. They then describe the objects, including identifying other attributes, such as weight and height, to a friend.

⑤ Evaluate | Formative Assessment

I Can

Have children describe to a partner in their own words how to demonstrate the skill for the I Can statement.

I can compare volume and identify other measurable attributes of objects by . . .

determining which container holds more. I can also describe how full an object is or how much space it takes up.

Exit Ticket

Use words or pictures to explain how to measure the volume of a cup using spoonfuls of gravel.

DIFFERENTIATED INSTRUCTION • Independent Activities

Grab and Go!
Version 2.0
Differentiated Centers Kit

Tabletop Flipchart
Mini-lessons for reteaching to targeted small groups

Readers
Supports key math skills and concepts in real-world situations.

Games
Reinforce math content and vocabulary

Activities
Meaningful and fun math practice

Practice and Homework

Compare Volume

Use the Practice and Homework pages to provide children with more practice of the concepts and skills presented in this lesson. Children master their understanding as they complete practice items.

1

- -

2

GLUE

DIRECTIONS 1. Circle the object that takes up less space. Mark an X on the object that takes up more space. 2. Circle the objects that have volume. Tell if each object is heavy or light. Tell if each object is tall or short.

Chapter 19 • Lesson 4 **789**

CROSS-CURRICULAR

SCIENCE

Materials clear cups, containers in different sizes and shapes, water, drawing paper, crayons

- Have pairs or small groups of children fill a clear cup with water and draw a picture to record what they see. Have them explore what happens to the water when they pour it into other containers that are different sizes and shapes. Have them draw pictures.

- Ask children to share their drawings and talk about their observations. Discuss the idea that a liquid can change the way it looks in different containers; it takes the shape of the container it is in.

SOCIAL STUDIES

Materials apple juice containers in different sizes

- Apples are grown in every state in the continental United States. Some apples are handpicked and sold in stores. Some apples are made into apple juice and applesauce.

- Display the different-size containers of apple juice that consumers may buy, from juice boxes to gallon jugs. Have children choose any two containers and guess which holds more and which holds less.

Lesson Check

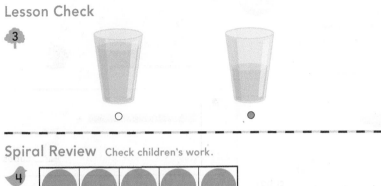

○   ●

- -

Spiral Review Check children's work.

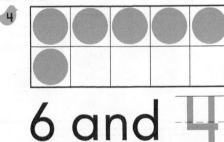

6 and 4

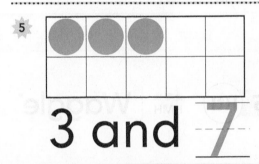

3 and 7

DIRECTIONS **3.** Mark under the glass that has less. **4–5.** Draw counters to make 10. Write the number to show how many counters you drew.

790 Go Math! Grade K

Summative Assessment

Use the **Chapter Review** to assess children's progress in Chapter 19.

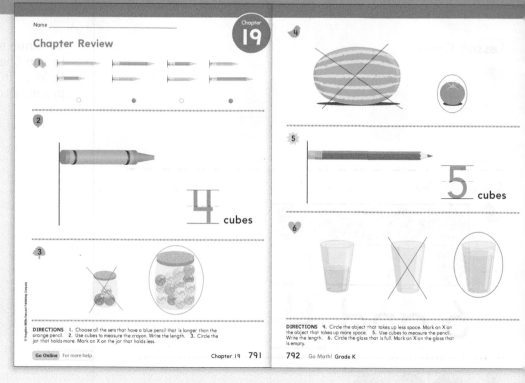

Online, Data-Driven Decision Making *MTSS* (RtI) HMH | Waggle®

Based on the results of the Chapter Review, use the following resources to review skills.

Item	Lesson	Content Focus	Intervene With
1, 2, 5, 9	19.1	Directly compare the lengths of two objects.	Reteach 19.1, Waggle
3, 4, 6, 12	19.4	Compare the volume of objects.	Reteach 19.4, Waggle
7, 8, 11	19.2	Directly compare the weights of two objects.	Reteach 19.2, Waggle
10	19.3	Describe several ways to measure one object.	Reteach 19.3, Waggle

7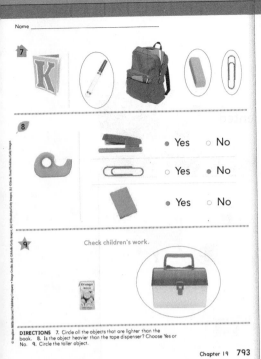

8

○ Yes   ○ No

○ Yes   ● No

● Yes   ○ No

9   Check children's work.

DIRECTIONS 7. Circle all the objects that are lighter than the book.   8. Is the object heavier than the tape dispenser? Choose Yes or No.   9. Circle the taller object.

10

11   Check children's work.

12

DIRECTIONS 10. Circle the object that is tall and heavy.   11. Look at the objects. Mark an X on the object that weighs less. Circle the object that weighs more.   12. Mark an X on the object that is short and full.

Performance Assessment Task

See the Performance Tasks to assess children's understanding of the content. For each task, you will find sample student work for each of the response levels in the task scoring rubric.

Performance Assessment Tasks may be used for portfolios.

Chapter Test

Summative Assessment

Use the **Chapter Test** to assess children's progress in Chapter 19.

Chapter Tests are found in the *Assessment Guide*. Test items are presented in formats consistent with high-stakes assessments.

data
checkpoint

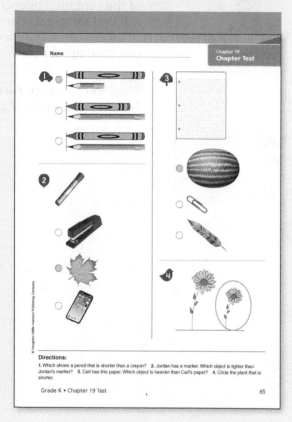

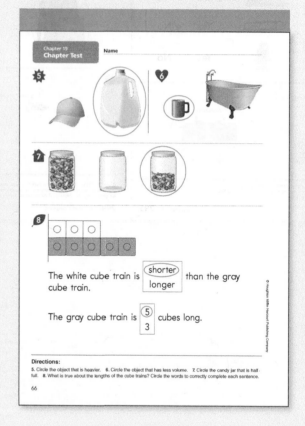

Teacher Notes

Chapter at a Glance

Data

	LESSON 20.1 • 1 Day	LESSON 20.2 • 1 Day	LESSON 20.3 • 1 Day
Lesson at a Glance	Sort by Shape and Size. 797A	Sort into Three or More Groups. 803A	Sort and Count 809A
I Can	I can collect and sort objects into categories by shape and size.	I can collect and sort objects into three categories.	I can solve problems by connecting mathematical concepts.
Learning Goal	Collect and sort objects into categories by shape and size.	Collect and sort objects into three or more categories.	Solve problems by using the *use logical reasoning* strategy.
Vocabulary	sort, size, big, small, classify	category	
Multilingual Support	**Strategy:** Define	**Strategy:** Model Language	**Strategy:** Describe

	LESSON 20.1	LESSON 20.2	LESSON 20.3
Practice and Fluency	◆ ■ Practice and Homework ■ Waggle	◆ ■ Practice and Homework ■ Waggle	◆ ■ Practice and Homework ■ Waggle ◆ Achieving Facts Fluency*
***MTSS* (RtI)** **Intervention and Enrichment**	■ Waggle ◆ ■ Reteach 20.1 ◆ ■ Tier 2 Intervention Skill S41/S43 ◆ ■ Tier 3 Intervention Skill E41/E43 ◆ Enrich 20.1	■ Waggle ◆ ■ Reteach 20.2 ◆ ■ Tier 2 Intervention Skill S41 ◆ ■ Tier 3 Intervention Skill E41 ◆ Enrich 20.2	■ Waggle ◆ ■ Reteach 20.3 ◆ ■ Tier 2 Intervention Skill S29/S41 ◆ ■ Tier 3 Intervention Skill E29/E41 ◆ Tabletop Flipchart ◆ Enrich 20.3

See the Grab-and-Go!™ Centers Kit for more small-group activities.

Version 2.0

Differentiated Centers Kit

The kit provides literature, games, and activities for small-group learning.

◆ Print/Printable Resource
■ Interactive Resource

LESSON 20.4 • 1 Day

Lesson at a Glance	Classify, Count, and Sort by Count 815A
I Can	I can classify objects and show the categories sorted by count.
Learning Goal	Classify objects into given categories and sort the categories by count.
Vocabulary	
Multilingual Support	**Strategy:** Scaffold Language

Practice and Fluency

LESSON 20.4

◆ ■ Practice and Homework
■ Waggle
◆ Achieving Facts Fluency*

MTSS (RtI)
Intervention and Enrichment

■ Waggle
◆ ■ Reteach 20.4
■ ■ Tier 2 Intervention Skill S46
■ ■ Tier 3 Intervention Skill E46
◆ Enrich 20.4

*For individual and class practice with counting automaticity and operational fluency, go to *Achieving Facts Fluency* pages located online.

> Consider ways in which you empower students to solve problems in their lives, community, and in the world.

CULTURALLY RESPONSIVE TEACHING

Cultural Competence

Provide students mathematics learning experiences that develop critical consciousness and empower them to use mathematics to understand and critique the world.

Image Credit: © HMH

◆ Print/Printable Resource
■ Interactive Resource

Teaching for Depth
Data

Classifying

Having children explain their reasoning about why objects do or do not belong to a particular group helps children deepen their understanding.

- Children should have extensive opportunities to develop the language needed to sort and classify objects.

- Children should be able to successfully sort using their own criteria (one or more attributes), and explain to others how they made their decisions.

- Children often sort collections of objects based on attributes other than those provided by the teacher.

- Children cannot sort collections of objects on attributes they cannot distinguish.

- Playing the game "Guess my Rule" that emphasizes attributes and sorting can develop deeper understanding (Clements & Sarama, 2009).

- Children who struggle to make data displays often do so because they have difficulty sorting data (NRC, 2001).

From the Research

"Allow children the opportunity to create categories for data. Encourage them to brainstorm possibilities and then debate the pros and cons of each one. By having to choose some categories and reject others, children become more aware of the limits of their visual display."

(Whitin, 2006, p. 38)

Vocabulary

You can deepen and enhance children's understanding of size words with activities such as these.

- Involve children in creative movements to crouch down and be very small, and then rise and grow bigger and bigger with outstretched arms.

- Focus on sizes as you share favorite old stories, such as "The Three Bears" and "Jack and the Beanstalk." These stories also provide opportunities to review position words, such as *above* and *below*.

- Work with children to make a list of words that describe size. Words that describe things that are big might be *giant, huge, large,* or *gigantic*. Words such as *tiny, little,* or *petite* might be words that children know for *small*.

Mathematical Practices and Processes

Construct arguments and critique reasoning of others.

As you allow children to create their own categories in this chapter, ask them to explain their reasoning. Question whether their categories make sense, and allow children to defend their choices. Allow other children to explain different ways they may have sorted the same objects. Discuss with children how there can be more than one way to sort the same set of objects.

For more professional learning, go online to Teacher's Corner.

nstructional Journey

While every classroom may look a little different, this instructional model provides a amework to organize small-group and whole-group learning for meaningful student learning.

Whole Group
Engage

5 minutes

Readiness
- Problem of the Day
- Fluency Builder or Vocabulary Builder
- Access Prior Knowledge

Engagement
- I Can
- Making Connections
- Learning Activity

Small and Whole Group
Explore

15–20 minutes

Exploration
- Listen and Draw, Unlock the Problem
- Multilingual Support and Strategy
- Common Errors

Small Group
Explain

15–20 minutes

Quick Check
☑ Share and Show

Differentiated Instruction

Version 2.0

Intervention
- Waggle
- Reteach
- Tier 2 and Tier 3 MTSS
- Tabletop Flipchart Mini Lessons

Language Support
- Vocabulary Activities
- Language Routines
- Multilingual Glossary

Enrichment
- Waggle Games
- Ready for More
- Enrich

Whole Group
Elaborate

5 minutes
- Math on the Spot Videos
- Higher-Order Thinking Problems

Evaluate

- I Can Reflection
- Exit Ticket
- Practice and Homework
- Fluency Practice
- Waggle

Assessment		
Diagnostic	Formative	Summative
• Show What You Know	• Lesson Quick Check	• Chapter Review • Chapter Test • Performance Assessment Task

Version 2.0

Differentiated Centers Kit

The kit provides literature, games, and activities for small-group learning.

Strategies for
Multilingual Learners

Understanding a child's language development is helpful in differentiating teaching and assessment. Assessing a child's understanding of mathematical concepts can be done by listening, speaking, reading, and writing. The level of support a child needs determines how best to assess that child's understanding of mathematical concepts.

Planning for Instruction

Language Support	Substantial (WIDA Level 1)*	Moderate (WIDA Levels 2 & 3)*	Light (WIDA Levels 4 & 5)*
Child's Use of Language	• uses single words • uses common short phrases • heavily relies on visual supports and use of manipulatives	• uses simple sentences • uses some academic vocabulary • relies on visual supports and use of manipulatives	• uses a variety of sentences • uses academic vocabulary • benefits from visual supports and manipulatives
Ways to Assess Understanding	**Listening:** points to pictures, words, or phrases to answer questions **Speaking:** answers *yes/no* questions **Reading:** matches symbols to math terms and concepts **Writing:** draws a visual representation of a problem	**Listening:** matches, categorizes, or sequences information based on visuals **Speaking:** begins to explain reasoning, asks math questions, repeats explanations from peers **Reading:** identifies important information to solve a problem **Writing:** uses simple sentences and visual representations	**Listening:** draws conclusions and makes connections based on what they heard **Speaking:** explains and justifies concepts and solutions **Reading:** understands information in math contexts **Writing:** completes sentences using some academic vocabulary

* For more information on WIDA Standards, visit their website at: https://wida.wisc.edu/.

• Look for strategies throughout the lesson to support multilingual learners.
• Log on to ED to find additional multilingual activities and Vocabulary Cards.

In This Chapter

Key Academic Vocabulary

Current Development • Vocabulary

sort, size, big, small, classify, category

Using Language Routines to Develop Understanding

 Language routines provide opportunities for children to develop an understanding of mathematical language and concepts by listening, speaking, reading, and writing. More information on these language routines can be found on the Language Support Cards.

Compare and Contrast

Children share their work with a partner to compare and contrast their strategies.

Language Support	Substantial (WIDA Level 1)*	Moderate (WIDA Levels 2 & 3)*	Light (WIDA Levels 4 & 5)*
Language Routine Differentiation	Children will physically point out similarities and differences on visual representations. They may use short phrases such as "the same" and "different" to verbally compare and contrast their strategies.	Children would rely on visual representations to inform their simple-sentence discussions as they compare and contrast their strategies.	Children would be able to use some academic vocabulary to compare and contrast their strategies with a partner or small group.
Possible Student Work	**Example:** **Teacher:** Are these circles in different groups because they are the same shape? **Child:** No. **Teacher:** Are these circles in different groups because they are different sizes? **Child:** Yes.	**Example:** **Teacher:** Why are these circles in different groups? **Child:** One circle is big. One circle is small.	**Example:** **Teacher:** How are these objects sorted? **Child:** The objects are sorted into big shapes and small shapes.

* For more information on WIDA Standards, visit their website at:
https://wida.wisc.edu/.

Assessing Prior Knowledge

Have children complete **Show What You Know** on their own. Items tested are the prerequisite skills for this chapter.

Diagnostic Interview Task

The alternative interview tasks below evaluate children's understanding of each **Show What You Know** skill. The diagnostic chart may be used for intervention on prerequisite skills.

Materials two-dimensional shapes

- Place three different shapes in front of the child. Have the child find a matching shape for each of the shapes.
- Choose a triangle. Ask the child to point to the sides and tell how many. Ask the child to point to the vertices and tell how many. Repeat with a square.

Some children may be able to identify the number of sides and vertices without explicitly counting them.

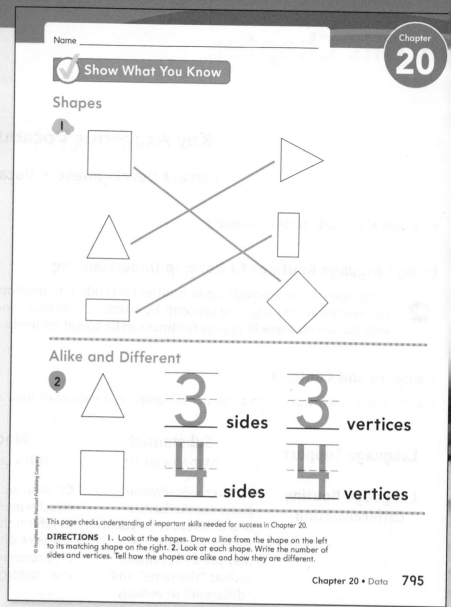

Show What You Know

Shapes

Alike and Different

3 sides   3 vertices
4 sides   4 vertices

This page checks understanding of important skills needed for success in Chapter 20.

DIRECTIONS 1. Look at the shapes. Draw a line from the shape on the left to its matching shape on the right. 2. Look at each shape. Write the number of sides and vertices. Tell how the shapes are alike and how they are different.

Chapter 20 • Data **795**

✓ Show What You Know • Diagnostic Assessment

Use to determine if children need intervention for the chapter's prerequisite skills.

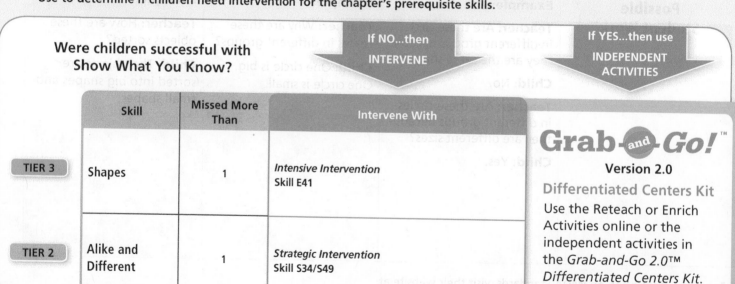

If NO...then INTERVENE

If YES...then use INDEPENDENT ACTIVITIES

	Skill	Missed More Than	Intervene With
TIER 3	Shapes	1	*Intensive Intervention* Skill E41
TIER 2	Alike and Different	1	*Strategic Intervention* Skill S34/S49

Grab-and-Go!
Version 2.0
Differentiated Centers Kit
Use the Reteach or Enrich Activities online or the independent activities in the *Grab-and-Go 2.0™ Differentiated Centers Kit*.

Go Online For more help

Vocabulary Builder

sort

Check children's work.

DIRECTIONS Look at the boxes. Tell how they are sorted. Circle a group of 4. Mark an X on a group of 6.

© Houghton Mifflin Harcourt Publishing Company

796 Go Math! Grade K

Vocabulary Builder

Children use multiple strategies to develop grade-appropriate vocabulary.

Have children complete the activities on the page by working alone or with partners.

Look at the page with children. Talk about and name the various fruits and vegetables.

- **Which fruits are red?** strawberries, apples
- **Which fruits are yellow?** lemons, bananas
- **How are the different fruits and vegetables sorted?** Accept reasonable answers.

Have children use color and shape words to describe the fruits and vegetables they see on the page.

Have children circle a group of 4 and mark an X on a group of 6.

 School-Home Letter is available in English and Spanish online, and in multiple other languages.

Intervention Options MTSS (RtI) Response to Intervention

Use Show What You Know, Lesson Quick Check, and Assessments to diagnose children's intervention levels.

TIER 1	TIER 2	TIER 3	ENRICHMENT
On-Level Intervention	**Strategic Intervention**	**Intensive Intervention**	**Independent Activities**
For children who are generally at grade level but need early intervention with the lesson concepts, use:	For children who need small-group instruction to review concepts and skills needed for the chapter, use:	For children who need one-on-one instruction to build foundational skills for the chapter, use:	For children who successfully complete lessons, use: • Waggle Practice and Games
 • Reteach • Tabletop Flipchart Mini Lesson • Waggle ▲ Tier 1 Activity	 ▲ Prerequisite Skills Activities ▲ Tier 2 Activity	 ▲ Prerequisite Skills Activities ▲ Tier 3 Activity	**Grab-and-Go!** Version 2.0 Differentiated Centers Kit • Ready for More Activity for every lesson • Enrich

Lesson at a Glance
Sort by Shape and Size

SNAPSHOT

Mathematical Standards
- Classify objects into given categories; count the numbers of objects in each category and sort the categories by count.

Mathematical Practices and Processes
- Model with mathematics.
- Attend to precision.
- Construct arguments and critique reasoning of others.
- Look for and make use of structure.

(I Can) Objective
I can collect and sort objects into categories by shape and size.

Learning Goal
Collect and sort objects into categories by shape and size.

Language Objective
Children will describe how to sort objects by shape and size.

MATERIALS
- MathBoard
- two-dimensional shapes

ACROSS THE GRADES

Grade K
Collect and sort objects into categories and compare the categories by counting the objects in each category. Report the results verbally, with a written numeral or with drawings.

After
Collect data into categories and represent the results using tally marks or picture graphs.

ABOUT THE MATH

In this lesson, children explore different ways to sort objects. While there is almost a limitless number of possible ways, this lesson focuses on the categories of shape and size. The category shape could include the actual geometric term for the shape or it could be a description of the shape, such as curved or not curved. Size could be big or small. Children will be asked to focus on one set of criteria during the sorting process, so while a big square and a small rectangle would both be sorted into the Not Curved category, in a different problem where size is the criteria, they would be in separate groups.

For more professional learning go online to Teacher's Corner.

DAILY ROUTINES

 Problem of the Day 20.1

Have children draw a rectangle, circle, triangle, and square. Check children's drawings.

Vocabulary sort, size, big, small, classify

- Interactive Student Edition
- Multilingual Glossary

Fluency Builder

Have children count aloud with a partner from 1 to 20.

FOCUSING ON THE WHOLE STUDENT

Access Prior Knowledge

Choose one or more of the following activities.

- Have children draw their own flower gardens, using whatever colors they like for the flowers.
- Write a class poem about planting flowers in a garden.

Social & Emotional Learning

Relationship Skills During the lesson, provide opportunities for children not only to ask questions, but also to answer questions to help others. *Does anyone have a useful strategy to classify by size? You can be a helper too! When you ask questions and talk about your learning, you help others as well as yourself. What questions did you ask or answer today?*

① Engage

with the Interactive Student Edition

I Can Objective

I can collect and sort objects into categories by shape and size.

Making Connections

Invite children to share what they know about sizes.

Hold up a few sheets of different-sized paper shapes and have children identify the size of of each shape (small, medium, or large). Have children name objects they know that are larger or smaller than the objects you are displaying.

Learning Activity

Tell a story about two stickers with kittens on them. One kitten sticker is shaped like a square, and the other is shaped like a circle. Direct children to think about the shapes of the stickers.

- **How many stickers are there?** 2
- **What shapes are the stickers?** a square and a circle
- **How are the stickers alike? How are they different?** Possible answers: They are alike because the stickers have kittens on them. They are different because they are different shapes.

Explore

Listen and Draw

Materials two-dimensional shapes

Have children look at the workspace. Read the following problem aloud as children listen. Have children use an assortment of two-dimensional shapes to complete the sorting activity on this page.

- **Look at the shapes and choose one of them. Which shape did you choose?** Possible answer: triangle

Have children draw the shape at the top left of the workspace. Read the label with children so that they know that shapes of their chosen shape go on the left and shapes that are not their chosen shape go on the right.

- **Find a shape that matches your shape. Place the shape on the workspace below where you drew your shape. This will be your first set. All the figures that match this shape go on this side of the workspace. All of the shapes that are not that shape go on the other side of the workspace.**

 Attend to precision.

Hold up a square.

- **Can we place this shape under the first shape?** no
- **Why?** Possible answer: It is not a triangle. **The square goes on the side of the workspace that is for shapes that are not triangles.**

Have children sort their shapes and then draw to show how they sorted.

Explain that we sort by placing the objects that are alike in some way in one category and the objects that are different in another category.

- **How would you describe the way you sorted the shapes?** Possible answer: They are sorted by shape. All of the shapes that are triangles are in one category and all of the shapes that are not triangles are in another category.

Name _____

Sort by Shape and Size

(I Can) collect and sort objects into categories by shape and size.

Listen and Draw

	not

Check children's work.

© Houghton Mifflin Harcourt Publishing Company

DIRECTIONS Choose a shape. Draw the shape at the top of each side. Sort and classify a handful of shapes into a set of the shape you chose and a set that is not that shape. Draw the shapes.

 Multilingual Support

STRATEGY: Define

Materials two-dimensional shapes

Children can practice their understanding by defining words.

- Put several different shapes out of various sizes.

- Write the word *big*. **What does big mean? Which shapes are big?** Answers may vary.

- Write the word *small*. **What does small mean? Which shapes are small?** Answers may vary.

Continue asking children questions such as:

- **Which shape is a triangle? How do you know?** Possible answer: This is a triangle because it has 3 sides.

- **Which shape is a circle? How do you know?** Possible answer: This is a circle because it has curves.

Allow children to define specific attributes in their responses to help strengthen their understanding of particular shapes and different ways to sort them.

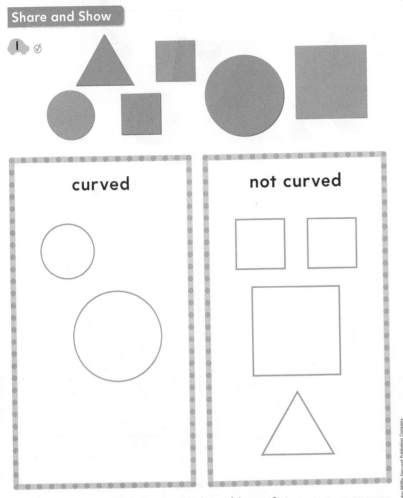

curved | not curved

DIRECTIONS 1. Use shapes like those shown at the top of the page. Sort the shapes into a set of curved shapes and a set of shapes that are not curved. Draw the shapes to show how you sorted them.

© Houghton Mifflin Harcourt Publishing Company

 Ready for More   Logical / Mathematical / Visual / Small Group

Materials lunch bags, construction paper shapes in four colors and two different sizes, index cards

Give children a collection of construction-paper shapes and two empty lunch bags.

- **Work together to think of a way to sort and classify these shapes into two sets. Count how many are in each set.**
- **Write the name of the category and how many are in each set on index cards. Place the cards in the bags with the matching paper shapes.**

Have children exchange bags with another group, look at the paper shapes in each bag, and guess how the shapes were sorted.

- **Look at the cards to check your guess. Count how many to check the number on the card.**

③ Explain

Share and Show

Have children find Problem 1. Explain that they will be using two-dimensional shapes like the shapes at the top of the page.

- **What categories will you use to sort these shapes?** curved and not curved

Tell children that they will sort the shapes into two categories. Explain that a category is a set or group of objects that are similar in some way. Read the shape descriptions aloud as you point to them on the page. Have children sort the shapes by whether or not they are curved.

(MP) Construct arguments and critique reasoning of others.

- **What do you notice about the shapes in each category on this page?** One category has circles, and the other has other shapes.
- **How have the shapes been sorted?** by shape

Hold up the red circle.

- **Why does this circle belong in the first category?** because it is curved
- **Why does this shape not belong in the next category?** because those shapes are not curved

Use similar questioning with other shapes. Then have children draw the shapes in each category.

Use the checked problem for Quick Check.

 **Quick Check   MTSS RtI**

If → a child misses the checked problem

Then → Differentiate Instruction with
- Reteach 20.1
- Waggle

! Common Errors

Error Children may not sort the shapes correctly.

Springboard to Learning Explain that this page is about sorting by the attributes of the shapes. Have children point to each shape in a category and tell whether it is curved. Then ask what the category is. Repeat for the other category, size.

Share and Show

 Look for and make use of structure.

Have children find Problem 2 and use the two-dimensional shapes that are pictured at the top of the page.

- **What sizes are the shapes?** big and small

Hold up the large red triangle and the large yellow square.

- **How are these two shapes alike?** They are both big.

Read the labels on the workspace aloud as you point to them on the page. Tell children to sort the shapes into categories by size.

- **What do you notice about the sizes of the shapes in each category on this page?** Each category is one size.

Hold up the small blue circle.

- **In which category does this shape belong?** small
- **Why does this shape not belong in the other category?** because it is not big

Use similar questioning for other shapes. Then have children draw the shapes in each category.

Higher-Order Thinking

 Model with mathematics.

- **Adam has big, medium, and small marbles. He wants to sort them by size. How many categories will he have?** 3

Children should be able to determine that there will be three categories, since they were told that Adam would sort by size and three sizes were listed.

Math on the Spot Use this video to help children model and solve this type of problem.

Name _____

small   big

DIRECTIONS 2. Use shapes like those shown at the top of the page. Sort the shapes by size. Draw the shapes to show how you sorted them.

Chapter 20 • Lesson 1   **799**

Meeting Individual Needs

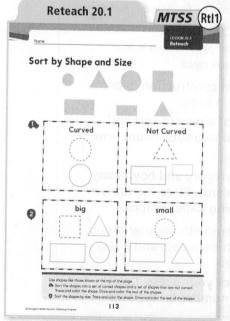

Reteach 20.1   **MTSS** **RtI1**

Sort by Shape and Size

Curved   Not Curved

big   small

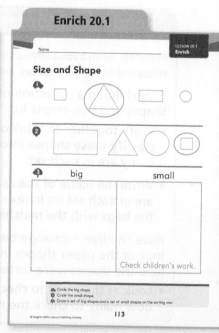

Enrich 20.1

Size and Shape

big   small

Check children's work.

 799   Go Math! Grade K

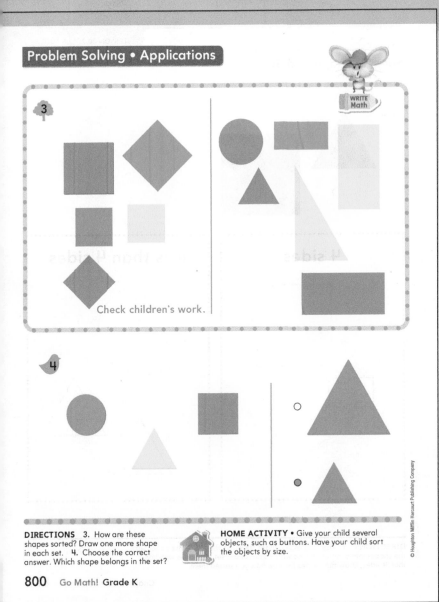

WRITE Math

3

Check children's work.

4

DIRECTIONS 3. How are these shapes sorted? Draw one more shape in each set. 4. Choose the correct answer. Which shape belongs in the set?

HOME ACTIVITY • Give your child several objects, such as buttons. Have your child sort the objects by size.

800 Go Math! Grade K

DIFFERENTIATED INSTRUCTION • Independent Activities

Grab-and-Go!™
Version 2.0
Differentiated Centers Kit

Tabletop Flipchart
Mini-lessons for reteaching to targeted small groups

Readers
Supports key math skills and concepts in real-world situations.

Games
Reinforce math content and vocabulary

Activities
Meaningful and fun math practice

---

④ Elaborate

Problem Solving Applications

 Construct arguments and critique reasoning of others.

Problem 3 Children explain how they will solve the problem.

- **What do you see in each category?** a category of squares and a category of not squares
- **How do you know how the categories are sorted?** I can tell they are sorted by shape because one category has all the squares shapes and the other category has all the other shapes.

Have children draw one more shape in each category to assess their understanding of sorting into two categories.

 Attend to precision.

Problem 4 Read the problem to the children.
- **Which shape belongs in the set?** small red triangle
- **Fill in the bubble for the correct answer.**

⑤ Evaluate | Formative Assessment

I Can
Have children write to describe the skill for the I Can statement.

I can collect and sort objects into categories by shape and size by . . . choosing either a shape or a size. I put all of the objects of that shape or size into one category, and I put all of the objects that are not that shape or size into another category.

Exit Ticket
Explain how to sort objects by size.

Sort by Shape and Size

Use the Practice and Homework pages to provide children with more practice of the concepts and skills presented in this lesson. Children master their understanding as they complete practice items.

Name _____

Sort by Shape and Size

1

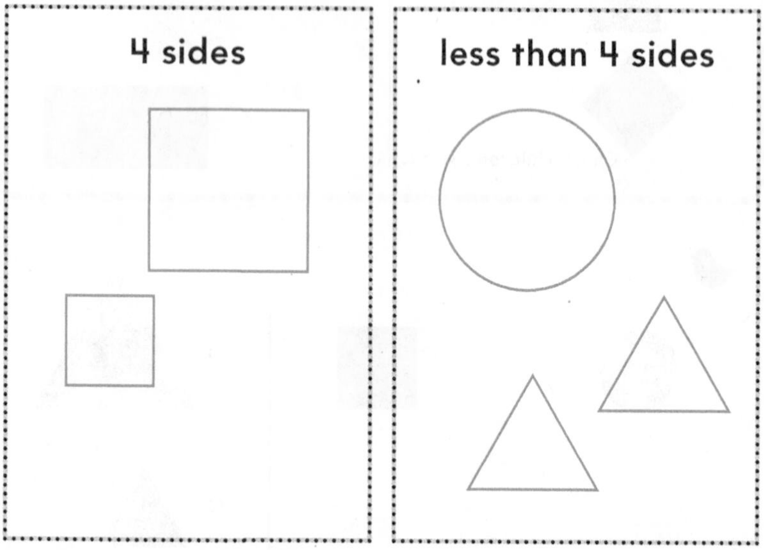

4 sides	less than 4 sides

DIRECTIONS 1. Use shapes like those shown at the top of the page. Sort the shapes into a set of shapes with 4 sides and a set of shapes with less than 4 sides. Draw the shapes to show how you sorted them.

Chapter 20 • Lesson 1   801

Lesson Check

2

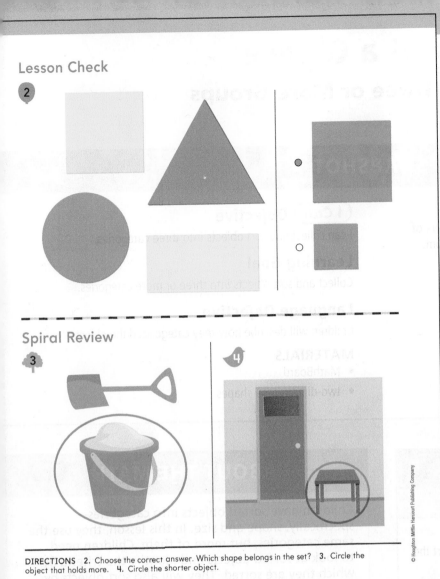

Spiral Review

3

4

© Houghton Mifflin Harcourt Publishing Company

DIRECTIONS **2.** Choose the correct answer. Which shape belongs in the set? **3.** Circle the object that holds more. **4.** Circle the shorter object.

Lesson at a Glance

Sort into Three or More Groups

SNAPSHOT

Mathematical Standards

● Classify objects into given categories; count the numbers of objects in each category and sort the categories by count.

Mathematical Practices and Processes

● Model with mathematics.

● Attend to precision.

● Construct arguments and critique reasoning of others.

● Look for and make use of structure.

● Reason abstractly and quantitatively.

(I Can) Objective

I can collect and sort objects into three categories.

Learning Goal

Collect and sort objects into three or more categories.

Language Objective

Children will describe how they categorized the objects.

MATERIALS

• MathBoard

• two-dimensional shapes

ACROSS THE GRADES

Grade K

Collect and sort objects into categories and compare the categories by counting the objects in each category. Report the results verbally, with a written numeral or with drawings.

After

Collect data into categories and represent the results using tally marks or picture graphs.

ABOUT THE MATH

Children have sorted objects into categories—specifically, shape and size. In this lesson, they use the same categories, but more of them. Children need to look at sorted objects and identify the criteria by which they are sorted. They will also sort objects by designated criteria.

For more professional learning go online to Teacher's Corner

DAILY ROUTINES

🖥 **Problem of the Day 20.2**

Draw a circle on top of a square.
Draw a triangle beside a rectangle.
Check children's drawings.

🖥 **Vocabulary** category

- Interactive Student Edition
- Multilingual Glossary

Fluency Builder

Have children count aloud backward from 20 to 1.

FOCUSING ON THE WHOLE STUDENT

Access Prior Knowledge

Choose one or more of the following activities.

- Have children talk about times when they played with or saw balloons.
- Help the class make a list of words and phrases that tell about balloons, such as *round*, *light*, and *fun*. Write the list on the board.

Supporting All Learners

As the school year draws to a close, think about the ways you pushed children to succeed. Consider where children have developed learning gaps, and ask what you can do to prevent that in your future classes. Take time to think about something positive in each child in your class, and express these positive sentiments in these remaining days of school. Ensure children go to first grade with the confidence that they can succeed in school and the knowledge that you believe in them.

➊ Engage

with the Interactive Student Edition

I Can Objective

I can collect and sort objects into three categories.

Making Connections

Invite children to tell you what they know about sorting objects into categories.

- **What are some different categories we can sort objects into?** Answers may vary; color, shape, etc.
- **What are some different objects we can sort into categories?** Answers may vary; colored markers, apples, flowers, etc.

Learning Activity

Show children a bunch of balloons with stars on them and a bunch of balloons that are striped. Tell children that these balloons will be used to decorate for a party.

Help children understand what it means to sort objects by attributes.

- **What kind of decorations will there be for the party?** balloons
- **Are the balloons all alike? Why or why not?** No, they are not all the same pattern.
- **What do you notice about the first group of balloons?** Possible answer: They have stars on them.

Explore

Listen and Draw

Materials two-dimensional shapes

 Model with mathematics.

Read aloud this problem as children listen.

Juan has a collection of toys. He has toy cars, toy trucks, and toy airplanes. How can Juan sort his collection of toys into three categories?

Have children use small circle, triangle, and square two-dimensional shapes. Hold up each type of shape and name it. Have children repeat the word after you.

 Look for and make use of structure.

- **What shapes do you see at the top of the workspace?** triangles, squares, and circles
- **How many categories did you sort shapes into in the last lesson?** 2

Explain that in this lesson children will be sorting objects into three categories.

Have children use the shapes pictured at the top of the page.

Hold up the red square.

 Construct arguments and critique reasoning of others.

- **In which category does this shape belong?** the middle, squares **How do you know?** Possible answer: It is a square, and the picture at the top of the column is a square.
- **How do you know that it doesn't belong in the other categories?** Possible answer: The other categories are for circles and triangles.

Use similar questioning for other categories. Then have children draw the shapes in each category to show how they sorted.

Reread the problem about Juan.

- **How can Juan sort his toys?** He can make three groups. He can put all of the cars together in a group, all of the trucks together in a group, and all of the airplanes together in a group.

Name _____

Sort into Three or More Groups

(I Can) collect and sort objects into three categories.

Listen and Draw

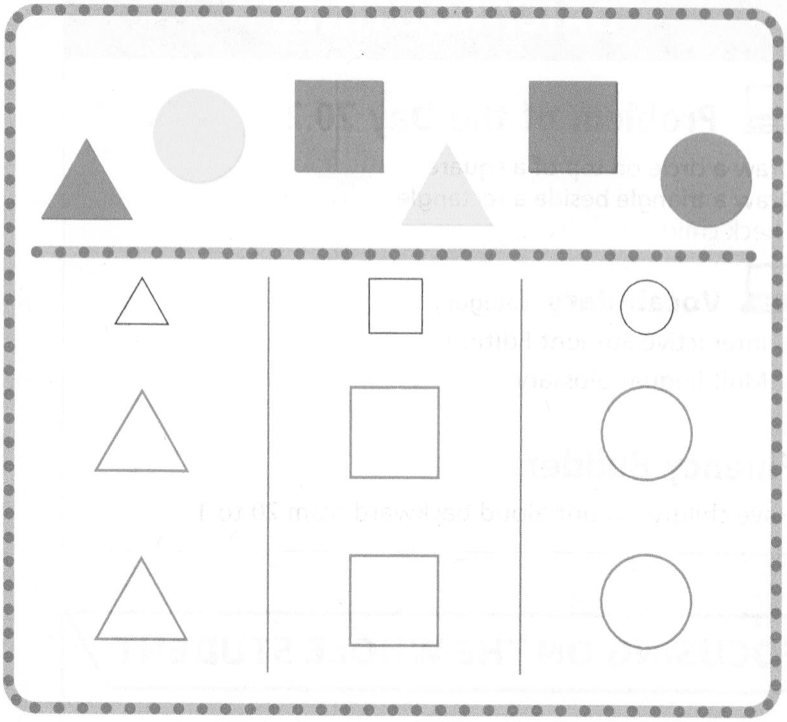

[shapes worksheet with triangle, circle, square, square, triangle, circle at top; columns of triangles, squares, and circles below]

DIRECTIONS Use shapes like those shown at the top of the page. Sort them by shape. Draw the shapes to show how you sorted them.

Chapter 20 • Lesson 2 **803**

 Multilingual Support

STRATEGY: Model Language

Materials markers, connecting cubes

Children can learn correct pronunciation by repeating words modeled by proficient speakers.

- Hold up a red cube. **This is a red cube.** Have children repeat.

- Have them divide a sheet of paper into three parts. Guide them to draw red objects in the first part, blue objects in the second part, and yellow objects in the third part. Have them use your sentence as a model for how to describe each object drawn by its color.

- Give children a red, blue, and yellow cube. Have them place each cube in the appropriate section of their drawings.

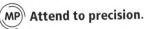

circle	square
○	☐

triangle	rectangle
△ △	▭ ▭ ▭

Check children's work.

DIRECTIONS 1. Place shapes as shown. Sort and classify by shape. Draw the shapes in each category.

© Houghton Mifflin Harcourt Publishing Company

Ready for More

 Visual / Verbal Partners

- Put children in partners and have them think of three categories to sort objects into.

- Have children work in pairs to write the categories in the top of a three-column chart and then look around the classroom to find objects to sort.

square	triangle	circle

- For each category, have children draw different classroom objects and explain their chart to the class. Accept all reasonable responses.

③ Explain

Share and Show Math Board

For Problem 1, have children take a handful of two-dimensional shapes. Explain that they will be sorting their shapes into four categories.

(MP) Attend to precision.

- **What shapes do you see?** circle, square, triangle, rectangle

Hold up a red triangle.

- **In which category should we put this shape?** in the bottom left category **Why?** because it is a triangle

- **Why does this shape not belong in the other categories?** because those categories are for other shapes

After children have finished sorting their shapes, have them draw the shapes to show how they sorted.
Use the checked problem for Quick Check.

✓ Quick Check MTSS RtI

If	a child misses the checked problem
Then	**Differentiate Instruction** with • Reteach 20.2 • Waggle

! Common Errors

Error Children may not sort by shape.

Springboard to Learning Remind children that objects can be sorted in different ways. On the last page, children sorted by shape. On this page, children are sorting by shape again. Have children name the shapes in the workspace.

Share and Show

Children will need a handful of small two-dimensional shapes to complete Problem 2. Explain that on this page, children will be sorting their shapes by number of straight sides.

- **What labels are at the top of the page?** 0 sides, 3 sides, 4 sides

Review how to count the straight sides of a shape.

 Reason abstractly and quantitatively.

Hold up a large rectangle.

- **In which category should we put this shape?** in the last category **Why?** because it has four sides

- **Why does this shape not belong in the other categories?** because those categories are for shapes with no sides and shapes with three sides

After children have finished sorting their shapes, have them draw the shapes to show how they sorted.

Higher-Order Thinking

 Construct arguments and critique reasoning of others.

- **Compare your page with one of your classmates. How are they alike?** They both have shapes. **How are they different?** The colors and sizes of the shapes are different. **Why are the two pages not exactly the same?** Possible answer: We used different handfuls of shapes.

Children should recognize that the pages are similar because they both have columns with shapes drawn in them. The first column has all circles, the second column has all triangles, and the third column has squares and rectangles. The pages are different because the colors of the shapes and their sizes are not the same. The children should conclude that the pages are not the same because the two children used different handfuls of shapes to complete the page.

Math on the Spot Use this video to help children model and solve this type of problem.

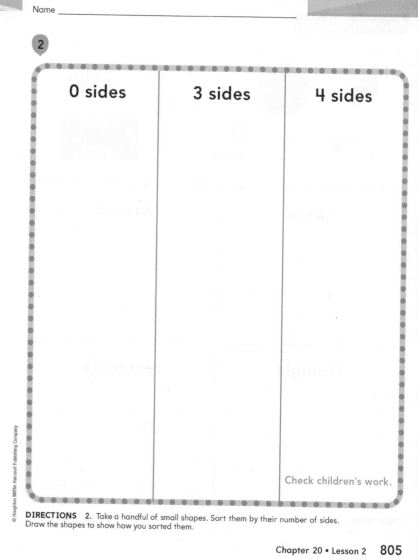

Name _____

0 sides	3 sides	4 sides

Check children's work.

DIRECTIONS 2. Take a handful of small shapes. Sort them by their number of sides. Draw the shapes to show how you sorted them.

© Houghton Mifflin Harcourt Publishing Company

Meeting Individual Needs

Reteach 20.2   MTSS (RtI1)

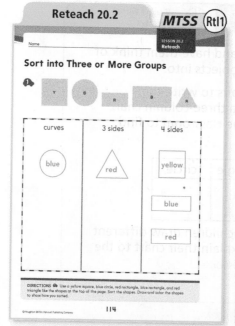

Enrich 20.2

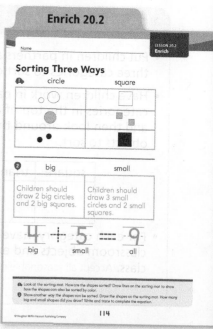

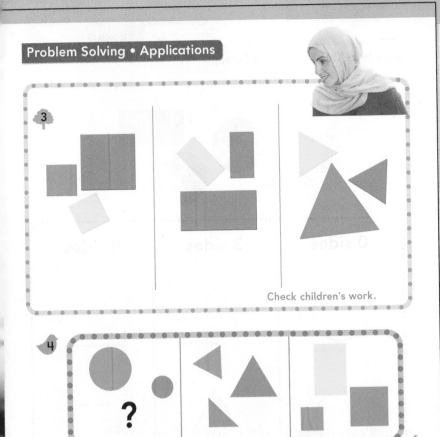

3

Check children's work.

4

?

○   ●

© Houghton Mifflin Harcourt Publishing Company • CHMH

DIRECTIONS 3. How are the shapes sorted? Draw one more shape in each set. **4.** Choose the correct answer. Look at how the shapes are sorted. Which shape belongs in the first set?

HOME ACTIVITY • Ask your child to explain how he or she sorted shapes on this page. Draw a square, a circle, or a triangle. Ask your child which set the shape goes in and why it goes there.

DIFFERENTIATED INSTRUCTION • Independent Activities

Grab and Go!™
Version 2.0
Differentiated Centers Kit

Tabletop Flipchart

Mini-lessons for reteaching to targeted small groups

Readers

Supports key math skills and concepts in real-world situations.

Games

Reinforce math content and vocabulary

Activities

Meaningful and fun math practice

---

④ Elaborate

Problem Solving Applications

(MP) Attend to precision.

Have children locate **Problem 3**.

- **What do you see in each category?** The first category has squares, the second category has rectangles, and the third category has triangles.
- **Were the shapes sorted by color, by size, or by shape?** by shape
- **Draw one more shape in each category.**

Read **Problem 4** with children.

- **Look at how the shapes are sorted. Which shape belongs in the first category?** red circle **Fill in the bubble for the correct answer.**

⑤ Evaluate | Formative Assessment

I Can

Have children describe in their own words how to demonstrate the skill for the I Can statement.

I can collect and sort objects into three categories by . . . choosing the categories, finding the objects that match those categories, and grouping them together into the correct categories.

Exit Ticket

Explain how you know to which category an object belongs.

Practice and Homework

Sort into Three or More Groups

Use the Practice and Homework pages to provide children with more practice of the concepts and skills presented in this lesson. Children master their understanding as they complete practice items.

Sort into Three or More Groups

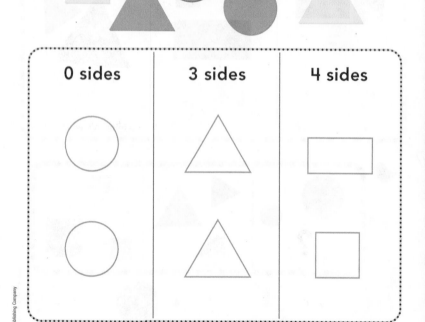

0 sides	3 sides	4 sides

DIRECTIONS 1. Sort the shapes at the top of the page by their number of sides. Draw the shapes to show how you sorted them.

Chapter 20 • Lesson 2   **807**

Lesson Check

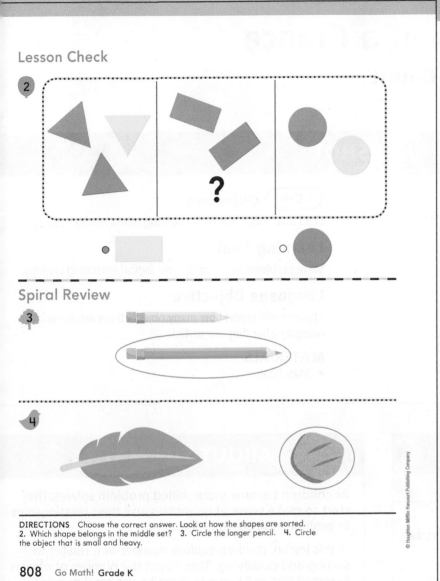

2

3

4

Spiral Review

DIRECTIONS Choose the correct answer. Look at how the shapes are sorted.
2. Which shape belongs in the middle set? 3. Circle the longer pencil. 4. Circle the object that is small and heavy.

SNAPSHOT

Mathematical Standards
- Classify objects into given categories; count the numbers of objects in each category and sort the categories by count.

Mathematical Practices and Processes
- Model with mathematics.
- Attend to precision.
- Look for and make use of structure.
- Reason abstractly and quantitatively.

(I Can) **Objective**
I can solve problems by connecting mathematical concepts.

Learning Goal
Solve problems by using the *use logical reasoning* strategy.

Language Objective
Children will report how many objects there are in each category after they are sorted.

MATERIALS
- MathBoard

ACROSS THE GRADES

Grade K
Collect and sort objects into categories and compare the categories by counting the objects in each category. Report the results verbally, with a written numeral or with drawings.

After
Collect data into categories and represent the results using tally marks or picture graphs.

ABOUT THE MATH

As children become more skilled problem solvers, they start to make sense of quantities and their relationships in problem-solving situations.

In this lesson, children explore number as it relates to sorting and classifying. They count the number of objects in sorted sets and begin to describe the total number of objects as the number in all of the objects in the sets. Children use sorted sets to complete the equations.

Children learn to use quantitative reasoning to create relationships between numbers and symbols. As they look at pictures of sorted shapes, children learn how the shapes relate to the numbers and how the numbers relate to the mathematical symbols + and =.

For more professional learning go online to Teacher's Corner.

🖥 Problem of the Day 20.3

What information does this concrete graph show? Are there more red counters or yellow counters?
how many red and yellow counters; red

How Many Counters?					
🔴	🔴	🔴	🔴		
🟡	🟡	🟡			

🖥 Vocabulary

- Interactive Student Edition
- Multilingual Glossary

Fluency Builder

Count on a Hundred Chart

Materials hundred chart, two pieces of construction paper

Have partners work with a hundred chart. One partner covers all but one row of the chart with the construction paper.

The other partner counts the visible numbers and then tries to continue counting through the next row without looking at the numbers. Children can then remove the construction paper to check their work.

Have children repeat the activity, leaving a different row of the hundred chart visible.

FOCUSING ON THE WHOLE STUDENT

Access Prior Knowledge

Provide each child with six to ten two-color counters. Have children turn over some of the counters to show yellow.

- **How many red counters do you have?**
- **How many yellow counters do you have?**
- **How many counters do you have in all?**
  Check children's answers.

---

❶ Engage

with the Interactive Student Edition

I Can Objective

I can solve problems by connecting mathematical concepts.

Making Connections

Invite children to tell you what they know about sorting objects into categories.

- **What are some different categories we can sort objects into?** Possible answers: shape; size; number of sides

- **Why might we want to count the objects after they are sorted?** to know how many objects are in each group

Learning Activity

Materials two-column sorting mat with blank addition equation, construction paper circles and squares of the same size and in two colors, paper bag

For each group, place some blue and red circle shapes and square shapes into a bag.

- **Have each child take shapes from the bag. Have children decide if the shapes should be sorted into two categories by size or shape.**

- **After the shapes are sorted, have a child count each set of shapes and write the number that tells how many are in each group.**

- **Children work together to check that the shapes are sorted and counted correctly. They then discuss which number tells how many in all.**

Explore

Unlock the Problem

(MP) **Reason abstractly and quantitatively.**

Read aloud this problem as children listen.

Steven has some shapes. How can he sort and classify them into two categories? How can he find how many shapes there are in all?

Have children look at the sorting mat as you read the labels.

- **What does this mat show?** shapes that are sorted by shape—circles and squares

- **How many circles are there on the mat?** 5 **Trace the number in the addition equation.**

- **How many squares are there?** 4 **Trace the number in the addition equation.**

- **How can you find out how many shapes there are in all?** add the two numbers **How many are there in all?** 9 **Trace the number.**

Read the addition equation with children. 5 plus 4 is equal to 9.

Reread the problem about Steven.

- **How can Steven sort and classify his shapes into two categories? How can he find how many in all?** He can sort and classify the shapes by shape. He can put all of the circles together and all of the squares together. He can count how many of each shape. Then he can add the numbers.

Name _____

Sort and Count

(I Can) solve problems by connecting mathematical concepts.

:: UNLOCK the Problem

$$5 + 4 = 9$$

all

© Houghton Mifflin Harcourt Publishing Company

DIRECTIONS Look at the sorting mat. How are the shapes sorted? How many circles? How many squares? Add the two sets. Trace the addition sentence.

Check children's work.

Chapter 20 • Lesson 3 **809**

(ML) **Multilingual Support**

STRATEGY: Describe

Materials two-dimensional shapes

Children can practice their comprehension by describing what they have seen or heard.

- Make a set of four squares and a set of three circles on the table. Have children describe how the shapes are sorted and classified. by shape

- **How many squares are in the first set?** 4 Write **4** on the board. **How many circles are in the second set?** 3 Write **+ 3** on the board next to the 4. **How many shapes are there in all?** 7 Write **= 7** on the board.

$$4 + 3 = 7$$

$6 + 4 = 10$

all

DIRECTIONS I. Look at the sorting mat. How are the shapes sorted? How many triangles? How many rectangles? Add the two sets. Write the numbers and trace the symbols to complete the addition sentence.

© Houghton Mifflin Harcourt Publishing Company

③ Explain

Try Another Problem

(MP) Look for and make use of structure.

Call attention to both sides of the sorting mat.

* **How are the shapes sorted and classified?** by shape

Point out the addition equation at the bottom of the page.

* **How many triangles?** 6
* **How many rectangles?** 4
* **Add the two sets. How many are there in all?** 10 Guide children to read the word *all*. Have children write the numbers and trace the symbols to complete the addition equation.

Read the addition equation with children. 6 plus 4 is equal to 10.

Use the checked problem for Quick Check.

✓ Quick Check   MTSS (RtI)

If	a child misses the checked problem
Then	**Differentiate Instruction** with • Reteach 20.3 • Waggle

---

⚠ Common Errors

Error Children may count the number of shapes incorrectly.

Example Children write 5 triangles instead of 6.

Springboard to Learning Have children place a check mark on each shape as they count.

Ready for More   🕐 | Kinesthetic Partners

Materials large and small squares, circles, triangles, and rectangles that are not squares from construction paper in four colors; two-column sorting mats with blank addition equation; spinners (3- and 4-section) with labels *Size, Color* Shape

Partners place the collection of shapes on a desk.

* One child spins the spinner and reads the label. He or she sorts and classifies the shapes on the sorting mat.

* Next, the partner checks to see if the sorting is accurate. Partners count each set of shapes, write the numbers, and complete the addition equation that shows how many in all.

* Have children repeat the activity and discuss any observations.

Share and Show

Math Board

(MP) Attend to precision.

Direct attention to the sorting mat. Read the labels.

- **How are the shapes sorted and classified?** by size
- **How many small shapes are there?** 5
- **How many big shapes are there?** 5
- **Add the two sets. How many are there in all?** 10 **Write the numbers and trace the symbols to complete the addition equation.**

Math on the Spot Use this video to help children model and solve this type of problem.

Higher-Order Thinking

(MP) Reason abstractly and quantitatively.

- **Suppose two small shapes are taken off the sorting mat. How would your answer change?** It would change to 3 + 5 = 8.

Children should know that removing small shapes would change the number of small shapes and the number of shapes in all. They should recognize that the number in all would be less than before.

Culturally Responsive Education

Children are likely to notice that the tables on pages 810 and 811 are the same, but that the categories have changed. Discuss how more than one attribute of an object can be measured at one time. To foster problem-solving skills, provide children the opportunity to create their own charts like the one on page 812 in groups. As responsive educators, we need to cultivate a positive classroom environment while working to help children become independent learners.

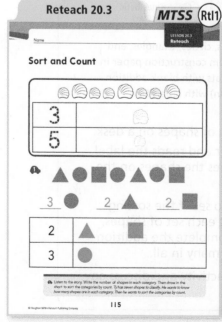

Name _____

Share and Show

2

DIRECTIONS 2. Look at the sorting mat. How are the shapes sorted? How many small shapes? How many big shapes? Add the two sets. Write the numbers and trace the symbols to complete the addition sentence.

Chapter 20 • Lesson 3   811

Meeting Individual Needs

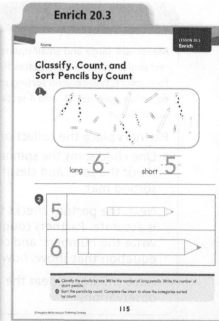

Reteach 20.3 **MTSS (RtI1)**

Sort and Count

Enrich 20.3

big   small

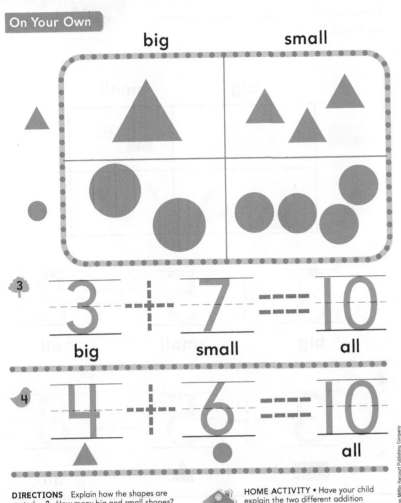

DIRECTIONS Explain how the shapes are sorted. **3.** How many big and small shapes? Write and trace to complete the addition sentence. **4.** How many triangles and circles? Write and trace to complete the addition sentence.

HOME ACTIVITY • Have your child explain the two different addition sentences on this page and tell how the shapes are sorted.

812   Go Math! **Grade K**

---

4 Elaborate

On Your Own

Draw children's attention to the sorting mat. Point out that the mat is divided into four categories. Read the labels.

- **How are the shapes sorted and classified?** by size, big and small, and by shape, triangle, and circle

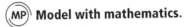 **Model with mathematics.**

- **For Problem 3, complete the number equation that shows how many big and small shapes there are.** There are 3 big shapes and 7 small shapes. The equation is 3 + 7 = 10.

- **For Problem 4, complete the equation that shows how many triangles and circles there are.** There are 4 triangles and 6 circles. The equation is 4 + 6 = 10.

5 Evaluate | Formative Assessment

I Can

Have children report how many objects there are in each category after they are sorted to demonstrate the skill for the I Can statement.

I can solve problems by connecting mathematical concepts by . . . sorting and classifying the information I have and then using logical reasoning to find an answer.

Exit Ticket

Draw some shapes and then describe how you can sort them.

DIFFERENTIATED INSTRUCTION • Independent Activities

Grab and Go!

Version 2.0

Differentiated Centers Kit

Tabletop Flipchart

Mini-lessons for reteaching to targeted small groups

Readers

Supports key math skills and concepts in real-world situations.

Games

Reinforce math content and vocabulary

Activities

Meaningful and fun math practice

Practice and Homework

Sort and Count

Use the Practice and Homework pages to provide children with more practice of the concepts and skills presented in this lesson. Children master their understanding as they complete practice items.

Name ____________________

LESSON 20.3
Practice and Homework

Sort and Count

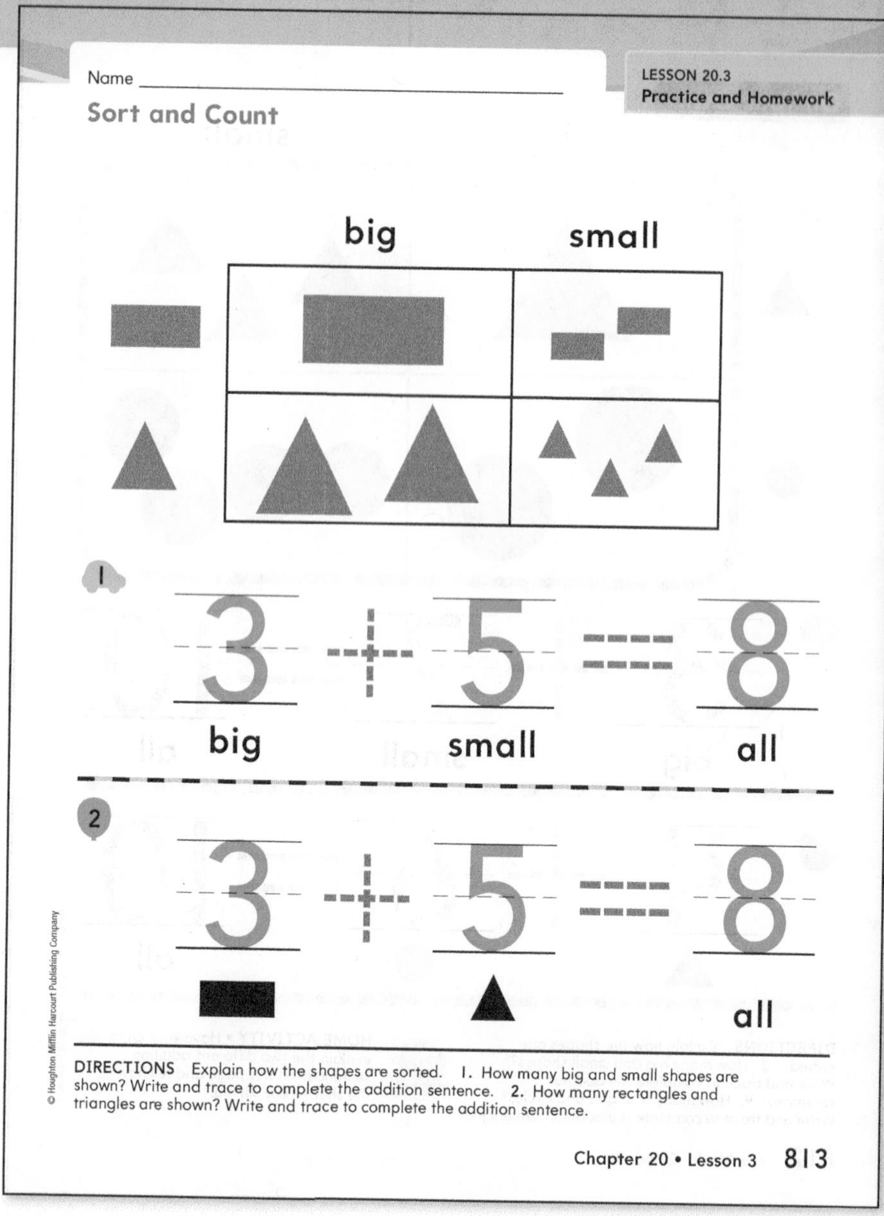

big | small

1. 3 + 5 = 8
big small all

2. 3 + 5 = 8
all

DIRECTIONS Explain how the shapes are sorted. **1.** How many big and small shapes are shown? Write and trace to complete the addition sentence. **2.** How many rectangles and triangles are shown? Write and trace to complete the addition sentence.

PROFESSIONAL LEARNING — MATH TALK IN ACTION

As children work on Problem 2, they discuss how they sorted and classified the shapes.

Teacher:	How many shapes in all did you find for Problem 2?
Betsy:	I found 8 shapes in all, just like for Problem 1.
Joe:	That is odd that we got 8 both times. And we sorted the shapes in different ways!
Carol:	Joe, you know that we started with the same group of shapes both times. Did you think that the number of shapes would change when we sorted them?
Joe:	Oh, I forgot that we started with the same group of shapes on both pages. That explains why the number in all is the same.
James:	It does not matter how we sort them, we will always have 8.
Teacher:	Many scientists have to sort and classify data when they do research. You are doing a great job getting started with data!

Lesson Check

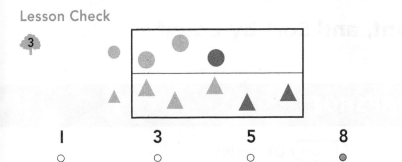

1   3   5   8

○   ○   ○   ●

Spiral Review

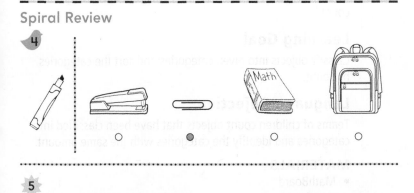

○ 17, 19, 20, 18   ○ 18, 19, 17, 20

● 17, 18, 19, 20   ○ 20, 19, 17, 18

DIRECTIONS 3. Look at the shapes on the sorting mat. Which number shows how many circles and triangles there are in all? Mark under your answer. 4. Which object weighs less than the marker? Mark under your answer. 5. Which set of numbers is in order? Mark beside your answer.

© Houghton Mifflin Harcourt Publishing Company

Continue to practice concepts and skills with Lesson Check. Use Spiral Review to engage children in previously taught concepts and to promote content retention.

Lesson at a Glance
Classify, Count, and Sort by Count

SNAPSHOT

Mathematical Standards
- Classify objects into given categories; count the numbers of objects in each category and sort the categories by count.

Mathematical Processes and Practices
- Reason abstractly and quantitatively.
- Construct arguments and critique reasoning of others.
- Model with mathematics.
- Attend to precision.
- Look for and make use of structure.
- Use appropriate tools strategically.

(I Can) **Objective**

I can classify objects and show the categories sorted by count.

Learning Goal

Classify objects into given categories and sort the categories by count.

Language Objective

Teams of children count objects that have been classified into categories and identify the categories with the same amount.

MATERIALS
- MathBoard
- connecting cubes

ACROSS THE GRADES

Grade K

Classify objects into given categories; count the numbers of objects in each category and sort the categories by count.

After

Use up to three categories to organize, represent, and interpret data; ask and answer questions about data points, including how many data points there are in each category, in one category as compared with another, and in all.

ABOUT THE MATH

Why Teach This?

In kindergarten, children identify ways that objects in a group are similar and different. Children understand that although objects may be grouped according to a common characteristic, the objects may differ in other ways. In this lesson, children will classify objects and sort the categories by count. As children experience classifying groups of objects by color, shape, or size, they explore different attributes by which items can be sorted. As children count the number of objects in each category and sort the categories by count, they practice representing the categories symbolically. These experiences provide the children with the understanding they will need, in later grades, to organize and represent data in graphs.

For more professional learning go online to Teacher's Corner

I Can Objective

I can classify objects and show the categories sorted by count.

Making Connections

Review classifying and counting by size. Display shapes of various colors in two groups of different-sized objects.

- **Did I classify these shapes by size, shape, or color? Tell how you know.** size; there are different shapes and colors in the same group, but all the shapes are about the same size.

- **What is the same about the shapes in each group?** One group has all small shapes, and one group has all large shapes.

Learning Activity

The chickens at a petting zoo laid eggs. Some of the eggs are brown, and some of the eggs are white. The zookeepers want to know how many brown eggs and how many white eggs there are.

Ask the following questions.

- **How can the zookeepers sort and count the eggs?** by color

- **What else do the zookeepers want to know?** how many brown eggs there are and how many white eggs there are

---

DAILY ROUTINES

🖥 Problem of the Day 20.4

Brad has a toy box full of his favorite toys. He has a red basketball, a red truck, a blue basketball, and a blue truck. Tell how Brad can sort and classify these toys.

Have children think of as many ways as they can to sort and classify these objects. Possible answers: red/blue, truck/ball, truck/not a truck, ball/not a ball

🖥 Vocabulary

- Interactive Student Edition
- Multilingual Glossary

Mental Math

Materials large and small classroom objects

Provide children with an assortment of large and small objects. Ask children to sort the objects by size, sorting into two categories—large and small. Call on a child to count the items in one category, and have another child check the count. Repeat for the other category.

FOCUSING ON THE WHOLE STUDENT

Access Prior Knowledge

Give small groups one red or yellow cube. Have groups take turns naming the color of their cube as you record their results in a table. Have children talk as a class about the table you made.

Explore

Listen and Draw

Materials connecting cubes

(MP) Model with mathematics.

Read the problem aloud as children listen.

Bo has 8 toy cars in 3 different colors. How can Bo sort the cars?

Provide pairs or small groups of children with 10 to 15 connecting cubes in orange, black, and green.

- **How can you sort and classify the cubes?**
  by color

Have children sort and classify the cubes into the columns of the workmat.

- **When you are finished sorting, draw to show the number of cubes (which represent Bo's cars) in each category. Use crayons to show the colors.**

- **After you draw to show the cubes (or cars), how can you find the number in each category?** I can count the cubes (or cars) that I drew in each column.

- **How will you record the number of cubes (or cars) in each category?** I will write the number of items at the bottom of the column.

- **Do any of the boxes of crayons have the same number of crayons?** Answers will vary. **When you know the number of items that are in several categories, you can use this information to sort the categories by count.**

(MP) Reason abstractly and quantitatively.

- **How would you sort these categories by count?** Possible answer: I sort the categories by the number of objects in each category. If there are categories with the same number of objects, they will be grouped together.

Name _____

Classify, Count, and Sort by Count

(I Can) classify objects and show the categories sorted by count.

Listen and Draw

Check children's work.

DIRECTIONS Bo has 8 toy cars in three different colors. How can Bo sort the cars? Use cubes to represent the story. Write how many cars are in each category.

Chapter 20 • Lesson 4   **815**

(ML) Multilingual Support

STRATEGY: Scaffold Language

Show children blue cubes and green cubes. Draw a chart. Ask volunteers to sort and classify the cubes and to help you place the cubes on the chart.

Ask children to use *classify*, *sort*, *category*, and *belong* to describe the information. Then add some cubes and ask children to describe the new information.

Check children's work.

3 ▪ 2 ● 2 ▲

| 2 | ● | ▲ |
| 3 | | ▪ |

DIRECTIONS 1. Classify the shapes. Write the number of shapes in each category. Sort the categories by count.

© Houghton Mifflin Harcourt Publishing Company

Ready for More

Logical
Small Group

Materials index cards, assorted objects (should vary in size, color, and shape)

Provide assorted objects for each small group. Have children discuss different ways that the shapes could be classified, and then classify the shapes in one way. Ask one child to count the objects in each category while another child uses the index cards to label each category. Together they should sort the categories by count.

Ask children to sort the objects in a different way. Have children count the objects in each category and use the index cards to label the categories. Ask children to sort the categories by count.

③ Explain

Share and Show

Read the directions aloud with the class, and then direct children's attention to the figures at the top of the page. Have children identify the different shapes that are on the page.

(MP) **Construct arguments and critique reasoning of others.**

Before beginning the task, have children describe and give examples in their own words of the meaning of the word *sort*. Have children discuss their examples. Prompt discussion by asking: **Do you agree or disagree? Why?**

- **How many kinds of figures are there?** three
- **How can you tell how many of each shape there are?** I can count the number of shapes in each category.
- **How can you sort the categories by count?** I find the row in the table for the number of shapes in a category. Then I draw one of each shape that matches that number.
- **How does knowing the number of objects in each category make it possible to sort the categories by count?** I use the numbers to classify and sort the categories.

Use the checked problem for Quick Check.

✓ Quick Check   MTSS (RtI)

If	a child misses the checked problem
Then	Differentiate Instruction with • Reteach 20.4 • Waggle

⚠ Common Errors

Error Children may count the label picture in each row as one of the objects.

Example Children write 4 instead of 3.

Springboard to Learning Point out the write-on lines next to the row labels. You may want children to cover each label picture when they count each type of object.

Share and Show

Read the directions to the class. Direct children's attention to the figures at the top of the page. Provide children with a handful of large and small objects (large and small counting bears, for example).

 Use appropriate tools strategically.

- **These objects will represent the shells at the top of the page. How will you sort and classify the objects (shells)?** by size
- **Place large objects onto the large shells, and small objects onto the small shells. Then, move the objects down into the correct columns of the table to classify the shells.**
- **What is the next step to solve the problem?** Write the number of shells in each category.
- **Now you know how many shells are in each category. What does this tell you about sorting these categories by count?** Possible answer: There are two different numbers of shells, one number for each category, so I will need two sorting rows. Each row will have only one picture.

Encourage children to share the strategies they used to sort the categories by count.

Higher-Order Thinking

 Attend to precision.

- **Look at the table that you made. If you found another large shell, would your table change? If so, how?** Yes; I would change the 2 that I wrote in that row to a 3.

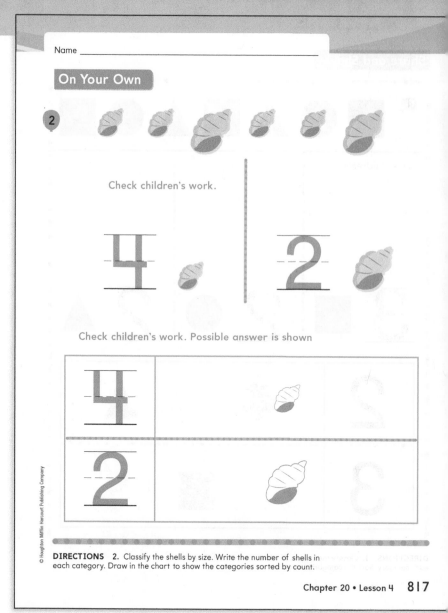

Name _____

On Your Own

2

Check children's work.

4   2

Check children's work. Possible answer is shown

DIRECTIONS 2. Classify the shells by size. Write the number of shells in each category. Draw in the chart to show the categories sorted by count.

Chapter 20 • Lesson 4   817

Meeting Individual Needs

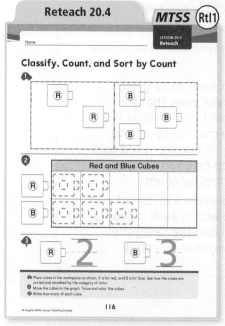

Reteach 20.4   MTSS (Rtl1)

Classify, Count, and Sort by Count

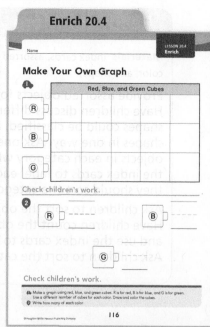

Enrich 20.4

Make Your Own Graph

3 Check children's work.

_____ | _____ | _____
buttons | buttons | buttons

DIRECTIONS 3. Color each button red, orange, or blue. Classify the buttons by color. Write the number of buttons in each category. Draw in the chart to show the categories sorted by count.

HOME ACTIVITY • Have your child describe how they sorted the buttons by count.

DIFFERENTIATED INSTRUCTION • Independent Activities

Grab and Go!™
Version 2.0
Differentiated Centers Kit

Tabletop Flipchart
Mini-lessons for reteaching to targeted small groups

Readers
Supports key math skills and concepts in real-world situations

Games
Reinforce math content and vocabulary

Activities
Meaningful and fun math practice

④ Elaborate

Problem Solving Applications

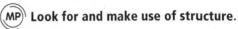

Read the directions for **Problem 3**. Ask children to explain how they will solve this open-ended problem. Children may wish to represent the buttons with red, orange, and blue connecting cubes before drawing on their papers.

- **How will you sort these button?** by color
- **How will you color the buttons to show the categories?** Children's answers should indicate that they will use the colors to determine the category into which each button should be sorted.

(MP) Look for and make use of structure.

Have children count and write the number of buttons in each category, and have them use these numbers to complete the table. Ask them to explain how the graph shows their answers.

- **Do you need to use all three rows in the table?** Children's answers should indicate, for example, that if the number of buttons is the same for two of the colors, both of those colors will go in the same row (and only two rows of the chart will be used).

⑤ Evaluate | Formative Assessment

I Can

After the buttons have been sorted into categories, have teams report how many buttons (or objects) there are in each category. This will demonstrate the skill needed for the I Can statement.

I can classify objects and show the categories sorted by count by . . . sorting the objects into categories, counting how many objects are in each category, and making a table to show the categories sorted by number of objects.

Exit Ticket

Melissa has 8 balloons in 3 different colors. Draw to show what Melissa's balloons might look like. Draw to show how to sort her balloons by color. Then draw a table to sort the categories by count.

Practice and Homework

Classify, Count, and Sort by Count

Use the Practice and Homework pages to provide children with more practice of the concepts and skills presented in this lesson. Children master their understanding as they complete practice items.

Classify, Count, and Sort by Count

1

Check children's work.

2

© Houghton Mifflin Harcourt Publishing Company

DIRECTIONS 1. Sort and classify the shapes by category. Draw and count the sorted shapes. 2. Complete the table to show the categories sorted by count.

Chapter 20 • Lesson 4   819

Lesson Check

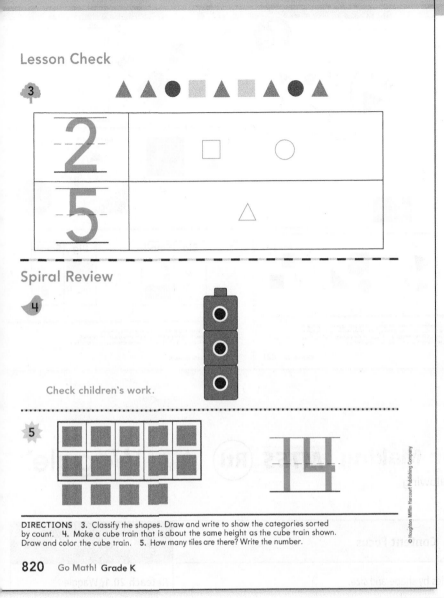

3

2

5

Spiral Review

4

Check children's work.

5

14

DIRECTIONS 3. Classify the shapes. Draw and write to show the categories sorted by count. 4. Make a cube train that is about the same height as the cube train shown. Draw and color the cube train. 5. How many tiles are there? Write the number.

820 Go Math! Grade K

Continue to practice concepts and skills with Lesson Check. Use Spiral Review to engage children in previously taught concepts and to promote content retention.

© Houghton Mifflin Harcourt Publishing Company

CHAPTER 20 Chapter Review

Summative Assessment

Use the **Chapter Review** to assess children's progress in Chapter 20.

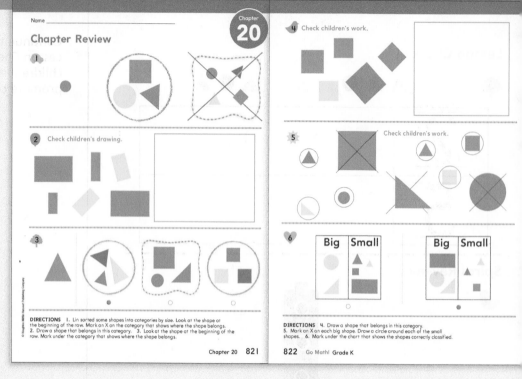

Chapter 20 821

822 Go Math! Grade K

Online, Data-Driven Decision Making *MTSS* (RtI) HMH | Waggle®

Based on the results of the Chapter Review, use the following resources to review skills.

Item	Lesson	Content Focus	Intervene With
1, 2, 3, 4, 5, 6	20.1	Collect and sort objects into categories by shape and size.	**Reteach 20.1,** Waggle
7	20.2	Collect and sort objects into three or more categories.	**Reteach 20.2,** Waggle
9, 10	20.3	Solve problems by using the use logical reasoning strategy.	**Reteach 20.3,** Waggle
8	20.4	Classify objects into given categories and sort the categories by count.	**Reteach 20.4,** Waggle

Name _____

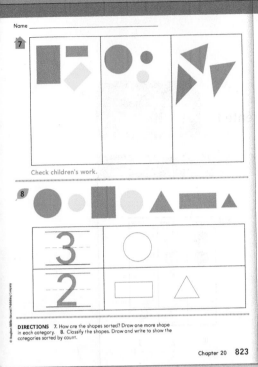

Check children's work.

7

8

3	◯
2	▭ △

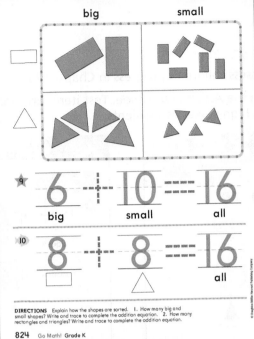

big   small

9 6 + 10 = 16
    big   small   all

10 8 + 8 = 16
    ▭   △   all

DIRECTIONS 7. How are the shapes sorted? Draw one more shape in each category. 8. Classify the shapes. Draw and write to show the categories sorted by count.

Chapter 20   823

DIRECTIONS Explain how the shapes are sorted. 1. How many big and small shapes? Write and trace to complete the addition equation. 2. How many rectangles and triangles? Write and trace to complete the addition equation.

824   Go Math! Grade K

Performance Assessment Task

See the Performance Tasks to assess children's understanding of the content. For each task, you will find sample student work for each of the response levels in the task scoring rubric.

Portfolio Performance Assessment Tasks may be used for portfolios.

CHAPTER 20

Chapter Test

Summative Assessment

Use the **Chapter Test** to assess children's progress in Chapter 20.

Chapter Tests are found in the *Assessment Guide*. Test items are presented in formats consistent with high-stakes assessments.

data checkpoint

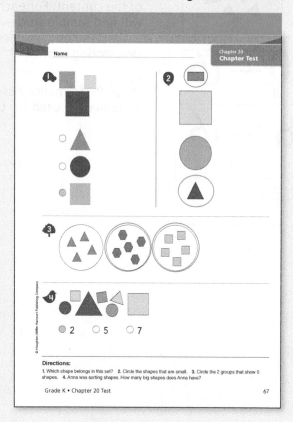

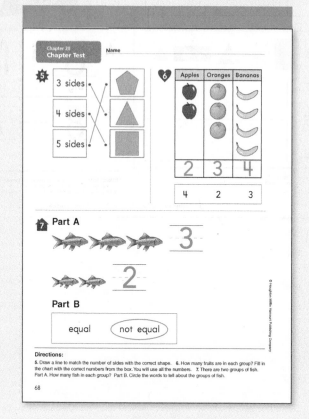

824A Go Math! **Grade K**

Teacher Notes

above [arriba, encima]

The kite is **above** the rabbit.

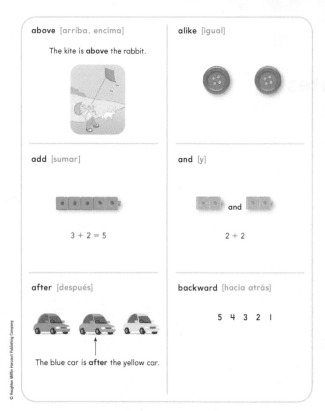

alike [igual]

add [sumar]

$3 + 2 = 5$

and [y]

and

$2 + 2$

after [después]

The blue car is **after** the yellow car.

backward [hacia atrás]

5 4 3 2 1

before [antes de]

The yellow car is **before** the blue car.

beside [al lado]

The tree is **beside** the bush.

behind [detrás]

The box is **behind** the girl.

big [grande]

big

below [debajo]

The rabbit is **below** the kite.

category [categoría]

fruits

toys

---

circle [círculo]

cone [cono]

classify [clasificar]

apples

not apples

corner [esquina]

corner

compare [comparar]

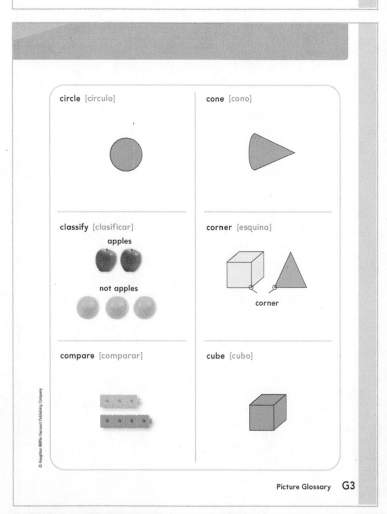

cube [cubo]

---

curve [curva]

difference [diferencia]

$4 - 3 = 1$

The **difference** is the number left after you subtract.
[Una **diferencia** es el número que queda después de restar.]

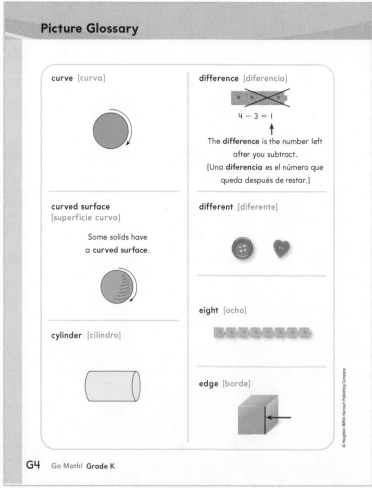

curved surface
[superficie curva]

Some solids have a **curved surface**.

different [diferente]

cylinder [cilindro]

eight [ocho]

edge [borde]

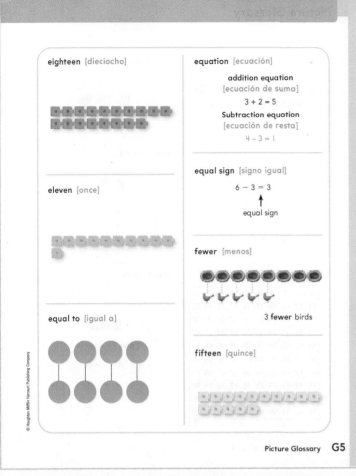

eighteen [dieciocho]

eleven [once]

equal to [igual a]

equation [ecuación]

addition equation
[ecuación de suma]
$3 + 2 = 5$
Subtraction equation
[ecuación de resta]
$4 - 3 = 1$

equal sign [signo igual]

$6 - 3 = 3$

↑
equal sign

fewer [menos]

3 **fewer** birds

fifteen [quince]

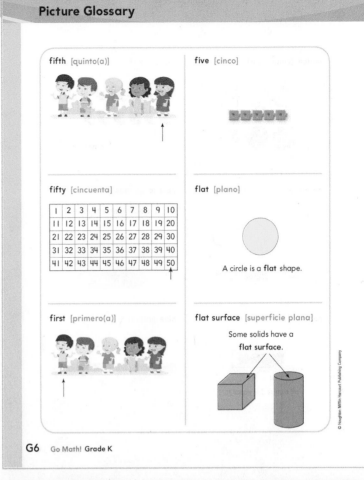

fifth [quinto(a)]

fifty [cincuenta]

1	2	3	4	5	6	7	8	9	10
11	12	13	14	15	16	17	18	19	20
21	22	23	24	25	26	27	28	29	30
31	32	33	34	35	36	37	38	39	40
41	42	43	44	45	46	47	48	49	50

first [primero(a)]

five [cinco]

flat [plano]

A circle is a **flat** shape.

flat surface [superficie plana]

Some solids have a
flat surface.

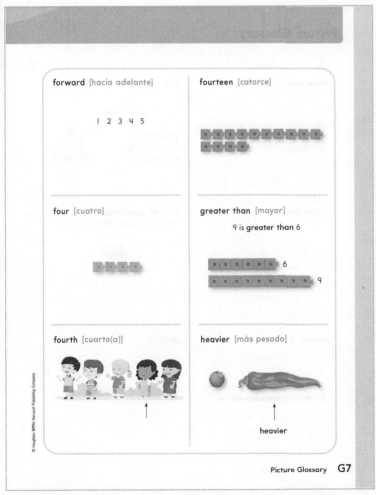

forward [hacia adelante]

1 2 3 4 5

four [cuatro]

fourth [cuarto(a)]

fourteen [catorce]

greater than [mayor]

9 is **greater than** 6

6

9

heavier [más pesado]

heavier

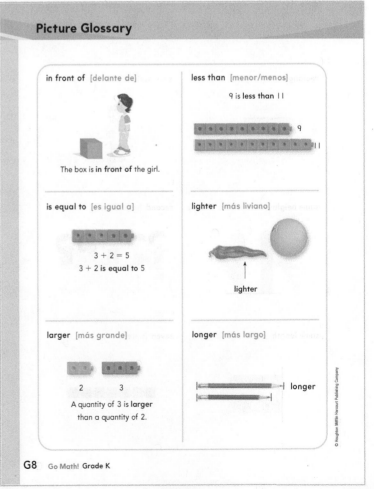

in front of [delante de]

The box is **in front of** the girl.

less than [menor/menos]

9 is **less than** 11

9

11

is equal to [es igual a]

$3 + 2 = 5$
$3 + 2$ is **equal to** 5

lighter [más liviano]

lighter

larger [más grande]

2

3

A quantity of 3 is **larger**
than a quantity of 2.

longer [más largo]

longer

match [emparejar]

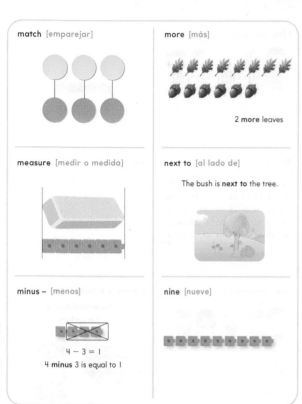

more [más]

2 more leaves

measure [medir o medida]

next to [al lado de]

The bush is **next to** the tree.

minus − [menos]

4 − 3 = 1

4 **minus** 3 is equal to 1

nine [nueve]

---

nineteen [diecinueve]

ones [unidades]

3 ones

one [uno]

pairs [pares]

3	
3	0
2	1
1	2
0	3

number **pairs** for 3

number line recta numérica

1 2 3 4 5 6 7 8 9 10

one hundred [cien]

1	2	3	4	5	6	7	8	9	10
11	12	13	14	15	16	17	18	19	20
21	22	23	24	25	26	27	28	29	30
31	32	33	34	35	36	37	38	39	40
41	42	43	44	45	46	47	48	49	50
51	52	53	54	55	56	57	58	59	60
61	62	63	64	65	66	67	68	69	70
71	72	73	74	75	76	77	78	79	80
81	82	83	84	85	86	87	88	89	90
91	92	93	94	95	96	97	98	99	100

plus + [más]

2 **plus** 1 is equal to 3

2 + 1 = 3

---

rectangle [rectángulo]

same weight [del mismo peso]

same height [de la misma altura]

second [segundo(a)]

same length [del mismo largo]

seven [siete]

---

seventeen [diecisiete]

side [lado]

side

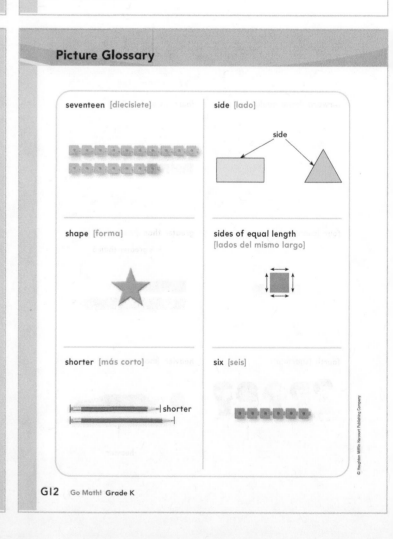

shape [forma]

sides of equal length
[lados del mismo largo]

shorter [más corto]

shorter

six [seis]

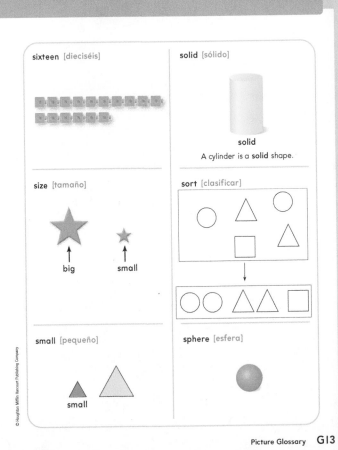

sixteen [dieciséis]

solid [sólido]

solid

A cylinder is a **solid** shape.

size [tamaño]

big

small

sort [clasificar]

small [pequeño]

small

sphere [esfera]

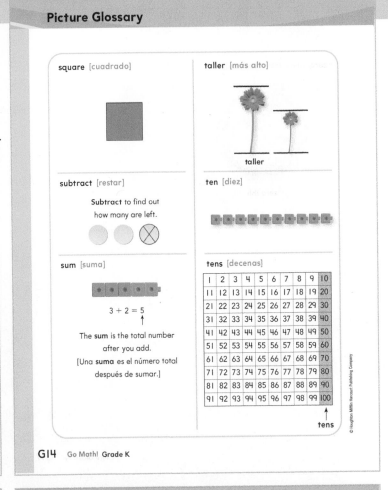

square [cuadrado]

taller [más alto]

taller

subtract [restar]

Subtract to find out
how many are left.

ten [diez]

sum [suma]

$3 + 2 = 5$

The **sum** is the total number
after you add.
[Una **suma** es el número total
después de sumar.]

tens [decenas]

1	2	3	4	5	6	7	8	9	10
11	12	13	14	15	16	17	18	19	20
21	22	23	24	25	26	27	28	29	30
31	32	33	34	35	36	37	38	39	40
41	42	43	44	45	46	47	48	49	50
51	52	53	54	55	56	57	58	59	60
61	62	63	64	65	66	67	68	69	70
71	72	73	74	75	76	77	78	79	80
81	82	83	84	85	86	87	88	89	90
91	92	93	94	95	96	97	98	99	100

tens

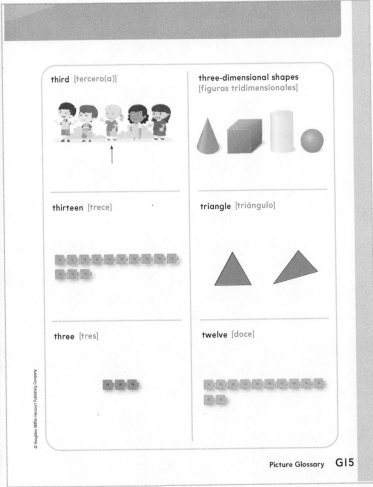

third [tercero(a)]

three-dimensional shapes
[figuras tridimensionales]

thirteen [trece]

triangle [triángulo]

three [tres]

twelve [doce]

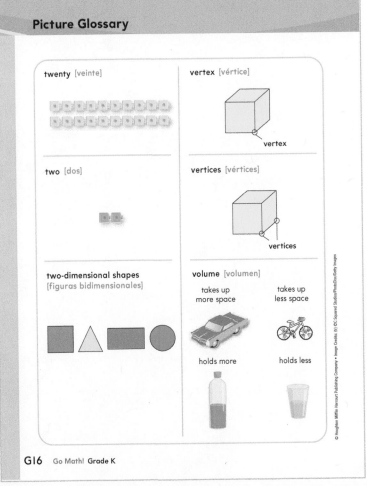

twenty [veinte]

vertex [vértice]

vertex

two [dos]

vertices [vértices]

vertices

two-dimensional shapes
[figuras bidimensionales]

volume [volumen]

takes up
more space

takes up
less space

holds more

holds less

zero, none [cero, ninguno]

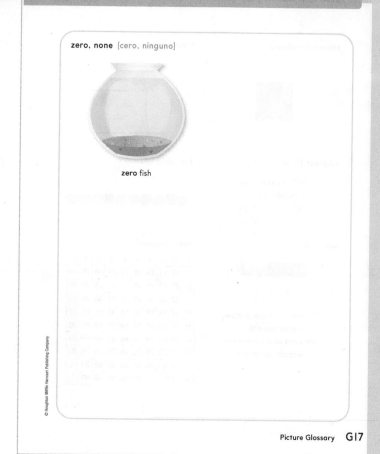

zero fish

Picture Glossary **G17**